More Short Stories

edited by

HENRY I. CHRIST
JEROME SHOSTAK

AMSCO SCHOOL PUBLICATIONS, INC.
315 Hudson Street / New York, N.Y. 10013

HENRY I. CHRIST has had a long and distinguished career as writer, editor, teacher, and supervisor. A specialist in language, literature, and composition, he has written more than a hundred textbooks in the field of English, including many published by Amsco. For nearly ten years, he was the editor of the teachers' magazine *High Points*. He has been active in professional organizations and has held office at the local, state, and national levels. A frequent speaker at English conventions and workshops throughout the United States, he has also lectured on educational television and participated in curriculum development and evaluation.

MARIE E. CHRIST has worked with Henry I. Christ as a partner throughout his writing career. She has provided many practical suggestions and usable materials. As always, her good judgment, common sense, and hard work played a major role in the development and preparation of this book.

JEROME SHOSTAK has experienced the many and various facets of teaching language arts: he has taught in every grade from the primary through the intermediate and senior levels; his students ranged from the gifted in electives to the reluctant in remedial courses. He has been faculty adviser to the school newspaper, literary magazine, and senior yearbook staffs. He has chaired a department and been an active participant in local and national organizations. He has written several series of workbooks in language skills and in preparation for high school and college entrance. In addition to the present group of collections of short stories, he has edited contemporary novels for classroom use.

When ordering this book, please specify:
either R 577 S or MORE SHORT STORIES, SOFTBOUND

ISBN 1-87720-761-5

Printed in the United States of America

1 2 3 4 5 6 7 8 9 10   00 99 98 97 96 95 94 93

Contents

1. ACROSS THE GENERATIONS

2. THE TURNING POINT

3. THE LIGHTER SIDE

4. THE MANY FACES OF LOVE

5. THE WILLING SUSPENSION OF DISBELIEF

6. MIXED MOTIVATIONS

7. CONFLICT

8. DATELINE—THE FUTURE

To the Student

Which, of all defects, has been the one most fatal to a good style? The not knowing when to come to an end.

Sir Arthur Helps

By their very nature, short stories seldom suffer from the defect of wordiness. The best short stories often have an opposite result: they leave the involved reader satisfied, sometimes even looking for more. The stories in this book have been chosen primarily to whet your interest and encourage discussion. Because they are short stories, they possess certain qualities: conciseness, economy, and compression. They tend to be sophisticated and challenging, encouraging varying points of view and productive analysis.

You will find many first-rate writers here: Ernest Hemingway, H. G. Wells, P. G. Wodehouse, Elizabeth Bowen, James Thurber, Shirley Jackson, and Kurt Vonnegut, Jr., to name a few. Some talented newcomers, like Ouida Sebestyen, a black writer, show us that basic human experiences are not restricted to race nor nation. There are classics, like Thomas Bailey Aldrich's "Marjorie Daw," and recent gems like Bel Kaufman's "Sunday in the Park." Our short stories cross national boundaries: Anton Chekhov's Russia, H. G. Wells' England, Jesse Stuart's America, and Gérard Klein's France.

The stories show a variety of theme and characterization. The division into units provides themes around which to build your discussions, but this division doesn't rule out comparisons and contrasts throughout the book. It is always instructive to compare ways in which authors develop characters: by their actions, by what they say, by what other characters say about them, by the author's own evaluations of the characters.

Each story is introduced by a quotation from the story and a "teaser" to get you started on the reading. Each story has objective-test questions, vocabulary-building exercises, discussion questions, and stories in words. Each unit includes questions that tie together the four stories in the unit.

The book has been planned with multiple goals in mind: the improvement of reading skills, growth in vocabulary, class evaluations of challenging stories. The first goal, however, has been providing stories that you will want to read for the sheer joy of the experience. May you find these to your taste.

Acknowledgments

Grateful acknowledgment is made to the following sources for permission to reprint copyrighted stories.

"Reading the Light," page 2. By Roger Pfingston. From THE AVAILABLE PRESS/PEN SHORT STORY COLLECTION. Copyright 1985 by Pen American Center. Reprinted by permission of PEN Syndicated Fiction Project.

"Charles," page 13. By Shirley Jackson. From THE LOTTERY. Copyright © 1948, 1949 by Shirley Jackson. Copyright renewed 1976, 1977 by Laurence Hyman, Barry Hyman, Mrs. Sarah Webster and Mrs. Joanne Schnurer. Reprinted by permission of Farrar, Straus and Giroux, Inc.

"Teenage Wasteland," page 22. By Anne Tyler. Copyright © 1984 by Ann Tyler. Reprinted by permission of Russell & Volkening as agents for the author.

"Another April," page 36. By Jesse Stuart. Copyright 1942, 1946 by Jesse Stuart. Copyright © 1970, 1974 renewed by Jesse Stuart. Used by permission of the Jesse Stuart Foundation, P.O. Box #391, Ashland, KY 41114.

"Welcome," page 54. By Ouida Sebestyen. From SIXTEEN SHORT STORIES BY OUTSTANDING WRITERS FOR YOUNG ADULTS edited by Donald R. Gallo. "Welcome" copyright © 1984 by Ouida Sebestyen. Reprinted by permission of Delacorte Press, a division of BANTAM, DOUBLEDAY, DELL PUBLISHING GROUP, INC.

"Reduced," page 67. By Elizabeth Bowen. From THE COLLECTED STORIES OF ELIZABETH BOWEN. Copyright © 1981 by Curtis Brown Ltd., Literary Executors of the Estate of Elizabeth Bowen. Reprinted by permission of Alfred A. Knopf, Inc.

"The Drum," page 82. By Monica Furlong. From WINTER'S TALE. Copyright by author 1986. Reprinted by permission of Sanford J. Greenburger Associates, Inc.

"Broken Treaty," page 96. By Dion Henderson. Copyright © 1954 by FIELD AND STREAM. Reprinted by permission of Larry Sternig Literary Agent.

"The Night the Bed Fell," page 112. By James Thurber. Copyright © 1933, 1961 James Thurber. From MY LIFE AND HARD TIMES, published by Harper & Row.

"Pig-Hoo-o-o-o-ey!" page 121. By P. G. Wodehouse. From BLANDINGS CASTLE. Copyright © 1934, Doubleday. Reprinted by permission of the author and the author's agents, Scott Meredith Literary Agency, Inc., 845 Third Avenue, New York, New York 10022.

"The Aviarian," page 142. By Patricia McConnel. Copyright © 1985 by Pen American Center. Published by Ballentine Books, Random House. Reprinted by permission of PEN Syndicated Fiction Project.

"Sunday in the Park," page 178. By Bel Kaufman. From THE AVAILABLE PRESS/PEN SHORT STORY COLLECTION. Ballentine Books. Copyright 1985 by Pen American Center. Reprinted by permission of PEN Syndicated Fiction Project.

"Weekend," page 186. By Shirley Hazzard. Copyright © 1962 by Shirley Hazzard. First published in *The New Yorker*. Reprinted by permission of McIntosh and Otis, Inc.

"The Magic Barrel," page 198. By Bernard Malamud. From THE MAGIC BARREL by Bernard Malamud. Copyright © 1954, 1958 by Bernard Malamud. Reprinted by permission of Farrar, Straus and Giroux, Inc.

"The Darling," page 217. By Anton Chekhov. Reprinted with permission of Macmillan Publishing Company from THE DARLING AND OTHER STORIES by Anton Chekhov. Translated from the Russian by Constance Garnett. Copyright 1916 by Macmillan Company; copyright renewed 1944 by Constance Garnett. Canadian copyright, the Estate of Anton Chekhov, translator Constance Garnett. By permission of Chatto & Windus/The Hogarth Press.

"The Witch's Cat," page 240. By Manly Wade Wellman. From TREASURY OF GREAT CAT STORIES, edited by Roger Caras. Copyright © 1987 by Roger Caras. Reprinted by permission of the publisher, Dulton/Truman Talley, an imprint of New American Library, a division of Penguin Books USA Inc.

"Tricky Customers," page 259. By James Chatto. From WINTER'S TALE. Copyright by author 1986. Reprinted by permission of the author and The Carol Smith Literary Agency.

"The Man Who Could Work Miracles," page 273. By H. G. Wells. From THE COMPLETE STORIES OF H. G. WELLS. Reprinted by permission of A. P. Watt Limited on behalf of The Literary Executor of the Estate of H. G. Wells.

"Desire," page 292. By James Stephens. Reprinted by permission of Macmillan Publishing Company from ETCHED IN MOONLIGHT by James Stephens. Copyright 1928 The Macmillan Company; copyright renewed © 1955 Cynthia Stephens.

"Wild Men of Borneo," page 310. By Susan M. Dodd. Reprinted from OLD WIVES' TALES by Susan M. Dodd, by permission of the University of Iowa Press. Copyright 1984 by University of Iowa Press.

"Winterblossom Garden," page 322. By David Low. Reprinted by permission of the author.

"The Patterns of Love," page 338. By William Maxwell. Copyright 1945 by William Maxwell. Reprinted from OVER BY THE RIVER AND OTHER STORIES by William Maxwell, by permission of Alfred A. Knopf, Inc.

"A Poetics for Bullies," page 349. By Stanley Elkin. From CRIERS AND KIBITZERS, KIBITZERS AND CRIERS. Published by Random House (1965), Thunder's Mouth Press (1990). Reprinted by permission of Georges Borchardt, Inc. for the author. Copyright © 1965 by Stanley Elkin.

"The Killers," page 374. By Ernest Hemingway. Reprinted by permission of Charles Scribner's Sons, an imprint of Macmillan Publishing Company, from MEN WITHOUT WOMEN by Ernest Hemingway. Copyright 1927 by Charles Scribner's Sons; copyright renewed 1955 by Ernest Hemingway.

"Graven Image," page 387. By John O'Hara. Copyright 1943 and renewed 1971 by John O'Hara. Reprinted from SELECTED SHORT STORIES OF JOHN O'HARA, by permission of Random House, Inc. Originally appeared in *The New Yorker.*

"The Old Man," page 396. By Daphne du Maurier. Copyright 1953 by Daphne du Maurier. From KISS ME AGAIN STRANGER by Daphne du Maurier. Used by permission of Doubleday, a division of BANTAM, DOUBLEDAY, DELL PUBLISHING GROUP, INC.

"The Avenging Chance," page 409. By Anthony Berkeley. Copyright © 1928 by The Society of Authors. Reprinted by permission of The Society of Authors.

"The Valley of Echoes," page 436. By Gérard Klein. Translated by Frank Zero from VIEW FROM ANOTHER SHORE edited by Franz Rottensteiner. English translation © 1973 by the Continuum Publishing Company. Reprinted by permission of the publisher.

"Cephes 5," page 449. By Howard Fast. Copyright © 1975 by Howard Fast. From TIME AND THE RIDDLE, Houghton Mifflin Company, 1980. Reprinted by permission of Sterling Lord Literistic, Inc.

"Harrison Bergeron," page 463. By Kurt Vonnegut, Jr. From WELCOME TO THE MONKEY HOUSE by Kurt Vonnegut, Jr. Copyright © 1961 by Kurt Von-

More Short Stories

There are many theories about the origin of language. One half-seriously suggests that the first human speech sounds were those of parents trying to communicate with their frisky young. Perhaps an early communication might have been translated something like this: "Watch out for that saber-toothed tiger!" Study of various animal species shows a close interaction between parents and young, with warnings of danger commonplace.

One of the enduring themes of literature is the generation gap . . . as one generation tries to understand another. The movies and television have presented many situations dealing with this not-always-successful effort. The four stories in this unit illuminate some of the bittersweet aspects of attempted communication across the generations.

1

Across the Generations

Each generation has a different language, and can't learn what former generations knew until it has been translated into their own words.

Katherine Butler Hathaway

The stories are varied in setting and characterization. In one story, a son tries to come to grips with the impending split between his mother and father. Another shows us the fantasies of early childhood and the confusion they engender in parents. A third considers one of the most distressing problems of all: the alienation of a teenager. Finally, as a kind of finale to generation-gap problems, the fourth shows us a person at the other end of the time scale: a quiet old man who is happy to meet another April.

All four stories analyze the thoughts, emotions, and actions of human beings trying to solve the problems of living with conflict, love, and concern.

Reading the Light

ROGER PFINGSTON

"I don't want to talk about it," Brian said. "I just want to go back to the house while I've still got plenty of film left."

"Film is no problem," David said. "I have lots of film in my camera bag. Don't you think we should talk about this a little before we go back?"

Brian didn't respond.

In *Anna Karenina,* Count Leo Tolstoy wrote, "Happy families are all alike; every unhappy family is unhappy in its own way." "Reading the Light" is a subtle examination of an "ideal" family—mother, father, son, daughter. A consuming interest in photography joins father and son in a pleasurable pursuit. A visit to the grandfather's provides the context for an absorbing story.

The basic situation is not set forth directly and obviously. Rather, the reader must look for clues, asking, "What kind of person is David? What is his relationship with his son? What is Brian thinking as he shoots picture after picture in the cold morning light?" When David says, "Seeing is the important thing," we realize later that this statement is ironic. Brian does see—only too clearly. His is a silent cry across the generations, a not uncommon cry in today's world.

A story title often has an indirect, symbolic meaning as well as an obvious one. Does "Reading the Light" have more meaning than just as a photographic term?

Reading the Light

Without a coat or hat, keys in hand, David Thompson ran out into the ten-degree weather. From inside the car the glow of light through the ice-encrusted windshield triggered a quick fantasy, as if he were a character in a Jack London survival story.

On the third try the engine roared with good news. Shivering, he pumped the gas pedal, holding it halfway to the floor for several seconds at a time. When he was sure the car would keep running on its own, he turned on the heat and defroster and ran back to the house where his wife stood behind the front door, peering through the glass and holding up his coat and hat as a gentle reprimand.

Inside, he rubbed his hands together and sat down near the window, where he could keep an eye on the car, hoping it wouldn't die.

His wife brought a large mug of coffee that he gulped while watching the exhaust puff up and whip around the car before dissipating in the clean, sharp light of morning. The ice was beginning to give way to the heat rushing up the windshield, forming curious abstractions that tempted him. He decided he would resist this time; besides, he'd shot that sort of thing often enough.

He checked his watch—8:30—and figured he'd better be on his way if he wanted to work with some of that good early light. He had loaded his cameras the night before, cleaned the lenses and filters, gone through the whole ritual of preparing himself, very much like a hunter, but in his case it was all for the glory of light, a phrase that he kept to himself since it would probably sound a little hokey to others, even his wife, who had lived with his obsession for nearly fifteen years.

Fifteen years of traveling back and forth between Indiana and Hoopeston, Illinois, sweet-corn capital of the world, never tiring of the farmland, passing the time while driving by playing a game of Count the Hawks with himself or his family, trying to spot the birds as they sailed or topped trees and telephone poles with their impressive silhouettes.

On the way over this time there'd been the back-lit, wind-driven snow near Crawfordsville, a couple of icy hills in Danville that challenged his driving skills, the kids sleeping through it all in the backseat, and then the final stretch over land that never ceased to intrigue him with its incredible flatness, rich and black. It was his wife's home ground, but he felt a nearness to it, a spiritual tie that resulted, he knew, from photographing it over the years through all the seasons.

They made the 150-mile trip from Bloomington to Hoopeston two or three times a year, and always at Christmas unless the weather made it impossible. In the summer, Hoopeston being a canning town, they could smell it before they ever saw it. Mostly it was the tomato pits that "did the dirty deed," as the kids described it. Like a lot of people in town, his wife had put in her time, usually summers between college years, chopping worms out of corn for Stokely–Van Camp.

The flash startled him. He turned to see his son bundled up, smiling at having caught a candid of his dad with a mouthful of coffee cup.

"What kept you?"

"I had trouble loading the film, but I think it's all right now. See?" Brian held the camera out so his dad could see the rewind knob turning as he advanced the film to the next frame.

"Looks good," David said. "You won't need the flash where we're going. No sense dragging it along. Remember, keep your shooting simple and unburdensome." He wished he hadn't said the latter. It was the teacher in him and he knew how his twelve-year-old son reacted to that most of the time. Brian looked up at his mother and frowned. He said he'd like to take the flash along, just in case.

David decided that it wasn't worth arguing over. He grabbed his coat and hat, his camera bag, and, after hesitating, a tripod, even though he was sure he wouldn't use it. Brian's words echoed in his head: *just in case*. . . .

As David pulled out of the driveway, he said to Brian that he thought they would head out west of town and cut through the cemetery so Brian could get a few shots of the snow-covered tank, World War I vintage. Even though he knew it was a memorial of sorts to the war dead, he always thought of it as a huge oddity among the tombstones.

David drove through the entrance and stopped directly in front of the tank, about twenty feet away. He suggested that Brian try a few head-on shots and then walk around the tank to see what other views might interest him.

Without saying much, Brian got out of the car, took the obligatory head-on shot, and then walked to the back of the tank, where he was out of sight for several minutes.

David started to get out of the car when Brian suddenly appeared on top of the tank, slipping now and then as he inched his way to the front. David was worried that he might damage the camera, or, worse, hurt himself. He also worried that someone passing by might wonder what was going on. As Brian straddled the protruding gun, he yelled something that

David couldn't understand. David rolled the window down and yelled back, "Brian, what are you up to? Don't forget that's a two-hundred-dollar camera you've got there!"

"Gun it, Dad! Gun the motor! I want lots of exhaust all around the car when I take the picture." He was sitting in about an inch of snow, his arms parallel to and tight against his body, the camera pressed to his right eye and resting firmly in the palm of his left hand as he focused with his thumb and forefinger, the forefinger of his right hand poised to release the shutter. He was doing everything that David had taught him.

Pressing the pedal to the floor, David smiled as the sunlit exhaust enveloped the car.

They drove through the cemetery and out the back entrance onto the narrow road, a straight shot of blacktop with plowed ground on either side and what seemed an endless rhythm of telephone poles on their left.

Brian asked his dad to pull over. David hung his camera over his shoulder, thinking they would shoot this one together. As they walked in front of the car, David started to explain how to expose for a silhouette when he realized that Brian had gone off to the right into the field, squatting low to shoot the contrasting effect of snow-covered hunks of black earth in the foreground with the cemetery in the background. It was a good shot. Pretty soon, Brian came over and shot a few verticals of the road and the telephone poles disappearing into infinity.

As they continued their drive, David commented that he thought Brian was getting some good shots.

"I hope so," Brian said. "They sure look good when I'm taking them. Do they always come out as good as they look in the camera?"

"Not always," David said. He went on to explain a little about the printing process, how seeing well and printing technique combined to make the final image. "But seeing is the important thing. Most people can learn to develop film and make fairly decent prints, but not everybody has a good eye for photographs."

Brian shook his head yes without saying anything. They both remained silent for the next two or three minutes until Brian suddenly asked if they could go back to the house.

More than a little surprised, David asked why. "We're just getting started," he said.

"I want to take some pictures of you and Mom together. We could walk down to the park and I could take pictures of you and Mom . . . just walking or standing by some trees."

"That's ridiculous, Brian. I thought we were going to spend the morning together. I'll show you some of the spots I've photographed over the past fifteen years—bridges, silos, one-lane roads running between fields. There's a pond east of here where we could get some good ice pictures."

Brian stared out the window, his fingers playing nervously with the focusing ring of his camera.

"I heard you and Mom talking to Grandpa Bill last night."

David felt a tightening in his chest. Cattle and farmhouses slid by on either side. At one point he considered stopping for a shot of a frozen stream winding past a dilapidated barn.

"Is it really such a surprise?" he asked. He figured Brian had heard enough to know what was going on. "I'm sure you know that your mother and I haven't been the best of friends lately."

"I don't want to talk about it," Brian said. "I just want to go back to the house while I've still got plenty of film left."

"Film's no problem," David said. "I have lots of film in my camera bag. Don't you think we should talk about this a little before we go back?"

Brian didn't respond. Instead, he turned his back to David and stared out the window. The landscape blurred to a soft focus as the tears started.

At the crossroads David slowed the car and made a U-turn. On the way back he kept wondering how Marcia would take this. Maybe he wouldn't say a thing about it, just walk to the park and let Brian take his pictures. Afterwards, maybe the three of them could talk about what was going on, get some things said before going home tomorrow. He wondered if Brian had said anything to his sister. He felt bad, too, about hitting Bill with all of this right here at Christmas, especially when he wasn't doing too well himself, being 75 and diabetic. He wished Ginny, Bill's wife for 52 years, were still alive.

As he pulled into the driveway, David suggested that Brian not say anything to his mother about what he'd heard last night—not yet.

As soon as he saw the two of them sitting at the kitchen table, David knew that Bill and Marcia had been talking about things again. She tried to smile at Brian, who stood back and waited. Obviously, she hadn't expected them back so soon.

"That was a short trip," Bill said. "Get too cold for you?" He looked at Brian and said, "You know, your dad and I used to go out when it was colder than this and spend the whole morning taking pictures. Sometimes our fingers would get so numb we could hardly advance the film. You want some hot chocolate?"

David looked at Marcia and said, "Brian wants us to walk to the park, where he can take some pictures of the two of us."

Marcia knew that something was wrong. She called to Melissa, their seven-year-old daughter, to see if she'd like to go for a walk to the park, but she said she'd rather watch TV.

Brian spoke up that he just wanted David and Marcia. "You and Dad," he said.

Bill said that he would make David and Brian some hot chocolate while Marcia dressed and got herself together for the two-block walk to the park.

Not much was said as they walked, Brian a few steps ahead, glancing back now and then, his camera swinging from his shoulder. David was thinking that Brian looked like a short photojournalist bent on some assignment that involved this somber, middle-aged couple treading through the snow as if they were being led to a place that required their presence in order to make the story complete. He imagined the story appearing in the Sunday magazine of the *Chicago Tribune*, or maybe *Life*. Maybe a *Life* cover, a stark black and white portrait of Marcia and himself, blurred snow stopped between them and the camera, and inside the magazine grainy blowups with deep, velvety blacks complementing a four-page story. David was trying to think what their story might be when he realized that they were in the park and that Brian was asking them to go and stand in the middle of the frozen pond.

The pond reflected the brilliance of the sun like a giant mirror. David knew that the built-in light meter in Brian's camera would be fooled by the brightness, resulting in underexposure, if he didn't first come up close and take a reading off their faces. He waited to see what his son would do.

Brian raised the camera to his eye and held it there for several seconds. David and Marcia smiled as best they could, their arms around each other. David kept waiting for the sound of the shutter. He even tried for a little humor, asking if they should say cheese, or better yet, cheese pleez.

In spite of the sun, it was getting awfully cold. The wind-chill factor must've been ten or fifteen below.

Suddenly Brian lowered the camera and walked up to them, saying that he remembered he'd better check the light.

They could see that he'd been crying, that his eyelashes were actually showing traces of frost. David wondered if he was having trouble focusing. When Marcia saw Brian's eyes she made a small cry and hugged him to her thick pea coat, one that David had worn in the navy. The three of them stood huddled in the glare of ice and sun.

And then, still determined to take his pictures, Brian raised the camera to their faces and read the light.

Reading for Understanding

☐ MAIN IDEA

1. Which of the following statements best expresses the main idea of the story? (a) Photography is always a demanding hobby. (b) Divorce can be a terrible experience for the child of a marriage. (c) A harsh climate provides many challenges for the amateur photographer. (d) An interest in a hobby makes a sound contribution toward mental health.

☐ DETAILS

2. The story takes place during (a) a raging blizzard in Illinois (b) a Thanksgiving trip to a grandfather's (c) a Christmas holiday season (d) Brian's birthday celebration.

3. The first photographic subject was (a) a gnarled tree (b) the car's exhaust (c) telephone poles (d) a tank.
4. Melissa is the name of (a) Brian's mother (b) Marcia's sister (c) David's daughter (d) Bill's niece.
5. The last picture taken by Brian was of (a) David and Marcia (b) Grandpa Bill (c) weather-beaten trees (d) Marcia alone.

☐ INFERENCES

6. The most important sentence in the story is the following: (a) "I have lots of film in my camera bag." (b) "But seeing is the most important thing." (c) "I heard you and Mom talking to Grandpa Bill last night." (d) He wished Ginny, Bill's wife for 52 years, were still alive.
7. The obsession mentioned on page 3 is (a) fast driving (b) photography (c) drinking coffee (d) reading stories by Jack London.
8. Brian's mood throughout the story might be characterized as (a) sad (b) joyous (c) destructive (d) enthusiastic.
9. Brian wants to take pictures of his parents together because (a) he realizes they are separating (b) he usually includes people in his photographs (c) his parents make an ideal couple (d) he is in a photo contest calling for people as subjects.

☐ AUTHOR'S ATTITUDE

10. The author's attitude toward Brian is (a) indifferent (b) sympathetic (c) annoyed (d) impatient.

☐ ORDER OF EVENTS

11. Arrange the items in the order in which they occurred. Use letters only.
    A. Marcia and David do not get along.
    B. David and Brian set out early for good pictures.
    C. Brian says he overheard David and Marcia talking to Bill.
    D. Brian takes a picture of his parents.
    E. Brian climbs on top of the tank.

☐ OUTCOMES

12. After the story, (a) Brian becomes a professional photographer (b) David gives up photography (c) Marcia and David separate (d) Bill blames David for all the trouble.

❑ CAUSE AND EFFECT

13. At first Brian fails to take the picture of Marcia and David because (a) a cloud has obscured the sun (b) his camera has frozen in the cold (c) somebody has moved (d) he is overcome by emotion.

❑ FACT OR OPINION

Tell whether each of the following is a fact or an opinion.

14. Marcia and David were cruel and inconsiderate.

15. Brian was a better photographer than David.

Words in Context

❑ A. GENERAL TERMS

1. "... where his wife stood ... holding up his coat and hat as a gentle *reprimand.*" ***Reprimand*** (page 3) means (a) reminder (b) commentary (c) scolding (d) symbol.

2. "... watching the exhaust puff up and whip around the car before *dissipating* in the clean, sharp light ..." ***Dissipating*** (3) means (a) scattering (b) falling (c) condensing (d) developing.

3. "The ice was beginning to give way ... forming curious *abstractions* that tempted him." ***Abstractions*** (3) means (a) forms (b) landscapes (c) questions (d) characters.

4. "He had ... gone through the whole *ritual* of preparing himself, very much like a hunter ..." ***Ritual*** (3) means (a) established custom (b) expense (c) religious statements (d) trouble.

5. "... a phrase that he kept to himself since it would probably sound a little *hokey* to others ..." ***Hokey*** (3) means (a) crude (b) too sharp (c) over-sentimental (d) too strong.

6. "... even his wife, who had lived with his *obsession* for nearly fifteen years." ***Obsession*** (3) means (a) stubbornness (b) preoccupation (c) hobby (d) childish fantasy.

7. "... so Brian could get a few shots of the snow-covered tank, World War I *vintage.*" ***Vintage*** (4) means (a) relic (b) period (c) framework (d) monument.

8. "Without saying much, Brian got out of the car, took the *obligatory* head-on shot, and then walked to the back ..." ***Obligatory*** (4) means (a) sensational (b) ordinary (c) rare (d) required.

9. "As Brian *straddled the protruding gun, . . .*" ***Straddled the protruding gun*** (4) means (a) shot the old-fashioned gun (b) examined the rusting gun (c) pointed at the long gun (d) sat on the gun that jutted out.

10. ". . . bent on some assignment that involved this somber, middle-aged couple *treading* through the snow . . ." ***Treading*** (6) means (a) hurrying (b) gliding (c) walking (d) crashing.

11. "Maybe a *Life* cover, a *stark* black and white portrait of Marcia and himself . . ." ***Stark*** (7) means (a) fearsome (b) subdued (c) telltale (d) harsh.

12. ". . . and inside the magazine grainy blowups with deep, velvety blacks *complementing* a four-page story." ***Complementing*** (7) means (a) in praise of (b) completing (c) creating contrast for (d) along with.

☐ B. TERMS FROM PHOTOGRAPHY

13. ". . . besides, he'd shot that sort of thing often enough" (3) means he had (a) seen (b) taken (c) sold (d) discussed similar pictures.

14. "He had loaded his cameras" (3) means he had (a) cleaned (b) checked (c) placed film in (d) placed the cameras in the car.

15. "On the way over this time there'd been the back-lit, wind-driven snow . . ." (3) means that he had been driving (a) toward the sun (b) away from the sun (c) at daybreak (d) at sunset.

16. "The flash startled him" (4) when his son (a) called out a warning (b) spoke to his wife (c) commented on the scenery (d) took a picture with added light.

17. "He turned to see his son bundled up, smiling at having caught a candid of his dad with a mouthful of coffee cup" (4) means that his son had taken (a) a good (b) an unposed (c) a carefully planned (d) an unfocused picture.

18. ". . . he advanced the film to the next frame" (4) means that the camera was (a) replaced in the case (b) taken out of the case (c) mishandled (d) ready to take the next picture.

19. "He grabbed . . . a tripod" (4) that he would use to (a) raise (b) steady (c) level (d) store the camera.

20. "He suggested that Brian try a few head-on shots" (4) by standing (a) closer to (b) farther away from (c) on an elevation away from (d) directly in front of the tank.

21. "He focused with his thumb" (5) to (a) snap the picture (b) adjust the light (c) move the film forward (d) sharpen the image.

22. "Pretty soon, Brian came over and shot a few verticals" (5) by holding the camera (a) sideways (b) upside down (c) tilted toward the ground (d) tilted upward.

23. "The landscape blurred to a *soft focus* as the tears started." In a ***soft focus*** (6) the main details become (a) clearer (b) sharply contrasted (c) less distinct (d) more understandable.

24. ". . . and inside the magazine *grainy blowups* . . . ***Grainy blowups***" (7) are (a) particles of snow (b) blended portraits (c) miniature portraits (d) enlargements with contrasting light and dark particles.

25. "Reading the light" is necessary to make certain that (a) everything is in focus (b) the shot is well composed (c) the picture has depth of focus (d) the true values of lightness and darkness are caught.

Thinking Critically About the Story

1. Would the story have been more effective if the author had included incidents and reasons that led to the impending breakup of the family? Explain.

2. How does Brian handle his father's repetitious need to tell him how to take the pictures? How does Brian's approach compare with yours? What could each of you learn from the method and approach of the other?

3. At what point does Marcia show that she is reading the light accurately? At what point does David show that he is reading the light with fuller understanding?

4. The author deliberately uses ambiguity to involve the reader: Why do the parents speak to Bill separately? Why aren't we told what they said? What is the significance of the last scene? What doesn't the author tell us about the last scene? What happens after the story ends? How does ambiguity affect the quality of the story? What does the ambiguity reveal about the author's purpose?

5. The story is told in a series of photographic snapshots. Which scene impressed you most? How does the author use these snapshots to develop the reader's insights?

Stories in Words

Dilapidated (page 6) derives from the Latin *lapis*, "stone." By derivation, *dilapidated* means "having stones fall down." Strictly speaking, the word should be restricted to crumbling *stone* walls and ruined *stone* castles, but the word has left its limits behind. A decaying wooden structure or an old wreck of a car may now be called *dilapidated.* Related words include *lapidary* ("a cutter of precious *stones*") and *lapis lazuli* ("azure *stone*").

Silhouette (page 5) arose from the name of a finance minister during the reign of Louis XV of France. He had been appointed to control the runaway expenditures of the French government, but when he tried to place restrictions on the spending of the king himself, he fell from favor. During his tenure of office, he instituted many small taxes that annoyed the nobility. The phrase *à la silhouette* meant "in a cheap way." Even portraits done in profile without other details were said to be done *à la silhouette*. The name remains even today for a featureless outline.

Focused (page 5) is related to a fireplace, hearth. The word *focus* now means "the point at which rays of light, heat, or sound come together." What connection does *hearth* have with photography? If a magnifying glass is held up to the sun, the point at which the sun's rays come together is the focus, or burning point. The first modern use of the word was by the German astronomer, Johannes Kepler, in 1604. He called *focus* "the burning point." The word was soon picked up by others, and the meanings extended to geometry, optics, and everyday life. There is a story that a ranch out West was called *Focus*, the place where "the sons raise meat" ("sun's rays meet").

Charles

SHIRLEY JACKSON

On Saturday I remarked to my husband, "Do you think kindergarten is too unsettling for Laurie? All this toughness and bad grammar, and this Charles boy sounds like such a bad influence."

"It'll be all right," my husband said reassuringly.

A *rite of passage* is a period in a person's life of crucial importance, a time of significant change. "Charles" is about a young boy who faces his own rite of passage: beginning school.

Laurie's personality changes when he attends kindergarten. He develops a new quality of independence, unfortunately tinged with disrespect. In his daily reports of school events, Laurie describes the escapades of a boy, Charles, who finds it difficult to fit into the routines of kindergarten. Charles is different from the other children, a person so colorful Laurie's mother cannot wait to meet Charles's mother. At last a partial opportunity arises, and Laurie's mother meets the teacher.

"Charles" is a lighthearted look at early childhood, at a time when options are still open and understanding is crucial in parenting. In this story, Shirley Jackson, author of "The Lottery," brings a little boy to life—with humor as well as insight. There is an interesting postscript: one of Shirley Jackson's own children was named *Laurie.*

Charles

The day my son Laurie started kindergarten he renounced corduroy overalls with bibs and began wearing blue jeans with a belt. I watched him go off the first morning with the older girl next door, seeing clearly that an era of my life was ended, my sweet-voiced nursery-school tot replaced by a long-trousered, swaggering character who forgot to stop at the corner and wave good-bye to me.

He came home the same way, the front door slamming open, his hat on the floor, and the voice suddenly become raucous shouting, "Isn't anybody *here*?"

At lunch he spoke insolently to his father, spilled his baby sister's milk, and remarked that his teacher said we were not to take the name of the Lord in vain.

"How *was* school today?" I asked, elaborately casual.

"All right," he said.

"Did you learn anything?" his father asked.

Laurie regarded his father coldly. "I didn't learn nothing," he said.

"Anything," I said. "Didn't learn anything."

"The teacher spanked a boy, though," Laurie said, addressing his bread and butter. "For being fresh," he added, with his mouth full.

"What did he do?" I asked. "Who was it?"

Laurie thought. "It was Charles," he said. "He was fresh. The teacher spanked him and made him stand in a corner. He was awfully fresh."

"What did he do?" I asked again, but Laurie slid off his chair, took a cookie, and left, while his father was still saying, "See here, young man."

The next day Laurie remarked at lunch, as soon as he sat down, "Well, Charles was bad again today." He grinned enormously and said, "Today Charles hit the teacher."

"Good heavens," I said, mindful of the Lord's name. "I suppose he got spanked again?"

"He sure did," Laurie said. "Look up," he said to his father.

"What?" his father said, looking up.

"Look down," Laurie said. "Look at my thumb. Gee, you're dumb." He began to laugh insanely.

"Why did Charles hit the teacher?" I asked quickly.

"Because she tried to make him color with red crayons," Laurie said. "Charles wanted to color with green crayons so he hit the teacher and she spanked him and said nobody play with Charles but everybody did."

The third day—it was Wednesday of the first week—Charles bounced a see-saw on the head of a little girl and made her bleed, and the teacher made him stay inside all during recess. Thursday Charles had to stand in a corner during story-time because he kept pounding his feet on the floor. Friday Charles was deprived of blackboard privileges because he threw chalk.

On Saturday I remarked to my husband, "Do you think kindergarten is too unsettling for Laurie? All this toughness and bad grammar, and this Charles boy sounds like such a bad influence."

"It'll be all right," my husband said reassuringly. "Bound to be people like Charles in the world. Might as well meet them now as later."

On Monday Laurie came home late, full of news. "Charles," he shouted as he came up the hill; I was waiting anxiously on the front steps. "Charles," Laurie yelled all the way up the hill, "Charles was bad again."

"Come right in," I said, as soon as he came close enough. "Lunch is waiting."

"You know what Charles did?" he demanded, following me through the door. "Charles yelled so in school they sent a boy in from first grade to tell the teacher she had to make Charles keep quiet, and so Charles had to stay after school. And so all the children stayed to watch him."

"What did he do?" I asked.

"He just sat there," Laurie said, climbing into his chair at the table. "Hi, Pop, y'old dust mop."

"Charles had to stay after school today," I told my husband. "Everyone stayed with him."

"What does this Charles look like?" my husband asked Laurie. "What's his other name?"

"He's bigger than me," Laurie said. "And he doesn't have any rubbers and he doesn't ever wear a jacket."

Monday night was the first Parent-Teachers meeting, and only the fact that the baby had a cold kept me from going; I wanted passionately to meet Charles's mother. On Tuesday Laurie remarked suddenly, "Our teacher had a friend come to see her in school today."

"Charles's mother?" my husband and I asked simultaneously.

"Naaah," Laurie said scornfully. "It was a man who came and made us do exercises, we had to touch our toes. Look." He climbed down from his chair and squatted down and touched his toes. "Like this," he said. He got solemnly back into his chair and said, picking up his fork, "Charles didn't even *do* exercises."

"That's fine," I said heartily. "Didn't Charles want to do the exercises?"

"Naaah," Laurie said. "Charles was so fresh to the teacher's friend he wasn't *let* do exercises."

"Fresh again," I said.

"He kicked the teacher's friend," Laurie said. "The teacher's friend told Charles to touch his toes like I just did and Charles kicked him."

"What are they going to do about Charles, do you suppose?" Laurie's father asked him.

Laurie shrugged elaborately. "Throw him out of school, I guess," he said.

Wednesday and Thursday were routine; Charles yelled during story hour and hit a boy in the stomach and made him cry. On Friday Charles stayed after school again and so did all the other children.

With the third week of kindergarten Charles was an institution in our family; the baby was being a Charles when he filled his wagon full of mud and pulled it through the kitchen; even my husband, when he caught his elbow in the telephone cord and pulled telephone, ashtray, and a bowl of flowers off the table, said, after the first minute, "Looks like Charles."

During the third and fourth weeks it looked like a reformation in Charles; Laurie reported grimly at lunch on Thursday of the third week, "Charles was so good today the teacher gave him an apple."

"What?" I said, and my husband added warily, "You mean Charles?"

"Charles," Laurie said. "He gave the crayons around and he picked up the books afterward and the teacher said he was her helper."

"What happened?" I asked incredulously.

"He was her helper, that's all," Laurie said, and shrugged.

"Can this be true, about Charles?" I asked my husband that night. "Can something like this happen?"

"Wait and see," my husband said cynically. "When you've got a Charles to deal with, this may mean he's only plotting."

He seemed to be wrong. For over a week Charles was the teacher's helper; each day he handed things out and he picked things up; no one had to stay after school.

"The PTA meeting's next week again," I told my husband one evening. "I'm going to find Charles's mother there."

"Ask her what happened to Charles," my husband said. "I'd like to know."

"I'd like to know myself," I said.

On Friday of that week things were back to normal. "You know what Charles did today?" Laurie demanded at the lunch table, in a voice slightly awed. "He told a little girl to say a word and she said it and the teacher washed her mouth out with soap and Charles laughed."

"What word?" his father asked unwisely, and Laurie said, "I'll have to whisper it to you, it's so bad." He got down off his chair and went around to his father. His father bent his head down and Laurie whispered joyfully. His father's eyes widened.

"Did Charles tell the little girl to say *that*?" he asked respectfully.

"She said it *twice*," Laurie said. "Charles told her to say it *twice*."

"What happened to Charles?" my husband asked.

"Nothing," Laurie said. "He was passing out the crayons."

Monday morning Charles abandoned the little girl and said the evil word himself three or four times, getting his mouth washed out with soap each time. He also threw chalk.

My husband came to the door with me that evening as I set out for the PTA meeting. "Invite her over for a cup of tea after the meeting," he said. "I want to get a look at her."

"If only she's there," I said prayerfully.

"She'll be there," my husband said. "I don't see how they could hold a PTA meeting without Charles's mother."

At the meeting I sat restlessly, scanning each comfortable matronly face, trying to determine which one hid the secret of Charles. None of them looked to me haggard enough. No one stood up in the meeting and apologized for the way her son had been acting. No one mentioned Charles.

After the meeting I identified and sought out Laurie's kindergarten teacher. She had a plate with a cup of tea and a piece of chocolate cake; I had a plate with a cup of tea and a piece of marshmallow cake. We maneuvered up to one another cautiously, and smiled.

"I've been so anxious to meet you," I said. "I'm Laurie's mother."

"We're all so interested in Laurie," she said.

"Well, he certainly likes kindergarten," I said. "He talks about it all the time."

"We had a little trouble adjusting, the first week or so," she said primly, "but now he's a fine little helper. With occasional lapses, of course."

"Laurie usually adjusts very quickly," I said. "I suppose this time it's Charles's influence."

"Charles?"

"Yes," I said, laughing, "you must have your hands full in that kindergarten, with Charles."

"Charles?" she said. "We don't have any Charles in the kindergarten."

Reading for Understanding

❑ MAIN IDEA

1. The main idea of the story is that Charles is (a) Laurie's brother (b) a friend of Laurie's (c) an imaginary person (d) Laurie's teacher.

☐ DETAILS

2. Laurie changed his personality (a) when he entered kindergarten (b) after being punished by his mother (c) in nursery school (d) after being spanked by his father.

3. Among Charles's misdeeds was (a) smoking on school grounds (b) being fresh to Laurie (c) striking a first-grader (d) injuring a girl on the see-saw.

4. There was a change in Charles when he (a) became ill (b) was teacher's helper (c) became especially friendly with Laurie (d) was expelled from school.

5. Laurie's mother found out about Charles (a) one day after school (b) when Laurie confessed (c) at the PTA meeting (d) through Laurie's father.

☐ INFERENCES

6. When the narrator says, "Anything," in line 17, she is (a) showing a lack of interest in Laurie (b) correcting a misuse of a word (c) rejecting an easy solution for Laurie's problems (d) suggesting that Laurie actually learned something.

7. Laurie's report of Charles's misdeeds was probably a form of (a) release from tension (b) understatement (c) intentional viciousness (d) desire to tell the truth at any cost.

8. In going to the meeting, Laurie's mother hoped to (a) scold the teacher (b) check Laurie's seating arrangement (c) find Laurie's lost mittens (d) meet Charles's mother.

9. In solving Laurie's problems, the teacher used (a) psychology (b) sarcasm (c) humor (d) endless repetition.

10. Laurie's wish-fulfillment fantasy comes through best in which of the following statements?
    (a) "Nothing. He was passing out the crayons."
    (b) "He's bigger than me. And he doesn't have any rubbers and he doesn't ever wear a jacket."
    (c) "He was her helper, that's all."
    (d) "The teacher spanked a boy though. For being fresh."

☐ AUTHOR'S PURPOSE

11. The author's purpose is to (a) provide a commentary on the teaching methods used in kindergarten (b) reveal a little boy's fantasy in a lighthearted way (c) study the interrelationships in a family when

the first child goes off to kindergarten (d) make a study in depth of a life-threatening personality flaw.

❑ ORDER OF EVENTS

12. Arrange the items in the order in which they supposedly occurred. Use letters only.
   A. Laurie's mother goes to school.
   B. Charles uses the wrong crayons.
   C. Charles hits the teacher.
   D. Laurie's mother learns the truth about Charles.
   E. Charles makes a positive change.

❑ OUTCOMES

13. After the end of the story, (a) Charles is thrown out of school (b) the teacher gives Charles another seat (c) Laurie's mother has a better understanding of him (d) Laurie's mother and father divorce.

❑ CAUSE AND EFFECT

14. Laurie's behavior in school (a) caused his teacher to try some positive strategy on him (b) won the approval of Charles (c) made his father especially proud (d) made the teacher almost uncontrollably angry.

❑ FACT OR OPINION

Tell whether the following is a fact or an opinion.

15. Laurie got into a number of difficulties in kindergarten.

Words in Context

1. "The day my son Laurie started kindergarten he *renounced* corduroy overalls with bibs . . ." ***Renounced*** (14) means (a) accepted (b) chose (c) abandoned (d) wore.
2. "'How was school today?' I asked, elaborately *casual*." ***Casual*** (14) means (a) low-keyed (b) enthusiastic (c) formal (d) anxious.
3. "'Charles's mother?' my husband and I asked *simultaneously*." ***Simultaneously*** (15) means (a) loudly (b) quietly (c) in one voice (d) looking at each other.

4. "'What?' I said, and my husband added *warily*, 'You mean Charles?'" ***Warily*** (16) means (a) cautiously (b) slowly (c) quickly (d) with annoyance.

5. "'What happened?' I asked *incredulously*." ***Incredulously*** (16) means (a) fearfully (b) quickly (c) firmly (d) unbelievingly.

6. "'Wait and see,' my husband said *cynically*. 'When you've got a Charles to deal with, this may mean he's only plotting.'" ***Cynically*** (16) means (a) knowingly (b) doubtingly (c) convincingly (d) with finality.

7. "At the meeting I sat restlessly, scanning each comfortable *matronly* face, trying to determine which one hid the secret of Charles." ***Matronly*** (17) means belonging to a (a) tricky person (b) sensitive woman (c) mature woman (d) pleasant adult.

8. "None of them looked to me *haggard* enough." ***Haggard*** (17) means (a) careworn (b) rugged (c) diabolical (d) impatient.

9. "'We had a little trouble adjusting, the first week or so,' she said *primly*." ***Primly*** (17) means (a) firstly (b) stiffly, properly (c) slowly, hesitatingly (d) firmly, candidly.

10. ". . . but now he's a fine little helper. With *occasional lapses*, of course." ***Occasional lapses*** (17) means (a) frequent misdeeds (b) infrequent backsliding (c) much encouragement (d) excellent cooperation.

Thinking Critically About the Story

1. Compare Charles's attitude in class with Laurie's at home. To what extent were the parents to blame for Laurie's conduct in school? Explain.

2. Neither the teacher nor the parents ever come to grips with Laurie's lying, blaming someone else for his misconduct. How would you handle a Laurie? If you were the teacher? The parent?

3. The author, Shirley Jackson, is noted for her ability to paint a sharply defined picture in a few words. Select an example of this; be prepared to read it to the class and to justify your choice.

4. The author leaves the conclusion of the story up to the imagination of the reader. You have to decide how the parents deal with Laurie when they arrive home after meeting the teacher. What would you do if you were one of the parents? Does this twist add to or subtract from the worth of the story? Explain. How would you have ended this story?

5. What happens to youngsters like Laurie as they grow older? What causes some to outgrow this inability to grasp reality while others fall prey to human weaknesses throughout their lives? Explain.

Stories in Words

Kindergarten (page 14) has an interesting history. Once upon a time, teaching methods for the very young were quite severe. But an educator named Friedrich Wilhelm August Froebel believed that young children should be taught according to their natural instincts, handled with kindness and patience. He believed the child's interests should be stimulated and his or her creativity developed. He developed the world's first kindergarten, or "children's garden," in 1837. At first his ideas were scorned and criticized, but in time his views prevailed.

Corduroy (page 14), now a rather plain cotton, was once a regal silk. The word itself has a disputed origin. A favorite explanation, now rejected, is that it came from the French *corde du Roi* ("cord of the king"), but no such word has ever been used by the French. Another explanation is that it came from *cord* + *duroy*, a coarse woolen fabric. Still another explanation is that it is named from the first manufacturer's name, *Corderoy*. The word's meaning has been extended to *corduroy road*, built of logs laid side by side transversely. Anyone who has ever seen the distinctive pattern of corduroy can appreciate the aptness of the expression.

Husband (page 15) goes far back into English history. The first citation for *husband* in the *Oxford English Dictionary* is dated nearly a thousand years ago (about the year 1000). Here it means "master of the house," "male head of a household." Indeed the first element, *hus, house* is tied to the second element, *band,* which is related to the verb *dwell.* Thus a *husband* was originally a *house dweller,* a *house owner* when few people owned their own land. A husband was a good catch, and gradually the word changed its meaning. The first citation for "a man joined to a woman in marriage" is 1290.

Teenage Wasteland

ANNE TYLER

"I'll tell you what. Let's you and me try working together three nights a week. Think you could handle that? We'll see if we can show that school of yours a thing or two. Give it a month; then if you don't like it, we'll stop. If *I* don't like it, we'll stop. I mean, sometimes people just don't get along, right? What do you say to that?"

Earl Wilson once wrote, "Snow and adolescence are the only problems that disappear if you ignore them long enough." Through the ages, the old have often wondered about the young, but the young eventually become old in turn. The generations tend to work out their problems somehow—though not always.

Adolescence is a difficult time of life. Childish and mature impulses struggle for mastery. The struggle is sometimes sadly compounded by unfortunate accidents, indifferent adults, or parental cruelty. Sometimes, though, things don't work out despite the best intentions of all concerned.

In "Teenage Wasteland," Anne Tyler has written a disturbing contemporary story that might be acted out anywhere in America. There needn't be any malicious villains. Well-intentioned people may strive to the limits of their strength, without making a difference. Here, three well-drawn characters—Daisy, Donny, and Cal—play out their destiny without a clear view of their fate.

Teenage Wasteland

He used to have very blond hair—almost white—cut shorter than other children's so that on his crown a little cowlick always stood up to catch the light. But this was when he was small. As he grew older, his hair grew darker, and he wore it longer—past his collar even. It hung in lank, taffy-colored ropes around his face, which was still an endearing face, fine-featured, the eyes an unusual aqua blue. But his cheeks, of course, were no longer round, and a sharp new Adam's apple jogged in his throat when he talked.

In October, they called from the private school he attended to request a conference with his parents. Daisy went alone; her husband was at work. Clutching her purse, she sat on the principal's couch and learned that Donny was noisy, lazy, and disruptive; always fooling around with his friends, and he wouldn't respond in class.

In the past, before her children were born, Daisy had been a fourth-grade teacher. It shamed her now to sit before this principal as a parent, a delinquent parent, a parent who struck Mr. Lanham, no doubt, as unseeing or uncaring. "It isn't that we're not concerned," she said. "Both of us are. And we've done what we could, whatever we could think of. We don't let him watch TV on school nights. We don't let him talk on the phone till he's finished his homework. But he tells us he doesn't *have* any homework or he did it all in study hall. How are we to know what to believe?"

From early October through November, at Mr. Lanham's suggestion, Daisy checked Donny's assignments every day. She sat next to him as he worked, trying to be encouraging, sagging inwardly as she saw the poor quality of everything he did—the sloppy mistakes in math, the illogical leaps in his English themes, the history questions left blank if they required any research.

Daisy was often late starting supper, and she couldn't give as much attention to Donny's younger sister. "You'll never guess what happened at . . ." Amanda would begin, and Daisy would have to tell her, "Not now, honey."

By the time her husband, Matt, came home, she'd be snappish. She would recite the day's hardships—the fuzzy instructions in English, the botched history map, the morass of unsolvable algebra equations. Matt would look surprised and confused, and Daisy would gradually wind down. There was no way, really, to convey how exhausting all this was.

In December, the school called again. This time, they wanted Matt to come as well. She and Matt had to sit on Mr. Lanham's couch like two bad children and listen to the news: Donny had improved only slightly, raising a D in history to a C, and a C in algebra to a B-minus. What was worse, he had developed new problems. He had cut classes on at least three occasions. Smoked in the furnace room. Helped Sonny Barnett break into a freshman's locker. And last week, during athletics, he and three friends had been seen off the school grounds; when they returned, the coach had smelled beer on their breath.

Daisy and Matt sat silent, shocked. Matt rubbed his forehead with his fingertips. Imagine, Daisy thought, how they must look to Mr. Lanham: an overweight housewife in a cotton dress and a too-tall, too-thin insurance agent in a baggy, frayed suit. Failures, both of them—the kind of people who are always hurrying to catch up, missing the point of things that everyone else grasps at once. She wished she'd worn nylons instead of knee socks.

It was arranged that Donny would visit a psychologist for testing. Mr. Lanham knew just the person. He would set this boy straight, he said.

When they stood to leave, Daisy held her stomach in and gave Mr. Lanham a firm, responsible handshake.

Donny said the psychologist was a moron and the tests were really dumb; but he kept all three of his appointments, and when it was time for the follow-up conference with the psychologist and both parents, Donny combed his hair and seemed unusually sober and subdued. The psychologist said Donny had no serious emotional problems. He was merely going through a difficult period in his life. He required some academic help and a better sense of self-worth. For this reason, he was suggesting a man named Calvin Beadle, a tutor with considerable psychological training.

In the car going home, Donny said he'd be damned if he'd let them drag him to some stupid tutor. His father told him to watch his language in front of his mother.

That night, Daisy lay awake pondering the term "self-worth." She had always been free with her praise. She had always told Donny he had talent, was smart, was good with his hands. She had made a big to-do over every little gift he gave her. In fact, maybe she had gone too far, although, Lord knows, she had meant every word. Was that his trouble?

She remembered when Amanda was born. Donny had acted lost and bewildered. Daisy had been alert to that, of course, but still, a new baby keeps you so busy. Had she really done all she could have? She longed—

she ached—for a time machine. Given one more chance, she'd do it perfectly—hug him more, praise him more, or perhaps praise him less. Oh, who can say . . .

The tutor told Donny to call him Cal. All his kids did, he said. Daisy thought for a second that he meant his own children, then realized her mistake. He seemed too young, anyhow, to be a family man. He wore a heavy brown handlebar mustache. His hair was as long and stringy as Donny's, and his jeans as faded. Wire-rimmed spectacles slid down his nose. He lounged in a canvas director's chair with his fingers laced across his chest, and he casually, amiably questioned Donny, who sat upright and glaring in an armchair.

"So they're getting on your back at school," said Cal. "Making a big deal about anything you do wrong."

"Right," said Donny.

"Any idea why that would be?"

"Oh, well, you know, stuff like homework and all," Donny said.

"You don't do your homework?"

"Oh, well, I might do it sometimes but not just exactly like they want it." Donny sat forward and said, "It's like a prison there, you know? You've got to go to every class, you can never step off the school grounds."

"You cut classes sometimes?"

"Sometimes," Donny said, with a glance at his parents.

Cal didn't seem perturbed. "Well," he said, "I'll tell you what. Let's you and me try working together three nights a week. Think you could handle that? We'll see if we can show that school of yours a thing or two. Give it a month; then if you don't like it, we'll stop. If *I* don't like it, we'll stop. I mean, sometimes people just don't get along, right? What do you say to that?"

"Okay," Donny said. He seemed pleased.

"Make it seven o'clock till eight, Monday, Wednesday, and Friday," Cal told Matt and Daisy. They nodded. Cal shambled to his feet, gave them a little salute, and showed them to the door.

This was where he lived as well as worked, evidently. The interview had taken place in the dining room, which had been transformed into a kind of office. Passing the living room, Daisy winced at the rock music she had been hearing, without registering it, ever since she had entered the house. She looked in and saw a boy about Donny's age lying on a sofa with a book. Another boy and a girl were playing Ping-Pong in front of the fireplace. "You have several here together?" Daisy asked Cal.

"Oh, sometimes they stay on after their sessions, just to rap. They're a pretty sociable group, all in all. Plenty of goof-offs like young Donny here."

He cuffed Donny's shoulder playfully. Donny flushed and grinned.

Climbing into the car, Daisy asked Donny, "Well? What did you think?"

But Donny had returned to his old evasive self. He jerked his chin toward the garage. "Look," he said. "He's got a basketball net."

Now on Mondays, Wednesdays, and Fridays, they had supper early—

the instant Matt came home. Sometimes, they had to leave before they were really finished. Amanda would still be eating her dessert. "Bye, honey. Sorry," Daisy would tell her.

Cal's first bill sent a flutter of panic through Daisy's chest, but it was worth it, of course. Just look at Donny's face when they picked him up: alight and full of interest. The principal telephoned Daisy to tell her how Donny had improved. "Of course, it hasn't shown up in his grades yet, but several of the teachers have noticed how his attitude's changed. Yes, sir, I think we're onto something here."

At home, Donny didn't act much different. He still seemed to have a low opinion of his parents. But Daisy supposed that was unavoidable—part of being fifteen. He said his parents were too "controlling"—a word that made Daisy give him a sudden look. He said they acted like wardens. On weekends, they enforced a curfew. And any time he went to a party, they always telephoned first to see if adults would be supervising. "For God's sake!" he said. "Don't you trust me?"

"It isn't a matter of trust, honey . . ." But there was no explaining to him.

His tutor called one afternoon. "I get the sense," he said, "that this kid's feeling . . . underestimated, you know? Like you folks expect the worst of him. I'm thinking we ought to give him more rope."

"But see, he's still so suggestible," Daisy said. "When his friends suggest some mischief—smoking or drinking or such—why, he just finds it very hard not to go along with them."

"Mrs. Coble," the tutor said, "I think this kid is hurting. You know? Here's a serious, sensitive kid, telling you he'd like to take on some grown-up challenges, and you're giving him the message that he can't be trusted. Don't you understand how that hurts?"

"Oh," said Daisy.

"It undermines his self-esteem—don't you realize that?"

"Well, I guess you're right," said Daisy. She saw Donny suddenly from a whole new angle: his pathetically poor posture, that slouch so forlorn that his shoulders seemed about to meet his chin . . . oh, wasn't it awful being young? She'd had a miserable adolescence herself and had always sworn no child of hers would ever be that unhappy.

They let Donny stay out later, they didn't call ahead to see if the parties were supervised, and they were careful not to grill him about his evening. The tutor had set down so many rules! They were not allowed any questions at all about any aspect of school, nor were they to speak with his teachers. If a teacher had some complaint, she should phone Cal. Only one teacher disobeyed—the history teacher, Miss Evans. She called one morning in February. "I'm a little concerned about Donny, Mrs. Coble."

"Oh, I'm sorry, Miss Evans, but Donny's tutor handles these things now . . ."

"I always deal directly with the parents. You are the parent," Miss Evans said, speaking very slowly and distinctly. "Now, here is the problem.

Back when you were helping Donny with his homework, his grades rose from a D to a C, but now they've slipped back, and they're closer to an F."

"They are?"

"I think you should start overseeing his homework again."

"But Donny's tutor says . . ."

"It's nice that Donny has a tutor, but you should still be in charge of his homework. With you, he learned it. Then he passed his tests. With the tutor, well, it seems the tutor is more of a crutch. 'Donny,' I say, 'a quiz is coming up on Friday. Hadn't you better be listening instead of talking?' 'That's okay, Miss Evans,' he says. 'I have a tutor now.' Like a talisman! I really think you ought to take over, Mrs. Coble."

"I see," said Daisy. "Well, I'll think about that. Thank you for calling."

Hanging up, she felt a rush of anger at Donny. A talisman! For a talisman, she'd given up all luxuries, all that time with her daughter, her evenings at home!

She dialed Cal's number. He sounded muzzy. "I'm sorry if I woke you," she told him, "but Donny's history teacher just called. She says he isn't doing well."

"She should have dealt with me."

"She wants me to start supervising his homework again. His grades are slipping."

"Yes," said the tutor, "but you and I both know there's more to it than mere grades, don't we? I care about the *whole* child—his happiness, his self-esteem. The grades will come. Just give them time."

When she hung up, it was Miss Evans she was angry at. What a narrow woman!

It was Cal this, Cal that, Cal says this, Cal and I did that. Cal lent Donny an album by the Who. He took Donny and two other pupils to a rock concert. In March, when Donny began to talk endlessly on the phone with a girl named Miriam, Cal even let Miriam come to one of the tutoring sessions. Daisy was touched that Cal would grow so involved in Donny's life, but she was also a little hurt, because she had offered to have Miriam to dinner and Donny had refused. Now he asked them to drive her to Cal's house without a qualm.

This Miriam was an unappealing girl with blurry lipstick and masses of rough red hair. She wore a short, bulky jacket that would not have been out of place on a motorcycle. During the trip to Cal's she was silent, but coming back, she was more talkative. "What a neat guy, and what a house! All those kids hanging out, like a club. And the stereo playing rock . . . gosh, he's not like a grown-up at all! Married and divorced and everything, but you'd think he was our own age."

"Mr. Beadle was married?" Daisy asked.

"Yeah, to this really controlling lady. She didn't understand him a bit."

"No, I guess not," Daisy said.

Spring came, and the students who hung around at Cal's drifted out to the basketball net above the garage. Sometimes, when Daisy and Matt arrived to pick up Donny, they'd find him there with the others—spiky and excited, jittering on his toes beneath the backboard. It was staying light much longer now, and the neighboring fence cast narrow bars across the bright grass. Loud music would be spilling from Cal's windows. Once it was the Who, which Daisy recognized from the time that Donny had borrowed the album. "*Teenage Wasteland,*" she said aloud, identifying the song, and Matt gave a short, dry laugh. "It certainly is," he said. He'd misunderstood; he thought she was commenting on the scene spread before them. In fact, she might have been. The players looked like hoodlums, even her son. Why, one of Cal's students had recently been knifed in a tavern. One had been shipped off to boarding school in midterm; two had been withdrawn by their parents. On the other hand, Donny had mentioned someone who'd been studying with Cal for five years. "Five years!" said Daisy. "Doesn't anyone ever stop needing him?"

Donny looked at her. Lately, whatever she said about Cal was read as criticism. "You're just feeling competitive," he said. "And controlling."

She bit her lip and said no more.

In April, the principal called to tell her that Donny had been expelled. There had been a locker check, and in Donny's locker they found five cans of beer and half a pack of cigarettes. With Donny's previous record, this offense meant expulsion.

Daisy gripped the receiver tightly and said, "Well, where is he now?"

"We've sent him home," said Mr. Lanham. "He's packed up all his belongings, and he's coming home on foot."

Daisy wondered what she would say to him. She felt him looming closer and closer, bringing this brand-new situation that no one had prepared her to handle. What other place would take him? Could they enter him in a public school? What were the rules? She stood at the living room window, waiting for him to show up. Gradually, she realized that he was taking too long. She checked the clock. She stared up the street again.

When an hour had passed, she phoned the school. Mr. Lanham's secretary answered and told her in a grave, sympathetic voice that yes, Donny Coble had most definitely gone home. Daisy called her husband. He was out of the office. She went back to the window and thought awhile, and then she called Donny's tutor.

"Donny's been expelled from school," she said, "and now I don't know where he's gone. I wonder if you've heard from him?"

There was a long silence. "Donny's with me, Mrs. Coble," he finally said.

"With you? How'd he get there?"

"He hailed a cab, and I paid the driver."

"Could I speak to him, please?"

There was another silence. "Maybe it'd be better if we had a conference," Cal said.

"I don't *want* a conference. I've been standing at the window picturing him dead or kidnapped or something, and now you tell me you want a—"

"Donny is very, very upset. Understandably so," said Cal. "Believe me, Mrs. Coble, this is not what it seems. Have you asked Donny's side of the story?"

"Well, of course not, how could I? He went running off to you instead."

"Because he didn't feel he'd be listened to."

"But I haven't even—"

"Why don't you come out and talk? The three of us," said Cal, "will try to get this thing in perspective."

"Well, all right," Daisy said. But she wasn't as reluctant as she sounded. Already, she felt soothed by the calm way Cal was taking this.

Cal answered the doorbell at once. He said, "Hi, there," and led her into the dining room. Donny sat slumped in a chair, chewing the knuckle of one thumb. "Hello, Donny," Daisy said. He flicked his eyes in her direction.

"Sit here, Mrs. Coble," said Cal, placing her opposite Donny. He himself remained standing, restlessly pacing. "So," he said.

Daisy stole a look at Donny. His lips were swollen, as if he'd been crying.

"You know," Cal told Daisy, "I kind of expected something like this. That's a very punitive school you've got him in—you realize that. And any half-decent lawyer will tell you they've violated his civil rights. Locker checks! Where's their search warrant?"

"But if the rule is—" Daisy said.

"Well, anyhow, let him tell you his side."

She looked at Donny. He said, "It wasn't my fault. I promise."

"They said your locker was full of beer."

"It was a put-up job! See, there's this guy that doesn't like me. He put all these beers in my locker and started a rumor going, so Mr. Lanham ordered a locker check."

"What was the boy's name?" Daisy asked.

"Huh?"

"Mrs. Coble, take my word, the situation is not so unusual," Cal said. "You can't imagine how vindictive kids can be sometimes."

"What was the boy's *name*," said Daisy, "so that I can ask Mr. Lanham if that's who suggested he run a locker check."

"You don't believe me," Donny said.

"And how'd this boy get your combination in the first place?"

"Frankly," said Cal, "I wouldn't be surprised to learn the school was in on it. Any kid that marches to a different drummer, why, they'd just love an excuse to get rid of him. The school is where I lay the blame."

"Doesn't *Donny* ever get blamed?"

"Now, Mrs. Coble, you heard what he—"

"Forget it," Donny told Cal. "You can see she doesn't trust me."

Daisy drew in a breath to say that of course she trusted him—a reflex. But she knew that bold-faced, wide-eyed look of Donny's. He had worn that look when he was small, denying some petty misdeed with the evidence plain as day all around him. Still, it was hard for her to accuse him outright. She temporized and said, "The only thing I'm sure of is that they've kicked you out of school, and now I don't know what we're going to do."

"We'll fight it," said Cal.

"We can't. Even you must see we can't."

"I could apply to Brantly," Donny said.

Cal stopped his pacing to beam down at him. "Brantly! Yes. They're really onto where a kid is coming from, at Brantly. Why, *I* could get you into Brantly. I work with a lot of their students."

Daisy had never heard of Brantly, but already she didn't like it. And she didn't like Cal's smile, which struck her now as feverish and avid—a smile of hunger.

On the fifteenth of April, they entered Donny in a public school, and they stopped his tutoring sessions. Donny fought both decisions bitterly. Cal, surprisingly enough, did not object. He admitted he'd made no headway with Donny and said it was because Donny was emotionally disturbed.

Donny went to his new school every morning, plodding off alone with his head down. He did his assignments, and he earned average grades, but he gathered no friends, joined no clubs. There was something exhausted and defeated about him.

The first week in June, during final exams, Donny vanished. He simply didn't come home one afternoon, and no one at school remembered seeing him. The police were reassuring, and for the first few days, they worked hard. They combed Donny's sad, messy room for clues; they visited Miriam and Cal. But then they started talking about the number of kids who ran away every year. Hundreds, just in this city. "He'll show up, if he wants to," they said. "If he doesn't, he won't."

Evidently, Donny didn't want to.

It's been three months now and still no word. Matt and Daisy still look for him in every crowd of awkward, heartbreaking teenage boys. Every time the phone rings, they imagine it might be Donny. Both parents have aged. Donny's sister seems to be staying away from home as much as possible.

At night, Daisy lies awake and goes over Donny's life. She is trying to figure out what went wrong, where they made their first mistake. Often, she finds herself blaming Cal, although she knows he didn't begin it. Then at other times she excuses him, for without him, Donny might have left earlier. Who really knows? In the end, she can only sigh and search for a cooler spot on the pillow. As she falls asleep, she occasionally glimpses something in the corner of her vision. It's something fleet and round, a ball—a basketball. It flies up, it sinks through the hoop, descends, lands in a yard littered with last year's leaves and striped with bars of sunlight as white as bones, bleached and parched and cleanly picked.

Reading for Understanding

☐ MAIN IDEA

1. The main point of the story is (a) the cruelty of adults toward teenagers (b) the deterioration of a disturbed teenager (c) the influence of rock music on teenagers (d) a successful relationship between parents and teenagers.

☐ DETAILS

2. When Daisy first worked with Donny and his homework, (a) he enjoyed the change (b) Donny's father joined in (c) Donny left his books at school (d) his grades improved slightly.
3. The tutor, Calvin Beadle, was suggested by (a) the psychologist (b) Mr. Lanham (c) Matt (d) Miriam.
4. The teacher who disregarded the arrangement and called Daisy about Donny was (a) Cal (b) Mr. Lanham (c) his history teacher (d) his English teacher.
5. Donny vanished (a) after an argument with Miriam (b) at the suggestion of Cal (c) after failing every subject (d) during final exams.

☐ INFERENCES

6. Because of the difficulties with Donny, the Cobles were actually (a) neglecting Amanda (b) going back to school themselves (c) learning how to handle teenagers (d) on the verge of divorce.
7. On balance, Cal's influence on Donny proved (a) to be the lifesaver for Donny (b) to have had no lasting, positive effect (c) far worse than anyone expected (d) that Cal was a master redeemer of lost children.
8. Miss Evans apparently (a) was jealous of Cal's influence (b) was an unsuccessful teacher of history (c) understood the Donny problem better than Daisy (d) risked her job by calling Mrs. Coble.
9. By constantly taking Donny's part, Cal actually (a) did himself a disservice (b) showed the right way to handle Donny (c) made lifelong friends of the Cobles (d) pioneered a new method of teaching school subjects.

☐ MOOD

10. The mood of the story is best characterized as (a) upbeat (b) despairing (c) indifferent (d) exuberant.

❑ AUTHOR'S ATTITUDE

11. The attitude of the author toward Mrs. Coble is one of (a) admiration for her clear-sighted view of what was needed (b) sympathy for her hopeless efforts (c) anger because of her indifference toward Donny (d) reluctant approval for the choices she made.

❑ ORDER OF EVENTS

12. Arrange the items in the order in which they occurred. Use letters only.
    A. Donny enters public school.
    B. Amanda is born.
    C. Donny disappears.
    D. In October, Daisy meets the school principal.
    E. Donny is expelled from private school.

❑ OUTCOMES

13. For Donny, the future looks (a) more promising than at the beginning of the story (b) unexpectedly successful (c) filled with happy surprises (d) grim.

❑ CAUSE AND EFFECT

14. Donny's situation (a) made Mr. Lanham a more sympathetic person (b) completely changed Cal's attitude toward young people (c) caused great tension in his parent's marriage (d) was the subject of a profound change in the school's policies.

❑ FACT OR OPINION

Tell whether the following is a fact or an opinion.

15. Cal's smile was "feverish and avid—a smile of hunger."

Words in Context

1. "She would recite the day's hardships . . . the *morass* of unsolvable algebra equations." A ***morass*** (24) is something that (a) pleases (b) traps or puzzles (c) enrages (d) conflicts with reality.
2. ". . .Donny combed his hair and seemed unusually *sober and subdued.*" ***Sober and subdued*** (24) means (a) angry and annoyed (b) alert and obedient (c) serious and calm (d) rebellious and stubborn.

3. "...and he *casually, amiably* questioned Donny ..." ***Casually, amiably*** (25) means (a) carefully, seriously (b) critically, loudly (c) angrily, forcefully (d) informally, good-naturedly.

4. "Cal didn't seem *perturbed*." ***Perturbed*** (25) means (a) troubled (b) interested (c) attentive (d) amused.

5. "Cal *shambled* to his feet." ***Shambled*** (25) means rose (a) quickly and easily (b) partially (c) awkwardly and noisily (d) with anger.

6. "He *cuffed* Donny's shoulder playfully." ***Cuffed*** (25) means (a) hit with hand (b) patted gently (c) touched (d) grabbed.

7. "But Donny had returned to his old *evasive* self." ***Evasive*** (25) means (a) anxious (b) truthful (c) deceptive (d) frank.

8. "'But see, he's still so *suggestible*,' Daisy said." ***Suggestible*** (26) means (a) disobedient (b) easily influenced (c) turned off (d) excitable.

9. "'That's okay, Miss Evans,' he says. 'I have a tutor now.' Like a *talisman*!" ***Talisman*** (27) means (a) a magical charm (b) piece of jewelry (c) judge (d) juror.

10. "He sounded *muzzy*." ***Muzzy*** (27) means (a) annoyed (b) excitable (c) muddled (d) absent-minded.

11. "Now he asked them to drive her to Cal's house *without a qualm*." ***Without a qualm*** (27) means lacking any (a) misgiving (b) consideration (c) feeling (d) reason.

12. "That's a very *punitive* school you've got him in ..." ***Punitive*** (29) means (a) inadequate (b) inefficient (c) punishing (d) controlling.

13. "You can't imagine how *vindictive* kids can be sometimes." ***Vindictive*** (29) means (a) uncooperative (b) cruel (c) vengeful (d) protective.

14. "She *temporized* and said, 'The only thing I'm sure of is that they've kicked you out of school ...'" ***Temporized*** (30) means (a) hedged (b) concluded (c) reached a decision (d) grew tense.

15. "She didn't like Cal's smile, which struck her now as *feverish and avid*—a smile of hunger." ***Feverish and avid*** (30) means (a) intense and cruel (b) cruel and hungry (c) sick and selfish (d) overeager and greedy.

Thinking Critically About the Story

1. Would the story be more effective if it were told from the point of view of Donny? Cal? Mr. Lanham? Matt?

2. Who is the villain? When could the movement toward disaster have been stopped? Who could have stopped it? How would you handle Donny if you were his teacher? Parent? Tutor? Friend?

3. Are we given a sympathetic picture of Donny? The parents? The tutor? The school? Is there anyone whom the author presents favorably? Explain. What was the author's purpose in telling this story?

4. Write the dictionary definitions of *wasteland* on the chalkboard. To what extent is each appropriate to the story?

5. Is this a dated story, or is it one that could easily happen today? Explain.

6. Explain the following quotation: "Because Donny is passive in his resistance, he is difficult to handle." What causes him to give up and let his life go smash?

7. Why is Donny attracted to Miriam? Why does Daisy discount Miriam so completely? Could Miriam help Donny find a place in the sun? Explain.

Stories in Words

October (page 23) was once the eighth month in the calendar. When July (for Julius Caesar) and August (for Augustus Caesar) were inserted, October became the tenth month. But like a fossil it retains the name of the eighth month, for *octo* means "eight" as in *octagon* ("eight-sided polygon"), *octave* ("musical interval of eight degrees"), *octet* ("composition for eight instruments or voices") and *octopus* ("mollusk with eight arms").

Talisman (page 27) means "a charm to ward off evil." To track the changes in meaning of this word is to lead a merry chase through language. It may have come to English from French, Spanish, or Italian, but it is clear that the original word borrowed was the Arabic *tilsam*. But *tilsam* itself came from the Middle Greek *telesma* ("sanctified object"), which in turn came from the Old Greek verb *telein*, meaning "to initiate into the mysteries." But *telein* in turn comes from *telos*, meaning "end." The modern word *teleology* is the "study of design and purpose in nature." *End* may suggest *purpose* as in "What is the end of life?" Thus the word *talisman* has had a varied history, but at every turn the meanings seem to deal with life and its purpose.

Muzzy (page 27) means "muddled or confused in mind." This is probably a blend of *muddy* and *fuzzy*. English often combines two words to form one. Most commonly, blends are proper nouns, as when the

Florilina motel combines *Carolina* and *Florida*. Indeed, the word *motel* itself is a blend of *motor* and *hotel*. Other common blends include *brunch* (*breakfast* + *lunch*), *chortle* (*chuckle* + *snort*), *travelogue* (*travel* + *monologue*), and *cheeseburger* (*cheese* + *hamburger*). The word *hamburger* itself, however, is named for the German city, Hamburg, and has nothing to do with ham. The most famous blend historically is *gerrymander*. Elbridge Gerry was governor of Massachusetts during a redrawing of election districts to favor the incumbent party. The resulting picture of the distorted districts looked like a salamander. "More like a gerrymander," declared Benjamin Russell, a newspaper editor.

Another April

JESSE STUART

"I'll be back to see you," Grandpa said. "I'm a-gettin' a little chilly; I'll be gettin' back to the house."

The terrapin twisted his wrinkled neck without moving his big body, poking his head deeper into the April wind as Grandpa pulled his bundled body up by holding to the sassafras tree trunk.

"Good-bye, old friend!"

To be interesting, a story needn't be filled with excitement and violence. An overdose of action can bore by repetition, dulling the senses. Some stories rely on characterization, allowing the reader to sense the inner struggles, tensions, and reconciliations. "Another April" is such a story.

There is no sensory overload here. Nothing much happens overtly as Grandpa goes out for his first walk of the springtime. Mom and the narrator watch him as he examines a pine cone and a dogwood blossom. The terse comments of Grandpa are presented against the backdrop of questions and answers between the two left behind. There are three generations presented here, but instead of conflict and turbulence, we find love, serenity, and understanding.

Another April

Now, Pap, you won't get cold," Mom said as she put a heavy wool cap over his head.

"Huh, what did ye say?" Grandpa asked, holding his big hand cupped over his ear to catch the sound.

"Wait until I get your gloves," Mom said, hollering real loud in Grandpa's ear. Mom had forgotten about his gloves until he raised his big bare hand above his ear to catch the sound of Mom's voice.

"Don't get 'em," Grandpa said, "I won't ketch cold."

Mom didn't pay any attention to what Grandpa said. She went on to get the gloves anyway. Grandpa turned toward me. He saw that I was looking at him.

"Yer Ma's a-puttin' enough clothes on me to kill a man," Grandpa said, then he laughed a coarse laugh like March wind among the pine tops at his own words. I started laughing but not at Grandpa's words. He thought I was laughing at them and we both laughed together. It pleased Grandpa to think that I had laughed with him over something funny that he had said. But I was laughing at the way he was dressed. He looked like a picture of Santa Claus. But Grandpa's cheeks were not cherry-red like Santa Claus' cheeks. They were covered with white thin beard—and above his eyes were long white eyebrows almost as white as percoon* petals and very much longer.

Grandpa was wearing a heavy wool suit that hung loosely about his big body but fitted him tightly round the waist where he was as big and as round as a flour barrel. His pant legs were as big round his pipe-stem legs as emptied meal sacks. And his big shoes, with his heavy wool socks dropping down over their tops, looked like sled runners. Grandpa wore a heavy wool shirt and over his wool shirt he wore a heavy wool sweater and then his coat over the top of all this. Over his coat he wore a heavy overcoat and about his neck he wore a wool scarf.

**percoon* mountain dialect for pecan tree

The way Mom had dressed Grandpa you'd think there was a heavy snow on the ground but there wasn't. April was here instead and the sun was shining on the green hills where the wild plums and the wild crab apples were in bloom enough to make you think there were big snowdrifts sprinkled over the green hills. When I looked at Grandpa and then looked out at the window at the sunshine and the green grass I laughed more. Grandpa laughed with me.

"I'm a-goin' to see my old friend," Grandpa said just as Mom came down the stairs with his gloves.

"Who is he, Grandpa?" I asked, but Grandpa just looked at my mouth working. He didn't know what I was saying. And he hated to ask me the second time.

Mom put the big wool gloves on Grandpa's hands. He stood there just like I had to do years ago, and let Mom put his gloves on. If Mom didn't get his fingers back in the glove-fingers exactly right Grandpa quarreled at Mom. And when Mom fixed his fingers exactly right in his gloves the way he wanted them Grandpa was pleased.

"I'll be a-goin' to see 'im," Grandpa said to Mom. "I know he'll still be there."

Mom opened our front door for Grandpa and he stepped out slowly, supporting himself with his big cane in one hand. With the other hand he held to the door facing. Mom let him out of the house just like she used to let me out in the spring. And when Grandpa left the house I wanted to go with him, but Mom wouldn't let me go. I wondered if he would get away from the house—get out of Mom's sight—and pull off his shoes and go barefooted and wade the creeks like I used to do when Mom let me out. Since Mom wouldn't let me go with Grandpa, I watched him as he walked slowly down the path in front of our house. Mom stood there watching Grandpa too. I think she was afraid that he would fall. But Mom was fooled; Grandpa toddled along the path better than my baby brother could.

"He used to be a powerful man," Mom said more to herself than she did to me. "He was a timber cutter. No man could cut more timber than my father; no man in the timber woods could sink an ax deeper into a log than my father. And no man could lift the end of a bigger sawlog than Pap could."

"Who is Grandpa goin' to see, Mom?" I asked.

"He's not goin' to see anybody," Mom said.

"I heard 'im say that he was goin' to see an old friend," I told her.

"Oh, he was just a-talkin'," Mom said.

I watched Grandpa stop under the pine tree in our front yard. He set his cane against the pine tree trunk, pulled off his gloves and put them in his pocket. Then Grandpa stooped over slowly, as slowly as the wind bends down a sapling, and picked up a pinecone in his big soft fingers. Grandpa stood fondling the pinecone in his hand. Then, one by one, he pulled the little chips from the pinecone—tearing it to pieces like he was hunting for

for something in it—and after he had torn it to pieces he threw the pine-cone stem on the ground. Then he pulled pine needles from a low hanging pine bough and he felt of each pine needle between his fingers. He played with them a long time before he started down the path.

"What's Grandpa doin'?" I asked Mom.

But Mom didn't answer me.

"How long has Grandpa been with us?" I asked Mom.

"Before you's born," she said. "Pap has been with us eleven years. He was eighty when he quit cuttin' timber and farmin'; now he's ninety-one."

I had heard her say that when she was a girl he'd walk out on the snow and ice barefooted and carry wood in the house and put it on the fire. He had shoes but he wouldn't bother to put them on. And I heard her say that he would cut timber on the coldest days without socks on his feet but with his feet stuck down in cold brogan shoes and he worked stripped above the waist so his arms would have freedom when he swung his double-bitted ax. I had heard her tell how he'd sweat and how the sweat in his beard would be icicles by the time he got home from work on the cold winter days. Now Mom wouldn't let him get out of the house for she wanted him to live a long time.

As I watched Grandpa go down the path toward the hog pen he stopped to examine every little thing along his path. Once he waved his cane at a butterfly as it zigzagged over his head, its polka-dot wings fanning the blue April air. Grandpa would stand when a puff of wind came along, and hold his face against the wind and let the wind play with his white whiskers. I thought maybe his face was hot under his beard and he was letting the wind cool his face. When he reached the hog pen he called the hogs down to the fence. They came running and grunting to Grandpa just like they were talking to him. I knew that Grandpa couldn't hear them trying to talk to him but he could see their mouths working and he knew they were trying to say something. He leaned his cane against the hog pen, reached over the fence, and patted the hogs' heads. Grandpa didn't miss patting one of our seven hogs.

As he toddled up the little path alongside the hog pen he stopped under a blooming dogwood. He pulled a white blossom from a bough that swayed over the path above his head, and he leaned his big bundled body against the dogwood while he tore each petal from the blossom and examined it carefully. There wasn't anything his dim blue eyes missed. He stopped under a redbud tree before he reached the garden to break a tiny spray of redbud blossoms. He took each blossom from the spray and examined it carefully.

"Gee, it's funny to watch Grandpa," I said to Mom, then I laughed.

"Poor Pap," Mom said, "he's seen a lot of Aprils come and go. He's seen more Aprils than he will ever see again."

I don't think Grandpa missed a thing on the little circle he took before he reached the house. He played with a bumblebee that was bending a windflower blossom that grew near our corncrib beside a big bluff. But

Grandpa didn't try to catch the bumblebee in his big bare hand. I wondered if he would and if the bumblebee would sting him, and if he would holler. Grandpa even pulled a butterfly cocoon from a blackberry briar that grew beside his path. I saw him try to tear it into shreds but he couldn't. There wasn't any butterfly in it, for I'd seen it before. I wondered if the butterfly with the polka-dot wings, that Grandpa waved his cane at when he first left the house, had come from this cocoon. I laughed when Grandpa couldn't tear the cocoon apart.

"I'll bet I can tear that cocoon apart for Grandpa if you'd let me go help him," I said to Mom.

"You leave your Grandpa alone," Mom said. "Let 'im enjoy April."

Then I knew that this was the first time Mom had let Grandpa out of the house all winter. I knew that Grandpa loved the sunshine and the fresh April air that blew from the redbud and dogwood blossoms. He loved the bumblebees, the hogs, the pinecones, and pine needles. Grandpa didn't miss a thing along his walk. And every day from now on until just before frost Grandpa would take this little walk. He'd stop along and look at everything as he had done summers before. But each year he didn't take as long a walk as he had taken the year before. Now this spring he didn't go down to the lower end of the hog pen as he had done last year. And when I could first remember Grandpa going on his walks he used to go out of sight. He'd go all over the farm. And he'd come to the house and take me on his knee and tell me about all that he had seen. Now Grandpa wasn't getting out of sight. I could see him from the window along all of his walk.

Grandpa didn't come back into the house at the front door. He tottled around back of the house toward the smokehouse and I ran through the living room to the dining room so I could look out at the window and watch him.

"Where's Grandpa goin'?" I asked Mom.

"Now never mind," Mom said. "Leave your Grandpa alone. Don't go out there and disturb him."

"I won't bother 'im, Mom," I said. "I just want to watch 'im."

"All right," Mom said.

But Mom wanted to be sure that I didn't bother him so she followed me into the dining room. Maybe she wanted to see what Grandpa was going to do. She stood by the window and we watched Grandpa as he walked down beside our smokehouse where a tall sassafras tree's thin leaves fluttered in the blue April wind. Above the smokehouse and the tall sassafras was a blue April sky—so high you couldn't see the sky-roof. It was just blue space and little white clouds floated upon this blue.

When Grandpa reached the smokehouse he leaned his cane against the sassafras tree. He let himself down slowly to his knees as he looked carefully at the ground. Grandpa was looking at something and I wondered what it was. I just didn't think or I would have known.

"There you are, my good old friend," Grandpa said.

"Who is his friend, Mom?" I asked.

Mom didn't say anything. Then I saw.

"He's playin' with that old terrapin, Mom," I said.

"I know he is," Mom said.

"The terrapin doesn't mind if Grandpa strokes his head with his hand," I said.

"I know it," Mom said.

"But the old terrapin won't let me do it," I said. "Why does he let Grandpa?"

"The terrapin knows your Grandpa."

"He ought to know me," I said, "but when I try to stroke his head with my hand, he closes up in his shell."

Mom didn't say anything. She stood by the window watching Grandpa and listening to Grandpa talk to the terrapin.

"My old friend, how do you like the sunshine?" Grandpa asked the terrapin.

The terrapin turned his fleshless face to one side like a hen does when she looks at you in the sunlight. He was trying to talk to Grandpa; maybe the terrapin could understand what Grandpa was saying.

"Old fellow, it's been a hard winter," Grandpa said. "How have you fared under the smokehouse floor?"

"Does the terrapin know what Grandpa is sayin'?" I asked Mom.

"I don't know," she said.

"I'm awfully glad to see you, old fellow," Grandpa said.

He didn't offer to bite Grandpa's big soft hand as he stroked his head.

"Looks like the terrapin would bite Grandpa," I said.

"That terrapin has spent the winters under that smokehouse for fifteen years," Mom said. "Pap has been acquainted with him for eleven years. He's been talkin' to that terrapin every spring."

"How does Grandpa know the terrapin is old?" I asked Mom.

"It's got 1847 cut on its shell," Mom said. "We know he's ninety-five years old. He's older than that. We don't know how old he was when that date was cut on his back."

"Who cut 1847 on his back, Mom?"

"I don't know, child," she said, "but I'd say whoever cut that date on his back has long been under the ground."

Then I wondered how a terrapin could get that old and what kind of a looking person he was who cut the date on the terrapin's back. I wondered where it happened—if it happened near where our house stood. I wondered who lived here on this land then, what kind of a house they lived in, and if they had a sassafras with tiny thin April leaves on its top growing in their yard, and if the person that cut the date on the terrapin's back was buried at Plum Grove, if he had farmed these hills where we lived today and cut timber like Grandpa had—and if he had seen the Aprils pass like Grandpa had seen them and if he enjoyed them like Grandpa was enjoying this April. I wondered if he had looked at the dogwood blossoms, the redbud blossoms, and talked to this same terrapin.

"Are you well, old fellow?" Grandpa asked the terrapin.

The terrapin just looked at Grandpa.

"I'm well as common for a man of my age," Grandpa said.

"Did the terrapin ask Grandpa if he was well?" I asked Mom.

"I don't know," Mom said. "I can't talk to a terrapin."

"But Grandpa can."

"Yes."

"Wait until tomatoes get ripe and we'll go to the garden together," Grandpa said.

"Does a terrapin eat tomatoes?" I asked Mom.

"Yes, that terrapin has been eatin' tomatoes from our garden for fifteen years," Mom said. "When Mick was tossin' the terrapins out of the tomato patch, he picked up this one and found the date cut on his back. He put him back in the patch and told him to help himself. He lives from our garden every year. We don't bother him and don't allow anybody else to bother him. He spends his winters under our smokehouse floor buried in the dry ground."

"Gee, Grandpa looks like the terrapin," I said.

Mom didn't say anything; tears came to her eyes. She wiped them from her eyes with the corner of her apron.

"I'll be back to see you," Grandpa said. "I'm a-gettin' a little chilly; I'll be gettin' back to the house."

The terrapin twisted his wrinkled neck without moving his big body, poking his head deeper into the April wind as Grandpa pulled his bundled body up by holding to the sassafras tree trunk.

"Good-bye, old friend!"

The terrapin poked his head deeper into the wind, holding one eye on Grandpa, for I could see his eye shining in the sinking sunlight.

Grandpa got his cane that was leaned against the sassafras tree trunk and hobbled slowly toward the house. The terrapin looked at him with first one eye and then the other.

Reading for Understanding

❑ MAIN IDEA

1. The main point of the story is (a) the increase in a young man's understanding of old age (b) the advantages of keeping a turtle as a pet (c) the beauty of springtime in the country (d) the influence of weather upon people.

❑ DETAILS

2. Grandpa differed from Santa Claus in his (a) height (b) weight (c) cheeks (d) attitude.

3. Grandpa was fussy about (a) his beard (b) the way his gloves were put on (c) the way he looked when he went outdoors (d) the way his grandson dressed.
4. The first animals visited were (a) the cattle (b) the sheep (c) the goats (d) the hogs.
5. The terrapin spent the winter (a) indoors (b) under the sassafras tree (c) under the ice (d) under the smokehouse.

❑ INFERENCES

6. A word to characterize Grandpa is (a) *unsound* (b) *proud* (c) *unkind* (d) *defeated.*
7. Grandpa lives with Mom because of (a) a disagreement with another relative (b) his friendship with the narrator (c) his age (d) a wish to be near his favorite dogwood.
8. The "friend" that Grandpa was going out to see was (a) a hog (b) an old dog (c) a turtle (d) an old neighbor down the road.
9. Mom cries at the end because she realizes that (a) Grandpa is failing (b) her son will soon leave her (c) April is a cruel month (d) her son has disobeyed her.
10. The date is mentioned to (a) show how old the terrapin is (b) give the year of Grandpa's birth (c) interest the son in history (d) compare the terrapin with other terrapins.

❑ AUTHOR'S PURPOSE

11. A main purpose of the author is to (a) set forth a series of nature notes (b) compare Grandpa and the terrapin (c) show that truth finally pays (d) tell a humorous story.

❑ ORDER OF EVENTS

12. Arrange the items in the order in which they occurred. Use letters only.
    A. Grandpa examines a butterfly cocoon.
    B. Mom puts on Grandpa's gloves.
    C. Grandpa studies a pine cone.
    D. Grandpa plays with the terrapin.
    E. Grandpa comes to live with Mom.

❑ OUTCOMES

13. Grandpa will probably (a) stay with another relative (b) stay indoors the rest of April (c) show the narrator how to fish (d) have very few more Aprils.

❑ CAUSE AND EFFECT

14. The terrapin allows Grandpa to stroke him because (a) of their long association (b) he allows everyone to do the same (c) most turtles don't mind (d) he's still affected by the cold weather.

❑ FACT OR OPINION

Tell whether the following is a fact or an opinion.

15. Grandpa was hard of hearing.

Words in Context

1. "He laughed a coarse laugh like March wind among the pine tops . . ." (37) His laugh was (a) melodious and rhythmical (b) soft and soothing (c) thunderous (d) raspy and harsh.
2. ". . . a heavy wool suit . . . fitted him tightly round the waist where he was as big and as round as a flour barrel." (37) Around the waist, Grandpa must have measured (a) less than 38 inches (b) between 38 and 45 inches (c) between 46 and 89 inches (d) more than 90 inches.
3. "His pant legs were as big round his pipe-stem legs as emptied meal sacks." (37) Grandpa's legs were (a) as heavy as the rest of his body (b) practically all bones (c) straight and powerful (d) overladened with fatty tissue.
4. "And his big shoes, with his heavy wool socks dropping down over their tops, looked like *sled runners*." (37) ***Sled runners*** are (a) short and stubby (b) long and narrow (c) glistening and icy (d) slippery and uncontrollable.
5. ". . . where the wild plums and the wild crab apples were in bloom enough to make you think there were big snowdrifts sprinkled over the green hills." (38) The intended mental picture contains (a) trees ladened with ripened fruit (b) promise (c) heavy snow (d) unripened fruit.
6. "'Who is he, Grandpa?' I asked, but Grandpa just looked at my mouth working. He didn't know what I was saying." (38) These two sen-

tences reveal that (a) Grandpa's hearing is impaired (b) Grandpa was daydreaming (c) Grandpa was very tense (d) The young boy has a speech defect.

7. "... and he stepped out slowly, supporting himself with his big cane in one hand. With the other hand he held to the door facing." (38) Grandpa used his empty hand to (a) hold on to the doorknob (b) adjust the doorjamb (c) steady himself (d) point the way.

8. "Grandpa *toddled* along the path better than my baby brother could." ***Toddled*** (38) means (a) meandered deliberately (b) hurried noisily (c) took short, unsteady steps (d) trudged.

9. "... he stopped under a blooming dogwood ... that grew near our *corncrib* beside a big *bluff*." ***Corncrib*** ... ***bluff*** (39) mean (a) storage place ... high, steep ridge (b) stalks ... stony cliff (c) seed container ... sharp precipice (d) husking place ... short promontory.

10. "He's playing with that old *terrapin*." A ***terrapin*** (41) is a (a) blizzard (b) raccoon (c) porcupine (d) turtle.

Thinking Critically About the Story

1. Jesse Stuart wrote mainly of "mountain folk." Cite some of the devices he used to make the reader aware of how these people are different from and how they are similar to other regional groups.
2. Turn to the first page of the story and reread the description that introduces Grandpa to us. How does the author, in the few pages that follow, make us sympathetic toward him?
3. How old is Grandpa? How does he compare with the older people you know? With the elderly people of today?
4. Cite some of the descriptions that reveal Grandpa's joy in meeting spring. How can you tell when spring arrives in your neighborhood?
5. Would the story be more effective if standard spelling had been used for the dialog? Explain.

Stories in Words

Polka-dot (39) suggests a dance craze that once swept the country. There have been many dance fads in America, but a century ago one of the most popular was the polka. Though the dance may not originally have been of Polish origin, the name stuck. Just as we have "square-dance ties" today, so dancers wore "polka gauze," "polka hats," and fabrics printed with "polka dots." The polka is a lively dance with the basic pattern of hop-step-close-step.

Santa Claus (37) has a fascinating history. The name is based originally on the legend of St. Nicholas, a bishop of Asia Minor in the fourth century. He gave gifts to three sisters as their dowry. Gift giving is an essential part of the Santa Claus story. The name *Santa Claus* is a contraction of the Dutch "Sant Nikolaas." The most famous Christmas poem, "The Night Before Christmas," was originally titled "A Visit from St. Nicholas."

Terrapin (41) is of Algonquian origin. When the settlers arrived in the new land, they came across many plants and animals that were new to them. They tried to learn the Indian names but sometimes changed the names in the process. *Muskrat,* for example, comes from the Indian word *musquash,* but the settlers saw resemblances to other rodents and used the word *muskrat. Raccoon* was derived from the Indian *arahkum.* Some Indian names for foods include *hominy, maize, pecan, succotash, squash,* and *persimmon.*

Across the Generations

Getting Technical

Terms

atmosphere	resolution	tragedy
epiphany	sympathetic scenery	

Definitions Match each of the above terms with its definition.

1. The outcome of the climax
2. The mood established by the story
3. Unavoidable fall from good fortune to bad
4. The external world reflecting the mood
5. Sudden perception of the meaning

Examples Match each of the following actions with the appropriate term.

1. Stormy weather appears when the heroine becomes deeply troubled by events.
2. As the story ends, readers suddenly realize why the father had seemingly refused to aid his wayward son.
3. The main character's pride slowly destroys him politically and financially.
4. The optimism of the mysterious stranger permeates all of the action in the story.
5. The gun duel is fought and the young cowhand is the victorious survivor.
6. The sun shone brightly, birds were singing in the blossoming trees, Henry was in love!

7. Joe was down the street when he muttered, "Why was I so stupid! So that was what he was aiming at! Dopey me!"

8. I'm going to watch that program tonight. It will be humorous enough to get me out of the blues.

Application Match each of the following quotations with the appropriate term.

1. "Charles?" she said. "We don't have any Charles in this kindergarten." The parents stood there in utter silence.

2. At night, Daisy lies awake and goes over Donny's life. She is trying to figure out what went wrong, where they made their first mistake. Why to Donny! Why to them!

3. Without a coat or hat, keys in hand, David Thompson ran out into the ten-degree weather. He couldn't run away from the cold terror that filled him.

4. "You leave your Grandpa alone," Mom said. "Let 'im enjoy April." She smiled contentedly and continued her daily chores.

5. And then, still determined to take his pictures, Brian raised the camera to their faces and read the light. It was their decision, not his, that had to be accepted.

6. At that moment . . . the sun was shining on the green hills where the wild plums and the wild crab apples were in bloom . . .

Thinking Critically About the Stories

1. A major character in each of these four stories is the mother. How do they compare with each other in handling life's problems? How close does each come to your idea of an ideal parent? How do they compare with the mother in a soap opera or movie you saw recently?

2. Brian, Danny, and Laurie are characters in revolt. How true to life are they? Explain. Compare the effectiveness of their approaches. How have people you know or read about faced similar predicaments? Who was injured most? At what point does tragedy become inevitable?

3. Use one or more of the following terms to classify the tone of each of these stories: bitter, ironic, angry, acceptant, humorous, objective. Did the tone add to or subtract from the force of the author's message? Explain.

4. The stories in the unit have a wide range of ideas. Which one has the

most significance to you? Which one stretched your imagination most? Which one do you think you will remember longest? Justify each of your choices.

5. Which adult in these stories: would you most like to know? did you admire least? hit closest to home? was most mature? Explain your choices.

Writing and Other Activities

1. Be prepared to lead a class panel in a discussion of one of the following:
   (a) To what extent the adolescent members should be involved in making major family decisions: mother taking a job; handling a large inheritance or sweepstake winning; divorce; moving out of the area or state.
   (b) Mistakes that parents make in handling older teenagers and what can be done about them.
   (c) Pivotal errors that older teenagers make and how deeply friends should become involved.
   (d) Facts and fictions about labels such as *mature* and *immature*. What are the qualities of maturity? What's wrong with remaining immature?
   (e) "Reading the Light": Some of the Do's and Don't's when using any of the following, especially with friends or members of your family:

sarcasm	bitterness	negative reactions
humor	sentimentalism	total acceptance

2. Write the setting and dialog for one of the following.
   (a) Miriam, the girl in "Teenage Wasteland," tells one of her friends about Donny's disappearance.
   (b) The youthful narrator in "Another April" tries to explain to his classmates Grandpa's reactions to the gift of another April.
   (c) Twenty-five years later, Laurie tries to explain to his wife why he doesn't want to make an issue of his five-year-old son's telling of how he fought and killed an unfriendly dinosaur.
   (d) Brian explains to his sister Melissa why he had interrupted the photography trip with his father.

3. Write an informal editorial to appear in the school newspaper on one of the following:
   (a) Enjoying the first day of summer
   (b) Endangered species, our grandparents
   (c) A picture in words for today
   (d) Handling the class troublemaker

4. Write the opening paragraphs that give the setting for:
   (a) A humorous short story taking place in the school cafeteria.
   (b) A tragic story in which the innocent bystander becomes involved in a brutal gang war.
   (c) A short-short story in which a high school freshman suddenly discovers that he is in love.
   (d) A stream-of-consciousness story in which a depressed high school senior walks through the local museum.

5. As a member of the Debating Team, write an explanation of your major reason for being for or against:
   (a) A world federation of nations without armies
   (b) Spending huge sums on exploring space
   (c) Outlawing private ownership of handguns
   (d) Life imprisonment for drug dealers
   (e) Compulsory college education

Stories in Words: A Review

A. corduroy	E. kindergarten	I. Santa Claus
B. dilapidated	F. polka-dot	J. silhouette
C. focused	G. muzzy	K. talisman
D. husband	H. October	L. terrapin

Answer the following questions by choosing a word from the list above. Use letters only.

Which of the words above . . .

1. ________ is probably a blend of two words?
2. ________ is a metaphor for a kind of road?
3. ________ suggests a magical charm?
4. ________ is based on a popular dance?
5. ________ is an Indian name?
6. ________ was named for a "cheapskate"?
7. ________ is related to the word for an eight-armed sea creature?
8. ________ was devised by an educator named Froebel?
9. ________ literally means "master of the house"?
10. ________ is based on an ancient legend in Asia Minor?

In his play *Dangerous Corner*, J. B. Priestley suggests that there are key moments in life that determine a person's entire future. A moment's hesitation, a second thought about speaking, an interruption—all these presumably might make a critical difference. Many people look back over a long life and say, "Yes, there was a moment in my life that made a difference. It was a turning point."

The stories in this unit suggest that indeed there are turning points that influence events to follow. In the first story, a mother, her daughter, and an aunt are on a visit to an old homestead. Old memories mesh with present anxieties. Then, the daughter turns the corner away from self-deception to a mature acceptance of reality. A flower from an unlikely source makes the turning point easier to accept.

2

The Turning Point

One's mind has a way of making itself up in the background, as it suddenly becomes clear what one means to do.

A. C. Benson

The second and third stories are paired for comparison and contrast. Both deal with nannies responsible for the child or children in their charge. Both stories develop and become richer as the reader is given insight into the essential conflicts. Both stories include a turning point as the children break through constraints to express themselves truly.

The turning point in the fourth story involves a dog—and his own turning point. The reader comes to know the dog and to sympathize with him, as he attempts to hold to the treaty he accepted many years before.

As you read the stories, decide for yourself what the turning point is in each story.

Welcome

OUIDA SEBESTYEN

My mother walked slowly away toward a worn stone. Years of wind had scoured off all the inscription except one line. It said, *beloved wife of.*

She began to cry, with the loud surprised sound of an animal in pain.

The best short stories somehow are able to capture in a few brief pages a long and involved history. "Welcome" is a masterpiece of subtle characterization, superb storytelling, and compassion.

Three women, of three different generations, are traveling to visit an elderly family member. As Aunt Dessie, Mary, and Tina travel, the conversation contains hints of various family relationships. In addition to the three travelers, there are three others. Noella is the aged family member, the person to be visited. Arley is her disadvantaged son. James is the father of Tina, husband of Mary. Though James doesn't appear physically in the story, his presence is felt, and his character is strongly hinted at. These are six sympathetic people with different problems. By the end of the story you will have looked into their hearts and been enriched by the experience.

The ingredients are not new, but the handling is first-rate. The image of the keys pervades the story. What are the things we try to lock in—or lock out? What is the turning point in the growing maturity of Tina?

It is not easy to be a human being, but with courage we can survive. The characters in "Welcome" display courage, though of several different kinds. When Mary finally says, "Some things don't change," we gain insight by her actions. Perhaps you will find new meaning in the French expression: "Tout comprendre c'est tout pardonner." ("To understand all is to forgive all.")

Welcome

My father's Aunt Dessie peered through the windshield at a road sign. "Slow up a little bit, Mary," she told my mother. "The last time I tried to find kinfolks I hadn't visited for a while, I got the house number and the street perfect, but I was in the wrong town." She turned to me in the back seat. "I ran across this yard yelling, 'Guess who's here, Annabelle,' and burst right in on a white lady. Perfect stranger."

I caught my mother's eyes in the rearview mirror and made a pretend smile for Aunt Dessie, thinking how I would describe her to my friend Sharon when I got home. *Picture this eighty-year-old drill sergeant? In drag? With this head of corn-row hair she must have made with a real hoe?* Sharon would double up. At least as far as she could double, now.

My mother slowed to a creep. Yesterday evening, bowling along through Texas on her way to see her parents, she had swerved off the interstate toward a dismal little town. Before I could figure what in blazes she was doing, we were spending the night on Aunt Dessie's let-down couch between two whatnots crammed with spinster junk. I had hissed, "What *is* this—I hate changes." But my mother just lay with her back to me, pretending to be asleep, while strange summer things from the piney woods tapped against the screens.

Aunt Dessie said, "Noella's going to be as surprised as I was. I still can't believe I'm riding along beside you, Mary. After seventeen years."

"Is it that long?" my mother said.

Aunt Dessie turned back to me. "And to finally get to see you, pretty thing. The image of your daddy."

"Are you sure this is the road?" my mother said sharply. "We've really got to keep this visit brief."

"Then why don't you stop at that little place up there and let me ask. Some of this backwoods is hazy in my mind."

We stopped. Aunt Dessie unfolded out of the car like a carpenter's ruler, and yanked open the screen door of a little grocery that had been waiting for a customer since the Great Depression.

I murmured, "Lordy mercy, as they say down here. Are we talking hazy or crazy?"

"That's enough smart lip," my mother warned me. "You be nice to her. She took us in like royalty. She didn't have to."

"If she tells me one more time I look like my daddy—"

"You do."

"I look like me." It mattered that I was my own special leg of the proud unsteady tripod my mother and father and I had always made. "I feel very guess-who's-here-Annabelle."

"Me too, a little. But suddenly I just wanted to see her and your great-aunt Noella again. I've never forgotten how they took me into the family. No questions. No testing. Just welcome." She was silent, remembering. "I guess I needed their blessing, or something. But I can't tell if Dessie knows."

She lifted the hot hair off her coffee-and-cream neck. She had always worn her hair long and straightened, to please my father. Reverse perm after reverse perm. But now the newest inch of it had its own natural crinkle, recording almost to the day, I guess, when they stopped loving each other. Old fears began to press me like fingers finding the deep secret acupuncture points of pain. "What do you mean, *if she knows*? What's to know? You're going to patch all this up. Like the other times, and everything's going to be fine again."

She put her hands on the wheel as if she needed to be driving.

"You are," I said.

"Tina, sometimes things—"

"No. You *are*."

Aunt Dessie came striding out, carrying a piece of paper in one hand and a bright canvas bag in the other.

"Lady in there makes these totes," she announced, handing it to me. "A souvenir."

I took it, surprised. "Thanks," I said, actually smiling in my confusion. Her old eyes studied me so long that I said too loudly, "Hey, I could embroider YUCK! on it and give it to Sharon for a diaper bag."

"Who's Sharon?" Aunt Dessie asked.

My mother started off with a jerk. "A bubble-headed little blonde Tina knows back home."

"Just my best friend," I said.

Aunt Dessie studied the scrap of paper someone had drawn a map on. "Ah," she nodded. "I see."

"Actually," my mother said, her voice accelerating with the car, "she's a strange little person who keeps trying to saddle Tina with all her problems. I hoped this trip would give them a vacation from each other."

Lie, I said to her back. *You'd rather run from that empty-feeling house than face up to your life.*

"She didn't saddle me," I told Aunt Dessie. "Somebody has to look after Sharon, she's so casual, so inconceivably—" I began to giggle crazily and couldn't stop. "I have to remind her what the doctor says to do, or she'll eat like she wants a French-fried baby with diet-cola blood."

"I think we can spare Aunt Dessie the details."

"Hey, all I did was ask if she could stay with us till the baby comes. And you went off like a ton of dynamite—rip, mangle, roar." My mother's eyes tried to grab mine in the mirror, but I wouldn't look. I wanted to give the details. Hadn't she driven miles out of her way to give her side of things to my father's aunts before he did? Okay, I wanted to tell about my friend who wasn't afraid to gulp down whole chunks of life I hadn't even dared to taste.

She said, "The last thing I need is a tenth-grade dropout with a fatherless child on the way."

"There's always a father," I objected. "She just doesn't want him around." I tried to think what the slang had been in my mother's day. "He's a creep. She doesn't really like him."

"Turn left," Aunt Dessie said. My mother swerved.

"It's the baby that's important," I said. "Sharon's going to have something really truly her very own. She's glad about it."

"My God," my mother said. She bore through a tunnel of pines riddled with sunlight shafts. "But not in my house."

I braced myself carefully. "But she *is* in our house. I gave her the key before we left."

The car lurched to a stop. My mother swung around in her seat. "Tina! You knew perfectly well how I felt about that."

"Where else could she go?"

"Good heavens, she has parents."

"Oh, sure, her mother's in Florida with four stepchildren and her dad got an ultimatum from his girl friend. Who's she supposed to turn to besides us? I'm her friend. I thought you were, too, the way you were always nice to her and laughed when she did weird things—"

Aunt Dessie said firmly, "Left again up there at that tree."

My mother started the car and drove past a field of sunflowers all staring at us with little happy faces. Slowly tears as hard as hailstones filled my throat. "I thought I could depend on you," I said, bumping along like the car. "To help her. But you slide out of things like a plate of noodles."

Aunt Dessie said, "I gather your daddy's away from home."

"He still travels, you know," my mother answered for me. "In his kind of work he has to, a great deal."

She slowed as the rutted road dipped for a creek. A little boy in overalls stood expectantly beside a mailbox. Suddenly I knew how my father had looked, growing up in those piney woods. Waiting for the mail carrier to come with something wonderful. I snapped my eyes shut to block him off. I didn't want to think about my father. I didn't even know how to think about him anymore. I just wanted everything to stand still, frozen like that little boy, so that nothing would ever have to arrive.

"How long has he been dead?" I heard my mother say. I jerked to attention, but she added, "Noella's husband."

"I guess two years now," Aunt Dessie said. "Bless her heart, it must be hard for her." She turned around in the seat, raising her voice in case I had gone deaf. "Noella's husband was your Granddaddy Mayhew's brother, you see, and I'm from your grandmother's side, so Noella and I aren't anything like blood kin."

My mother said, "Why have you kept up with each other all these years?"

Aunt Dessie craned to read the name of a small wooden church we were passing. "I guess we just feel related." She turned back to me. "Your daddy stayed with me four years, so he could be close to a better school. I loved that boy."

I gazed at the crooked rows of her gray hair, wondering what age she had been when she stared into a mirror at her horse face and rawboned body and knew no man was ever going to love her.

We passed a square unpainted house smothering under a trumpet vine. "Whoa!" Aunt Dessie commanded. "It says Mayhew on the mailbox."

"This is it?" My mother stopped and backed up. At the side of a barn two pigs lay in a juicy wallow. Some little granny in clodhopper shoes just had to be around the corner, stewing the wash in a black pot. "Good heavens," she murmured. "I wouldn't live out here all alone for the world."

"Well, Noella's not alone, you remember. She's still got Arley with her." Aunt Dessie flipped her stiff old hand at a hill nearby. "And the old Mayhew cemetery's up there. There's family around."

We stopped in front of the house. The screen opened and a little dried-apple woman came to the edge of the porch. Aunt Dessie unfolded and strode up the steps into her arms.

"Who do you think I brought to see you, Noella?" she demanded. "Here's Jimmie's wife, Mary."

Jimmie? I thought. My father could never have been anyone but James. Cool, upwardly mobile James.

"Of course it's Mary," Noella said in a quavery voice as tender as cake. "You precious thing. I'm so thankful to see you again." She wound her arms around my mother like roots.

Aunt Dessie said, "And this is Jimmie's daughter. This is Tina." Then I was inside that root-hold, as helpless as a rock being broken by long gentle pressure.

"I would have known you," Noella said. I braced myself. "You have his face, your daddy's face. I always hoped I'd get to see you." She looked beyond me at the empty car.

My mother looked, too, as if she had just recalled the trips we used to take when my father would wake up in the back seat, yelling, "Hey, we've *arrived*—why didn't you tell me?" while we laughed. "James would have liked to come, I'm sure. But he's a busy man these days."

Noella took her arm. "Tell him I miss him."

"Yes," my mother said, glancing sharply at me to make sure I didn't blurt out, *How can she tell him when he moved out a month ago?*

We sat in Noella's cramped little living room while she slushed around in her slippers, bringing us iced tea. She and Aunt Dessie took big breaths and brought each other up-to-date on who had died since they last visited. They made me nervous, reminding me how life changes and the people we love fall away.

I stared out the window through a bouquet of plastic flowers that was never going to die. All at once I realized that a man's bearded face was staring in at me.

I screamed, giving a start that filled my lap with iced tea.

Noella said calmly, "It's just Arley, precious. He wants to see who you are, but he's shy." The face scowled, punctured by a gaping mouth, and disappeared. She patted my skirt with everyone's pink paper napkins and sent me out into the sun to dry.

Aunt Dessie strolled out behind me. "Who's Arley?" I whispered, afraid I'd see that face again peeking through the beanpoles of the garden.

"Noella's son," Aunt Dessie said.

"But he's middle-aged." It sounded stupid, but I couldn't recall ever seeing a retarded adult. I guess I thought they stayed children.

"Of course he is. We grow, whether we're ready or not. We do the best we can." She picked a skinny red-pepper pod and bit off the end. "Mercy! Jalapeño." She fanned her tongue.

We walked along the garden rows while my skirt dried. Behind a hedge a bear-shaped shadow stayed even with us.

"Your mother seems very sad," Aunt Dessie said.

I shrugged. "Really?" Suddenly it would have been a relief to pour out the whole They've-split-again-and-it's-awful-and-I'm-scared story.

"Trouble at home?"

I kept shrugging. "Not exactly. Well, maybe a little, but they'll work it out. They always do."

"Ah," Aunt Dessie said.

When we went into the kitchen, my mother was setting plates around a table that practically sagged under bowls of macaroni and cheese and sliced tomatoes and fried okra and chowchow and peaches that perfumed the room. All at once I was famished.

Noella piled food on a tray and took it to the door, saying, "Arley wants to eat on the porch. It takes him a little while to get used to new people."

I stuffed myself. Aunt Dessie kept right up with me, begging her gall-bladder to forgive and forget. My mother ate in silence, watching the two old faces opposite her like a play.

Noella said, "The last time Dessie came for a visit she brought me the most beautiful crocheted bedspread you ever set eyes on. I'll show it to you. Are you still doing bedspreads?"

"Can't afford the thread anymore," Aunt Dessie said. "Now it's bootees and little sacques* and caps. I sell some for baby showers and give the rest away to whoever's expecting."

**sacque* infant's short jacket that fastens at the neck

Noella asked, "What kind of projects keep you busy, Mary?"

My mother opened her mouth and nothing came out. I waited with them, curious. *Tell them your hobby is collecting little keys that lock out the things in your life that scare you. And lock you in.*

A glass shattered out on the porch. We jumped again as something crashed against the wall. A blubbering growl rose and faded as footsteps pounded off the porch and away.

Noella took a broom and went out. We waited. My mother pressed a careful furrow in her food and we all studied it like a divination. She asked, "Who will take care of him when she dies?"

Aunt Dessie nodded, musing. "Yes. When he's alone. She worries terribly about that."

Unexpectedly my mother reached across the table and laid her hand on Aunt Dessie's. Aunt Dessie put her other hand on top of theirs and we all looked at the funny fragile layers of hands until Noella came back with the tray full of spilled food and broken glass.

In the hurting silence I found myself offering to do the dishes while they visited, but Noella shooed us out, saying she could do dishes when she didn't have us. I hung at the kitchen door, feeling somehow drawn to her, as she put up the food. "I'm sorry I screamed," I said. "I didn't know."

"Of course you didn't, sugar." She took a dozen gorgeous peaches off the windowsill and put them in a sack. "When Arley was little and I finally knew he was never going to be right, I screamed too. Screamed and screamed." She put the sack into my hands. "Take these with you. Your mother said you're on your way to see her folks."

I wished she hadn't reminded me. "She never did this before." As if I had taken the bottom piece of fruit out of the pyramid at the market, everything began to tumble. "Left home, I mean. To go talk to her folks about it. Like this time it was—it was—" I felt silly tripping over a simple word like *serious*.

"Bless your heart," Noella said.

When we went into the living room, Aunt Dessie asked us, "We do have time to go up to the cemetery a minute, don't we?"

My mother shook her head. "I'm afraid it's getting—"

"We have time," I said. I offered my arm to Noella and we went out past my mother's surprised face.

She and Aunt Dessie followed us up a shade-spattered road to the top of the hill. Noella opened a gate in a wire fence and let us into the little graveyard filled with dark cedars. "Used to be a church here, at the beginning," she said. I looked around, wondering why I had wanted so suddenly and urgently, back at the house, to stand up there with my kin.

Noella led us through the high weeds to a grave with a neat concrete cover. A jar with the stem of a rose in it stood beside the nameplate. Dried petals lay around it. "Arley comes," Noella said.

Aunt Dessie pulled two weeds and brushed the nameplate with their leafy tops. "He was a good kind man, Noella." They looked down in silence. "You were fortunate."

"Oh, yes," Noella said, and put her thin arm through Aunt Dessie's bony one.

My mother walked slowly away toward a worn stone. Years of wind had scoured off all the inscription except one line. It said, *beloved wife of.*

She began to cry, with the loud surprised sound of an animal in pain.

"Oh, precious," Noella exclaimed. "Are you sick?"

My mother pivoted blindly into Aunt Dessie's arms. A sob broke through her fingers. They both caught her tight, not understanding. But I knew.

Fear froze me. My voice made a long arc. "Nooo—you can fix it, you can work it out, you're adults!"

My mother's head rocked back and forth, her long hair sliding.

"Oh, Mary," Aunt Dessie said. "No hope at all?"

"No hope," my mother sobbed.

"What?" Noella asked. "What?"

"The marriage," Aunt Dessie said. "Over."

I whirled and ran. Before the fact could touch me. Over the humps of graves lost in the weeds. "No!" I insisted, with every gasp of breath.

But I knew the fact was right behind me, riding piggyback the way it always had, and there was no way I could ever run fast enough. My father had escaped. Oh, God, I knew it wasn't his fault that he had to keep growing. Out of the piney woods. Out of a marriage with somebody who was growing at a different speed. But I wished I could have hunted for that little boy he had been once, and coaxed him out, and made friends with him.

The fence loomed up. I grabbed the rusty wire and hung over it, listening to myself gulping air as though nothing in me had died.

When I lifted my head, a hand was reaching toward me from behind a gravestone. I recoiled into the weeds before I saw that it was holding out a yellow flower.

Arley peeped out. "I'm nice," he whispered. "Don't cry." His soft wet mouth crumpled with anxiety. "I don't scare you." He pushed the flower closer.

I cringed away before I could stop myself. He did scare me. All the things I didn't understand scared me. Losing the people I had belonged to. Letting a special person change my life someday. Or mess it up, the way Sharon had let someone mess up hers. I had collected as many keys as my mother to lock the changes out.

Carefully, Arley sniffed the flower to show me what he wanted me to do. He held it out again, smiling, with pollen on his nose.

"Don't cry," he begged. "I'm nice." He had my father's deep eyes. The family face. Mine.

"I know," I said shakily. I could see he was. A big, bearded man-child distressed to see me sad. "It's not you." A year's collection of tears tried to burst out, sweeping my breath away again. I pointed up the hill. "It's that."

He looked up and nodded solemnly, as if he knew all about divorces, and all about the key I'd given Sharon so she'd hang out at our house like always and teach me to be brave. He smiled as if he could explain why people kept rearranging themselves into families so they could take care of each other.

I looked up the slope. My mother was walking toward me, between Aunt Dessie and Noella. Her face was calm. She held their hands. She would cut her hair, I thought. She would let it go natural.

Slowly I reached out and took Arley's flower.

I wondered if he would nod if I suddenly said that, in spite of everything, I knew I was lucky. Lucky to be able to go on from this, without too much to handle like Sharon, or starting from scratch like my mother.

Noella came to me and held me close in her root arms. She gave me a brisk pat. "I don't have a brain cell working. I forgot to show you Dessie's bedspread."

We went through the gate and down the road again. Behind me, my mother said, "Tina?" I felt the tips of her fingers brush my back. "If you're giving Sharon the diaper bag, maybe I could give her some bootees."

I stumbled around to look at her. My voice wiggled as I said, "Would you? It would mean a lot."

Aunt Dessie smiled. "What color shall they be, for this modern little mother? Purple, with orange ribbons?"

"Just a nice traditional white, I would think," my mother said. "Some things don't change."

Reading for Understanding

❑ MAIN IDEA

1. Which of the following quotations best expresses the main idea of the story?
   (a) Tell them your hobby is collecting little keys that lock out the things in your life that scare you. And lock you in.
   (b) "James would have liked to come, I'm sure. But he's a busy man these days."
   (c) I hung at the kitchen door, feeling somehow drawn to her, as she put up the food.
   (d) "The last time I tried to find kinfolks I hadn't visited for a while, I got the house number and the street perfect, but I was in the wrong town."

❑ DETAILS

2. Sharon was (a) a cousin of Noella's (b) a friend of Tina's (c) James's second wife (d) Aunt Dessie's sister.
3. The Mayhew mailbox identified (a) Aunt Dessie's home (b) the country post office (c) the house of a friendly neighbor (d) Noella's land.
4. At first, Tina was frightened by (a) news from Sharon (b) Aunt Dessie's strong voice (c) Arley (d) the graveyard.
5. Noella and Aunt Dessie (a) havc the same interests (b) are not blood kin (c) are cousins (d) disliked James.

❑ INFERENCES

6. The very first paragraph suggests to the reader that the three travelers (a) dislike each other (b) are black (c) have no sense of responsibility (d) are foreign born.
7. Aunt Dessie can be characterized as (a) strong and warm (b) flighty and unreliable (c) weak but sensitive (d) helpless but charming.
8. The events in the story (a) made Tina dislike Aunt Dessie (b) showed the viciousness in people (c) helped Tina grow up (d) annoyed Noella.
9. Arley (a) displayed an underlying warmth (b) was aware of all the problems (c) was cruel to Tina (d) was outgoing and extroverted.
10. The difficulty between Mary and James was essentially (a) cruelty on the part of James (b) infidelity on the part of Mary (c) differences over Tina (d) differences in growth.

❑ AUTHOR'S IMAGERY

11. An example of a perceptive figure of speech is the following:
    (a) "I've never forgotten how they took me into the family."
    (b) "Who will take care of him when she dies?"
    (c) Aunt Dessie unfolded out of the car like a carpenter's ruler.
    (d) "I'm her friend. I thought you were, too, the way you were always nice to her and laughed when she did weird things."

❑ ORDER OF EVENTS

12. Arrange the items in the order in which they occurred. Use letters only.
    A. Arley says, "I don't scare you."
    B. Tina gives Sharon the keys to the house.

C. James and Mary separate.
D. Mary speaks kindly and warmly about Sharon.
E. Aunt Dessie notices the Mayhew mailbox.

❑ OUTCOMES

13. After the end of the story, (a) Mary and Jim get back together (b) Aunt Dessie moves in with Noella (c) Arley goes back with Tina and Mary (d) The characters are more reconciled to the sadnesses they've experienced.

14. The visit to Noella (a) made Aunt Dessie determined not to visit again (b) gave Tina greater insight into her father's personality (c) widened the gulf between Mary and Tina (d) showed Noella's indifference to family.

❑ FACT OR OPINION

Tell whether the following is a fact or an opinion.

15. The coming divorce was the fault of James, not Mary.

Words in Context

1. ". . .she had swerved off the *interstate* toward a dismal little town." ***Interstate*** (55) means (a) crossroad (b) main street (c) ocean highway (d) major highway.

2. ". . . we were spending the night on Aunt Dessie's let-down couch between two *whatnots* crammed with *spinster junk*." ***Whatnots . . . spinster junk*** (55) mean (a) tables . . . toys (b) shelves . . . curios (c) chairs . . . display dishes (d) closets . . . drying clothes.

3. "'Lady in there makes these *totes*,' she announced, handing it to me. 'A souvenir.'" ***Totes*** (56) means (a) candy bars (b) bread sticks (c) dolls (d) carry-alls.

4. "My mother started off with a jerk. 'A *bubble-headed* little blond Tina knows back home.'" ***Bubble-headed*** (56) means (a) loud-mouthed (b) heavyset (c) quiet and pretty (d) flighty and not bright.

5. "The car *lurched* to a stop. My mother swung around in her seat." ***Lurched*** (57) means (a) swerved (b) hurried (c) braked hard (d) came gradually.

6. "... her mother's in Florida with four stepchildren and her dad got an *ultimatum* from his girl friend." ***Ultimatum*** (57) means (a) inheritance (b) final warning (c) encouraging sign (d) lease.

7. "... she stared into a mirror at her horse face and *rawboned* body and knew no man was ever going to love her." ***Rawboned*** (58) means (a) heavyset (b) thin (c) tall (d) ill-formed.

8. "My father could never have been anyone but James. Cool, *upwardly mobile* James." ***Upwardly mobile*** (58) means (a) rising to a higher social position (b) unwilling to accept responsibility (c) unstable (d) driven by need for money.

9. "'Of course it's Mary,' Noella said in a *quavery* voice as tender as cake." ***Quavery*** (58) means (a) thin (b) booming (c) melodious (d) trembling.

10. "My mother pressed a careful furrow in her food and we all studied it like a *divination*." ***Divination*** (60) means (a) ancient idol (b) symbol of thought (c) look into the future (d) waste of time.

Thinking Critically About the Story

1. "I've never forgotten how they took me into the family. No questions. No testing. Just welcome . . ." What is Mary's attitude toward family? What does Tina learn on this trip about the meaning of family? What role should relatives outside the immediate family play in our lives? Do yours come up to your expectations? Which ones do you respect the most? Explain. Explain what errors relatives make when on the plane of teenagers.

2. The fullest amplitude of the meaning of friendship is reached in the relationship between Tina and her friend Sharon. How does Tina's definition compare with yours? Your friend's? Does friendship have limits? Explain.

3. "Tell them your hobby is collecting little keys that lock out the things in your life that scare you. And lock you in." What did Tina mean? Why did she object to this way of handling problems? How valid is Tina's generalization? What would be a better way? Why doesn't Mary take it?

4. One character central to the story, James, Tina's father, never makes an appearance. What do you learn about him from the other characters? Do you sympathize with him? Explain. Is there any better way in which he could have handled his inner conflict?

5. Why does Arley startle Tina at first? What changes her attitude toward him? What does she learn about herself from him? Are her responses to him typical of those of most of us when meeting exceptional people? Explain. How does Arley compare with the exceptional people you have met or read about?

Stories in Words

Spinster (page 55) as a term for an unmarried woman has a long history. Alfred the Great referred to the females in his family as "the spindle side." Each young woman had to learn to spin and weave. She was expected to create all the household linens she'd need when she married. Not very long ago, young ladies had "hope chests" in which they stored the linens (not necessarily handwoven) they hoped to bring to their marriages. Though young ladies no longer have to spin and weave, the old word has remained for an unmarried woman.

Tripod (page 56), meaning "a three-footed stool or altar," displays two useful Greek roots. *Tri* appears in such diverse words as *triceratops* ("a three-horned dinosaur"), *tricycle* ("a three-wheeled vehicle"), *trigonometry* ("the branch of mathematics based on triangles"), *trilingual* ("versed in three languages"), *trilogy* ("series of three books"), *trimeter* ("line of verse with three metrical feet"), *tripartite* ("having three parts"), and *triptych* ("a painting with three panels"). The Latin *tri*, related to the Greek prefix, gives us many other "three" compounds, like *triangle, triple,* and *trilingual. Pod,* "foot," appears in *podiatrist* ("foot specialist"). The word seems to be replacing *chiropodist* ("hand and foot specialist"). *Gastropod* literally means "stomach foot," because mollusks seem to slide along on their stomachs.

Ultimatum (page 57) comes from the Latin *ultimus*, meaning "last." An *ultimatum* is the last word before some action is to be taken. The root appears in *ultimately* and a strange word, *ultimogeniture.* In English law *primogeniture* declares that the oldest son inherits. Though not exactly fair, the law has kept English estates from being subdivided into tiny parcels. *Ultimogeniture* is the opposite situation, declaring that the youngest son inherits the estate. The root also appears in *penultimate*, meaning "next to the last." *Pen*, meaning "almost," appears in *peninsula*—literally "almost an island."

Reduced

ELIZABETH BOWEN

"She was accused of murder," said Miss Rice, as though giving a history lesson, "tried last spring, acquitted but never properly cleared. So she disappeared, hoping to be forgotten."

"Good God," exclaimed Frank. "Where would a woman go to, after a show like that?"

"She is fortunate to be anywhere."

A household rife with tension, a competent and underpaid governess, two children once victims of a heartless nanny—these are the ingredients of this perceptive story. Two houseguests, quite different in personalities, precipitate a crisis in the family's nervous existence and disturb the uneasy equilibrium.

"Reduced" and "The Drum" (page 82) provide an interesting pair of stories, suggesting obvious comparisons and subtle contrasts. Both deal with governesses who seem to understand children, but Paul in "The Drum" is far more complex than Claudia or Penny. "Reduced" focuses principally on the inner life of the governess. "The Drum" is mainly concerned with the repressed psyche of the young child. Both stories depend upon the subtle interaction of personalities for their insight and appeal. In both stories there is a turning point that suggests the direction of events that will follow.

Reduced

I

The Carburys' two little girls, Penny and Claudia, went upstairs again with their governess, Miss Rice, as soon as lunch was over: their steps could be heard retreating along the pitch-pine gallery round the hall. The visitors were disappointed—Mrs. Laurie liked children, and Frank Peele had been hoping to see more of the governess. Rain drummed on the hall skylight; still smoking their host Godwin Carbury's rather musty cigarettes, the grown-ups allowed themselves to be driven into the library. Here no chair invited you, the uninviting books must have been bought in lots and looked gummed in the shelves. It could have been a pretty September day; the plum-tree leaves in the tilting orchards round were bright yellow, but for days the Forest of Dene had been clouded and sodden.

Mrs. Laurie, who was vivacious and had married at nineteen, and Mrs. Carbury, who was muddled and dim, had been friends years ago in India when they were both young girls. They had kept in touch, Mrs. Carbury having no other vivacious friend, life having taught Mrs. Laurie that there was no knowing when anybody devoted might not come in useful—besides, she had always been sorry for Mima.

Mima's life had been unrewarding. She returned flatly from India after her friend's wedding, and it had not been till she was twenty-seven or eight that she met Godwin Carbury, who at forty was looking round for a wife. He had the reputation of being the most unpopular man in his part of the country, and that reputation followed him up to London. He was careful, savagely careful, about money, and not careful enough about seeing this was not known. Added to this, he had a dour self-importance. It was understood that economy kept him single as long as his mother had lived to keep house at Pendlethwaite. Possibly Mima saw something in him that no one else saw; she was anxious to "settle" suitably and not herself accustomed to being liked. At all events, they married, and had had after some years these two thin, remote little girls. They had few neighbors at Pendlethwaite, and Godwin's peculiarities cut them off more and more from anybody there was. Whatever misgivings she had, Mima pandered to him blindly. On her own account she had just a little money, so once or twice a year she came up to London, gazed into shop windows, met Mrs. Laurie (now widowed) and bought reduced coats and shoes for the little girls. She had begun lately to talk of giving up London; the girls' education would be a heavy expense, she said.

It surprised Mrs. Laurie to find herself at Pendlethwaite, but she had been at a loose end, with nowhere to go for a week. So she thought, "Try the Carburys," and had written to Mima. She was a shiftless woman, maintaining herself by the exercise of a good deal of charm: she could say daring things without sounding impertinent, and determined to get a little fun out of Godwin—apart from this, she did not expect very much.

Pendlethwaite was not a lovable house. Built about 1880 of unpleasing maroon brick, it creaked inside with pitch-pine: its churchlike windows peered narrowly at the smiling landscape round; its grounds darkened a valley with belts of laurel and stiff, damp-looking clumps of unindigenous firs. The house looked dedicated to a perpetual January: sunnier seasons beat back from its walls. The bloomy red plums and mellow apples bending the boughs this month were pagan company for it. Indoors, there was no electricity, panels absorbed the lamplight; before October, no fires were lit till night. It had not even the insidious charm of decay, for Godwin had great ideas of "keeping things up"; the laurels were kept clipped, the thrifty meals served formally. . . . Mrs. Laurie had been diverted to find that she had a fellow guest, but this did not see her far. Frank Peele, just back on leave from Siam, was Mima's second cousin. He must have asked himself here because he had to be somewhere; she thought he was not a man you would scramble to entertain. At about thirty, he was a haggard schoolboy—shambling, facetious, huffy, forlorn, melancholic, with perhaps (she feared most of all) a romantic soul. She supposed Mima must enjoy being even sorrier for him than she need be for herself. . . . Entertaining on this scale must be a plunge for the Carburys. Mrs. Laurie could almost hear Godwin saying to Mima: "Well then, in for a penny, in for a pound." He went through with his duties as host with glum correctness. "But if one stayed a day too long he'd cut off supplies." As it was, his rigid economies hit you everywhere.

The one startling un-economy was the governess. Mrs. Laurie, though unhappily childless, knew an expensive governess when she saw one. Miss Rice's technique was perfect. Her first appearance, at lunch, took Nella's breath away with its serene unobtrusiveness. Penny and Claudia—their dark eyes set close in, tucking their long fair hair back behind their shoulders primly—clearly revolved round her. "Those two little mice adore her," thought Mrs. Laurie, recalling the composed retreat after lunch: three people going back to a world of their own. But the adoration was kept within nice bounds. "How does Mima *keep* the woman in this mausoleum? She might be anywhere. Mima can't be such a fool as I thought. . . . I must find out."

In the library, she lost no time doing this. In the bow window, Frank Peele with his hands in his pockets stood looking out unexpectingly at the rain; Mima poured out thin coffee; Godwin glumly handed the cups round. Mrs. Laurie said affably: "So you got a governess? Last time we met, you were busy looking for one."

"Yes, oh yes. We did," Mima said in her flustered way.

"Miss Rice came in May," said Godwin firmly.

"She seems a great success. . . ."

Frank Peele grunted.

"When she first came in," went on Mrs. Laurie, "I felt certain I'd seen her somewhere. I wonder where she was before? She's startlingly good-looking, but in such a tactful way. Hag-ridden—but that's the life, I suppose."

"She appears content with us," said Godwin, handing the sugar to Mrs. Laurie bitterly. "Mima, what are your plans for this afternoon?" His wife looked blank.

"Our guests should be entertained."

"It struck me," said Frank, wheeling round, "as one of the few faces I had *not* seen before."

"Really?" said Godwin.

Mima touched the coffee-tray clumsily; everything on it skidded. Did she not want cousin Frank to fall for the governess? The nicest women like having unattached men around. "She must be full of brains," said Mrs. Laurie vaguely.

"She teaches wonderfully; she's got the children *on* so. They seem to be learning everything."

"Can we have them all down after tea to play Up Jenkin or something?"

"They do preparation then," said Godwin repressively. ("Set," thought his guest, "on getting his money's worth.") Mima's eyes, oddly overwrought in her pink creased face, stole to meet her husband's. "Frank," Godwin continued, "I could show you those maps now." Clearly, any discussion of Miss Rice was closed.

"Not today, thanks," said Frank, "I've got a crick in my neck." Godwin, after one more forbidding look at Mima, left them, shutting the door reprovingly. Frank loafed along the bookshelves, pulled out *Monasteries of the Levant**, and folded himself in a chair with an air of resigned discomfort. A man with a book is practically not present. Mrs. Laurie whipped out her *petit point*, and the two women, pulling their chairs together zestfully, settled down for a talk. Rain streamed down the windows, paper rustled inside the cold grate.

Mima saw so few friends that talk went to her head like wine. Evenly sing-song, the women's voices began rising and falling. After half an hour

**Levant* Eastern Mediterranean countries

Frank's book slipped on to his knee; his head rolled back, jaw dropping; he let out a sharp snore. "Really . . ." exclaimed Mima, stopping the talk to titter. "A tropical habit," said Mrs. Laurie. This was better than Frank with a book, they were quite alone. She hopped back to her topic.

"Mima, what's Godwin got up his sleeve about Miss Rice?"

"Miss Rice?—nothing," Mima said, overacting.

"His one wicked extravagance?"

"No," faltered Mima. "That's just the point—she's not."

"A bargain? You amaze me. Can she be at all fishy?"

"My *dear* Nella—she's good with the children, isn't she?" Mima fixed her friend with such oddly imploring eyes that Mrs. Laurie, startled, put down her work: "She's made princesses of them," she said extravagantly. "How wise you have been, Mima!"

"You do really think so? Godwin and I wanted the best we could get, you see: he has such ideas for Penny and Claudia."

"It does him credit," said Mrs. Laurie warmly.

"I suppose so," blurted out Mima, then, looking wretched, put her hand to her cheek. "I've never quite liked—I mean if she—I can't help wondering—"

"Why did Godwin snap me up when I said I thought I knew her face?"

"We'd hoped no one *would* think that," said Mima surprisingly. "As a rule, you see, almost nobody comes here, and in every other way she seemed quite ideal: she is. In the ordinary way, we never could have afforded her. It *did* seem such an opportunity. You see, we could not offer a high salary."

"That would narrow things down. . . . "

"It did. All the ones I had interviewed were so vulgar and pushing, besides seeming to know nothing at all. The agency woman said, 'For *that*, what can you expect?' I was in despair."

"Oh? So then—?"

"I came round more and more to Godwin's idea. As he said, it was practically a charity. It did seem unfair that the thing should count against her. When she had paid for her defense she hadn't a penny, and no other future, of course. And she *was* acquitted."

"What on earth do you mean?"

Looking thoroughly frightened, Mima caught herself up. "Oh dear," she said, "and I swore never to speak of it. Nella, will you *swear* to let this go no further? It's such a relief to tell you: it's on my mind the whole time. You see, Godwin had followed all the evidence carefully. The witnesses gave her such magnificent testimonials; almost all her former employers were called. Even the Prosecution didn't make out she wasn't a good *governess*. And after all, she *was* cleared. (If only they'd found who'd done it. . . .)"

"Begin at the beginning."

"Well. . . . Do you ever read murder trials?"

"Hardly ever miss one."

"Do you remember that Sir Max Rant dying suddenly?"

"Mima—she's not *Henrietta Post?*"

"Sssh—sssh," whispered Mima, glancing Frank's way cautiously. Then she nodded at Nella with frightened important eyes.

Mrs. Laurie stared, galvanized, at her hostess. Then: "She's lucky to be alive," she said, "it was touch and go."

"He was a dreadful old man, apparently. At the very worst, they said nothing against her *morals*."

"No wonder she's haunted-looking. That was an appalling ordeal. . . . But, after that, how on earth . . .?"

"Godwin got me to write to her three weeks after the trial, offering her a new life and twenty-five pounds a year. . . ."

"Godwin is on the spot! Well, they're your children, not mine—*Henrietta Post*!"

Immovably, without batting a closed eyelid, Frank said, "Who is Henrietta Post?"

II

"Miss Rice's hands are cold again," said Penny.

Claudia went on painting a moment longer, then, balancing her brush on the glass jar of paint-water, which gave out a prussic smell and had a red sediment, looked intently across the table at Penny, who stood by Miss Rice's chair, chafing her right hand. Their governess, with her book propped on the table, her pale cheek on her left hand, read on, smiling unnoticingly. Once she withdrew her hand from Penny's to turn over a page.

"Whatever will she do in winter?" said Claudia.

"There'll be fires then."

"This fire never burns much." They shared the same desperate thought: "Suppose our darling should leave us?"

This afternoon, the black chill of the grate focused your fancy as firelight might have done. The schoolroom had a faded sea-blue wallpaper cut into by pitch-pine presses and two doors: not a color warmed it; the high windows looked into a rain-blurred hill. Miss Rice had put nothing of her own on the mantelpiece, along which marched a file of plastic animals modeled by the little girls. About the room were products of other hobbies good governesses encourage children to have: on the windowsill a nursery-garden in pots. Pink-cheeked "Bubbles" and "Cherry Ripe" looked queerly down at the bleak room where these three people were living as best they could.

Miss Rice put away the book, and with it her happy, forgetful smile—the book had been *Emma*. "Have you stopped painting?" she said.

She had given them for the subject a Greek temple. Claudia's temple had a sunset behind it, Penny had filled in the columns with Mediterranean blue. Miss Rice came round and looked. "A sunset like that would make reflections on white stone, Claudia. Penny, on such a fine day there would be shadows." They saw. She always thought of something they had not thought of: they wrinkled up their foreheads in ecstatic despair. "Penny, if you are stopping, wash that blue off your paintbrush."

"Are paints poison?"

"Sometimes. Well, are you cold, too?"

They would admit nothing that could distress her.

"Then push the table back and get the skipping-ropes out."

The little girls were alike, though there were two years between them, as though they could not decide to part in any particular. There was not much difference in size, as though Penny had waited for Claudia. Their voices were pitched on the same persuasive note; when their vehement dark eyes met they seemed to consult. What they thought of being alive their parents would never know: their characters were like batteries storing something up. Before Miss Rice was here, the doctor's sister had come in every morning to give them lessons. They had known before how to read and write, so all they had learnt from the doctor's sister was what every one else knew: just why their house was avoided, how bitterly father was laughed at and mother pitied because of him. They learnt that it was wretched to be themselves. They marked the contempt with which every morning she bicycled up their avenue, and how insolently she ate what there was at lunch. Her raspy fingertips, the pearls screwed tight in her fleshy ears, her horsesense, all seemed part of her power to mortify them. She was the world and they prayed she might die, but she married. After that they waited, in armor. Then came Miss Rice.

"If you want to keep warm you must hurry," said Miss Rice.

Claudia unwound the skipping-ropes and they took one each: they stood with their arms out, gripping the handles eagerly. "One, two, three—go!" The ropes zip-zipped on the oilcloth. Penny stumbled at fifty-six but Claudia kept in and skipped seventy-eight: her toes bounced and bounced, her hair flopped, her eyes started out of her head. At last the rope caught her toe. "That's the record," said Miss Rice, "but Penny may beat it next time." Both breathless, they knelt on the hearthrug, life tingling up through them from their toes to their cheeks.

"If *you* skipped," said Claudia, "you might skip a hundred."

"The rope is too short," said Miss Rice.

"What else used you to do—dance?"

"Yes, once."

They had never seen anyone dancing except in pictures of ballrooms: they preferred to imagine Miss Rice not on the crook of an arm, but floating alone round a floor, with her ageless, shining white face, unfrivolous as an angel. At this happy moment, near her and warm from skipping, they felt on the edge of the story she did not tell. . . . But *she* looked down at the skipping-ropes on the floor. "Better put those away," she said. Except when she was reading she never stayed quiet long: something they could feel creep up behind her chair would make her speaking eyes go suddenly cold and dark as the grate. Against this their love was powerless. This dreadful expectation seemed wrong in their darling—mother without her worries would not be anyone, father was there to stare and bite his moustache, but *she* seemed to them born to inherit light. . . . Feeling their enemy here now the children, helpless, got up to put the skipping-ropes back in the press.

"Someone's coming!" said Penny. They heard the baize door at the far end of their passage swing to behind somebody, then a man's step. A knuckle rapped the door once, unconfidently. Miss Rice and the children waited. "Come in!" she said.

Frank Peele peered round the door. "Oh?" he said. "May I come in? Sorry. I was exploring. Looking for secret passages. Exercise before tea." Miss Rice smiled composedly. "So here you all are," he went on. He looked at the table. "Painting?"

"Yes."

"What a day!" he said to Miss Rice humbly. "Very cheery up here, though. You believe in fresh air?" Then he saw that both windows were bolted: what he felt were the drafts. Miss Rice had moved to the table where she had been reading; Frank dropped into the wicker chair with a creak. The children shut their paintboxes up. "Must be getting on tea-time," remarked Frank.

"Are you hungry, Cousin Frank?" said Claudia gently.

Frank looked relieved at hearing someone say something. "I don't deserve tea; I slept like a log in the library. Your mother and Mrs. Laurie complain I snored." He looked round the schoolroom wistfully, like a dog. "They were talking nineteen to the dozen. When I dropped off they were well away about India, when I came to it was one Henrietta Post."

Penny laughed, "Who's Henrietta Post?" she said.

"Don't ask *me*," said Frank,"—Miss Rice, who's Henrietta Post?"

Miss Rice pondered while the clock ticked several seconds and a cart rattled off into silence behind the wet orchards. The children turned to see how she took Frank's joke. She looked twice at him with steady, considering, dark eyes. "Surely you know?" she said at last.

"I don't know a soul," said Frank, "I've been in Siam."

"But you get the papers there, don't you?"

"She's a celebrity, is she?"

"She was accused of murder," said Miss Rice, as though giving a history lesson, "tried last spring, acquitted but never properly cleared. So she disappeared, hoping to be forgotten."

"Good God," exclaimed Frank. "Where would a woman go to, after a show like that?"

"She is fortunate to be anywhere."

"—Stop! it's coming back!" Frank said, delighted to have a topic. "Wasn't she that governess? The old swine whose house she was in had been making up to her, so when someone did him in they tried to fix it on her. I remember I thought at the time—"

Miss Rice's marked unresponse reminded Frank where he was. Chidden, he stopped awkwardly, with a glance at the children. *They* sat stone-still, clasped hands thrust down between their knees; you could not possibly tell what was going on in their heads, which were both turned intently away from their governess. Frank kicked himself. But for the life of him he couldn't stop blurting out: "She was very good-looking, wasn't she?"

"You never saw any photographs?"

"Out where I am I only get *The Times*, you see. No pretty pictures in it."

"I see."

Frank went on violently: "I know I thought at the time, what a shocking unfair thing to happen to any woman!" . . . Miss Rice with her cold smile looked thoughtfully into the grate as though there were a fire burning there: she said nothing more. Her charges' agonized tension became startling. Frank hummed and beat a nonplussed tattoo on his knee. They were waiting to see the last of him. Whatever brick one had dropped, they were all very odd up here. . . .

III

This wet autumn evening closed in so early that the children had to stop work and wait for the lamp to come; when Mrs. Carbury looked in they were all in the dark. "Why, whatever are you doing?" she said nervously. "Where's Miss Rice? Why doesn't she ring for the lamp?"

"It never comes any sooner."

"Father wouldn't like you wasting your time like this. Where *is* Miss Rice?"

"In her room," Penny said, so indifferently that there seemed to be something foolish about the fuss. At this point a band of light appeared in the passage; the housemaid brought in the lamp and Mima saw her daughters facing each other like images across the table of lesson books, their unchildish eyes dark in the sudden lamplight. She sat down, acting calm while the housemaid was in the room; all the same, her manner made the girl so jumpy that she went away again without drawing down the blinds. Mrs. Carbury sat eyeing the other door: the children's bedroom opened off the schoolroom and Miss Rice's room was beyond, connecting with theirs. Her relief at *not* finding the governess was tremendous: all the same, she felt she was being defied.

"Does she always leave you to do preparation alone?"

"She's tired," said Claudia. "Cousin Frank was up here."

"Oh? . . . Well, tell her I want to speak to her. Then you can leave your lessons, just for this evening, and go downstairs; Mrs. Laurie says she will play games with you."

The children looked at their books without stirring, and Mima for the first time felt mutiny in the air. . . . Mima had had to brace herself to come in; twice already since tea she had started up to the schoolroom, then turned back before the baize door to that wing. Ever since her revelation to Mrs. Laurie she had been in a fearful state: the way Mrs. Laurie took it brought her own most persistent throttling fears to the top. "*Henrietta Post. . . . Well, they're your children, not mine.*" What Nella said was what anybody who knew would say. Mima had shrunk back from the schoolroom door, feeling: "No, I really cannot face her." Then she had been forced to think: "But that is the woman my children are with the whole time. . . ." Once she had got as far as Godwin's study to tell him he must agree to send Miss Rice away tomorrow, but the way he had looked up at her settled that. "Nothing has changed since I agreed to engage her." Mima knew too well that her husband found her a fool. "I will give her notice first, then tell Godwin. It won't be so bad with Nella here in the house. Nella will back me up. *But when Godwin hears I've told Nella?* . . . He said before she came to stay: "Suppose your friend is inquisitive?" . . . What are they doing up there? What does she say to them? What goes on the whole time? My own children are strangers; they don't like being downstairs now. *What was it the prosecution said about influence?*" That thought had brought Mima past the schoolroom door.

Mima raised her voice. "Run along now at once, children: Mrs. Laurie is waiting."

"We would much rather not, mother."

"Then you're very ungrateful. Besides, I have got something to say to Miss Rice—Penny and Claudia, don't look at each other like that! It's rude to look at each other when mother speaks!"

"Miss Rice is tired," repeated Claudia gently.

"If you give us the message," said Penny, "we'll tell her."

"No, I want to talk to Miss Rice," said Mima, her voice unnatural.

"Do you, mother?" said Penny. "You don't generally."

The wicker chair Mima sat in creaked convulsively. "When we're alone again you may learn to make mother happy. You may understand mother then and not be unkind to her. Tomorrow, Miss Rice will be going away, children."

Penny and Claudia looked at the chair their mother now sat in, then up at *Emma* left on the edge of the mantelpiece. Claudia looked at their row of young plants in the window-sill, sharp in the lamplight against the rain-lashed dark outside, Penny at the wrinkled rug where that afternoon they had knelt at their darling's feet. Then their gentle, vehement, dark eyes, meeting, paused to consult again. They said in their quiet voices: "Then we will go too."

Reading for Understanding

❑ MAIN IDEA

1. The main point of the story is the (a) tension arising from a sordid event in the past (b) wrong way to raise children (c) thoughtlessness of houseguests (d) unexpected joys of a happy marriage.

DETAILS

2. Mrs. Laurie and Mrs. Carbury (a) are related (b) compare their children (c) had met in India (d) have both been divorced.
3. The name of the visiting friend is (a) Mima (b) Penny (c) Claudia (d) Nella.
4. Henrietta Post was (a) convicted of murder (b) a friend of Frank Peele's (c) Miss Rice (d) Mima's houseguest.
5. Mima finally decides to (a) ask Frank Peele to leave (b) ask Mrs. Laurie to stay an extra week (c) tell the governess to leave (d) send the girls off to boarding school.

INFERENCES

6. A word that would best describe Mr. Carbury is (a) *kindly* (b) *domineering* (c) *adventurous* (d) *sensitive.*
7. Frank Peele is pictured as (a) cheery but sometimes moody (b) dull and uninteresting (c) energetic and vibrant (d) cruel and vindictive.
8. The governess's behavior throughout was (a) secretly mocking (b) cold and destructive (c) loud and selfish (d) professional but warm.
9. The two who had the best understanding of the governess's worth were (a) Claudia and Penny (b) Mrs. Carbury and Mrs. Laurie (c) Mr. Carbury and Frank Peele (d) Mrs. Laurie and Frank Peele.

IMAGERY

10. The statement "The house looked dedicated to a perpetual January" was intended to be (a) unflattering (b) warmly approving (c) serenely indifferent (d) intentionally challenging.
11. "Its churchlike windows peered narrowly at the smiling landscape round" is an example of (a) simile (b) hyperbole (c) understatement (d) personification.

ORDER OF EVENTS

12. Arrange the items in the order in which they occurred. Use letters only.
    A. Henrietta Post goes on trial.
    B. Mima tells Nella about the new governess.
    C. Mr. Carbury hires Miss Rice.
    D. Nella comes to visit Mima.
    E. The girls present their ultimatum to Mima.

❑ OUTCOMES

13. After the conclusion of the story, a probable next step was that (a) the Carburys divorced (b) the governess stayed (c) Mrs. Laurie married Frank Peele (d) an old murder trial was reopened.

❑ CAUSE AND EFFECT

14. Mima's fateful decision was prompted by (a) Frank's love for Claudia (b) Mrs. Laurie's anxiety (c) Mr. Carbury's desire to save money (d) Penny's dislike of the governess.

❑ FACT OR OPINION

Tell whether the following is a fact or an opinion.

15. Miss Rice was the best governess any child ever had.

Words in Context

1. "The Carbury's two little girls, Penny and Claudia, went upstairs again with their *governess* . . ." ***Governess*** (68) means (a) companion (b) private woman teacher (c) supervising relative (d) guardian.
2. ". . . but for days the Forest of Dene had been clouded and *sodden.*" ***Sodden*** (68) means (a) thoroughly soaked (b) impenetrable (c) gloomy and threatening (d) dry and brittle.
3. "*He was careful, savagely careful, about money* . . ." This is a fitting description (68) of a (a) spendthrift (b) modest person (c) penniless person (d) penny-pincher.
4. "Whatever *misgivings* she had, Mima *pandered to* him blindly." ***Misgivings*** . . . ***pandered to*** . . . (69) mean (a) affection . . . followed (b) preferences . . . obeyed (c) doubts . . . catered (d) qualms . . . worshipped.
5. ". . . its grounds darkened a valley with belts of *laurel* and stiff, damp-looking clumps of *unindigenous* firs." ***Laurel*** . . . ***unindigenous*** . . . (69) mean (a) grass . . . forbidding (b) ground cover . . . dwarfed (c) flowers . . . towering (d) evergreens . . . not native.
6. ". . . Mrs. Laurie had been *diverted* to find that she had a fellow guest, but this did not see her far." ***Diverted*** (69) means (a) upset (b) surprised (c) disappointed (d) amused.
7. "At about thirty, he was a *haggard* schoolboy—*shambling, facetious,* huffy, forlorn, melancholic . . ." ***Haggard*** . . . ***shambling*** . . . ***face-***

tious . . . (69) mean (a) former . . . stuttering . . . comical (b) careworn . . . shuffling . . . wisecracking (c) gossipy . . . lazy . . . sarcastic (d) overgrown . . . awkward . . . humorous.

8. "Her first appearance, at lunch, took Nella's breath away with its *serene unobtrusiveness.*" ***Serene unobtrusiveness*** (69) means (a) majestic self-control (b) quiet arrogance (c) quiet presence (d) unruffled observation.

9. "Mrs. Laurie said *affably,* 'So you got a governess? Last time we met, you were busy looking for one.'" ***Affably*** (70) means (a) pryingly (b) pleasantly (c) with great interest (d) quietly.

10. "Mima's eyes, *oddly overwrought* in her pink creased face, stole to meet her husband's." ***Oddly overwrought*** (70) means (a) strangely agitated (b) unusually angry (c) unexpectedly sad (d) extremely close to tears.

11. "Frank loafed along the bookshelves . . . and folded himself in a chair with an air of *resigned* discomfort." ***Resigned*** (70) means (a) intense (b) reluctantly accepted (c) carefully planned (d) visible.

12. "Mrs. Laurie stared, *galvanized,* at her hostess. Then: 'She's lucky to be alive,' she said, 'it was touch and go.'" ***Galvanized*** (72) means (a) terrified (b) sadly (c) sympathetically (d) startled.

13. "No wonder she's haunted-looking. That was an *appalling ordeal.*" ***Appalling ordeal*** (72) means (a) dangerous experience (b) dreadful nightmare (c) fiendish trick (d) unique torment.

14. "Claudia . . . looked intently across the table at Penny, who stood by Miss Rice's chair, *chafing* her right hand." ***Chafing*** (72) means (a) holding out (b) clenching (c) rubbing (d) pointing.

15. "Frank hummed and beat a *nonplussed tattoo* on his knee. They were waiting to see the last of him." ***Nonplussed tattoo*** (75) means (a) loud rhythm (b) soft set of tappings (c) intermittent set of tappings (d) confused set of rappings.

Thinking Critically About the Story

1. To what extent is the following statement true of the characters in this story? "All of the people seem to be reduced to a single trait, but that trait so dominates their lives that they appear to be living, breathing human beings."

2. **coincidence** *n:* a sequence of events that happen at the same time by accident but seem to have been planned or arranged;

also any of these occurrences. *synonyms:* accident, chance, happenstance, luck, fate

Evaluate the author's use of coincidence in this story. Give examples in support.

3. Be prepared to read to the class quotations from the story to illustrate the validity of the following generalization: "The author painted most of the characters with a brush dipped in acid." What does the author gain and lose by using this approach?

4. What evidence is there in the story by which we can judge the competence of Miss Rice as a governess? How does she compare with child-care employees or teachers you have known or read about? Why do the girls "love her"?

5. Why was Miss Rice so vulnerable? How did she try to protect herself? How could she have avoided the humiliation she suffered at Pendlethwaite? Are the vulture-like reactions of the characters in this story to be expected from most people? How can the vulnerable protect themselves from the vultures?

Stories in Words

Widowed (69) suggests, in its origin, the grief associated with the name. The root of *widow* is *videre*, "to separate." The root appears in *divide* and *dividend.* Sadly, a widow has been *separated* by death from her husband. An interesting expression, *widow's peak,* is used to describe the point of hair growing down the middle of the forehead. An old superstition held that a woman with such a growth would become a widow early in life.

Mausoleum (69) is related to the Seven Wonders of the Ancient World. It contains a story of unusual devotion. When Queen Artemisia of Caria lost her husband Mausolus, she was inconsolable. She took the irrational step of mixing a portion of her husband's ashes with her daily drink. She died of grief three years later. Before her death, she had commissioned a monument to be erected in his memory. It was built on a base 230 × 250 feet and towered 100 feet in the air. It contained outstanding works of art and was an imposing sight. It lasted almost 1,800 years and finally crumbled in an earthquake in 1375. It shared its fame with six other Wonders: the Pyramid of Khufu, the Hanging Gardens of Babylon, the Colossus of Rhodes, the Olympian Zeus, the Pharos (lighthouse) at Alexandria, and the temple of Artemis at Ephesus. Only the Pyramid still stands.

Extravagance (71) suggests a vivid image in the elements that make it up. *Extra* is a useful prefix meaning "beyond." It appears in *extracurricular* ("*beyond* the curriculum"), *extraordinary* ("*beyond* the ordinary"), *extrasensory* ("*beyond* the senses"), and *extraterrestrial* ("*beyond* our earth"). The *vag* root, meaning "wander," appears in *vagrant* ("*wanderer* without a home"), *vagary* ("unpredictable action or idea"), and *vagabond* ("wanderer"). Putting the roots together gives us *wandering beyond normal limits.* Extravagance is spending beyond reasonable restraints.

The Drum

MONICA FURLONG

Waves of tension seemed to be passing through him, crumpling and stretching his body; somebody was in terrible pain, was so angry that it was not possible to feel such anger and live. He looked desperately about the room for some relief from the ferocity that filled him and his eye fell on the drum.

Child abuse, too often a part of the day's news, is not always obvious. Physical abuse may leave scars, but mental cruelty has results that are not always apparent.

This sensitive story has three principal characters, though one of them barely appears. In this triangle, there is a struggle for the soul of a young boy. Two governesses attempt opposing strategies, and one succeeds. Both nannies are seen through the eye of the child. Both come clear for the reader, even though the child sees at first with prejudice.

Like "Reduced" (page 67), "The Drum" deals with a nanny somewhat different from the usual. "Reduced" is like a miniature detective story. We are interested in the events, and the "mystery." The action of "The Drum" is more internal, occurring in the heart and soul of the child. The turning point in "The Drum" is extremely dramatic and positive. What paved the way for the desirable change?

Autism, an extreme withdrawal from reality, is difficult to treat. Autistic individuals live in a world apart. In "The Drum," we are given some hope that love will begin to prevail.

The Drum

Paul stood on the window seat and looked down on Miss Brown as she walked out to the waiting cab. The horse, which was big and black, stamped its foot on the frozen road, and the steam of its breath rose into the air. Miss Brown was wearing her felt hat with a bit of grizzled black fur on it which Paul had always thought was made out of her own rough hair. She was carrying her brown leather case. Just looking at her thin back told him that she was angry with him. She opened the door and climbed in without a glance at him, and the cabbie gave an order to the horse, which moved unwillingly off. Paul felt that someone, somewhere, was in pain and that if *She* permitted crying he would have cried. He continued to stand there gazing at the road where the cab had been. Emily, who was polishing the brass handles with a big yellow duster, spoke to him.

"Like a peppermint?" She produced a tattered paper bag from her pocket. The hot taste on his tongue, or just Emily's kindness, did make him feel a bit better. He turned away from the window to put the peppermint in his mouth and Emily sat down beside him and pulled him on to her lap. He liked the feel of her big floppy body and the warm, stale smell of her clothes; he leaned against her, sucking his peppermint.

"She give you that?" Paul mutely handed her the book in his hand. It had dark blue leather covers with gold writing on the front. They were soft, not like the covers of Papa's books, and inside was thin paper like Mary used under the tiny chocolate cakes; the edges of the pages shone with gold. At the back (he had discovered when he dropped it) were pictures of sheep and men wearing sheets. There was one of a woman about to hammer a big piece of wood through somebody's head which was interesting (he tried to imagine how it would feel to have a piece of wood hammered into your head), and another of a woman with long red hair kneeling on the floor and pouring a jar of honey over a man's feet. He liked the pictures.

"You'll be able to read it when you're a big boy." Emily's eye fell on the unpolished coal scuttle. She lifted Paul down to the floor.

"She'll be here for lunch," she said. Paul moved away towards the heavy felt cloth that hung over the table when it was not in use; he crawled underneath it and lay full length smelling the dust of the carpet. The gentle gloom of this place, as of somewhere far beneath the sea—the stormy waves clashing too far above his head to trouble him—always soothed him. Even *She* had not forbidden it. It was Emily who eventually summoned him out.

He walked very slowly down the stairs, passing his favorite picture with the boy playing his pipe with his dog beside him, the grazing sheep, the bathing girls, and the man with goat's feet and lovely curly hair. He often imagined going down the path, over the bridge, past the girls (whistling to his dog as he did so), to the meadow beyond. He could roll in the meadow and then find a farmhouse in the blue hills beyond. Possibly *She* would come and look after him. Papa could come sometimes, and smoke his cigar and take him out to eat croissants dipped in coffee at the French bakery.

The sound of his mother's voice brought him back to the staircase. The drawing room door was open.

". . . worried . . ." she was saying. Mama's little lapdog, Confucius, was always developing illnesses and troubling Mama. He stood uncertainly in the doorway, looking only at Mama who wore a blue dress which matched her eyes. Her golden hair was in a big bunch behind her head and the color of it was like one of the fields in the picture where they were cutting the grass with long knives. Mama was pretty but he did not want her in his blue house. As he got nearer to her there was the smell like lots of flowers that he remembered was what he did not like about her. It made it hard to breathe. *She*, on the other hand, smelled of carbolic soap and that stuff they put on you when you cut yourself. Her clothes were all rough.

"Paul, this is Nannie," Mama said, holding out a hand to him. He took her hand, but did not raise his head. Mama drew him to her and he smelled the suffocating flower smell and felt the slimy touch of silk. He stood with hung head until he buried his face in Mama's side. Confucius, who did not like Paul to touch Mama, snarled.

"There now, you've made Confucius cross," said Mama in a laughing voice, and Paul moved away from her. He could feel the strange person's eyes boring into his back and, not knowing what to do, he hung his head again.

"Why don't you take her upstairs and show her the nursery?"

Paul did not move and after a fraction of a second the new person said, "Well, I think I can find it. Coming, Paul?" Without waiting to see whether he followed she moved rather lightly across the room and went out of the door and up the stairs. He could feel Mama's surprise and he was surprised himself.

"If you are good you will like her," Mama said, and he could tell from her voice that the conversation was over. She gave him a little push towards the door, and for want of anything better to do Paul went out and up the stairs. The new person was standing in front of his picture on the landing and examining it carefully. He passed her with blank eyes and went sullenly past her and on up the stairs. She came after him in that light springing way she did everything.

"Race you to the top of the stairs!" she said. He ignored her—*She* had told him never to run upstairs—and continued stolidly on his way. She shot past him laughing, which made him crosser than ever, but then waited for him at the top of the stairs.

"I'm sorry," she said. "It wasn't fair. I took you by surprise." He had no idea what she meant, but he could not avoid looking at her, though he quickly looked away again. Her hair was a strange reddish color, and her skin creamy white beneath it. There were tiny brown spots over the bridge of her nose, and her eyes were brown. He didn't like her.

"Now," she said, "would you show me which room is mine? I'm longing to see it." He ignored her and went straight into the sitting room where the present *She* had given him still lay on the window seat. Desperately he picked it up; alone with this strange person he had no idea what to do. He could hear her cheerfully opening doors and talking to him and suddenly he saw the tablecloth. He crawled under it again, still clutching his present, and lay on the dusty carpet.

He stayed there for ages until he began to wonder whether the new person had found her room or was wandering disconsolately round the house; he hoped she was. He listened but could hear no sound of any kind. He went out into the corridor; still no sound. He stood outside *Her* room where the new person was to sleep, but could still hear nothing. Finally he turned the handle and pushed the door violently open. The new person had a box on the floor and had taken out clothes and objects and flung them around the room.

"Paul," she said with pleasure. "Have you come to help?"

He just stood and stared, first at her and her box, then at the room which had changed in a most odd way. There had been some writing in a frame over the bed with forget-me-nots painted round the edge which Paul liked a lot. It said "Thou God Seest Me" he had been told, and he always had a look round while he was in her room to see if there was an eye hidden somewhere—perhaps in the tiles round the fireplace or the plaster flowers in the ceiling—watching *Her* and him. Perhaps now the eye was watching *Her* in some other room. On the table there had been a big book with little pretty markers in it. He had taken them out and played with them once or twice but she had been very angry with him. There had been a glass by the bed which he had once seen full of teeth which interested him a lot. The glass still stood by the bed but there were no interesting teeth in it now.

"Look, I've brought you a drum," the new person said. She pulled the shining drum out of her box. It was painted on the sides in red and blue and had a red leather string to go round your neck. She pushed it towards him and hunted in the box again for the sticks. When he made no move she seemed puzzled and came across the room to him, lifting the drum and putting the string over his head. She handed a stick to him, but he let it fall to the floor, and he lifted the drum string back over his head, without expression, and lowered the drum to the carpet.

"Oh *Paul*," she said with a maddening laugh in her voice. "I'll tidy this up later. Let's go and have lunch." She picked up the drum and sticks and walked out of the room; she put them down on the windowseat beside the book.

After lunch, in the time when *She* used to doze in her chair and had made him sit perfectly still and silent so as not to disturb her, the new person sprang to her feet.

"I'm dying to go out, aren't you?" she said. "I love this weather. Go and get your things while I get ready." When she returned in long shiny boots and a coat with a grey swirly skirt and mother-of-pearl buttons, he was still standing there. She went into his room without comment, found his leggings and the buttonhook and lifted him on to the table where she did up the rows of little buttons.

"It's going to be lovely in the Park today," she told him. She eased his arms into his coat, buttoned it up, tucked in his scarf, wriggled his fingers into his gloves, all without help from him. She was not quick and sharp, did not pinch and wrench his fingers, nor appear to be cross at all, but touched him lightly as he might touch a flower he liked. It was odd.

"It's more fun to put on your own things," she remarked, as to some other child who might have been present in the room.

They moved out into the frozen world. The sky was a clear blue and the air so cold that breathing was like eating—you had to think about doing it. He held the new person's hand because *She* had trained him to hold her hand in the street. That other hand had felt quite different, though; it had gripped him in a hard, bony embrace as if it would never let him go. The new person's hand was warm and seemed to have a whole range of expression; when he first took hold of it outside the house she squeezed it gently, when they got to the Gardens it was so light it was scarcely like holding a hand at all. It made him uneasy.

As on the day before the big boys were sliding on the Round Pond; yesterday he had wanted to be released so that he might go nearer to them. He would not have dared to go on the Pond itself—*She* had told him how little boys could fall through holes in the ice and freeze to death because they could not scramble out again—but he could have run and jumped along the edge in the hope that the big boys would notice him. Now, as if she read his thoughts, the new person said, "Wouldn't you like to have a run?" Paul ignored her, and continued primly to hold her hand in silent reproof. Next minute she did something he never forgot. One of the big boys, accidentally or on purpose, had thrown a snowball in their direction, which landed at their feet. The new person let go of his hand, bent down and scooped up a handful of snow. She molded it quickly with her other hand, then threw it back, laughing; it caught the boy on the shoulder and he laughed too.

"My brother's about his age," she told Paul. For a moment he hoped she might go on about her brother but she walked on with her light springing step, not speaking, but humming to herself.

"Can you whistle?" she asked him after a bit. When she started to whistle a tune he had heard the messenger boys whistle in the street it was really very hard not to push his lips forward to see what sound came out; she had somehow guessed one of his dearest wishes.

"I'll teach you someday soon," she said in a friendly way, just as if he had told her what he felt.

By the time they reached home again Paul realized that he was puzzled by her. She had asked him a number of questions, not insistently, but as things came up, and she seemed not to notice that she never got answers. Had they not told her about him? Perhaps she was stupid, or, more likely, she planned to trick him.

At bathtime he was surprised that the water did not stop his breath with its cruel, numbing touch, but was warm like a glove. Nor did it hurt when she washed his face and his ears, though he braced himself for pain. As she bathed him she sang in a clear voice that echoed from the tiled walls, not a messenger-boy tune.

"That's an Irish song," she said to him.

When she had finished washing him she pretended the nailbrush was a boat which the enemy wanted to sink with the pumice stone. She splashed a lot and made the walls and floor wet, something Paul had been forbidden to do. He was coldly disapproving. Then when he stood up in the bath she wrapped a big towel round him and took him by surprise by lifting him bodily out, and sitting him on her lap while she dried his toes. She never stopped talking to him and he began to want to be alone in a place where she was not.

Once in bed he lay, as he had been trained to do, with his hands over the sheet.

"Wouldn't you like Rag Doll in beside you?" she asked, and without waiting for a reply she tucked the doll in beside him as if it was real. He thought her very silly. At the same time she picked up the sheet and blanket and tucked his hands down underneath them, smoothing the bed and tucking it in at the sides. It was intolerable. He pulled out his hands, picked up Rag Doll by a leg and dropped her on the floor by the bed.

"Maybe you'll want her later," the new person said without malice. Then she began to tell him a story. He used magic to will her to go away, to leave him to silence and sleep, but in spite of himself it was difficult not to listen to her story about the woodcutter's youngest son and difficult not to laugh when she told him about all the people stuck to the goose in a long line and unable to get away. One day, he thought, he would like to go into the world to seek his fortune.

Finally she stood up, bent over him, and kissed him softly on the cheek, ruffling his hair gently as she did so. She turned out the lamp by his bed and went out of the room, but had left a tiny lamp alight on the mantelpiece; he supposed she had forgotten it.

He woke in the night after one of his horrible dreams, but he knew better than to call out. Suddenly, however, he remembered Rag Doll, lying neglected on the floor beside the bed, and he put out a hand and pulled her into bed; seeing the dim little light and burying his face in the doll's stringy hair he could just bear the pain and eventually he went back to sleep.

The next day, and in the days that followed, the book and the drum continued to lie side by side on the windowseat. The new person seemed to feel no need to tidy either of them away, although one day, absent-mindedly, she picked up the drumsticks and played a roll on the drum. It was a splendid sound.

Two days after she came it was Saturday, and as she drew Paul's curtains and came over to sit on his bed—a liberty it seemed to him—she seemed merrier than ever.

"Mama and Papa are going to take you out today," she told him, as if giving him a lovely piece of news and she sprang up and took his best clothes out of the wardrobe. Actually, he did like Saturdays when Papa was home, but he did not see how she could know that. *She* had hated Saturdays and had always been cross when he returned from an outing; that was one of the ways he knew *She* loved him. The new person wanted to get rid of him for a day and he would be glad to get away from her.

Naturally when he returned she denied it.

"I've missed you, Paul," she said. There was a toffee-apple lying on the table. She did not say that she had bought it, and Paul wondered what to do about it. Perhaps Emily had left it for him? He put out a tentative hand and picked it up. He rustled the paper loudly as he undid it, still prepared to renounce it altogether if she laid any claim to having brought it for him as a gift, but she was reading a newspaper she had bought and did not look up. Paul addressed himself to the hard brown glaze.

After that he began to discover little gifts quite often; he would find a sweet exactly in the middle of his counterpane, crayons and paper on the table in his bedroom, a book with fairy pictures in it lying on the nursery hearthrug. It gave him a lovely warm feeling, but the new person, who was either stupid or cunning, never seemed to notice that he was being showered with gifts. Well, a couple of times she did. One day he came home from a walk and on a chair by the fire there was a mouth organ. He knew what it was because he had seen a beggar playing one in the street near Kensington Gardens. Trembling with excitement, he picked it up, dazed by the glitter of the sun on its beautiful polished wood surface. He breathed into the holes and a harsh, terrible sound came out; he had breathed too hard. Now he breathed again, softly, and the sound was strong and rich. He tried breathing farther along the mouthpiece and the note was high and piercing. Now almost frantic with delight, he sat down on the floor, and gave himself up without remainder to the mouth organ. He had no idea how long he had been playing when he looked up and saw the new person watching him. It spoiled his absorption, though she at once returned to reading her book; a sad story she must be reading because she had a tear on her cheek. How stupid she must be not to wonder where the mouth organ came from.

On another day he discovered in his room a clay pipe and a bowl of frothy water. This put him in a dilemma; he had no idea what it was for. He tried drinking the water through the stem of the pipe but it tasted awful. He tried putting the bowl of the pipe in the water and blowing down it; perhaps it was a musical instrument like the mouth organ. It made a gratifying sound but he soon tired of it. There was a secret about this present which he did not know and he could not bear not knowing. There was only one thing for it and he picked up the bowl and pipe and carried it into the new person's bedroom, pushing the door open with his foot. He noticed, vaguely, that it had changed since the last time he was there. A picture of fields and the sea hung over the bed where the forget-me-not writing had been. There was a vase of flowers on the table and photographs—one of the new person herself with her hair down her back standing with some children and grown-ups. There was a lovely red shawl hanging over a chair. The whole room seemed full of color and light.

The new person was sitting sewing beside the table and he marched straight to her and put the bowl down beside her.

"What shall I do with it, Paul?" she asked him. He pointed to it.

"What shall I do with it?" she asked him again. Again he pointed and again she looked at him expectantly. After a bit she very slowly picked up the pipe, and put it to her lips. She began to blow and a huge bubble, with curved window shapes white against its soapy blue and rose iridescence, bulged out of the bowl of the pipe, while Paul watched in astonishment. Suddenly it left the pipe and floated across the room; Paul ran after it and tried to catch it but before he could do so it touched the curtain and burst. He wanted to cry out, but by then the new person had blown another one and this time he did cry out because it was so fairylike. His voice came out faint, batlike, not like a voice at all, but the new person did not seem to have heard it. What he knew he must not do is give her the satisfaction of thinking he could make noises; he could imagine her smug pleasure. Yet suddenly he wanted to make noises.

He felt very angry with the new person and he longed for *She* and for the safety of being her good, silent boy who had only to do what he was told for her to be pleased. The new person made everything so difficult and painful. In a sudden longing for *She* he went to the window seat and picked up the book, turning the pages to find his favorite picture of the woman with the jar of honey. There she was, crouching at the foot of the man, her long, beautiful hair falling from her shoulders; she had got the top off the honey, and, in her outrageous way, was starting to tip it over his ankles. As on other occasions, Paul imagined himself as the man, sitting there in his lordly way, letting the woman abase herself. This time, however, it was different. The hair let loose over the woman's shoulders reminded him of the girl in the photograph in the new person's room, and the rich auburn of her hair reminded him of the dazzling pile on the new person's head, and of the wayward strands that escaped and framed her face as she bathed him.

Paul dropped the book and stood up. He was puzzled by a fierce shaking that took his body and worried it like a terrier shaking a rat. Waves of tension seemed to be passing through him, crumpling and stretching his body; somebody was in terrible pain, was so angry that it was not possible to feel such anger and live. He looked desperately about the room for some relief from the ferocity that filled him and his eye fell on the drum. He picked up a drumstick and beat on the drum with all his strength, as he did so uttering a high dreadful cry of hatred and destruction. He was killing the new person, bashing her face in, smashing her head, smattering her limbs, turning her into raspberry jam, and it was wonderful. His voice emerged stronger and stronger as he approached the crescendo of his strength and to his amazement it shaped itself into words. He had often wondered where words came from, how people found them, and everyone but himself had them. Now they hurtled out of him like an express train coming out of a dark tunnel.

"I hate . . . I hate . . ." Although he had smashed through the skin of the drum he still kept beating on it, beating on the new person till there was nothing left of the brown eyes that looked at him, the freckled nose, the light hands, the quick step, the twitching mouth, above all of the joyful laugh.

At last he was exhausted. Like someone who has been in another place he came back into his body; his throat hurt with the sounds that had been torn out of it, and he had cut his hand on the drum. Bewildered, he turned round, and there behind him was a young woman looking at him with kindness in her brown eyes. For a few moments they stood and looked at one another, neither making any movement, and then, gracefully, like one who knew what he was doing, he held out his bleeding hand to her and she took it, saying matter-of-factly, "We must find a bandage."

Reading for Understanding

❑ MAIN IDEA

1. The main idea of the story is that (a) those who take care of children are usually cruel (b) some children are stubborn and unreasonable (c) a drum is one toy that should be in every nursery (d) love can help a child leave fears and hatreds behind.

❑ DETAILS

2. The pronoun *She* refers to (a) Emily (b) Miss Brown (c) Mama (d) the new nanny.

3. One of the first things the new nanny did was (a) offer to find her own room (b) scold Paul (c) give Paul a peppermint (d) disagree with Mama.

4. The drum was (a) left behind by the former nanny (b) Papa's drum when he was a child (c) a gift from the new nanny (d) never noticed by Paul.

5. Paul was captivated by (a) the soap bubbles (b) the advice given by Miss Brown (c) Confucius (d) close friends.

❑ INFERENCES

6. The former nanny might be characterized as (a) prim but sprightly (b) generous and forgiving (c) firm and unfeeling (d) helpful in Paul's development.

7. A phrase that might characterize Paul is (a) light and cheerful (b) openly adventurous (c) vicious and cruel (d) seriously introverted.

8. The new nanny's influence on Paul was (a) well-intentioned but negative (b) helpful and positive (c) neither good nor bad (d) frightening.

9. The snowball incident was included to show how (a) cruel boys can be (b) normal the new nanny was (c) courageous Paul was (d) thoughtless Mama was.

❑ PURPOSE

10. A major purpose of the author was to (a) poke fun at the habits of the well-to-do (b) demonstrate her ability to work with words in various situations (c) contrast the effect of two nannies on a sensitive, impressionable child (d) depict a hopeless cause.

❑ SYMBOLISM

11. Staying underneath the table was introduced to symbolize (a) Paul's isolation from the real world (b) a place of fun and normal living (c) a place where pets could cavort (d) the warmth that surrounded Paul on every side.

❑ ORDER OF EVENTS

12. Arrange the events in the order in which they occurred. Use letters only.

A. Paul meets the new nanny.
B. Paul beats the drum feverishly.

C. The new nanny offers to race Paul to the top of the stairs.
D. The old nanny departs.
E. Emily gives Paul a peppermint.

☐ OUTCOME

13. At the conclusion of the story, Paul (a) runs away from home (b) asks to have the old nanny returned (c) never speaks to the new nanny (d) feels release after beating the drum.

☐ CAUSE AND EFFECT

14. The new nanny's methods (a) gradually drew Paul from his shell (b) went against Mama's express orders (c) were actually unsound (d) depended upon fear for their effectiveness.

☐ FACT OR OPINION

Tell whether the following is a fact or an opinion.

15. Miss Brown drove off without a glance back at Paul.

Words in Context

1. "Miss Brown was wearing her felt hat with a bit of *grizzled* black fur on it . . ." ***Grizzled*** (83) means (a) shabby (b) streaked with gray (c) crescent shaped (d) inexpensive.

2. "Emily's eye fell on the unpolished coal *scuttle*. She lifted Paul down to the floor." ***Scuttle*** (83) means (a) stove lid (b) shovel (c) furnace (d) bucket.

3. "Papa could come sometimes, . . . and take him out to eat *croissants* dipped in coffee at the French bakery." ***Croissants*** (84) means (a) crescent-shaped rolls (b) jelly doughnuts (c) danish pastry (d) slices of fresh oat bread.

4. "He ignored her—*She* had told him never to run upstairs—and continued *stolidly* on his way." ***Stolidly*** (85) means (a) noiselessly (b) impassively (c) humming to himself (d) with his head held high.

5. ". . . he began to wonder whether the new person had found her room or was wandering *disconsolately* round the house." ***Disconsolately*** (85) means (a) hysterically (b) calmly (c) silently (d) forlornly.

6. "Paul ignored her, and continued *primly* to hold her hand in silent *reproof*." ***Primly*** . . . ***reproof*** (86) mean (a) smugly . . . criticism

(b) sullenly . . . acceptance (c) sternly . . . approval (d) politely . . . disapproval

7. ". . . she pretended the nailbrush was a boat which the enemy wanted to sink with the *pumice stone*." The ***pumice stone*** (87) was used to (a) stop the flow of water (b) make the soap lather (c) anchor the towel (d) act as a mild abrasive.

8. "'Maybe you'll want her later,' the new person said without *malice*." ***Malice*** (87) means (a) tact (b) laughter (c) hesitation (d) spitefulness.

9. "He rustled the paper loudly . . . still prepared to *renounce* it altogether if she laid any claim to having brought it for him as a gift . . ." ***Renounce*** (88) means (a) reject (b) disregard (c) criticize (d) destroy.

10. "He would find a sweet exactly in the middle of his *counterpane*, crayons and paper on the table . . ." ***Counterpane*** (88) means (a) toys (b) hearthrug (c) bedspread (d) platc.

11. ". . . when he looked up and saw the new person watching him. It spoiled his *absorption* . . ." ***Absorption*** (88) means (a) enjoyment (b) playing (c) preoccupation (d) ability to interpret.

12. ". . . and a huge bubble, with curved window shapes white against its soapy blue and rose *iridescence*, bulged out of the bowl of the pipe." ***Iridescence*** (89) means (a) fragility (b) transparence (c) waviness (d) rainbow effects.

13. "Paul imagined himself as the man, sitting there in his lordly way, letting the woman *abase* herself." ***Abase*** (89) means (a) degrade (b) explain (c) control (d) forget.

14. ". . . the rich auburn of her hair reminded him of . . . thc *wayward strands* that escaped and framed her face . . ." ***Wayward strands*** (90) means (a) shafts of light (b) lovely songs (c) startling sunbeams (d) ungovernable wisps.

15. "His voice emerged stronger and stronger as he approached the *crescendo* of his strength . . ." ***Crescendo*** (90) means (a) weakening (b) peak (c) increase in volume (d) realization.

Thinking Critically About the Story

1. This story is told from the point of view of Paul. Would it have been more effective if it were told by Emily, the maid? Mama? The new nanny? Explain.

2. How does Paul's definition of love change from the opening to the closing of the story? Cite incidents to support your statements.
3. What is the turning point in the story? What did nanny do to pave the way for the change? Can tender loving care be a cure-all in real life as it is in this story? To support your answer, compare incidents in the story with ones you have seen or been told about.
4. Be prepared to read to the class excerpts that prove the validity of the following quotation: "We learn the character of Miss Brown, Mama, the new nanny through bits of action seen by Paul." Are these characters true to life? Explain.
5. "Symbolism is one of the basic devices relied upon by the author to enrich the impact of this story." Explain the symbolism in: Paul's mutism, the presents the two governesses give Paul, little Confucius, the breaking of the drum head, Paul's first words, "I hate . . . I hate." Did the symbolism impede or aid the flow of the story? Explain.

Stories in Words

Croissant (84) is the French equivalent of the English word *crescent*. The delicious breakfast roll is so named because it is formed in the shape of a crescent. The word *crescent*, in turn, is so named because it resembles the crescent moon. The root is *crescere*, "to grow." When the moon is in its crescent phase, it is growing, eventually becoming full. Oddly, the phase between third quarter and new moon is also called *crescent*, even though the apparent size of the moon is diminishing. On page 90, the word *crescendo* comes from the same root, *crescere*. A crescendo is a gradual increase in volume in a musical passage.

Saturday (88) is the *day of Saturn*. In ancient Roman mythology, Saturn was the god of harvests. His reign was called the *Golden Age*. He was later overthrown by his children, the Olympian gods: Jupiter, Juno, Ceres, Pluto, and Neptune. A December festival in his honor, the Saturnalia, was a time of gift giving, rejoicing, and celebration. Schools and courts were closed. Slaves and masters ate at the same table. Other day names refer to ancient gods: Tuesday—Tiu, Norse god of war; Wednesday—Woden, Norse supreme god; Thursday—Thor, Norse god of thunder and strength; Friday—Freya, Norse goddess of beauty and love.

Cunning (88) is a word whose roots can be traced back to the ancient Indo-European tongue, the ancestor of a huge family of modern languages. The earliest traceable root is *gno*, "to know." A surprising number of words derive from *gno,* though the form is sometimes concealed in varied spellings. Through the Germanic family, we have *know-how, knowledge,* and *uncouth;* from the Romance family we have *notice, notify, notion, recognize,* and *ignorant.* A *connoisseur* is "one who knows." A *cunning* person knows how to use his special skills for personal advantage.

Broken Treaty

DION HENDERSON

"Fifteen years ago," Doc said, sounding partly proud and partly exasperated, "my father told Wreck to look after me, and he's still doing it. When I was a kid and wanted to go fishing in the canoe by myself, he used to make me take Wreck with me, and he'd say, 'Look after the kid, Wreck.'"

Probably there is no bond between an animal and a person stronger than a bond involving a dog and a person. Real life and fiction abound with stories that demonstrate the deep devotion of a dog for its master or mistress. "Broken Treaty" introduces a dog who goes beyond the usual.

Golden Recollection, nicknamed *Wreck*, is an old dog, a dog with dignity, a dog with a responsibility. He has accepted a contract between himself and his old master. The death of the master doesn't break the contract, and Wreck honors it with all his strength.

Old age can be a time of sadness, but it can also be a time of purpose and resolve, a time to go down fighting. Wreck's old age may be a source of pity, but looked at in another way, it is a source of rejoicing at the indomitable will of a weary old dog. When Wreck's new master says, "I hope I do not grow so old," the narrator says, "Or if you do, that you grow old as beautifully as Wreck."

There are problems, though, and life cannot go on as before. Wreck faces a turning point and decides whether the treaty is still valid.

Broken Treaty

We had walked down the beach and around the bay and finally out to where the point stabbed into the lake to watch the ducks come home from the cornfields. While we were watching the ducks we saw Doc's old dog and watched him, too. He was old, incredibly old, more than a hundred years old as you reckon the age of a man, and he walked very carefully on the little stones as though he knew that everything inside him was very fragile and might break if he jarred any of it.

We watched him move down the steps, a big taffy-colored dog, still very handsome, as some golden retrievers are, and at the bottom of the steps he did not hesitate at all but turned after us, tracking easily on the beach. "Old, old," Doc said. "Golden Recollection. I hope I do not grow so old."

"Or if you do, that you grow old as beautifully as Wreck," I added.

"What's the difference?" Doc asked. "You get so terribly old, and then you are at the end of it."

I didn't say anything. Maybe it makes no difference how you get there. Maybe it does. The old dog was still tracking us, not wasting any motion, and down at the far end of the bay he stopped altogether. For a moment I thought he was resting, but he hadn't stopped for that. It was something the wind told him, and he had turned his head out toward the lake.

The ducks were coming in occasionally now, crossing us high up and heading for their rafts in open water, and the bay was rippling lightly in the breeze. Earlier the wind had been stronger from the bluffs, and now the water was flecked with floating oak leaves.

Abruptly the old dog gathered himself and slid into the water, still being very careful but clearly very determined, too.

"Chasing a leaf," Doc said wearily. "And with his rheumatism. It'll take me an hour to rub some life back into him."

But it wasn't a leaf. You do not smell a leaf, and the old dog went into the water because the nose he had by rightful inheritance from Lord Tweedmouth's long-ago bloodhound told him to go. He swam very low in the water and so slowly that it sometimes seemed he did not move at all. Nearly a hundred yards out a leaf that was not a leaf flapped a startled wing and quacked once in alarm as it was engulfed. The old dog then veered toward the nearest shore, which was very close to us. He took a long time, and you could hear him breathing all the way. When he was in shallow water, he stopped and let the water support him until his breathing was even again. Then he came out and started casting for our trail again, and Doc called him.

Wreck came on, wavering a little, and sat down proudly with the crippled duck and held it until Doc said, "Thank you, sir," and put out his hand. The old dog put the bird there and stood up to shake, but he could not quite make it. He tried, looked up with a wry expression on his face as though it did not surprise him greatly, and then lay down on the stones and suddenly was exhausted. I took the duck, and Doc wrapped the big dog in his jacket and carried him all the way home.

"You see what I mean?" Doc said over his shoulder. "What can you do with a dog like this?"

"I don't know," I replied, because I did not want any part of the decision he was trying to make. "I don't know very much about retrievers."

When the old kennel hands begin to talk of memorable dogs, one of the things they remember best is the royal manner—the flashing stride, the relentless courage, the flare of style, and the champion's heart. Such dogs do not always achieve royal standing in the world of dog competitions because they do not always have the chance, but when they do, they know that they do, and they are as proud as a man of the achievement.

Golden Recollection won his bench championship on the main line when the majors were few and far between, and he had finished the campaigning with a sporting-group win. His field work was very distinguished, too, although his best seasons were before the face-to-face competition of the National as it is today. He was aging during the time of the compiled championships, and I suppose you would say he was the dawn of the goldens' day that came in with Midas, who either won or did not win the first real National, and Nitro Express, and the later great ones.

He wasn't Doc's dog, you understand. His registration was dated the year Doc had entered fourth grade, and this summer that they came to the lakeshore together was the year Doc finished his internship. It did not seem possible that a dog's life could span such a time. Most people have to accustom themselves to living through several generations of dogs. But in Wreck's case it was reversed, and he was well along in his second generation of people, because men don't live forever, either.

So Doc and the dog who had been his father's contemporary were living in the same house again, but conditions were changed considerably from the time they had been the famous champion and the schoolboy, and naturally there were many complications. For one thing, Doc got married in the spring before he was quite ready to set up a practice, and he had quite a few problems that were strictly his own. His wife was very pretty and very brave, as any girl has to be who marries a young doctor, and she was very good about the dog, too.

But there is one thing about a handsome and polite dog you pet occasionally when you visit his home, and it is another thing entirely to have a heedless old monarch with all the weakness of that age and condition accept you as his handmaiden. I don't think she complained, then or later, about the obvious nuisance that Wreck was around the house. The first morning I met her, when she and Doc came to the old cottage from the city, I heard something special in the way she looked at the dog and said, "Poor old fellow."

There is a way a woman has of saying things like that; you can tell when you hear the sadness in her voice. She does not say exactly what she means, and maybe she does not even know exactly what she means; but you know, and a dog knows, too, after a while. So I did not become involved any of the times that Doc asked sort of casually, "What do you do with an old dog?" The time I came closest was the day after Wreck went for the duck. It was a cool morning, the dew not quite a frost but glistening very close to it on the shady side of the trees.

Doc and his wife were having breakfast on the porch and called me in for coffee. Wreck was lying where the morning sun streamed in on him, and once I heard him move and looked at him sharply. He was inching his way across the floor to keep fully in the sun, because that was how he had to move, with the chill and dampness of night heavy on the old bones. But he saw me watching him, and though he looked back at me he did not invite help, so I let him alone. Two or three other times he moved the same way, but when I left an hour later the sun had soaked through the caramel-colored hide and the blood was moving. A warm dog is not nearly so old as a cold dog.

Outside, Doc explained, "It hurts his pride if you help him. What are you going to do with a dog like that?"

"It depends on you and it depends on the dog," I said. "And it depends on the association that has developed between you and the way each of you has accepted it and a number of other things that there is no point discussing."

"We've negotiated a treaty," Doc said. "The old guy is happy—I guess he's happy."

And I guess he was, in his way. He did not really feel very bad about being old. He moved carefully always, and on warm, dry afternoons when he had been in the sun quite a while he would play very sedately all by himself. Then he would draw a very clear line to the playing and look at you wryly, and you knew he was up against the boundary he had made for himself. It was a little like being around a famous old athlete who occasionally worked out ever so little, in imitation of himself as a young man, then paused apologetically because he could not in modesty indicate just how beautifully and easily he had done the physical things that hardly anyone could do so well anymore.

And plainly Golden Recollection did not think of himself as a nuisance, not to anybody. Sometimes when he was sleeping on the pier and the sun moved away from him behind the trees he could not move very well, but he was very patient and expected someone would come for him after a while. Someone always did and might say, "Poor old dog," which made a strange, flat look come in his eyes, as though he heard what I heard in the words.

"He earned a lot of things in his time," Doc said. "I guess he figures he earned enough to retire on."

Then it was getting to be time for Doc and his wife to move back to the city to a little apartment, and there got to be a feeling of strain around the cottage. Every time his wife looked at Wreck she looked as though she might cry, and one time Doc told her, "You couldn't take a dog who's been a house dog all that length of time and put him in a boarding kennel. You might as well kill him outright."

When he said that, his wife did start to cry, and I thought it was a pretty good time for me not to be around anymore. Doc walked out with me and we headed along the shore toward my place, but he did not say anything and neither did I. Opposite the point, we stopped for a while and watched the big mergansers working in the bay. Presently there was a rustling in the leaves behind us, and there was Wreck, walking very carefully but coming on just the same.

"Fifteen years ago," Doc said, sounding partly proud and partly exasperated, "my father told Wreck to look after me, and he's still doing it. When I was a kid and wanted to go fishing in the canoe by myself, he used to make me take Wreck with me, and he'd say, 'Look after the kid, Wreck.' And all the time we were fishing, the dog would lie there in the canoe and watch me."

"I remember. He pulled you out once, didn't he?"

"He sure did." Doc grinned a little. "It was in four feet of water, but it was swimming depth for him, so he pulled me out. Pretty near broke my arm in the process, but Dad thought it was fine."

The dog reached us by then and sat down next to Doc and looked at him briefly with those old, old eyes.

"That's the same expression." Doc was almost angry. "He doesn't really give a hoot about me. But the old man said he should look out for me, and he'll do it if he has to live thirty years more."

I guess that pretty well stated the case. Wreck did not really love anyone anymore; he had outlived all his young loves, but he still had a job to do, and he did not propose to quit. You never know what goes on in a dog's head. He will do a thing, and there are various ways to explain it. The best way usually is the simple and instinctive way, but I am not sure it is always right. In the end there is really no way to tell.

The next day I went past Doc's cottage in a boat, well out, but I could see they were taking down screens and putting boxes in the car. I wondered about the dog. It was automatic to think of him at that point, and soon I saw the golden heap lying in the sun in sight of everything or at least in range of ear and nose. When you have dogs for a long time and keep them for the quality they have that is quite beyond compromise, you make many treaties that are hard to keep.

I thought about the dogs and treaties, and I was grateful for the dog in the boat with me. She was one of the German dogs who was far from home and who, knowing she would never see her home again, looked at the world with ice-cold eyes. She did her work marvelously and she gave me puppies who would love passionately and cling hard to life, but she did not offer anything like that and she wouldn't accept it, and I was grateful for her.

But however they are, you do whatever you have to do, and I expected that Doc and his wife would take the old dog with them. Long after dark the two of them came to my door.

"Wreck's gone," Doc blurted out. "We've been looking for hours."

"My boots are in the closet," I said. "Just a minute. What happened?"

"He followed Doc out in the field." His wife had been crying again. "Then he started to come back by himself and got lost."

I stopped putting on my boots. There was an expression on Doc's face.

"All right. What happened?" I asked.

"He left me." Doc's voice was a little hoarse. "The gun misfired, and he looked at me and left me."

"No," his wife said. "You didn't!"

"It seemed like the best thing to do," Doc said. "I didn't plan it. I could have given him an intravenous a lot more easily. But then he'd have known. The way it was, I heard crows tormenting something up in the field, and I took the gun and went back to see what it was. I was away back there watching them, and Wreck came along trailing me. It wasn't a good day for him, and he had a lot of trouble walking. Once he fell down, and I was afraid he couldn't get up again, but he did. He got up to me, breathing very hard and pretty shaky, but he gave me that quick glance, then went on out into the field to see what the crows were doing." Doc was sweating now.

"All of a sudden I thought, Here it is. No fuss, and it won't hurt him at all. And I brought up the gun and pulled the trigger." He wiped his face like a kid, and the sweat followed right after it. "It misfired," he said. "It never did that before. And there he was, looking at me right down the barrel, with the little gold bead right on his head. I put the gun down, and I knew that I couldn't ever do it again and that we'd keep him as long as he was happy. And I called him to come."

"But he didn't come," I prompted.

"No," Doc said. "He looked at me in a way that he'd never looked before, sort of relieved, and took a big breath and walked away from me better than he's walked for months."

"And you thought he was going home?"

"No," Doc said. "I knew he wasn't going home. I knew it, all right."

There was not much else for anyone to say, and there really wasn't any need to look for him that night. In the morning we went out to the field and lined ourselves up with the place that had been home to Wreck for so long and then suddenly was not home anymore, and we walked in a straight line away from it. After a while we came to the water's edge, and there was all that remained of Golden Recollection.

"I wonder what happened," said Doc's wife.

"He did not need to live anymore," I told her. "Your husband knows what that means."

"Yes," Doc said. "Now I do."

Reading for Understanding

❑ MAIN IDEA

1. The main point of the story is the sense of (a) ingratitude (b) selfishness (c) duty (d) recklessness.

❑ DETAILS

2. Wreck was a (a) collie (b) German shepherd (c) golden retriever (d) Labrador retriever.

3. When Wreck "chased a leaf," he (a) was deceived because of poor eyesight (b) had to be rescued from drowning (c) swam as vigorously as a young dog (d) brought back a duck.

4. Wreck was (a) Doc's father's dog (b) the narrator's dog (c) a good dog but never a champion (d) a noisy dog.

5. Wreck disappeared (a) when Doc's father died (b) after the gun misfired (c) when Doc got married (d) when the narrator left.

❑ INFERENCES

6. Which of the following statements is true? (a) Both men respected Wreck's old age. (b) Wreck disobeyed Doc throughout because he was so old. (c) Wreck put his own welfare above that of his master's. (d) Doc's wife was cruel to Wreck.

7. A major crisis arose because (a) Wreck suddenly developed a nasty streak (b) Wreck became seriously ill (c) Doc and his wife were moving into a small apartment (d) the narrator tried to buy Wreck from Doc.

8. Doc's basic motive in pulling the trigger on Wreck was (a) jealousy (b) kindness (c) cruelty (d) contempt.

9. This story might be considered (a) a tall story with little truth (b) a study of cultural differences (c) an attempt to explain death (d) a tribute to courageous old age.

❑ AUTHOR'S ATTITUDE

10. The author's attitude toward Wreck was one of (a) indifference (b) disapproval (c) tolerance (d) admiration.

❑ ORDER OF EVENTS

11. Arrange the items in the order in which they occurred. Use letters only.
    A. Wreck "chased a leaf."
    B. Golden Recollection wins a bench championship.
    C. Doc's father buys Wreck.
    D. Wreck disappears.
    E. The gun misfires.

❑ OUTCOME

12. After Doc finds Wreck, (a) everyone rejoices (b) Doc and his wife miss Wreck (c) the narrator breaks off his friendship with Doc (d) friends criticize Doc for cruelty.

❑ CAUSE AND EFFECT

13. Doc refuses to have Wreck put to sleep out of a (a) sense of loyalty (b) desire to impress his wife (c) fear of his friend's disapproval (d) fear of his father's anger.

❑ FACT OR OPINION

Tell whether each of the following is a fact or an opinion.

14. Wreck was unable to do many of the things he could do earlier.

15. Doc was not unkind but thoughtless.

Words in Context

1. "He . . . might break if he *jarred* any of it." ***Jarred*** (97) means (a) preserved (b) shook up (c) collected (d) disregarded.

2. ". . . still very handsome, as some golden *retrievers* are . . ." ***Retrievers*** (97) are popular hunting dogs because they can easily be trained to (a) run fast (b) follow animal tracks (c) find and bring back game (d) be faithful.

3. "The old dog *veered* toward the nearest shore . . ." ***Veered*** (98) means (a) looked (b) turned (c) swam (d) raced.

4. "Then he came out and started *casting for* our trail . . ." ***Casting for*** (98) means (a) turning about (b) looking for (c) pointing toward (d) pawing the ground for.

5. "Wreck came on, *wavering* a little, and sat down proudly with the crippled duck and held it . . ." ***Wavering*** (98) means (a) fluttering (b) staggering (c) giving way (d) changing.

6. "He . . . looked up with a *wry* expression on his face . . ." ***Wry*** (98) means (a) amused (b) sad (c) angry (d) terrified.

7. ". . . one of the things they remember best is . . . the *relentless* courage, the flare of style . . ." ***Relentless*** (98) means (a) uncompromising (b) wavering (c) quiet (d) unquestioned.

8. ". . . and it is another thing entirely to have a heedless old monarch . . . accept you as his *handmaiden* . . ." ***Handmaiden*** (99) means (a) contemporary (b) companion (c) confidante (d) servant.

9. ". . . Doc asked sort of *casually*, 'What do you do with an old dog?'" ***Casually*** (99) means (a) anxiously (b) loudly (c) offhandedly (d) emphatically.

10. ". . . he would play very *sedately* all by himself." ***Sedately*** (99) means (a) awkwardly (b) noisily (c) imaginatively (d) calmly.

11. "You might as well kill him *outright*." ***Outright*** (100) means (a) on the spot (b) through neglect (c) through overfeeding (d) painlessly.

12. ". . . we . . . watched the big *mergansers* working in the bay." ***Mergansers*** (100) are a type of (a) sailboat (b) duck (c) freshwater fish (d) canoe.

13. "'Fifteen years ago,' Doc said, sounding partly proud and partly *exasperated*, 'my father told Wreck to look after me, and he's still doing it.'" ***Exasperated*** (100) means (a) exhausted (b) concerned (c) acceptant (d) irritated.

14. "The best way usually is the simple and *instinctive* way, but I am not sure it is always right." ***Instinctive*** (100) means (a) most humane (b) fastest (c) quietest (d) natural.

15. "I could have given him an *intravenous* a lot more easily." ***Intravenous*** (101) means (a) a poisoned biscuit (b) an injection into a vein (c) an electric shock (d) a pill.

Thinking Critically About the Story

1. The story is told from the point of view of an unnamed narrator. Would it have been just as effective if it were told by Doc? Doc's wife? The veterinarian?

2. Real life and fiction abound with stories that demonstrate the deep devotion of a dog for its master or mistress. What is your favorite dog story in this area? Real life? TV? Books?
3. What is the treaty negotiated between Doc and Wreck? What brings it to an end?
4. Be prepared to read to the class examples of description that reveal the author's depth of familiarity with dogs and natural scenery.
5. "What do you do with an old dog?" What options are open to Doc? What was your reaction to his choice? Which one would you have chosen? Explain.

Stories in Words

Wry (98) means "twisted, distorted." A wry sense of humor if offbeat. The *wr* root in *wry* suggests *turning, twisting*. Perhaps if we traveled far back in language, we'd find the following words related: *wring, wrinkle, wreath, wriggle, wrench, wrest, wrestle, wrangle, wrist, writhe, wrong, awry, wroth*—all of which contain the idea of *twist* or *turn*. Similarly, *sn* words often suggest the nose: *snout, snooty, sniff, snuff, snuffle, snarl, snore, sneeze, snicker, sniffle, snivel, sneer*. Though not all of these seem directly related to each other, the connection with the nose is interesting.

Contemporary (98), meaning "at the same time," contains the *temp* root. *Temporary* is for a brief *time*. To *temporize* is to gain *time* by evasion. *Temporal* is "lasting for a time." *Tempo* is a measure of *time*. Though less obvious, the words *temple, contemplate,* and *temperature* are also related. Time has the idea of something cut, measured, marked out. A *temple* was a space marked out for the worship of a god. *Contemplate* is to mark out space for observation. It is directly related to *temple*. *Temperature* is the marking out of the degrees of heat or cold. Tracing word origins is like reading a good detective story.

Monarch (99), by derivation, is a "sole ruler." The *arch* root, meaning "rule" or "first," appears in *archbishop, archduke, archipelago, archive, archaic, archaeology, archangel, archenemy, architect, archetype, anarchy, patriarch,* and *matriarch*. The *mon* root, meaning "one," appears in *monochrome, monocle, monogamy, monolith, monologue, mononucleosis, monoplane, monopoly, monorail, monosyllable, monotone,* and *monotony*. Greek roots, like *mon* and *arch*, easily combine to form recognizable words whose meanings can be deduced from the parts.

The Turning Point

Getting Technical

Terms

climax	empathy	tone
in medias res	narrator	

Definitions Match each of the above terms with its definition.

1. Experiencing the emotions of another
2. That which reveals the author's attitude toward his material or audience or both
3. Point of maximum tension preceding a resolution
4. Author; teller of a story in a story
5. In the middle rather than at the beginning of an episode or story

Examples Match each of the following actions with the appropriate term.

1. Dear Diary: There I was trapped on the ledge of the towering cliff. It was all Henry's fault!
2. After many jarring incidents, the final showdown has arrived. The two opposing groups move slowly toward each other.
3. The deputy sheriff had seen it all, and he is the one who tells the jury what had happened.
4. I too bowed my head in shame and felt every pang that wracked the poor heroine's heart.
5. It wasn't his words that inspired us. It was his sincerity and general attitude.

6. As she walks into the bank, she finds herself face to face with the open end of a gun pointed at her forehead!
7. I was so engrossed that I felt the pain of each blow that the challenger threw at the falling champion.
8. I am Harvey Williams, sound of mind and limb. I swear to the truth of what I am about to tell you.

Application Find the choice that best completes each of the following.

1. In "Reduced" the reader usually finds it most easy to empathize with (a) the visitors (b) the mother (c) the father (d) the governess.
2. The climax in "The Drum" occurs when (a) Paul sees Miss Brown leave (b) she throws the snowball (c) he speaks for the first time (d) he finds the mouth organ.
3. The tone of "Welcome" is (a) despondent (b) upbeat (c) defiant (d) carefree.
4. The narrator in "Broken Treaty" is most likely the (a) doctor (b) doctor's wife (c) vet (d) author.
5. The author of "Welcome" began her story *in medias res* to (a) confuse the reader (b) involve the reader (c) lengthen the story (d) prevent reader confusion.
6. The climax of "Broken Treaty" was reached when (a) Wreck did not return (b) the gun misfired (c) the dog saved Doc's life (d) Doc's father died.

Thinking Critically About the Stories

1. Which story has the most significance for you? What are some of the *Do's* and *Don't's* emphasized in these four stories? What are the chances of achieving happiness for:

   Miss Rice   Penny and Claudia   Paul   James
2. How does Claudia and Penny's mother compare with Tina's? Are they both true to life? How do they compare with the mother in a movie you saw recently?
3. Compare Doc's approach to his problem with Mary's, with Mima Carbury's, with Henrietta Post's, with Nanny's. Which do you think is most effective? Least effective?
4. We meet a wide variation in personalities in these four stories. Which one did you consider the most mature? The most knowledgeable?

The most admirable? The least likable? The most adaptable? The one you would be most willing to choose as a friend? Explain.

5. Which author do you consider the most skillful in developing characters? In arousing interest? In revealing springs of action? Which do you consider the best storyteller? Explain.

Writing and Other Activities

1. Write the setting and dialog for one of the following:
   (a) The maid Emily tells one of the kitchen help about how the drum was broken.
   (b) Years later Doc explains to his son why Wreck has a memorial in the family cemetery.
   (c) Frank Peele describes to a member of his club his meeting with Henrietta Post.
   (d) Miss Brown tells a governess-to-be how to "train" a child.
   (e) Tina tells her friend Sharon how she came by the white bootees.

2. Be prepared to lead a class panel in a discussion on one of the following:
   (a) What your generation can gain by digging up family roots. What is the best way to go about doing so?
   (b) The Ten Commandments for baby watchers, baby-sitters and teacher's helpers.
   (c) How can sibling rivalry be changed to sibling cooperation?
   (d) How to control jealousy and envy in school and in the home.

3. Write an editorial for the school newspaper on one of the following:
   (a) Positive criticism, Yes! Negative criticism, No!
   (b) Empathy—putting yourself into the other person's shoes—the magic key to understanding yourself and others
   (c) What you should know before you take that part-time job in the local fast-food eatery
   (d) Why college should be in your plans for the future

4. Write the dialog for a story in which a high school senior and her (his) parent (parents) have a (three-way) discussion on one or more of the following:
   (a) Taking a year off before going on to college
   (b) Getting and supporting a car
   (c) What's wrong with the way the parents are handling the kid brother (sister)
   (d) Role to be played by the income from your part-time job

5. Describe the scene and write the inner dialog for a slice-of-life story dealing with one of the following:
   (a) What the senior substitute would like to tell the coach who has kept him out of most games all season
   (b) The advice-lecture on first dates the senior would give to the kid brother (sister) he (she) never had
   (c) The reply never given to the bullying supervisor in charge of part-time workers
   (d) What the favorite victim would never say to the practical joker of the class

Stories in Words: A Review

A. contemporary	E. mausoleum	I. tripod
B. croissant	F. monarch	J. ultimatum
C. cunning	G. Saturday	K. widowed
D. extravagance	H. spinster	L. wry

Answer the following questions by choosing a word from the list above. Use letters only.

Which of the words above . . .

1. ______ is named for one of the Seven Wonders of the Ancient World?
2. ______ suggests the *last word*?
3. ______ is related to the word *divide*?
4. ______ is related by derivation to a phase of the *moon*?
5. ______ is related to the word *connoisseur*?
6. ______ is named for an ancient Roman god?
7. ______ comes from a root suggesting *twisting*?
8. ______ comes from a Greek root meaning *one*?
9. ______ contains the idea of *time*?
10. ______ once referred to an activity expected of young women?

One of the sharpest criticisms of anyone is the statement, "He has no sense of humor." We all seem to know what humor is; yet no one has ever devised a completely satisfactory definition. Definitions touch upon incongruity, as when a bruising wrestler walks his dog, a tiny poodle. Definitions mention the unexpected, as when the husband's blind date turns out to be his own wife. We all remember movie scenes that we considered funny. We also realize that what is funny to one person may not be to another.

Now that we have mentioned the varieties of humor and suggested the impossibility of nailing it down, we can turn to four stories that demon-

3

The Lighter Side

Any man will admit, if need be, that his sight is not good, or that he cannot swim, or shoots badly with a rifle, but to touch upon his sense of humor is to give him a mortal affront.

Stephen Leacock

strate the extremes of humor. The first two stories retell outrageous events with colorful and funny characters. The third changes the pace somewhat and finds humor in a more subtle presentation, in the depiction of a character who is not funny in herself but who brings on grimly funny results. The last story finds its gentle humor in the conflicting characterizations of two friends, separated in place but linked by correspondence. The Thurber story may bring a gasp of laughter. The Aldrich story will bring a smile and an appreciation for a clever author.

All four stories present aspects of humor, but they cover a range of possibilities.

The Night the Bed Fell

JAMES THURBER

> "I'm glad," said mother, who always looked on the bright side of things, "that your grandfather wasn't here."

Too bad. Grandfather would undoubtedly have added an extra touch of madness to a hilariously funny situation. But then Grandfather was away worrying about the Army of the Potomac.

In the history of humor, there are those humorists who deal in understatement, who describe in a deadpan narrative style some of the wildest events ever conceived. James Thurber is such a humorist. He manages to tell, without a touch of self-conscious humor, some of the funniest episodes in fiction. His matter-of-fact statement at the very beginning sets the tone.

The events are funny because the characters are funny. If we may judge by Grandfather's disappearance, he is a fit member of the family. But those who are present on the night the bed fell are choice examples of colorful humanity. Mother and Father are interesting to begin with. Cousin Briggs is a classic neurotic character. The aunts are distinguished by their unusual quirks. Herman and Roy have their own special characteristics. The writer himself is eccentric. Even the dog Rex belongs to this unusual family.

In television skits, many attempts at comedy are lost because the comedians laugh at themselves, "break up," implying, "We know this is hilariously funny, so funny we can scarcely keep our composure." The most successful comedy is deadpan. The characters take themselves seriously. The humor comes through by the contrast between the seriousness of the participants and the absurdity of their actions. Thurber's family members take themselves seriously!

The Night the Bed Fell

I SUPPOSE that the high-water mark of my youth in Columbus, Ohio, was the night the bed fell on my father. It makes a better recitation (unless, as some friends of mine have said, one has heard it five or six times) than it does a piece of writing, for it is almost necessary to throw furniture around, shake doors, and bark like a dog, to lend the proper atmosphere and verisimilitude to what is admittedly a somewhat incredible tale. Still, it did take place.

It happened, then, that my father had decided to sleep in the attic one night, to be away where he could think. My mother opposed the notion strongly because, she said, the old wooden bed up there was unsafe: it was wobbly and the heavy headboard would crash down on father's head in case the bed fell, and kill him. There was no dissuading him, however, and at a quarter past ten he closed the attic door behind him and went up the narrow twisting stairs. We later heard ominous creakings as he crawled into bed. Grandfather, who usually slept in the attic bed when he was with us, had disappeared some days before. (On these occasions he was usually gone six or eight days and returned growling and out of temper, with the news that the federal Union was run by a passel of blockheads and that the Army of the Potomac didn't have any more chance than a fiddler's bitch.)

We had visiting us at this time a nervous first cousin of mine named Briggs Beall, who believed that he was likely to cease breathing when he was asleep. It was his feeling that if he were not awakened every hour during the night, he might die of suffocation. He had been accustomed to setting an alarm clock to ring at intervals until morning, but I persuaded him to abandon this. He slept in my room and I told him that I was such a light sleeper that if anybody quit breathing in the same room with me, I would wake instantly. He tested me the first night—which I had suspected he would—by holding his breath after my regular breathing had convinced him I was asleep. I was not asleep, however, and called to him.

This seemed to allay his fears a little, but he took the precaution of putting a glass of spirits of camphor on a little table at the head of his bed. In case I didn't arouse him until he was almost gone, he said, he would sniff the camphor, a powerful reviver. Briggs was not the only member of his family who had his crotchets. Old Aunt Melissa Beall (who could whistle like a man, with two fingers in her mouth) suffered under the premonition that she was destined to die on South High Street, because she had been born on South High Street and married on South High Street. Then there was Aunt Sarah Shoaf, who never went to bed at night without the fear that a burglar was going to get in and blow chloroform under her door through a tube. To avert this calamity—for she was in greater dread of anesthetics than of losing her household goods—she always piled her money, silverware, and other valuables in a neat stack just outside her bedroom, with a note reading: "This is all I have. Please take it and do not use your chloroform, as this is all I have." Aunt Gracie Shoaf also had a burglar phobia, but she met it with more fortitude. She was confident that burglars had been getting into her house every night for forty years. The fact that she never missed anything was to her no proof to the contrary. She always claimed that she scared them off before they could take anything, by throwing shoes down the hallway. When she went to bed she piled, where she could get at them handily, all the shoes there were about her house. Five minutes after she had turned off the light, she would sit up in bed and say "Hark!" Her husband, who had learned to ignore the whole situation as long ago as 1903, would either be sound asleep or pretend to be sound asleep. In either case he would not respond to her tugging and pulling, so that presently she would arise, tiptoe to the door, open it slightly and heave a shoe down the hall in one direction and its mate down the hall in the other direction. Some nights she threw them all, some nights only a couple of pair.

But I am straying from the remarkable incidents that took place during the night that the bed fell on father. By midnight we were all in bed. The layout of the rooms and the disposition of their occupants is important to an understanding of what later occurred. In the front room upstairs (just under father's attic bedroom) were my mother and my brother Herman, who sometimes sang in his sleep, usually "Marching Through Georgia" or "Onward, Christian Soldiers." Briggs Beall and myself were in a room adjoining this one. My brother Roy was in a room across the hall from ours. Our bull terrier, Rex, slept in the hall.

My bed was an army cot, one of those affairs which are made wide enough to sleep on comfortably only by putting up, flat with the middle section, the two sides which ordinarily hang down like the sideboards of a drop-leaf table. When these sides are up, it is perilous to roll too far toward the edge, for then the cot is likely to tip completely over, bringing the whole bed down on top of one with a tremendous banging crash. This, in fact, is precisely what happened, about two o'clock in the morning. (It was my mother who, in recalling the scene later, first referred to it as "the night the bed fell on your father.")

Always a deep sleeper, slow to arouse (I had lied to Briggs), I was at first unconscious of what had happened when the iron cot rolled me onto the floor and toppled over on me. It left me still warmly bundled up and unhurt, for the bed rested above me like a canopy. Hence I did not wake up, only reached the edge of consciousness and went back. The racket, however, instantly awakened my mother, in the next room, who came to the immediate conclusion that her worst dread was realized: the big wooden bed upstairs had fallen on father. She therefore screamed, "Let's go to your poor father!" It was this shout, rather than the noise of my cot falling, that awakened my brother Herman, in the same room with her. He thought that mother had become, for no apparent reason, hysterical. "You're all right, mamma!" he shouted, trying to calm her. They exchanged shout for shout for perhaps ten seconds: "Let's go to your poor father!" and "You're all right!" That woke up Briggs. By this time I was conscious of what was going on, in a vague way, but did not yet realize that I was under my bed instead of on it. Briggs, awakening in the midst of loud shouts of fear and apprehension, came to the quick conclusion that he was suffocating and that we were all trying to "bring him out." With a low moan, he grasped the glass of camphor at the head of his bed and instead of sniffing it poured it over himself. The room reeked of camphor. "Ugf, ahfg!" choked Briggs, like a drowning man, for he had almost succeeded in stopping his breath under the deluge of pungent spirits. He leaped out of bed and groped toward the open window, but he came up against one that was closed. With his hand, he beat out the glass, and I could hear it crash and tinkle in the alleyway below. It was at this juncture that I, in trying to get up, had the uncanny sensation of feeling my bed above me! Foggy with sleep, I now suspected, in my turn, that the whole uproar was being made in a frantic endeavor to extricate me from what must be an unheard-of and perilous situation. "Get me out of this!" I bawled. "Get me out!" I think I had the nightmarish belief that I was entombed in a mine. "Gugh!" gasped Briggs, floundering in his camphor.

By this time my mother, still shouting, pursued by Herman, still shouting, was trying to open the door to the attic, in order to go up and get my father's body out of the wreckage. The door was stuck, however, and wouldn't yield. Her frantic pulls on it only added to the general banging and confusion. Roy and the dog were now up, the one shouting questions, the other barking.

Father, farthest away and soundest sleeper of all, had by this time been awakened by the battering on the attic door. He decided that the house was on fire. "I'm coming, I'm coming!" he wailed in a slow, sleepy voice—it took him many minutes to regain full consciousness. My mother, still believing he was caught under the bed, detected in his "I'm coming!" the mournful, resigned note of one who is preparing to meet his Maker. "He's dying!" she shouted.

"I'm all right!" Briggs yelled, to reassure her. "I'm all right!" He still believed that it was his own closeness to death that was worrying mother. I found at last the light switch in my room, unlocked the door, and Briggs and I joined the others at the attic door. The dog, who never did like Briggs, jumped for him—assuming that he was the culprit in whatever was going on—and Roy had to throw Rex and hold him. We could hear father crawling out of bed upstairs. Roy pulled the attic door open, with a mighty jerk, and father came down the stairs, sleepy and irritable but safe and sound. My mother began to weep when she saw him. Rex began to howl. "What is going on here?" asked father.

The situation was finally put together like a gigantic jigsaw puzzle. Father caught a cold from prowling around in his bare feet but there were no other bad results. "I'm glad," said mother, who always looked on the bright side of things, "that your grandfather wasn't here."

Reading for Understanding

❑ MAIN IDEA

1. The main idea of the story is that (a) cots are unsafe (b) a fear of anesthetics is a terrible problem (c) misunderstandings can lead to a humorous turmoil (d) members of the writer's family are calm and stable.

❑ DETAILS

2. Father decided to sleep in the attic because (a) he had had a row with Mother (b) his back had been bothering him (c) he was a light sleeper (d) he wanted to think.
3. Briggs Beall used an alarm clock to (a) prevent his suffocation (b) keep from oversleeping (c) allow him to check the time throughout the night (d) throw at an intruder who might enter his room.
4. When the cot collapsed under the writer, he (a) went back to sleep (b) awakened Briggs (c) thought the bed had fallen on father (d) was slightly injured.
5. The soundest sleeper in the entire house was (a) Mother (b) Father (c) Aunt Melissa (d) Roy.

❑ INFERENCES

6. The best word to describe the characters in this story is (a) *moody* (b) *dull* (c) *eccentric* (d) *courageous.*
7. "The night the bed fell on your father" is (a) Mother's erroneous interpretation of events (b) a fairly accurate description of what happened (c) Aunt Gracie's way of characterizing what happened (d) Aunt Melissa's favorite story.

8. The person who really started the events in motion was (a) Herman (b) the writer (c) Briggs (d) Father.

9. Mother might accurately be described as (a) *melancholy* (b) *thoughtful* (c) *indifferent* (d) *excitable.*

❑ AUTHOR'S TONE

10. "The Night the Bed Fell" might best be described as (a) a study in multiple personalities (b) a lighthearted romp (c) a subtle character study (d) an analysis of serious mental disturbances.

❑ ORDER OF EVENTS

11. Arrange the items in the order in which they occurred. Use letters only.
    A. Father yells, "I'm coming!"
    B. Grandfather disappears.
    C. The cot collapses.
    D. Rex almost bites Briggs.
    E. Briggs douses himself with camphor.

❑ OUTCOMES

12. After the events in the story, Briggs Beall probably (a) congratulated Roy on getting father's door open (b) was never again afraid of suffocating (c) regretted ever coming to stay at his cousin's house (d) bravely asked to sleep in the attic bed.

❑ CAUSE AND EFFECT

13. Briggs's dose of camphor (a) infuriated Rex, the dog (b) enraged Father (c) almost caused the result he feared most (d) amused both aunts.

❑ FACT OR OPINION

Tell whether each of the following is a fact or an opinion.

14. Father did not fall out of bed.

15. Of the three aunts, Aunt Gracie Shoaf was the strangest.

Words in Context

1. "I suppose that the *high-water mark* of my youth in Columbus, Ohio, was the night the bed fell on my father." The ***high-water mark***

(113) signifies the (a) culmination (b) beginning (c) apex (d) tragedy.

2. ". . . to lend the proper atmosphere and *verisimilitude* to . . . a somewhat incredible tale." ***Verisimilitude*** (113) means sense of (a) horror (b) humor (c) history (d) truthfulness.

3. "There was no *dissuading* him, however, and at a quarter past ten he closed the attic door . . ." ***Dissuading*** (113) means (a) persuading (b) discouraging (c) reasoning with (d) consoling.

4. "We later heard *ominous* creakings as he crawled into bed." ***Ominous*** (113) means (a) sinister (b) extraordinary (c) thunderous (d) mysterious.

5. ". . . the federal Union was run by a *passel* of blockheads. . . ." ***Passel*** (113) means (a) small number (b) great number (c) select group (d) thieving group.

6. "This seemed to *allay* his fears a little . . ." ***Allay*** (114) means (a) increase (b) ease (c) explain (d) uncover.

7. ". . . he took the *precaution* of putting a glass of spirits of camphor on a little table . . ." ***Precaution*** (114) means (a) safety measure (b) risk (c) suggestion (d) approach.

8. "Briggs was not the only member of his family who had his *crotchets*." ***Crotchets*** (114) means (a) problems (b) needs (c) quirks (d) financial difficulties.

9. ". . . under the premonition that she was *destined* to die on South High Street, because she had been born on South High Street and married on South High Street." ***Destined*** (114) means (a) ready (b) due (c) disheartened (d) not going.

10. "Aunt Grace Shoaf also had a burglar *phobia*, but she met it with more *fortitude*." ***Phobia . . . fortitude*** (114) mean (a) alarm . . . wishful thinking (b) fear . . . courage to endure (c) impulse . . . anxiety (d) record . . . force.

11. ". . . the *disposition* of their occupants is important to an understanding of what later occurred." ***Disposition*** (114) means (a) arrangement (b) wishes (c) outlook (d) habits.

12. ". . . the two sides which ordinarily hang down like the sideboards of a *drop-leaf* table." ***Drop-leaf*** (114) means (a) having folding legs (b) useful in large dining rooms (c) having fold-down extensions (d) having sturdy supports.

13. "Briggs, awakening in the midst of loud shouts of fear and *apprehension*, came to the quick conclusion that he was suffocating . . ." ***Apprehension*** (115) means (a) anger (b) laughter (c) misunderstanding (d) anxiety.

14. "The room reeked of camphor . . . for he had almost succeeded in stopping his breath under the *deluge* of *pungent* spirits." ***Deluge* . . . *pungent*** (115) mean (a) spray . . . intoxicating (b) whiff . . . sweet-smelling (c) dose . . . life-saving (d) flood . . . acrid.

15. "It was at this *juncture* that I . . . had the uncanny sensation of feeling my bed above me!" ***Juncture*** (115) means (a) hour (b) catastrophe (c) critical point (d) contrast in space.

Thinking Critically About the Story

1. The varieties of humor have an awesome range from genial to bitter, from sheer nonsense to universal truths, from laughing at to laughing with. Into which category does this story belong? Why do some people almost resent this type of humor? How do you react? Which current humorists and sit-coms on TV fall into the same category? Retell some TV instances that had you "rolling in the aisles" or didn't move you at all!

2. Be prepared to read to the class an excerpt from this story that you found funniest or that should have made you smile but didn't. Get the class consensus on these. How does your HQ (Humor Quotient) for this type of humor compare with that of the other members of the class?

3. James Thurber wrote this story more than three generations ago. Except for possibly the reference to Grandpa's war, is this story dated? Could it have been written two hundred years ago? Is it dateless, universal? Explain.

4. Which of the characters did you find most unusual? To be pitied rather than to be laughed at? Resembles you or someone you know?

5. What is the author's attitude toward his characters? Why does he tell us about them? What do they teach us about life?

Stories in Words

Crotchet (114) here means a peculiar, eccentric opinion or manner. It has a lot of relatives. It can be traced back to an old Norse word meaning "hook." A hook is something bent, crooked. And so we have *crochet*: to knit with a long hooked needle; the game of *croquet*, originally played with a hooked stick; *crutch*, a supporting staff, with a propping crosspiece; a *crozier*, a shepherd's staff with a hook; even the game of *lacrosse*, played with a stick somewhat resembling a crosier. A *crook* is someone who is crooked, bent from normal behavior.

Phobia (114), meaning "a deep-seated fear," is related to a great many colorful English words. Here are some of them.

Word	*Fear of*
acrophobia	heights
agoraphobia	open spaces
ailurophobia	cats
claustrophobia	closed spaces
ergophobia	work
triskaidekaphobia	the number 13

Sometimes *phob* words and *phil* words are contrasted. An *Anglophobe* dislikes things English. An *Anglophile* admires and likes things English.

Jigsaw (116) is related to the dance: jig. The word *jig* comes from a Middle French word meaning "to hop about, dance." It may be related to a still older word from Old High German: *giga*, meaning "a fiddle." Fiddles and dancers are old partners. A jigsaw has a blade that "dances" up and down. The product of a jigsaw is a puzzle in many pieces, the meaning here in the text.

Pig-Hoo-o-o-o-ey!

P. G. WODEHOUSE

> Resting his hands on the rail before him, James Belford swelled before their eyes like a young balloon. The muscles on his cheekbones stood out, his forehead became corrugated, his ears seemed to shimmer. Then at the very height of the tension, he let it go like, as the poet beautifully puts it, the sound of a great Amen.

Some critics point out that American humor is often based on exaggeration, as in the writings of Mark Twain. English humor, by contrast, is often based on understatement. P. G. Wodehouse is the master of understatement and absurdity. In the perspective of Lord Emsworth, a pig's problems are much more important than a serious problem involving his niece's love.

That magnificent pig, the Empress of Blandings, has begun to fast only a short time before the Shropshire Agricultural Show. There is nothing dearer to the pig-loving heart of Lord Emsworth than a silver medal in the Fat Pigs class. All seems to be lost, but then a happy coincidence suggests a solution, but will the remedy come in time?

For generations the stories of P. G. Wodehouse have enchanted readers. Jeeves, Mr. Mulliner, Bertie Wooster, Aunt Agatha, and other deathless characters have ensured the survival of stories that have a dated charm, picturing an age of innocence that has long since disappeared. "Pig-Hoo-o-o-o-ey" is an excellent example of the Wodehouse genius at work.

Pig-Hoo-o-o-o-ey!

Thanks to the publicity given to the matter by *The Bridgnorth, Shifnal, and Albrighton Argus* (with which is incorporated *The Wheat-Growers' Intelligence and Stock Breeders' Gazetteer*), the whole world today knows that the silver medal in the Fat Pigs class at the eighty-seventh annual Shropshire Agricultural Show was won by the Earl of Emsworth's black Berkshire sow, Empress of Blandings.

Very few people, however, are aware how near that splendid animal came to missing the coveted honor.

Now it can be told.

This brief chapter of Secret History may be said to have begun on the night of the eighteenth of July, when George Cyril Wellbeloved (twenty-nine), pig-man in the employ of Lord Emsworth, was arrested by Police-Constable Evans of Market Blandings for being drunk and disorderly in the taproom of the Goat and Feathers. On July the nineteenth, after first offering to apologize, then explaining that it had been his birthday, and finally attempting to prove an alibi, George Cyril was very properly jugged for fourteen days without the option of a fine.

On July the twentieth, Empress of Blandings, always hitherto a hearty and even a boisterous feeder, for the first time on record declined all nourishment. And on the morning of July the twenty-first, the veterinary surgeon called in to diagnose and deal with this strange asceticism, was compelled to confess to Lord Emsworth that the thing was beyond his professional skill.

Let us just see, before proceeding, that we have got these dates correct:

July 18.–Birthday Orgy of Cyril Wellbeloved.

July 19.–Incarceration of Ditto.

July 20.–Pig Lays off the Vitamins.

July 21.–Veterinary Surgeon Baffled.

Right.

The effect of the veterinary surgeon's announcement on Lord Emsworth was overwhelming. As a rule, the wear and tear of our complex modern life left this vague and amiable peer unscathed. So long as he had sunshine, regular meals, and complete freedom from the society of his younger son Frederick, he was placidly happy. But there were chinks in his armor, and one of these had been pierced this morning. Dazed by the news he stood at the window of the great library of Blandings Castle, looking out with unseeing eyes.

As he stood there, the door opened. Lord Emsworth turned; and having blinked once or twice, as was his habit when confronted suddenly with anything, recognized in the handsome and imperious looking woman who had entered, his sister, Lady Constance Keeble. Her demeanor, like his own, betrayed the deepest agitation.

"Clarence," she cried, "an awful thing has happened."

Lord Emsworth nodded dully. "I know. He's just told me."

"What! Has he been here?"

"Only this moment left."

"Why did you let him go? You must have known I would want to see him."

"What good would that have done?"

"I could at least have assured him of my sympathy," said Lady Constance stiffly.

"Yes, I suppose you could," said Lord Emsworth, having considered the point. "Not that he deserves any sympathy. The man's an idiot."

"Nothing of the kind. A most intelligent young man, as young men go."

"Young? Would you call him young? Fifty, I should have said, if a day."

"Are you out of your senses? Heacham fifty?"

"Not Heacham. Smithers."

As frequently happened to her in conversation with her brother, Lady Constance experienced a swimming sensation.

"Will you kindly tell me, Clarence, in a few simple words, what you imagine we are talking about?"

"I'm talking about Smithers. Empress of Blandings is refusing her food, and Smithers says he can't do anything about it. And he calls himself a vet!"

"Then you haven't heard? Clarence, a dreadful thing has happened. Angela has broken off her engagement to Heacham."

"And the Agricultural Show on Wednesday week!"

"What on earth has that got to do with it?" demanded Lady Constance, feeling a recurrence of the swimming sensation.

"What has it got to do with it?" said Lord Emsworth warmly. "My champion sow, with less than ten days to prepare herself for a most searching examination in competition with all the finest pigs in the county, starts refusing her food—"

"Will you stop maundering on about your insufferable pig and give your attention to something that really matters? I tell you that Angela—your niece Angela—has broken off her engagement to Lord Heacham and expresses her intention of marrying that hopeless ne'er-do-well, James Belford."

"The son of old Belford, the parson?"

"Yes."

"She can't. He's in America."

"He is not in America. He is in London."

"No," said Lord Emsworth, shaking his head sagely. "You're wrong. I remember meeting his father two years ago out on the road by Meeker's twenty-acre field, and he distinctly told me the boy was sailing for America next day. He must be there by this time."

"Can't you understand? He's come back."

"Oh? Come back? I see. Come *back*?"

"You know there was once a silly sentimental sort of affair between him and Angela; but a year after he left she became engaged to Heacham and I thought the whole thing was over and done with. And now it seems she met this young man Belford when she was in London last week, and it has started all over again. She tells me she has written to Heacham and broken the engagement."

There was a silence. Brother and sister remained for a space plunged in thought. Lord Emsworth was the first to speak.

"We've tried acorns," he said. "We've tried skim milk. And we've tried potato peel. But, no, she won't touch them."

Conscious of two eyes raising blisters on his sensitive skin, he came to himself with a start.

"Absurd! Ridiculous! Preposterous!" he said, hurriedly. "Breaking the engagement? Pooh! Tush! What nonsense! I'll have a word with that young man. If he thinks he can go about the place playing fast and loose with my niece and jilting her without so much as a—"

"Clarence!"

Lord Emsworth blinked. Something appeared to be wrong, but he could not imagine what. It seemed to him that in his last speech he had struck just the right note—strong, forceful, dignified.

"Eh?"

"It is Angela who has broken the engagement."

"Oh, Angela?"

"She is infatuated with this man Belford. And the point is, what are we to do about it?"

Lord Emsworth reflected.

"Take a strong line," he said firmly. "Stand no nonsense. Don't send 'em a wedding-present."

There is no doubt that, given time, Lady Constance would have found and uttered some adequately corrosive comment on this imbecile suggestion; but even as she was swelling preparatory to giving tongue, the door opened and a girl came in.

She was a pretty girl, with fair hair and blue eyes which in their softer moments probably reminded all sorts of people of twin lagoons slumbering beneath a southern sky. This, however, was not one of those moments. To Lord Emsworth, as they met his, they looked like something out of an oxyacetylene blowtorch; and, as far as he was capable of being disturbed by anything that was not his younger son Frederick, he was disturbed.

Angela, it seemed to him, was upset about something; and he was sorry. He liked Angela.

To ease a tense situation, he said:

"Angela, my dear, do you know anything about pigs?"

The girl laughed. One of those sharp, bitter laughs which are so unpleasant just after breakfast.

"Yes, I do. You're one."

"Me?"

"Yes, you. Aunt Constance says that, if I marry Jimmy, you won't let me have my money."

"Money? Money?" Lord Emsworth was mildly puzzled. "What money? You never lent me any money."

Lady Constance's feelings found vent in a sound like an overheated radiator.

"I believe this absentmindedness of yours is nothing but a ridiculous pose, Clarence. You know perfectly well that when poor Jane died she left you Angela's trustee."

"And I can't touch my money without your consent till I'm twenty-five."

"Well, how old are you?"

"Twenty-one."

"Then what are you worrying about?" asked Lord Emsworth, surprised. "No need to worry about it for another four years. God bless my soul, the money is quite safe. It is in excellent securities."

Angela stamped her foot. An unladylike action, but how much better than kicking an uncle with it, as her lower nature prompted.

"I have told Angela," explained Lady Constance, "that, while we naturally cannot force her to marry Lord Heacham, we can at least keep her money from being squandered by this wastrel on whom she proposes to throw herself away."

"He isn't a wastrel. He's got quite enough money to marry me on, but he wants some capital to buy a partnership in a—"

"He is a wastrel. Wasn't he sent abroad because—"

"That was two years ago. And since then—"

"My dear Angela, you may argue until—"

"I'm not arguing. I'm simply saying that I'm going to marry Jimmy, if we both have to starve in the gutter."

"What gutter?" asked his lordship, wrenching his errant mind away from thoughts of acorns.

"Any gutter."

"Now, please listen to me, Angela."

It seemed to Lord Emsworth that there was a frightful amount of conversation going on. He had the sensation of having become a mere bit of flotsam upon a tossing sea of female voices. Both his sister and his niece appeared to have much to say, and they were saying it simultaneously and *fortissimo*. He looked wistfully at the door.

It was smoothly done. A twist of the handle, and he was beyond those voices where there was peace. Galloping joyfully down the stairs, he charged out into the sunshine.

His joyfulness was not long-lived. Free at last to concentrate itself on the really serious issues of life, his mind grew somber and grim. Once more there descended upon him the cloud which had been oppressing his soul before all this Heacham-Angela-Belford business began. Each step that took him nearer to the sty where the ailing Empress resided seemed a heavier step than the last. He reached the sty; and, draping himself over the rails, peered moodily at the vast expanse of pig within.

For, even though she had been doing a bit of dieting of late, Empress of Blandings was far from being an ill-nourished animal. She resembled a captive balloon with ears and a tail, and was as nearly circular as a pig can be without bursting. Nevertheless, Lord Emsworth, as he regarded her, mourned and would not be comforted. A few more square meals under her belt, and no pig in all Shropshire could have held its head up in the Empress's presence. And now, just for lack of those few meals, the supreme animal would probably be relegated to the mean obscurity of an "Honorably Mentioned." It was bitter, bitter.

He became aware that somebody was speaking to him; and, turning, perceived a solemn young man in riding breeches.

"I say," said the young man.

Lord Emsworth, though he would have preferred solitude, was relieved to find that the intruder was at least one of his own sex. Women are apt to stray off into side issues, but men are practical and can be relied on to stick to the fundamentals. Besides, young Heacham probably kept pigs himself and might have a useful hint or two up his sleeve.

"I say, I've just ridden over to see if there was anything I could do about this fearful business."

"Uncommonly kind and thoughtful of you, my dear fellow," said Lord Emsworth, touched. "I fear things look very black."

"It's an absolute mystery to me."

"To me, too."

"I mean to say, she was all right last week."

"She was all right as late as the day before yesterday."

"Seemed quite cheery and chipper and all that."

"Entirely so."

"And then this happens—out of a blue sky, as you might say."

"Exactly. It is insoluble. We have done everything possible to tempt her appetite."

"Her appetite? Is Angela ill?"

"Angela? No, I fancy not. She seemed perfectly well a few minutes ago."

"You've seen her this morning, then? Did she say anything about this fearful business?"

"No. She was speaking about some money."

"It's all so dashed unexpected."

"Like a bolt from the blue," agreed Lord Emsworth. "Such a thing has never happened before. I fear the worst. According to the Wolff-Lehmann feeding standards, a pig, if in health, should consume daily nourishment amounting to fifty-seven thousand eight hundred calories, these to consist of proteins four pounds five ounces, carbohydrates twenty-five pounds—"

"What has that got to do with Angela?"

"Angela?"

"I came to find out why Angela has broken off our engagement."

Lord Emsworth marshalled his thoughts. He had a misty idea that he had heard something mentioned about that. It came back to him.

"Ah, yes, of course. She has broken off the engagement, hasn't she? I believe it is because she is in love with someone else. Yes, now that I recollect, that was distinctly stated. The whole thing comes back to me quite clearly. Angela has decided to marry someone else. I knew there was some satisfactory explanation. Tell me, my dear fellow, what are your views on linseed meal?"

"What do you mean, linseed meal?"

"Why, linseed meal," said Lord Emsworth, not being able to find a better definition. "As a food for pigs."

"Oh, curse all pigs!"

"What!" There was a sort of astounded horror in Lord Emsworth's voice. He had never been particularly fond of young Heacham, for he was not a man who took much to his juniors, but he had not supposed him capable of anarchistic sentiments like this. "What did you say?"

"I said, 'Curse all pigs!' You keep talking about pigs. I'm not interested in pigs. I don't want to discuss pigs. Blast every pig in existence!"

Lord Emsworth watched him, as he strode away, with an emotion that was partly indignation and partly relief—indignation that a landowner and a fellow son of Shropshire could have brought himself to utter such words, and relief that one capable of such utterance was not going to marry into his family. He had always in his woolen-headed way been very fond of his niece Angela, and it was nice to think that the child had such solid good sense and so much cool discernment. Many girls of her age would have been carried away by the glamor of young Heacham's position and wealth; but she, divining with an intuition beyond her years that he was unsound on the subject of pigs, had drawn back while there was still time and refused to marry him.

A pleasant glow suffused Lord Emsworth's bosom, to be frozen out a few moments later as he perceived his sister Constance bearing down upon him. Lady Constance was a beautiful woman, but there were times when the charm of her face was marred by a rather curious expression; and from nursery days onward his lordship had learned that this expression meant trouble. She was wearing it now.

"Clarence," she said, "I have had enough of this nonsense of Angela and young Belford. The thing cannot be allowed to go drifting on. You must catch the two o'clock train to London."

"What! Why?"

"You must see this man Belford and tell him that, if Angela insists on marrying him, she will not have a penny for four years. I shall be greatly surprised if that piece of information does not put an end to the whole business."

Lord Emsworth scratched meditatively at the Empress's tank-like back. A mutinous expression was on his mild face.

"Don't see why she shouldn't marry the fellow," he mumbled.

"Marry James Belford?"

"I don't see why not. Seems fond of him and all that."

"You never have had a grain of sense in your head, Clarence. Angela is going to marry Heacham."

"Can't stand that man. All wrong about pigs."

"Clarence, I don't wish to have any more discussion and argument. You will go to London on the two o'clock train. You will see Mr. Belford. And you will tell him about Angela's money. Is that quite clear?"

"Oh, all right," said his lordship moodily. "All right, all right."

The emotions of the Earl of Emsworth, as he sat next day facing his luncheon-guest, James Bartholomew Belford, across a table in the main dining room of the Senior Conservative Club, were not of the liveliest and most agreeable. It was bad enough to be in London at all on such a day of golden sunshine. To be charged, while there, with the task of blighting the romance of two young people for whom he entertained a warm regard was unpleasant to a degree.

For, now that he had given the matter thought, Lord Emsworth recalled that he had always liked this boy Belford. A pleasant lad, with, he remembered now, a healthy fondness for that rural existence which so appealed to himself. By no means the sort of fellow who, in the very presence and hearing of Empress of Blandings, would have spoken disparagingly and with oaths of pigs as a class. It occurred to Lord Emsworth, as it has occurred to so many people, that the distribution of money in this world is all wrong. Why should a man like pig-despising Heacham have a rent roll that ran into the tens of thousands, while this very deserving youngster had nothing?

These thoughts not only saddened Lord Emsworth—they embarrassed him. He hated unpleasantness, and it was suddenly borne in upon him that, after he had broken the news that Angela's bit of capital was locked up and not likely to get loose, conversation with his young friend during the remainder of lunch would tend to be somewhat difficult.

He made up his mind to postpone the revelation. During the meal, he decided, he would chat pleasantly of this and that; and then later, while bidding his guest good-bye, he would spring the thing on him suddenly and dive back into the recesses of the club.

Considerably cheered at having solved a delicate problem with such adroitness, he started to prattle.

"The gardens at Blandings," he said, "are looking particularly attractive this summer. My head-gardener, Angus McAllister, is a man with whom I do not always find myself seeing eye to eye, notably in the matter of hollyhocks, on which I consider his views subversive to a degree; but there is no denying that he understands roses. The rose garden—"

"How well I remember that rose garden," said James Belford, sighing slightly and helping himself to brussels sprouts. "It was there that Angela and I used to meet on summer mornings."

Lord Emsworth blinked. This was not an encouraging start, but the Emsworths were a fighting clan. He had another try.

"I have seldom seen such a blaze of color as was to be witnessed there during the month of June. Both McAllister and I adopted a very strong policy with the slugs and plant lice, with the result that the place was a mass of flourishing Damasks and Ayrshires and—"

"Properly to appreciate roses," said James Belford, "you want to see them as a setting for a girl like Angela. With her fair hair gleaming against the green leaves she makes a rose garden seem a veritable Paradise."

"No doubt," said Lord Emsworth. "No doubt. I am glad you liked my rose garden. At Blandings, of course, we have the natural advantage of loamy soil, rich in plant food and humus; but, as I often say to McAllister, and on this point we have never had the slightest disagreement, loamy soil by itself is not enough. You must have manure. If every autumn a liberal mulch of stable manure is spread upon the beds and the coarser parts removed in the spring before the annual cultivating—"

"Angela tells me," said James Belford, "that you have forbidden our marriage."

Lord Emsworth choked dismally over his chicken. Directness of this kind, he told himself with a pang of self-pity, was the sort of thing young Englishmen picked up in America. Diplomatic circumlocution flourished only in a more leisurely civilization, and in those energetic and forceful surroundings you learned to Talk Quick and Do It Now, and all sorts of uncomfortable things.

"Er—well, yes, now you mention it, I believe some informal decision of that nature was arrived at. You see, my dear fellow, my sister Constance feels rather strongly—"

"I understand. I suppose she thinks I'm a sort of prodigal."

"No, no, my dear fellow. She never said that. Wastrel was the term she employed."

"Well, perhaps I did start out in business on those lines. But you can take it from me that when you find yourself employed on a farm in Nebraska belonging to an applejack-nourished patriarch with strong views on work and a good vocabulary, you soon develop a certain liveliness."

"Are you employed on a farm?"

"I was employed on a farm."

"Pigs?" said Lord Emsworth in a low, eager voice.

"Among other things."

Lord Emsworth gulped. His fingers clutched at the tablecloth.

"Then perhaps, my dear fellow, you can give me some advice. For the last two days my prize sow, Empress of Blandings, has declined all nourishment. And the Agricultural Show is on Wednesday week. I am distracted with anxiety."

James Belford frowned thoughtfully.

"What does your pig-man say about it?"

"My pig-man was sent to prison two days ago. Two days!" For the first time the significance of the coincidence struck him. "You don't think that can have anything to do with the animal's loss of appetite?"

"Certainly. I imagine she is missing him and pining away because he isn't there."

Lord Emsworth was surprised. He had only a distant acquaintance with George Cyril Wellbeloved, but from what he had seen of him he had not credited him with this fatal allure.

"She probably misses his afternoon call."

Again his lordship found himself perplexed. He had had no notion that pigs were such sticklers for the formalities of social life.

"His call?"

"He must have had some special call that he used when he wanted her to come to dinner. One of the first things you learn on a farm is hog-calling. Pigs are temperamental. Omit to call them, and they'll starve rather than put on the nose bag. Call them right, and they will follow you to the ends of the earth with their mouths watering."

"God bless my soul! Fancy that."

"A fact, I assure you. These calls vary in different parts of America. In Wisconsin, for example, the words 'Poig, Poig, Poig' bring home—in both the literal and the figurative sense—the bacon. In Illinois, I believe they call 'Burp, Burp, Burp,' while in Iowa the phrase 'Kus, Kus, Kus' is preferred. Proceeding to Minnesota, we find 'Peega, Peega, Peega' or alternatively, 'Oink, Oink, Oink,' whereas in Milwaukee, so largely inhabited by those of German descent, you will hear the good old Teuton 'Komm Schweine, Komm Schweine.' Oh, yes, there are all sorts of pig-calls, from the Massachusetts 'Phew, Phew, Phew' to the 'Loo-ey, Loo-ey, Loo-ey' of Ohio, not counting various local devices such as beating on tin cans with axes or rattling pebbles in a suitcase. I knew a man out in Nebraska who used to call his pigs by tapping on the edge of the trough with his wooden leg."

"Did he, indeed?"

"But a most unfortunate thing happened. One evening, hearing a woodpecker at the top of a tree, they started shinning up it; and when the man came out he found them all lying there in a circle with their necks broken."

"This is no time for joking," said Lord Emsworth, pained.

"I'm not joking. Solid fact. Ask anybody out there."

Lord Emsworth placed a hand to his throbbing forehead.

"But if there is this wide variety, we have no means of knowing which call Wellbeloved . . ."

"Ah," said James Belford, "but wait. I haven't told you all. There is a master word."

"A what?"

"Most people don't know it, but I had it straight from the lips of Fred Patzel, the hog-calling champion of the Western States. What a man! I've known him to bring pork chops leaping from their plates. He informed me that, no matter whether an animal has been trained to answer to the Illinois 'Burp' or the Minnesota 'Oink,' it will always give immediate service in response to this magic combination of syllables. It is to the pig world what the Masonic grip is to the human. 'Oink' in Illinois or 'Burp' in Minnesota, and the animal merely raises its eyebrows and stares coldly. But go to either State and call 'Pig-hoo-oo-ey!' . . ."

The expression on Lord Emsworth's face was that of a drowning man who sees a lifeline.

"Is that the master word of which you spoke?"

"That's it."

"Pig—?"

"—hoo-oo-ey."

"Pig-hoo-o-ey?"

"You haven't got it right. The first syllable should be short and staccato, the second long and rising into a falsetto, high but true."

"Pig-hoo-o-o-ey."

"Pig-hoo-o-o-ey."

"Pig-hoo-o-o-ey!" yelled Lord Emsworth, flinging his head back and giving tongue in a high, penetrating tenor which caused ninety-three Senior Conservatives, lunching in the vicinity, to congeal into living statues of alarm and disapproval.

"More body to the 'hoo,'" advised James Belford.

"Pig-hoo-o-o-o-ey!"

The Senior Conservative Club is one of the few places in London where lunchers are not accustomed to getting music with their meals. White-whiskered financiers gazed bleakly at bald-headed politicians, as if asking silently what was to be done about this. Bald-headed politicians stared back at white-whiskered financiers, replying in the language of the eye that they did not know. The general sentiment prevailing was a vague determination to write to the Committee about it.

"Pig-hoo-o-o-o-ey!" caroled Lord Emsworth. And, as he did so his eye fell on the clock over the mantelpiece. Its hands pointed to twenty minutes to two.

He started convulsively. The best train in the day for Market Blandings was the one which left Paddington station at two sharp. After that there was nothing till the five-five.

He was not a man who often thought; but, when he did, to think was with him to act. A moment later he was scudding over the carpet, making for the door that led to the broad staircase.

Throughout the room which he had left, the decision to write in strong terms to the Committee was now universal; but from the mind, such as it was, of Lord Emsworth the past, with the single exception of the word "Pig-hoo-o-o-o-ey!" had been completely blotted.

Whispering the magic syllables, he sped to the cloakroom and retrieved his hat. Murmuring them over and over again, he sprang into a cab. He was still repeating them as the train moved out of the station; and he would doubtless have gone on repeating them all the way to Market Blandings, had he not, as was his invariable practice when traveling by rail, fallen asleep after the first ten minutes of the journey.

The stopping of the train at Swindon Junction woke him with a start. He sat up, wondering, after his usual fashion on these occasions, who and where he was. Memory returned to him, but a memory that was, alas, incomplete. He remembered his name. He remembered that he was on his way home from a visit to London. But what it was that you said to a pig when inviting it to drop in for a bite of dinner he had completely forgotten.

It was the opinion of Lady Constance Keeble, expressed verbally during dinner in the brief intervals when they were alone, and by means of silent telepathy when Beach, the butler, was adding his dignified presence to the proceedings, that her brother Clarence, in his expedition to London to put matters plainly to James Belford, had made an outstanding idiot of himself.

There had been no need whatever to invite the man Belford to lunch; but, having invited him to lunch, to leave him sitting, without having clearly stated that Angela would have no money for four years, was the act of a congenital imbecile. Lady Constance had been aware ever since their childhood days that her brother had about as much sense as a—

Here Beach entered, superintending the bringing-in of the savory, and she had been obliged to suspend her remarks.

This sort of conversation is never agreeable to a sensitive man, and his lordship had removed himself from the danger zone as soon as he could manage it. He was now seated in the library, sipping port and straining a brain which Nature had never intended for hard exercise in an effort to bring back that word of magic of which his unfortunate habit of sleeping in trains had robbed him.

"Pig—"

He could remember as far as that; but of what avail was a single syllable? Besides, weak as his memory was, he could recall that the whole gist or nub of the thing lay in the syllable that followed. The "pig" was a mere preliminary.

Lord Emsworth finished his port and got up. He felt restless, stifled. The summer night seemed to call to him like some silver-voiced swineherd calling to his pig. Possibly, he thought, a breath of fresh air might stimulate his brain-cells. He wandered downstairs; and, having dug a shocking old slouch hat out of the cupboard where he hid it to keep his sister Constance from impounding and burning it, he strode heavily out into the garden.

He was pottering aimlessly to and fro in the parts adjacent to the rear of the castle when there appeared in his path a slender female form. He recognized it without pleasure. Any unbiased judge would have said that his niece Angela, standing there in the soft pale light, looked like some dainty spirit of the Moon. Lord Emsworth was not an unbiased judge. To him Angela merely looked like Trouble. The march of civilization has given the modern girl a vocabulary and an ability to use it which her grandmother never had. Lord Emsworth would not have minded meeting Angela's grandmother a bit.

"Is that you, my dear?" he said nervously.

"Yes."

"I didn't see you at dinner."

"I didn't want any dinner. The food would have choked me. I can't eat."

"It's precisely the same with my pig," said his lordship. "Young Belford tells me—"

Into Angela's queenly disdain there flashed a sudden animation.

"Have you seen Jimmy? What did he say?"

"That's just what I can't remember. It began with the word 'Pig'—"

"But after he had finished talking about you, I mean. Didn't he say anything about coming down here?"

"Not that I remember."

"I expect you weren't listening. You've got a very annoying habit, Uncle Clarence," said Angela maternally, "of switching your mind off and just going blah when people are talking to you. It gets you very much disliked on all sides. Didn't Jimmy say anything about me?"

"I fancy so. Yes, I am nearly sure he did."

"Well, what?"

"I cannot remember."

There was a sharp clicking noise in the darkness. It was caused by Angela's upper front teeth meeting her lower front teeth; and was followed by a sort of wordless exclamation. It seemed only too plain that the love and respect which a niece should have for an uncle were in the present instance at a very low ebb.

"I wish you wouldn't do that," said Lord Emsworth plaintively.

"Do what?"

"Make clicking noises at me."

"I will make clicking noises at you. You know perfectly well, Uncle Clarence, that you are behaving like a bohunkus."

"A what?"

"A bohunkus," explained his niece coldly, "is a very inferior sort of worm. Not the kind of worm that you see on lawns, which you can respect, but a really degraded species."

"I wish you would go in, my dear," said Lord Emsworth. "The night air may give you a chill."

"I won't go in. I came out here to look at the moon and think of Jimmy. What are you doing out here, if it comes to that?"

"I came here to think. I am greatly exercised about my pig, Empress of

Blandings. For two days she has refused her food, and young Belford says she will not eat until she hears the proper call or cry. He very kindly taught it to me, but unfortunately I have forgotten it."

"I wonder you had the nerve to ask Jimmy to teach you pig-calls, considering the way you're treating him."

"But—"

"Like a leper, or something. And all I can say is that, if you remember this call of his, and it makes the Empress eat, you ought to be ashamed of yourself if you still refuse to let me marry him."

"My dear," said Lord Emsworth earnestly, "if through young Belford's instrumentality Empress of Blandings is induced to take nourishment once more, there is nothing I will refuse him—nothing."

"Honor bright?"

"I give you my solemn word."

"You won't let Aunt Constance bully you out of it?"

Lord Emsworth drew himself up.

"Certainly not," he said proudly. "I am always ready to listen to your Aunt Constance's views, but there are certain matters where I claim the right to act according to my own judgment." He paused and stood musing. "It began with the word 'Pig'—"

From somewhere near at hand music made itself heard. The servants' hall, its day's labors ended, was refreshing itself with the housekeeper's record player. To Lord Emsworth the strains were merely an additional annoyance. He was not fond of music. It reminded him of his younger son Frederick, a flat but persevering songster both in and out of the bath.

"Yes. I can distinctly recall as much as that. Pig—Pig—"

"WHO—"

Lord Emsworth leaped in the air. It was as if an electric shock had been applied to his person.

"WHO stole my heart away?" howled the record player. "Who—"

The peace of the summer night was shattered by a triumphant shout.

"Pig-HOO-o-o-o-ey!"

A window opened. A large, bald head appeared. A dignified voice spoke.

"Who is there? Who is making that noise?"

"Beach!" cried Lord Emsworth. "Come out here at once."

"Very good, your lordship."

And presently the beautiful night was made still more lovely by the added attraction of the butler's presence.

"Beach, listen to this."

"Very good, your lordship."

"Pig-hoo-o-o-o-ey!"

"Very good, your lordship."

"Now you do it."

"I, your lordship?"

"Yes. It's a way you call pigs."

"I do not call pigs, your lordship," said the butler coldly.

"What do you want Beach to do it for?" asked Angela.

"Two heads are better than one. If we both learn it, it will not matter should I forget it again."

"By Jove, yes! Come on, Beach. Push it over the thorax," urged the girl eagerly. "You don't know it, but this is a matter of life and death. At-a-boy, Beach! Inflate the lungs and go to it."

It had been the butler's intention, prefacing his remarks with the statement that he had been in service at the castle for eighteen years, to explain frigidly to Lord Emsworth that it was not his place to stand in the moonlight practicing pig-calls. If, he would have gone on to add, his lordship saw the matter from a different angle, then it was his, Beach's, painful duty to tender his resignation, to become effective one month from that day.

But the intervention of Angela made this impossible to a man of chivalry and heart. A paternal fondness for the girl, dating from the days when he had stooped to enacting—and very convincingly, too, for his was a figure that lent itself to the impersonation—the *role* of a hippopotamus for her childish amusement, checked the words he would have uttered. She was looking at him with bright eyes, and even the rendering of pig-noises seemed a small sacrifice to make for her sake.

"Very good, your lordship," he said in a low voice, his face pale and set in the moonlight. "I shall endeavor to give satisfaction. I would merely advance the suggestion, your lordship, that we move a few steps farther away from the vicinity of the servants' hall. If I were to be overheard by any of the lower domestics, it would weaken my position as a disciplinary force."

"What chumps we are!" cried Angela, inspired. "The place to do it is outside the Empress's sty. Then, if it works, we'll see it working."

Lord Emsworth found this a little abstruse, but after a moment he got it.

"Angela," he said, "you are a very intelligent girl. Where you get your brains from, I don't know. Not from my side of the family."

The bijou residence of the Empress of Blandings looked very snug and attractive in the moonlight. But beneath even the beautiful things of life there is always an underlying sadness. This was supplied in the present instance by a long, low trough, only too plainly full to the brim of succulent mash and acorns. The fast, obviously, was still in progress.

The sty stood some considerable distance from the castle walls, so that there had been ample opportunity for Lord Emsworth to rehearse his little company during the journey. By the time they had ranged themselves against the rails, his two assistants were letter-perfect.

"Now," said his lordship.

There floated out upon the summer night a strange composite sound that sent the birds roosting in the trees above shooting off their perches like rockets. Angela's clear soprano rang out like the voice of the village blacksmith's daughter. Lord Emsworth contributed a reedy tenor. And the bass notes of Beach probably did more to startle the birds than any other one item in the program.

They paused and listened. Inside the Empress's boudoir there sounded the movement of a heavy body. There was an inquiring grunt. The next moment the sacking that covered the doorway was pushed aside, and the noble animal emerged.

"Now!" said Lord Emsworth again.

Once more that musical cry shattered the silence of the night. But it brought no responsive movement from Empress of Blandings. She stood there motionless, her nose elevated, her ears hanging down, her eyes everywhere but on the trough where, by rights, she should now have been digging in and getting hers. A chill disappointment crept over Lord Emsworth, to be succeeded by a gust of petulant anger.

"I might have known it," he said bitterly. "That young scoundrel was deceiving me. He was playing a joke on me."

"He wasn't," cried Angela indignantly. "Was he, Beach?"

"Not knowing the circumstances, Miss, I cannot venture an opinion."

"Well, why has it no effect, then?" demanded Lord Emsworth.

"You can't expect it to work right away. We've got her stirred up, haven't we? She's thinking it over, isn't she? Once more will do the trick. Ready, Beach?"

"Quite ready, Miss."

"Then when I say three. And this time, Uncle Clarence, do please for goodness' sake not yowl like you did before. It was enough to put any pig off. Let it come out quite easily and gracefully. Now, then. One, two—three!"

The echoes died away. And as they did so a voice spoke.

"Community singing?"

"Jimmy!" cried Angela, whisking round.

"Hullo, Angela. Hullo, Lord Emsworth. Hullo, Beach."

"Good evening, sir. Happy to see you once more."

"Thanks. I'm spending a few days at the Vicarage with my father. I got down here by the five-five."

Lord Emsworth cut peevishly in upon these civilities.

"Young man," he said, "what do you mean by telling me that my pig would respond to that cry? It does nothing of the kind."

"You can't have done it right."

"I did it precisely as you instructed me. I have had, moreover, the assistance of Beach here and my niece Angela—"

"Let's hear a sample."

Lord Emsworth cleared his throat. "Pig-hoo-o-o-o-ey!"

James Belford shook his head.

"Nothing like it," he said. "You want to begin the 'Hoo' in a low minor of two quarter notes in four-four time. From this build gradually to a higher note, until at last the voice is soaring in full crescendo, reaching F sharp on the natural scale and dwelling for two retarded half-notes, then breaking into a shower of accidental grace-notes."

"God bless my soul!" said Lord Emsworth, appalled. "I shall never be able to do it."

"Jimmy will do it for you," said Angela. "Now that he's engaged to me, he'll be one of the family and always popping about here. He can do it every day till the show is over."

James Belford nodded.

"I think that would be the wisest plan. It is doubtful if an amateur could ever produce real results. You need a voice that has been trained on the open prairie and that has gathered richness and strength from competing with tornadoes. You need a manly, wind-scorched voice with a suggestion in it of the crackling of corn husks and the whisper of evening breezes in the fodder. Like this!"

Resting his hands on the rail before him, James Belford swelled before their eyes like a young balloon. The muscles on his cheek-bones stood out, his forehead became corrugated, his ears seemed to shimmer. Then at the very height of the tension, he let it go like, as the poet beautifully puts it, the sound of a great Amen.

"Pig-HOOOOO-OOO-OOO-O-O-ey!"

They looked at him, awed. Slowly, fading off across hill and dale, the vast bellow died away. And suddenly, as it died, another, softer sound succeeded it. A sort of gulpy, gurgly, plobby, squishy, woffle-some sound, like a thousand eager men drinking soup in a foreign restaurant. And, as he heard it, Lord Emsworth uttered a cry of rapture.

The Empress was feeding.

Reading for Understanding

❑ MAIN IDEA

1. The main point of the story is (a) the love affair between Angela and James Belford (b) Lord Emsworth's concern about the pig's fast (c) the persistence of Aunt Constance (d) the vacillating fancies of Angela.

❑ DETAILS

2. Clarence is (a) the veterinarian (b) the father of James Belford (c) the butler (d) Lord Emsworth.

3. Angela's first love was (a) Heacham (b) Frederick (c) James (d) Smithers.

4. The person who solves the problem is (a) the veterinarian (b) Angela's suitor (c) Lord Emsworth himself (d) Beach.

5. James had gained his farm skills (a) at home (b) in Milwaukee (c) in Market Blandings (d) in Nebraska.

☐ INFERENCES

6. The expression "Curse all pigs" effectively doomed the marital hopes of (a) Heacham (b) James (c) George Wellbeloved (d) Smithers.

7. Lord Emsworth can best be described as (a) eccentric (b) stingy (c) reckless (d) intelligent.

8. Lady Constance's attitude toward James probably (a) drew Angela closer to him (b) had the hearty endorsement of Lord Emsworth (c) provoked a fight between Heacham and James (d) proved to be an effective strategy for her cause.

9. In his dealings with Lady Constance, Lord Emsworth (a) tried not to get involved (b) asked her advice about the problem with Empress of Blandings (c) furthered the cause of Heacham (d) followed her conversations carefully.

10. The comment about the man who called pigs by tapping on a trough with his wooden leg is intended to be (a) informative (b) argumentative (c) tongue-in-cheek (d) understated.

☐ AUTHOR'S TONE

11. The tone of the story can best be described as (a) intense (b) thoughtful (c) lighthearted (d) inspirational.

☐ ORDER OF EVENTS

12. Arrange the items in the order in which they occurred. Use letters only.
    A. James goes to America.
    B. The Empress refuses to eat.
    C. George Cyril Wellbeloved is arrested.
    D. "Lord Emsworth uttered a cry of rapture."
    E. James arrives at Blandings.

☐ OUTCOMES

13. After the conclusion of the story, (a) Lady Constance congratulates Lord Emsworth on his work with the Empress (b) Heacham manages to persuade Lord Emsworth to back his suit (c) Angela and James are united (d) the Empress goes on another hunger strike.

☐ CAUSE AND EFFECT

14. Lord Emsworth failed in his pig calling because (a) James gave him the wrong information (b) the Empress really had pneumonia

(c) he had the words but not the melody (d) the weather had turned chilly.

❑ FACT OR OPINION

Tell whether the following is a fact or an opinion.

15. Heacham would have made Angela an excellent husband.

Words in Context

1. "Very few people, however, are aware how near that splendid animal came to missing the *coveted* honor." ***Coveted*** (122) means (a) valuable (b) unusual (c) traditional (d) highly desirable.

2. "July 19.—*Incarceration* of *Ditto*." ***Incarceration* . . . *Ditto*** (122) mean (a) seizure . . . evidence (b) surrender . . . guilty one (c) imprisonment . . . same person (d) locking up . . . wine cellar.

3. "Her *demeanor*, like his own, betrayed the deepest agitation." ***Demeanor*** (123) means (a) manner (b) costume (c) voice (d) walk.

4. "Will you stop *maundering on* about your *insufferable* pig and give your attention to something that really matters?" ***Maundering* . . . *insufferable*** (123) mean (a) worrying . . . ailing (b) talking foolishly . . . unbearable (c) thinking . . . overstuffed (d) being so sad . . . worthless.

5. "Lady Constance's feelings found *vent* in a sound like an overheated radiator." ***Vent*** (125) means (a) comfort (b) expression (c) sadness (d) disaster.

6. "'What gutter?' asked his lordship, wrenching his *errant* mind away from thoughts of acorns." ***Errant*** (125) means (a) troubled (b) fickle (c) faulty (d) wandering.

7. "He had the sensation of having become a mere bit of *flotsam* upon a tossing sea of female voices." ***Flotsam*** (125) means (a) quiet humanity (b) unimportant data (c) irrelevance (d) useless wreckage.

8. "Both his sister and his niece appeared to have much to say, and they were saying it *simultaneously* and *fortissimo*." ***Simultaneously* . . . *fortissimo*** . . . (125) mean (a) sharply . . . most earnestly (b) logically . . . too softly (c) without listening . . . not strongly (d) at the same time . . . very loudly.

9. "And now, just for the lack of those few meals, the supreme animal would probably be *relegated* to the *mean* obscurity of an 'Honorable Mention.'" ***Relegated . . . mean*** (126) mean (a) banished . . . lowly (b) doomed . . . disgraceful (c) condemned . . . meaningless (d) pushed . . . distinguished.

10. "By no means the sort of fellow who . . . would have spoken *disparagingly* and with oaths of pigs as a class." ***Disparagingly*** (128) means (a) openly (b) boastfully (c) defiantly (d) belittlingly.

11. "Considerably cheered at having solved a delicate problem with such *adroitness,* he started to *prattle.*" ***Adroitness . . . prattle*** (128) mean (a) speed . . . feel smug (b) skill . . . babble (c) tactfulness . . . think of other problems (d) ease . . . pat himself on his back

12. "White-whiskered financiers gazed *bleakly* at bald-headed politicians, as if asking silently what was to be done about this." ***Bleakly*** (131) means (a) pleadingly (b) angrily (c) cheerlessly (d) fearlessly.

13. "A moment later he was *scudding* over the carpet, making for the door that led to the broad staircase." ***Scudding*** (131) means (a) sailing (b) moving swiftly (c) walking (d) slithering.

14. ". . . to leave him sitting, without having clearly stated that Angela would have no money for four years, was the act of a *congenital imbecile.*" A ***congenital imbecile*** (132) is a person who is (a) feebleminded from birth (b) unwilling to plan ahead (c) without foresight (d) a shrewd manipulator.

15. "Lord Emsworth found this a little *abstruse,* but after a moment he got it." ***Abstruse*** (135) means (a) startling (b) farfetched (c) ridiculous (d) hard to understand.

Thinking Critically About the Story

1. By referring to specific incidents and characterizations, show how this story illustrates the truth of the following statement: "P. G. Wodehouse is the master of understatement and absurdity."

2. Which series of dialog did you find most humorous? Explain. Be prepared—with a classmate—to read it aloud to the class.

3. P. G. Wodehouse was a master of descriptive phrases that leap off the page. Which one did you enjoy most? Be prepared to read it aloud to the class and to explain the reason for your choice.

4. What are some generalizations about people that you can garner from the words and actions of Wodehouse's people? What piece of truth

do you find in Lord Emsworth? In Lady Constance? In Angela? In James Belford? To what extent do they resemble real people? Characters in TV dramas?

5. What was the author's purpose in writing this story? Did he plan social satire or humor for its own sake? Explain. Which TV shows and sitcoms does it resemble?

Stories in Words

Preposterous (page 124), by derivation, means "the before coming after!" *Pre,* meaning "before," and *post,* meaning "after," are common prefixes in words like *prehistoric* and *postpone. Post* is embedded in the Latin word *posterus,* "after." Since the *before* cannot come *after,* a *preposterous* statement is absurd, impossible. A version of the modern expression "to put the cart before the horse" can be traced to the orator Cicero in 61 B.C. It is an ancient proverb in German, French, and Italian as well as English.

Flotsam (page 125) is usually combined with *jetsam,* but the words should be distinguished. *Flotsam* is derived from an Old English word for *float. Jetsam* is related to *jettison* and is ultimately derived from a Latin root meaning "to throw." In old law, flotsam was the wreckage floating on the sea after a ship disaster. Flotsam belonged to the English Crown. Jetsam was the cargo thrown overboard intentionally to lighten a ship in an emergency. Jetsam belonged to the lord of the manor where the debris came ashore. The distinction was not always easy to apply. *Flotsam* and *jetsam* are often used loosely for any floating wreckage.

Dismally (page 129) has two important roots: *dies* meaning "day" and *mal* meaning "evil." Though *dismal* now means "gloomy," "depressing," it once had a more sinister meaning. The Romans believed there were two unlucky days each month. These "dies mali" were anniversaries of great disasters. Romans avoided these days for any event of importance. The belief continued into medieval times. Here are a few examples: January 1 and 25; February 4 and 26; March 1 and 28.

The Aviarian

PATRICIA McCONNEL

It seemed to Mr. Pippin that she was decidedly *too* cheerful, and he began to repeat in his head, "Go home, Winifred, go home," until it became a chant that he hoped would magic her away.

The aviarian, a keeper of birds, is Winifred Oglethorpe, self-appointed caregiver to Mr. Pippin. It is Mr. Pippin who owns the nine parakeets that comprise the modest aviary. Winifred usually "knows what is best" for other people and accepts no obstacles in the path of her self-appointed duty. Mr. Pippin is the not-altogether-willing recipient of her vigorous intentions.

Though the subject matter seems grim enough, "The Aviarian" has a great many touches of humor: the name of the fashion store, the description of Winifred Oglethorpe, the title of the trailer park, Winifred's selective love of nature's creatures, her overwhelming presence, her offhand acceptance of the feathery catastrophes. This is not the extravagant and obvious humor of "The Night the Bed Fell." This is a darker humor that calls for wry smiles rather than loud guffaws.

Are there persons of apparently good intentions who somehow manage, often unknowingly, to run roughshod over the feelings of other people? How do you regard Winifred Oglethorpe?

The Aviarian

The very day that Winifred Oglethorpe turned sixty-two, she quit her job at Van Klamp's Bake Shop and went downtown to the Social Security office to have her pension turned on. Her next stop was Millie's Madcap Fashions for Mature Ladies, where she bought an orange and magenta flowered muumuu, and from there she went to Union Station, bought a book of crossword puzzles, and boarded the 3:08 train for Miami. She took with her only those worldly possessions that would fit in one navy surplus footlocker and two cardboard boxes. On her lap, so as not to crush it, she carried the starched Dutch-girl cap she had worn while selling tea cakes for twenty-five years.

In Miami she found a hotel catering to thrift-minded people and used it for her temporary headquarters while she looked for a permanent home. The other senior residents of the hotel were unanimous in the opinion that a retired lady of limited means could do no better than to buy a trailer, as trailer park rentals were cheap if you went out of the tourist zone. They sent her to North Miami to Helen's Hibiscus Heaven Trailer Home, which catered to senior citizens.

The Hibiscus Heaven had just the thing, a lovely little trailer only recently vacated by a lady gone on to a more idyllic retirement, as the manager put it. There had been no heirs, and the manager explained that she was willing to pass her little windfall along to Mrs. Oglethorpe for practically nothing, which in this case amounted to five-hundred dollars. The trailer was very tiny, and its plywood walls were warped and cracked from too many years' exposure to Florida sun and rain, but the price was right, and it sat under a magnificent magnolia tree.

The first thing Winifred Oglethorpe did was to paint the trailer lavender inside and out, and the second thing she did was to go about indulging her lifelong interest in birds. She built a birdbath under the magnolia tree and concealed herself behind some hibiscus with *The Bird Lover's Guide to Tropical Birds*.

The days passed pleasantly, and the little birds that frequented Mrs. Oglethorpe's birdbath grew fat on the tidbits the benevolent lady put out for them. Only one thing marred the perfection of Mrs. Oglethorpe's bird

Eden—the catbirds picked on the smaller birds mercilessly, driving them away from the birdbath and hogging the choicest bits of bird feed. But lack of resourcefulness had never been one of Winifred Oglethorpe's failings, and so she fashioned a slingshot from a forked branch and a strip from an old inner tube and soon became a remarkably good shot. Mrs. Oglethorpe killed catbirds with the vengeance of a knight slaying dragons.

So that is how it happened that Mrs. Oglethorpe was hiding in a clump of hibiscus when Mr. Pippin moved into Trailer No. 82. (There were vacancies in the rented trailers at Hibiscus Heaven only when someone died, usually, but Miss Tillie Wheelright, the former occupant of Trailer No. 82, had been forcibly ejected by the management for the questionable way in which she supplemented her retirement pension.)

From her vantage point in the hibiscus, Mrs. Oglethorpe discreetly took inventory of Mr. Pippin's belongings as he moved them in. She noted that he had a good many books and surmised that he was a man of culture. He had very few clothes, some cooking utensils, and nine parakeets. In fact, Mr. Pippin rather resembled a tiny gray bird himself, for he was a small-boned man, thin and frail-looking. Mrs. Oglethorpe reflected that any man who owned nine parakeets must have a sensitive nature, and she determined to know him.

Mrs. Oglethorpe emerged from the hibiscus and went over to introduce herself. She offered to help get Mr. Pippin settled and went home for cleaning supplies without giving him a chance to make a polite refusal. When she returned, she set about scouring the stove, which was crusted with burnt-on pizza sauce, and then she cleaned the tiny icebox, which reeked of sardines, beer, and papaya, all in various stages of decay. While she worked she filled Mr. Pippin in on the biographies and characterologies of the residents of the trailer park, with some editorial comments on who was worth cultivating and who was not.

Mr. Pippin did not seem to resent the intrusion but twittered to and fro, fussing with his parakeets and accomplishing very little. Mrs. Oglethorpe, for one thing, being slightly plump, completely blocked the passage between the rear of the trailer and the door, and Mr. Pippin did not want to try to squeeze past, for fear of being misunderstood. He was confined, therefore, to putting things away in his sleeping area.

In the course of her cleaning, Mrs. Oglethorpe inquired where Mr. Pippin intended to keep his parakeets. "I'll let them have the run of the trailer as soon as they are used to being here," he replied. "The screened porch area is almost like being outdoors. That's the reason I rented this particular trailer; I want my birds to be comfortable and happy. They should like it here, don't you think?"

Mrs. Oglethorpe agreed.

It was the beginning of a cordial, pleasant relationship. Mrs. Oglethorpe went every day to cook and clean, although Mr. Pippin had never asked her to. On the other hand, he never objected when she did. Once in a while he felt that perhaps he might enjoy puttering for himself, but then he couldn't quite bring himself to reject Mrs. Oglethorpe's kindness. It seemed an ungrateful thing to do. If occasionally he protested mildly at some extravagant generosity, Mrs. Oglethorpe looked so injured that he quickly retracted his protest. He had a vague feeling that to reject her kindness was to risk losing her friendship, and he was, after all, a lonely man.

Mrs. Oglethorpe, on the other hand, ecstatically welcomed the opportunity to look after someone. She had survived three husbands, each of them sickly, and she had dedicatedly nursed each one of them right up till his dying moment. It had been a long time now since she had had someone to take care of.

And so the terms were set. When Mrs. Oglethorpe was in the trailer, Mr. Pippin sat perched on the edge of his chair in the porch and watched her with beady bright eyes.

The parakeets soon had their run of the trailer and they seemed to enjoy the porch, as Mr. Pippin had predicted. On the eighth day, however, there was an unfortunate accident. Mrs. Oglethorpe was taking a cup of sassafras tea to Mr. Pippin in the porch, when one of the parakeets tried to dart through the screen door that separated the trailer from the porch. The door, alas, had a strong spring that snapped the door quickly back into place, and the parakeet was not fast enough.

Mrs. Oglethorpe was most upset, of course, but Mr. Pippin was philosophical. "He took a gamble and he lost, my dear. He shouldn't have been so daring. Freddie was always given to sudden decisions and impulsive actions. You must not blame yourself."

Mrs. Oglethorpe, who was one of those wonderful people who are always able to take charge in a tragedy, regained her composure, and they had a little burial ceremony by the birdbath that very afternoon. It was marred somewhat, however, by the fact that Mr. Pippin collapsed right in the middle of Mrs. Oglethorpe's eulogy. Mrs. Oglethorpe, who was also very good at emergencies, managed to drag him to his bed and called the doctor.

Mr. Pippin seemed unable to speak or move, but the doctor from County Welfare could find nothing wrong with him. He asked Mrs. Oglethorpe if she knew of any extreme stress situation in Mr. Pippin's life that could cause great feelings of anxiety and helplessness. Mrs. Oglethorpe replied, "Why, no, Mr. Pippin hasn't a care in the world. I spend every day with him, and he seems as free as a bird."

The doctor said that unless Mr. Pippin could arrange home nursing care for himself, he would have to be moved to the county hospital. Mrs. Oglethorpe, who had not left her friend's side since the collapse except to call the doctor, of course declared that she herself would care for him.

Seeing a look of distress in her mute friend's eyes, she assured him, "It's no trouble, Mr. Pippin. I'll move a cot into the porch so I can hear you in the night. I'm lonely, you know, and it will give me something to do."

Mr. Pippin's little beaklike nose quivered with emotion. Mrs. Oglethorpe was happy to have saved her friend from the county hospital, for he certainly couldn't afford home nursing on his pension. That very night she began to sleep—fully clothed, of course—on the porch, and although she spilled over both sides of the cot, she did not complain. The next morning she fashioned a perch for the birds over Mr. Pippin's bed and conscientiously cleaned the bird droppings from the coverlet as fast as they fell.

Mrs. Oglethorpe lavished attention on her charge, and he lacked nothing in care or entertainment. In a few days he had recovered enough to speak, although weakly, and he suggested that people might be gossiping about her living in the trailer with him, even though he was partially paralyzed, and that to satisfy propriety perhaps she should go home at night.

But Mrs. Oglethorpe declared that if anybody cared to peek, they could see her sleeping fully clothed on the porch at night, and that furthermore she wouldn't think of leaving him alone in his condition, even if she were to lose her reputation. So the subject was closed.

In the course of her daily cleaning, Mrs. Oglethorpe noticed that spiders had taken up residence in all the nooks and corners of the porch, and, horrified by the idea of their crawling over her at night, she sprayed the porch generously with her Flit gun. Within an hour five parakeets lay dead on the grass rug. Mrs. Oglethorpe, hysterical with grief, slammed the screen door on a sixth as she ran in to tell the horrible news to Mr. Pippin, and slammed the door again on a seventh when she returned to the porch to gather up the bodies.

Mr. Pippin had a new seizure immediately and completely lost what little mobility and speech he had regained.

There was now only one parakeet left, and this one showed a distinct reluctance to return to the porch. Mrs. Oglethorpe was distraught with grief about what happened, of course, but she realized that her first concern was for Mr. Pippin and that no matter how bad she felt, she must keep up a cheerful countenance for his sake.

It seemed to Mr. Pippin that she was decidedly *too* cheerful, and he began to repeat in his head, "Go home, Winifred, go home," until it became a chant that he hoped would magic her away. But Winifred stuck to her duties, and Mr. Pippin resigned himself. "I'm ungrateful," he thought. "After all, she is devoting her life to me."

That evening Mrs. Oglethorpe was boiling a pot of soup on the stove when she noticed a fly buzzing around the sink. A fastidious woman, Mrs. Oglethorpe gave chase with a flyswatter, but the fly was agile and quick-witted, and Mrs. Oglethorpe's attempts to flatten him grew more and more energetic. Finally the fly lit on the kitchen table, and at the exact moment that Mrs. Oglethorpe let go with a stupendous swat, the one remaining parakeet flew in her path on its way to a favorite perch on top of the sugar bowl. The bird might have survived had Mrs. Oglethorpe not batted him straight into the soup.

This was too much for poor Mrs. Oglethorpe. She couldn't bring herself to tell Mr. Pippin what had happened. She was staring numbly at the soup when the idea came to her. Quickly she turned off the fire under the pot, fished the bird out with a spoon, and wrapped it in a newspaper. She put on her hat and took her purse down from a hook by the door.

"Mr. Pippin, I have an errand to do," she sang. "I'll be back in a very short while."

Mrs. Oglethorpe hummed happily to herself as she hurried to the bus stop, pausing only long enough to deposit the last parakeet in the trash barrel (a funeral for every bird seemed impractical at this point). She was possessed by inspiration for a surprise that would surely cheer up Mr. Pippin and make everything all right again.

By the time she got back from Woolworth's, her excitement was uncontainable. "Mr. Pippin, Mr. Pippin," she cried as she struggled through the door with her cumbersome load. "I have a surprise for you!"

She hurried into the trailer and laid her gift on the coverlet. Mr. Pippin stared at the nine lively parakeets in the cage, then his eyes began to move from bird to bird, as if he were counting them. He looked at Winifred's face with disbelief, then he counted the birds again. His eyes widened as he understood that the last of his pets must be gone and that Winifred was starting over. Then his eyes glassed over and he was very still.

"He is overcome," thought Winifred happily. "Mr. Pippin, how do you like your new birds?"

Mr. Pippin did not make any sign. He did not even blink his eyes. He was so still that finally Mrs. Oglethorpe knew something must be wrong. She put her hand in front of his mouth and felt no breath, then she looked for a pulse and found none. She sighed and looked sadly at her friend. "Ah me," she sighed, remembering her three dead husbands, "I suppose it was inevitable."

Then she looked at the birds twittering busily in the cage—her wasted gift. After a moment she smiled and leaned over so that her nose pressed through the bars of the cage. "Don't worry, little fellows," she chirped, "you can come and live with *me*!"

Reading for Understanding

❑ MAIN IDEAS

1. The main point of the story can be expressed best in which of the following titles? (a) Birds of a Feather (b) The Problems of Aging (c) Killed by Kindness (d) When Evil Triumphs

❑ DETAILS

2. Immediately upon retirement, Winifred headed for (a) Hawaii (b) Miami (c) California (d) Phoenix.

3. Winifred showed an especial liking for the color (a) red (b) green (c) yellow (d) lavender.

4. Winifred's cleaning visits were (a) daily (b) weekly (c) monthly (d) irregular.

5. The last of the parakeets died (a) in a watery grave (b) by being caught in a door (c) from poison (d) at the claws of a neighbor's cat.

❑ INFERENCES

6. The "idyllic retirement" referred to on page 143 is (a) a nursing home (b) a return to the old homestead (c) full coverage by Social Security (d) death.

7. Winifred was hiding in a clump of hibiscus, so that she could (a) wait for Mr. Pippin's arrival (b) kill catbirds (c) see how her trailer looked from a distance (d) trick the owner of the trailer park.

8. Winifred successfully played upon Mr. Pippin's (a) loneliness (b) love of good cooking (c) stubbornness (d) hatred of snakes.

9. The sentence that best expresses Mr. Pippin's shock and subsequent death was the following: (a) "I have a surprise for you." (b) Mr. Pippin seemed unable to speak or move. (c) Winifred was starting over. (d) Mr. Pippin's little beaklike nose quivered with emotion.

❑ AUTHOR'S ATTITUDE

10. The author's attitude toward Winifred is one of amused respect tinged with (a) a mild dislike (b) a deep affection (c) a deep-seated horror (d) unsatisfied curiosity.

❑ IRONY

11. The last sentence in the story suggests that (a) the parakeets are facing disaster (b) Winifred will get more birds to keep these company (c) she'll weep inconsolably for days over Mr. Pippin (d) the trailer-park owner will object.

❑ ORDER OF EVENTS

12. Arrange the items in the order in which they occurred. Use letters only.

   A. Mr. Pippin has no pulse.
   B. Winifred meets Mr. Pippin.
   C. Winifred buys a ticket at Union Station.
   D. The first parakeet meets his untimely end.
   E. Winifred takes over Mr. Pippin's home-nursing care.

❑ OUTCOMES

13. After the end of the story, Winifred will probably (a) move back North (b) look for another person to take care of (c) cruelly kill the new parakeets (d) visit Mr. Pippin's grave every week.

❑ CAUSE AND EFFECT

14. Mr. Pippin's suggestions to Winifred that she leave (a) persuaded her that he was right (b) did not affect her determination to stay (c) were overheard by a sympathetic neighbor (d) were seconded by the doctor.

❑ FACT OR OPINION

Tell whether the following is a fact or an opinion.

15. Winifred was an unselfish, greathearted person.

Words in Context

1. "Her next stop was Millie's Madcap Fashions for Mature Ladies, where she bought an orange and *magenta* flowered *muumuu*." ***Magenta*** . . . ***muumuu*** . . . (143) mean (a) yellow . . . handbag . . . (b) pale green . . . pair of sneakers . . . (c) purplish red . . . loose-fitting long dress . . . (d) skin-tone . . . leotard . . .
2. "The Hibiscus Heaven had just the thing, a lovely little trailer only recently *vacated by a lady gone on to a more idyllic retirement*, as the manager put it." The former owner (143) had (a) moved away (b) remarried (c) passed away (d) sold the trailer to the manager.
3. "There had been no heirs, and the manager . . . was willing to pass her little *windfall* along to Mrs. Oglethorpe for practically nothing." ***Windfall*** (143) means (a) unexpected gain (b) share in the estate (c) secret (d) investment.
4. ". . . the little birds . . . grew fat on the tidbits the *benevolent* lady put out for them." ***Benevolent*** (143) means (a) thoughtless (b) active (c) warmhearted (d) newly arrived.
5. "But lack of *resourcefulness* had never been one of Winifred Oglethorpe's failings . . ." ***Resourcefulness*** (144) means (a) ingenuity (b) bravado (c) skullduggery (d) brawn.
6. "From her *vantage point* in the hibiscus, Mrs. Oglethorpe *discreetly* took inventory of Mr. Pippin's belongings . . ." ***Vantage point*** . . . ***discreetly*** . . . (144) means (a) hiding place . . . quickly (b) favor-

able spot . . . incautiously (c) command post . . . cautiously (d) overview . . . thoughtfully

7. "She noted that he had a good many books and *surmised* that he was a man of culture." ***Surmised*** (144) means (a) conjectured (b) dreamed (c) saw (d) declared.

8. "While she worked she filled Mr. Pippin in on *the biographies and characterologies of the residents* . . ." She told him (144) (a) all the gossip (b) whom to avoid (c) whom he would like (d) the-who-and-what of the other owners and renters.

9. "Mrs. Oglethorpe . . . always able to take charge in a tragedy, regained her *composure* . . ." ***Composure*** (145) means (a) self-control (b) confidence (c) insight (d) dignity.

10. "It was marred somewhat, however, by the fact that Mr. Pippin collapsed right in the middle of Mrs. Oglethorpe's *eulogy*." ***Eulogy*** (145) means (a) ceremony (b) plans (c) speech (d) living room.

11. ". . . he suggested that . . . to satisfy *propriety* perhaps she should go home at night." ***Propriety*** (146) means (a) rules and regulations (b) owner's rights (c) respectability (d) his wishes.

12. "Mrs. Oglethorpe was *distraught with* grief about what happened, of course . . ." ***Distraught with*** (146) means (a) willing to forgive and forget (b) beside herself (c) willing to accept the full blame (d) unable to understand what had happened.

13. "A *fastidious* woman, Mrs. Oglethorpe gave chase with a flyswatter, but the fly was *agile* and quick-witted . . ." ***Fastidious . . . agile*** . . . (146) mean (a) sensitive . . . noisy (b) determined . . . uninjured (c) fussy . . . nimble (d) hysterical . . . experienced

14. "Finally the fly lit on the kitchen table, and at the exact moment that Mrs. Oglethorpe let go with a *stupendous swat* . . ." ***Stupendous swat*** (146) means (a) loud shriek (b) clever maneuver (c) anguished groan (d) incredible blow.

15. "By the time she got back from Woolworth's, her excitement was *uncontainable*." ***Uncontainable*** (147) means (a) dissipated (b) very obvious (c) mounting (d) beyond control.

Thinking Critically About the Story

1. Are there really people of apparently good intentions who somehow manage, often unknowingly, to run roughshod over the feelings of other people? Have you met any? How do you regard Winifred Oglethorpe?

2. Why does Mrs. Oglethorpe move to the trailer park? How does she keep herself busy at first? What do other retirees do to while away the hours? What is ironic about her killing catbirds? What options are open to her? What would you have done?
3. Why does Mrs. Oglethorpe take possession of Mr. Pippin? What makes him so vulnerable? Could he have saved himself? Is the ending inevitable? Explain.
4. Mr. Pippin needs friendship and then help. Mrs. Oglethorpe is capable and willing. What goes wrong? What is the symbolism behind the parakeets and their fate? What is the author laughing at? Explain.
5. What kind of humor is found in this story? Where does the humor end and a more serious reaction—pathos or pity—set in? At what point does the reader cease empathizing with Mrs. Oglethorpe? Would you call this a humorous story? Explain.

Stories in Words

Aviarian (142) contains a familiar root: *avis,* the Latin root for *bird.* An *aviary* is an enclosure for *birds. Aviculture* is the care and raising of *birds.* An *aviator* (or feminine *aviatrix*) is a person who flies "like a *bird.*" *Avionics* is a blend of *aviation* and *electronics,* referring to the development and production of electrical devices used in aviation. *Avionics* is an example of a common language event in English: the blending of two words to make one. *Smog* is a blend of *smoke* and *fog. Brunch* is a blend of *breakfast* and *lunch. Motel* is a blend of *motor* and *hotel.*

Benevolent (143) contains two common Latin roots: *bene* meaning "good," "well" and *vol* meaning "wish." A *benevolent* person is someone who wishes someone well and then does something about it. *Bene* appears in words like *benefit, benediction, benign, benefactor,* and *beneficial. Vol* appears in *malevolent,* in which the "good" root is changed for the "evil" root (*mal*). It also appears in *volunteer, voluntary,* and *volition.*

Philosophical (145) contains two Greek roots: *phil,* meaning "love" and *soph,* meaning "wisdom." A *philosopher "loves wisdom." Phil* appears in *Philadelphia,* the City of Brotherly *Love; philanthropic,* a *lover* of mankind; *Philip,* a *lover* of horses; and *philately,* a *lover* of stamps. *Soph* appears in *sophomore,* a *wise* fool; *sophist,* a kind of teacher; *Sophie,* a *wise* child, and *sophisticated,* worldly-*wise.*

Marjorie Daw

THOMAS BAILEY ALDRICH

> Sometimes in the morning, and oftener in the afternoon, when the sun has withdrawn from that part of the mansion, a young woman appears on the piazza with some mysterious Penelope web of embroidery in her hand, or a book. There is a hammock over there—of pineapple fiber it looks from here. A hammock is very becoming when one is eighteen, and has golden hair, and dark eyes.

And so begins a description that encourages a lovesick romance with a strange girl whom the correspondent has never met. Little by little, the would-be lover becomes entangled in a web of intrigue. Though the story starts off quite leisurely, the tempo increases as the fateful meeting between the incurable romantic and the elusive object of his affections approaches.

In the 18th century, novels were often told in the form of letters, but the practice lost favor. An occasional thriller like Bram Stoker's *Dracula* (1897) uses the letter form, but the difficulty of writing a good yarn in letters discourages imitators. "Marjorie Daw" is a classic—not only because of its unusual form but because of the sympathetic story it tells. Most readers will feel for John Flemming as he resolves, no matter what the difficulties may be, to meet and ultimately win the girl of his dreams: Marjorie Daw.

There is much humor in this story, but it is the quiet humor that comes to grips with human failings and gently illuminates them. There is nothing uproarious in the love affair between John and Marjorie Daw, but there are a great many touches of gentle humor, as he falls madly in love with . . . but that remains to be seen.

Marjorie Daw

I.—DR. DILLON TO EDWARD DELANEY, ESQ., AT THE PINES, NEAR RYE, N.H.

August 8

My dear Sir: I am happy to assure you that your anxiety is without reason. Flemming will be confined to the sofa for three or four weeks, and will have to be careful at first how he uses his leg. A fracture of this kind is always a tedious affair. Fortunately, the bone was very skillfully set by the surgeon who chanced to be in the drugstore where Flemming was brought after his fall, and I apprehend no permanent inconvenience from the accident. *Flemming is doing perfectly well physically*; but I must confess that the irritable and morbid state of mind into which he has fallen causes me a great deal of uneasiness. He is the last man in the world who ought to break his leg. You know how impetuous our friend is ordinarily, what a soul of restlessness and energy, never content unless he is rushing at some object, like a sportive bull at a red shawl; but amiable withal. He is no longer amiable. His temper has become something frightful. Miss Fanny Flemming came up from Newport, where the family are staying for the summer, to nurse him; but he packed her off the next morning in tears. He has a complete set of Balzac's works, twenty-seven volumes, piled up near his sofa, to throw at Watkins whenever that exemplary serving-man appears with his meals. Yesterday I very innocently brought Flemming a small basket of lemons. You know it was a strip of lemon-peel on the curbstone that caused our friend's mischance. Well, he no sooner set his eyes upon these lemons than he fell into such a rage as I cannot adequately describe. This is only one of his moods, and the least distressing. At other times he sits with bowed head regarding his splintered limb, silent, sullen, despairing. When this fit is on him—and it sometimes lasts all day—nothing can distract his melancholy. He refuses to eat, does not even read the newspapers; books, except as projectiles for Watkins, have no charms for him. His state is truly pitiable.

Now, if he were a poor man, with a family depending on his daily labor, this irritability and despondency would be natural enough. But in a young fellow of twenty-four, with plenty of money and seemingly not a care in the world, the thing is monstrous. If he continues to give way to his vagaries in this manner, he will end by bringing on an inflammation of the fibula. It was the fibula he broke. I am at my wits' end to know what to prescribe for him. I have anesthetics and lotions, to make people sleep and to soothe pain; but I've no medicine that will make a man have a little common sense. That is beyond my skill, but maybe it is not beyond yours. You are Flemming's intimate friend. Write to him, write to him frequently, distract his mind, cheer him up, and prevent him from becoming a confirmed case of melancholia. Perhaps he has some important plans disarranged by his present confinement. If he has, you will know, and will know how to advise him judiciously. I trust your father finds the change beneficial? I am, my dear sir, with great respect, etc.

II.—EDWARD DELANEY TO JOHN FLEMMING, WEST 38TH STREET, NEW YORK

August 9

My dear Jack: I had a line from Dillon this morning, and was rejoiced to learn that your hurt is not so bad as reported. Like a certain personage, you are not so black and blue as you are painted. Dillon will put you on your pins again in two or three weeks, if you will only have patience and follow his counsels. Did you get my note of last Wednesday? I was greatly troubled when I heard of the accident.

I can imagine how tranquil and saintly you are with your leg in a trough! It is deuced awkward, to be sure, just as we had promised ourselves a glorious month together at the seaside; but we must make the best of it. It is unfortunate, too, that my father's health renders it impossible for me to leave him. I think he has much improved; the sea air is his native element; but he still needs my arm to lean upon in his walks, and requires someone more careful than a servant to look after him. I cannot come to you, dear Jack, but I have hours of unemployed time on hand, and I will write you a whole post office full of letters if that will divert you. Heaven knows, I haven't anything to write about. It isn't as if we were living at one of the beach houses; then I could do you some character studies, and fill your imagination with groups of sea goddesses, with their (or somebody else's) raven and blond manes hanging down their shoulders. You should have Aphrodite in morning wrapper, in evening costume, and in her prettiest bathing suit. But we are far from all that here. We have rooms in a farmhouse, on a crossroad, two miles from the hotels, and lead the quietest of lives.

I wish I were a novelist. This old house, with its sanded floors and high wainscots, and its narrow windows looking out upon a cluster of pines that turn themselves into Aeolian harps every time the wind blows would be the place in which to write a summer romance. It should be a story with the odors of the forest and the breath of the sea in it. It should be a novel like one of that Russian fellow's—what's his name?—Tourguénieff, Turguenef, Turgenif, Toorguniff—nobody knows how to spell him. Yet I wonder if even a Liza or an Alexandra Paulovna could stir the heart of a man who is in constant pain. I wonder if one of our own Yankee girls of the best type, haughty and spirited, would be of any comfort to you in your present deplorable condition. If I thought so, I would hasten down to the Surf House and catch one for you; or, better still, I would find you one over the way.

Picture to yourself a large white house just across the road, nearly opposite our cottage. It is not a house, but a mansion, built, perhaps, in the colonial period, with rambling extensions, and gambrel roof, and a wide piazza on three sides—a self-possessed, high-bred piece of architecture, with its nose in the air. It stands back from the road, and has an obsequious retinue of fringed elms and oaks and weeping willows. Sometimes in the morning, and oftener in the afternoon, when the sun has withdrawn from that part of the mansion, a young woman appears on the piazza with some mysterious Penelope web of embroidery in her hand, or a book. There is a hammock over there—of pineapple fiber, it looks from here. A hammock is very becoming when one is eighteen, and has golden hair, and dark eyes, and an emerald-colored illusion dress looped up after the fashion of a Dresden china shepherdess. All this splendor goes into that hammock, and sways there like a pond-lily in the golden afternoon. The window of my bedroom looks down on that piazza—and so do I.

But enough of this nonsense, which ill becomes a sedate young attorney taking his vacation with an invalid father. Drop me a line, dear Jack, and tell me how you really are. State your case. Write me a long, quiet letter. If you are violent or abusive, I'll take the law to you.

III.—JOHN FLEMMING TO EDWARD DELANEY

August 11

Your letter, dear Ned, was a godsend. Fancy what a fix I am in—I who never had a day's sickness since I was born. My left leg weighs three tons. It is embalmed in spices and smothered in layers of fine linen, like a mummy. I can't move. I haven't moved for five thousand years. I'm of the time of Pharaoh.

I lie from morning till night on a lounge, staring into the hot street. Everybody is out of town enjoying himself. The brownstone-front houses across the street resemble a row of particularly ugly coffins set up on end. A green mold is settling on the names of the deceased, carved on the silver doorplates. Sardonic spiders have sewed up the keyholes. All is silence and dust and desolation. I interrupt this a moment, to take a shy at Watkins with the second volume of *César Birotteau*. Missed him! I think I could bring him down with a copy of Sainte-Beuve or the *Dictionnaire Universel*, if I had it. These small Balzac books somehow don't quite fit my hand; but I shall fetch him yet. I've an idea Watkins is tapping the old gentleman's rare French wine. Duplicate key of the wine cellar. Happy soirees in the front basement. Young royal Egyptian prince upstairs, snug in his cerements. Watkins glides into my chamber, with that colorless, hypocritical face of his drawn out long like an accordion; but I know he grins all the way downstairs, and is glad I have broken my leg. Was not my evil star in the very zenith when I ran up to town to attend that dinner at Delmonico's? I didn't come up altogether for that. It was partly to buy Frank Livingstone's roan mare, Margot. And now I shall not be able to sit in the saddle these two months. I'll send the mare down to you at The Pines—is that the name of the place?

Old Dillon fancies that I have something on my mind. He drives me wild with lemons. Lemons for a mind diseased! Nonsense. I am only as restless as the devil under this confinement—a thing I'm not used to. Take a man who has never had so much as a headache or a toothache in his life, strap one of his legs in a section of waterspout, keep him in a room in the city for weeks, with the hot weather turned on, and then expect him to smile and purr and be happy! It is preposterous. I can't be cheerful or calm.

Your letter is the first consoling thing I have had since my disaster, ten days ago. It really cheered me up for half an hour. Send me a screed, Ned, as often as you can, if you love me. Anything will do. Write me more about that little girl in the hammock. That was very pretty, all that about the Dresden china shepherdess and the pond-lily; the imagery a little mixed, perhaps, but very pretty. I didn't suppose you had so much sentimental furniture in your upper story. It shows how one may be familiar for years with the reception room of his neighbor, and never suspect what is directly under his mansard. I supposed your loft stuffed with dry legal parchments, mortgages and affidavits; you take down a package of manuscript, and lo! there are lyrics and sonnets and canzonettas. You really have a graphic descriptive touch, Edward Delaney, and I suspect you of anonymous love-tales in the magazines.

I shall be a bear until I hear from you again. Tell me all about your pretty *inconnue* across the road. What is her name? Who is she? Who's her father? Where's her mother? Who's her lover? You cannot imagine how this will occupy me. The more trifling, the better. My imprisonment has weakened me intellectually to such a degree that I find your epistolary gifts quite considerable. I am passing into my second childhood. In a week or two I shall take to India-rubber rings and prongs of coral. A silver cup, with an appropriate inscription, would be a delicate attention on your part. In the meantime, write!

IV.—EDWARD DELANEY TO JOHN FLEMMING

August 12

The sick pasha shall be amused. He wills it so. If the storyteller becomes prolix and tedious—the bow-string and the sack, and two Nubians to drop him into the river! But, truly, Jack, I have a hard task. There is literally nothing here—except the little girl over the way. She is swinging in the hammock at this moment. It is to me compensation for many of the ills of life to see her now and then put out a small kid boot, which fits like a glove, and set herself going. Who is she, and what is her name? Her name is Daw. Only daughter of Mr. Richard W. Daw, ex-colonel and banker. Mother dead. One brother at Harvard, elder brother killed at the battle of Fair Oaks, nine years ago. Old, rich family, the Daws. This is the homestead, where father and daughter pass eight months of the twelve; the rest of the year in Baltimore and Washington. The New England winter too many for the old gentleman. The daughter is called Marjorie—Marjorie Daw. Sounds odd at first, doesn't it? But after you say it over to yourself half a dozen times, you like it. There's a pleasing quaintness to it, something prim and violet-like. Must be a nice sort of girl to be called Marjorie Daw.

I had mine host of The Pines in the witness-box last night, and drew the foregoing testimony from him. He has charge of Mr. Daw's vegetable-garden, and has known the family these thirty years. Of course I shall make the acquaintance of my neighbors before many days. It will be next to impossible for me not to meet Mr. Daw or Miss Daw in some of my walks. The young lady has a favorite path to the sea-beach. I shall intercept her some morning, and touch my hat to her. Then the princess will bend her fair head to me with courteous surprise not unmixed with haughtiness. Will snub me, in fact. All this for thy sake, O Pasha of the Snapt Axle-tree! . . . How oddly things fall out! Ten minutes ago I was called down to the parlor—you know the kind of parlors in farmhouses on the coast, a sort of amphibious parlor with seashells on the mantelpiece and spruce branches in the chimney place—where I found my father and Mr. Daw doing the antique polite to each other. He had come to pay his respects to his new neighbors. Mr. Daw is a tall, slim gentleman of about fifty-five, with a florid face and snow-white mustache and side-whiskers. Looks like Mr. Stuffed Shirt or as Mr. Stuffed Shirt would have looked if he had served a few years in the British Army. Mr. Daw was a colonel in the late war, commanding the regiment in which his son was a lieutenant. Plucky old boy, backbone of New Hampshire granite. Before taking his leave, the colonel delivered himself of an invitation as if he were issuing a general order. Miss Daw has a few friends coming, at 4 P.M., to play croquet on the lawn (parade ground) and have tea (cold rations) on the piazza. Will we honor them with our company? (or be sent to the guardhouse). My father declines on the plea of ill health. My father's son bows with as much suavity as he knows, and accepts.

In my next I shall have something to tell you. I shall have seen the little beauty face to face. I have a presentiment, Jack, that this Daw is a most unusual person! Keep up your spirits, my boy, until I write you another letter—and send me along word how's your leg.

V.—EDWARD DELANEY TO JOHN FLEMMING

August 13

The party, my dear Jack, was as dreary as possible. A lieutenant of the navy, the rector of the Episcopal church at Stillwater, and a society swell from Cape Cod. The lieutenant looked as if he had swallowed a couple of his buttons, and found the bullion rather indigestible; the rector was a pensive youth, of the daffydowndilly sort; and the swell from Cape Cod was a very weak tidal wave indeed. The women were much better, as they always are; the two Miss Kingsburys of Philadelphia, staying at the Sea-shell House, two bright and engaging girls. But Marjorie Daw!

The company broke up soon after tea, and I remained with the colonel on the piazza. It was like seeing a picture to see Miss Marjorie hovering around the old soldier, and doing a hundred gracious little things for him. She brought the cigars and lighted the tapers with her own delicate fingers, in the most enchanting fashion. As we sat there, she came and went in the summer twilight, and seemed, with her white dress and pale gold hair, like some lovely phantom that had sprung into existence out of the smoke wreaths. If she had melted into air, like a Greek goddess in a play, I should have been more sorry than surprised.

It was easy to perceive that the old colonel worshiped her, and she him. I think the relation between an elderly father and a daughter just blooming into womanhood the most beautiful possible. There is in it a subtle sentiment that cannot exist in the case of mother and daughter, or that of son and mother. But this is getting into deep water.

I sat with the Daws until half past ten, and saw the moon rise on the sea. The ocean, that had stretched motionless and black against the horizon, was changed by magic into a broken field of glittering ice, interspersed with marvelous silvery fjords. In the far distance the Isles of Shoals loomed up like a group of huge bergs drifting down on us. The Polar Regions in a June thaw! It was exceedingly fine. What did we talk about? We talked about the weather—and *you*! The weather has been disagreeable for several days past—and so have you. I glided from one topic to the other very naturally. I told my friends of your accident; how it has frustrated all our summer plans, and what our plans were. I played quite a spirited solo on the fibula. Then I described you; or, rather, I didn't. I spoke of your amiability, of your patience under this severe affliction; of your touching gratitude when Dillon brings you little presents of fruit; of your tenderness to your sister Fanny, whom you would not allow to stay in town to nurse you, and how you heroically sent her back to Newport, preferring to remain alone with Mary, the cook, and your man Watkins, to whom, by the way, you were devotedly attached. If you had been there, Jack, you wouldn't have known yourself. I should have excelled as a criminal lawyer, if I had not turned my attention to a different branch of jurisprudence.

Miss Marjorie asked all manner of leading questions concerning you. It did not occur to me then, but it struck me forcibly afterwards, that she evinced a singular interest in the conversation. When I got back to my room, I recalled how eagerly she leaned forward, with her full, snowy throat in strong moonlight, listening to what I said. Positively, I think I made her like you!

Miss Daw is a girl whom you would like immensely, I can tell you that. A beauty without affectation, a high and tender nature—if one can read the soul in the face. And the old colonel is a noble character, too.

I am glad the Daws are such pleasant people. The Pines is an isolated spot, and my resources are few. I fear I should have found life here somewhat monotonous before long, with no other society than that of my excellent sire. It is true, I might have made a target of the defenseless invalid; but I haven't a taste for artillery, *moi.*

VI.—JOHN FLEMMING TO EDWARD DELANEY

August 17

For a man who hasn't a taste for artillery, it occurs to me, my friend, you are keeping up a pretty lively fire on my inner works. But go on. Cynicism is a small brass fieldpiece that eventually bursts and kills the artilleryman.

You may abuse me as much as you like, and I'll not complain; for I don't know what I should do without your letters. They are curing me. I haven't hurled anything at Watkins since last Sunday, partly because I have grown more amiable under your teaching, and partly because Watkins captured my ammunition one night, and carried it off to the library. He is rapidly losing the habit he had acquired of dodging whenever I rub my ear, or make any slight motion with my right arm. He is still suggestive of the wine cellar, however. You may break, you may shatter Watkins, if you will, but the scent of the fruit of the vineyard will hang round him still.

Ned, that Miss Daw must be a charming person. I should certainly like her. I like her already. When you spoke in your first letter of seeing a young girl swinging in a hammock under your chamber window, I was somehow strangely drawn to her. I cannot account for it in the least. What you have subsequently written of Miss Daw has strengthened the impression. You seem to be describing a woman I have known in some previous state of existence, or dreamed of in this. Upon my word, if you were to send me her photograph, I believe I should recognize her at a glance. Her manner, that listening attitude, her traits of character, as you indicate them, the light hair and the dark eyes—they are all familiar things to me. Asked a lot of questions, did she? Curious about me? That is strange.

You would laugh in your sleeve, you wretched old cynic, if you knew how I lie awake nights thinking of The Pines and the house across the road. How cool it must be down there! I long for the salt smell in the air. I picture the colonel smoking his cheroot on the piazza. I send you and Miss Daw off on afternoon rambles along the beach. Sometimes I let you stroll with her under the elms in the moonlight, for you are great friends by this time, I take it, and see each other every day. I know your ways and your manners! Then I fall into a truculent mood, and would like to destroy somebody. Have you noticed anything in the shape of a lover hanging around the entranceway? Does that lieutenant of the horse-marines or that young Stillwater parson visit the house much? Not that I am pining for news of them, but any gossip of the kind would be in order. I wonder, Ned, you don't fall in love with Miss Daw. I am ripe to do it myself. Speaking of photographs, couldn't you manage to slip one of her snapshots from her album—she must have an album, you know—and send it to me? I will return it before it could be missed. That's a good fellow! Did the mare arrive safe and sound? It will be a capital animal this autumn for Central Park.

O—my leg? I forgot about my leg. It's better.

VII.—EDWARD DELANEY TO JOHN FLEMMING

August 20

You are correct in your surmises. I am on the most friendly terms with our neighbors. The colonel and my father smoke their afternoon cigar together in our sitting room or on the piazza opposite, and I pass an hour or two of the day or the evening with the daughter. I am more and more struck by the beauty, modesty, and intelligence of Miss Daw.

You ask me why I do not fall in love with her. I will be frank, Jack; I have thought of that. She is young, rich, accomplished, uniting in herself more attractions, mental and personal, than I can recall in any girl of my acquaintance; but she lacks the something that would be necessary to inspire in me that kind of interest. Possessing this unknown quantity, a woman neither beautiful nor wealthy nor very young could bring me to her feet. But not Miss Daw. If we were shipwrecked together on an uninhabited island—let me suggest a tropical island, for it costs no more to be picturesque—I would build her a bamboo hut, I would fetch her breadfruit and coconuts, I would fry yams for her, I would lure the ingenuous turtle and make her nourishing soups, but I wouldn't make love to her—not under eighteen months. I would like to have her for a sister, that I might shield her and counsel her, and spend half my income on threadlaces and camel's-hair shawls. (We are off the island now.) If such were not my feeling, there would still be an obstacle to my loving Miss Daw. A greater misfortune could scarcely befall me than to love her. Flemming, I am about to make a revelation that will astonish you. I may be all wrong in my premises and consequently in my conclusions; but you shall judge.

That night when I returned to my room after the croquet party at the Daws', and was thinking over the trivial events of the evening, I was suddenly impressed by the air of eager attention with which Miss Daw had followed my account of your accident. I think I mentioned this to you. Well, the next morning, as I went to mail my letter, I overtook Miss Daw on the road to Rye, where the post office is, and accompanied her thither and back, an hour's walk. The conversation again turned on you, and again I remarked that inexplicable look of interest which had lighted up her face the previous evening. Since then, I have seen Miss Daw perhaps ten times, perhaps oftener, and on each occasion I found that when I was not speaking of you, or your sister, or some person or place associated with you, I was not holding her attention. She would be absentminded, her eyes would wander away from me to the sea, or to some distant object in the landscape; her fingers would play with the leaves of a book in a way that convinced me she was not listening. At these moments if I abruptly changed the theme—I did it several times as an experiment—and dropped some remark about my friend Flemming, then the somber blue eyes would come back to me instantly.

Now, is not this the oddest thing in the world? No, not the oddest. The effect which you tell me was produced on you by my casual mention of an unknown girl swinging in a hammock is certainly as strange. You can conjecture how that passage in your letter of Friday startled me. Is it possible, then, that two people who have never met, and who are hundreds of miles apart, can exert a magnetic influence on each other? I have read of such psychological phenomena, but never credited them. I leave the solution of the problem to you. As for myself, all other things being favorable, it would be impossible for me to fall in love with a woman who listens to me only when I am talking of my friend!

I am not aware that anyone is paying marked attention to my fair neighbor. The lieutenant of the navy—he is stationed at Rivermouth—sometimes drops in of an evening, and sometimes the rector from Stillwater; the lieutenant the oftener. He was there last night. I would not be surprised if he had an eye to the heiress; but he is not formidable. Mistress Daw carries a neat little spear of irony, and the honest lieutenant seems to have a particular facility for impaling himself on the point of it. He is not dangerous, I should say; though I have known a woman to satirize a man for years, and marry him after all. Decidedly, the lowly rector is not dangerous; yet, again, who has not seen the religious victorious when competing with the worldly?

As to the photograph. There is an exquisite candid shot of Marjorie on the drawing room mantelpiece. It would be missed at once, if taken. I would do anything reasonable for you, Jack; but I've no burning desire to be hauled up before the local justice of the peace, on a charge of petty larceny.

P.S.—Enclosed is a spray of mignonette, which I advise you to treat tenderly. Yes, we talked of you again last night, as usual. It is becoming a little dreary for me.

VIII.—EDWARD DELANEY TO JOHN FLEMMING

August 22

Your letter in reply to my last has occupied my thoughts all the morning. I do not know what to think. Do you mean to say that you are seriously half in love with a woman whom you have never seen—with a shadow, a chimera? for what else can Miss Daw be to you? I do not understand it at all. I understand neither you nor her. You are a couple of ethereal beings moving in finer air than I can breathe with my commonplace lungs. Such delicacy of sentiment is something I admire without comprehending. I am bewildered. I am of the earth earthy, and I find myself in the incongruous position of having to do with mere souls, with natures so finely tempered that I run some risk of shattering them in my awkwardness.

Reflecting on your letter, I am not sure it is wise in me to continue this correspondence. But no, Jack; I do wrong to doubt the good sense that forms the basis of your character. You are deeply interested in Miss Daw; you feel that she is a person whom you may perhaps greatly admire when you know her: at the same time you bear in mind that the chances are ten to five that, when you do come to know her, she will fall far short of your ideal, and you will not care for her in the least. Look at it in this sensible light, and I will hold back nothing from you.

Yesterday afternoon my father and myself rode over to Rivermouth with the Daws. A heavy rain in the morning had cooled the atmosphere and laid the dust. To Rivermouth is a drive of eight miles, along a winding road lined all the way with wild barberry bushes. I never saw anything more brilliant than these bushes, the green of the foliage and the pink of the coral berries intensified by the rain. The colonel drove, with my father in front, Miss Daw and I on the back seat. I resolved that for the first five miles your name should not pass my lips. I was amused by the artful attempts she made, at the start, to break through my reticence. Then a silence fell upon her; and then she became suddenly spirited. That keenness which I enjoyed so much when it was exercised on the lieutenant was not so satisfactory directed against myself. Miss Daw has great sweetness of disposition, but she can be disagreeable. She is like the young lady in the rhyme, with the curl on her forehead.

"When she is good,
She is very, very good,
And when she is bad, she is horrid!"

I kept to my resolution, however; but on the return home I relented, and talked of your mare! Miss Daw is going to try a sidesaddle on Margot some morning. The animal is a trifle too light for my weight. By the by, I nearly forgot to say Miss Daw sat for a picture yesterday to a Rivermouth artist. If the negative turns out well, I am to have a copy. So our ends will be accomplished without crime. I wish, though, I could send you the candid shot in the drawing room; it is cleverly colored, and would give you an idea of her hair and eyes, which of course the other will not.

No, Jack, the spray of mignonette did not come from me. A man of twenty-eight doesn't enclose flowers in his letters—to another man. But don't attach too much significance to the circumstances. She gives sprays of mignonette to the rector, sprays to the lieutenant. She has even given a rose to your slave. It is her jocund nature to scatter flowers, like Spring.

If my letters sometimes read disjointedly, you must understand that I never finish one at a sitting, but write at intervals, when the mood is on me.

The mood is not on me now.

IX.—EDWARD DELANEY TO JOHN FLEMMING

August 23

I have just returned from the strangest interview with Marjorie. She has all but confessed to me her interest in you. But with what modesty and dignity! Her words elude my pen as I attempt to put them on paper; and, indeed, it was not so much what she said as her manner; and that I cannot reproduce. Perhaps, it was of a piece with the strangeness of this whole business, that she should tacitly acknowledge to a third party the love she feels for a man she has never beheld! But I have lost, through your aid, the faculty of being surprised. I accept things as people do in dreams. Now that I am again in my room, it all appears like an illusion—the black masses of shadow under the trees, the fireflies whirling fitfully among the shrubbery, the sea over there, Marjorie sitting on the hammock!

It is past midnight, and I am too sleepy to write more.

Thursday Morning.

My father has suddenly taken it into his head to spend a few days at the Shoals. In the meanwhile you will not hear from me. I see Marjorie walking in the garden with the colonel. I wish I could speak to her alone, but shall probably not have an opportunity before we leave.

X.—EDWARD DELANEY TO JOHN FLEMMING

August 28

You were passing into your second childhood, were you? Your intellect was so reduced that my epistolary gifts seemed quite considerable to you, did they? I rise superior to the sarcasm in your favor of the 11th instant, when I notice that five days' silence on my part is sufficient to throw you into the depths of despondency.

We returned only this morning from Appledore, that enchanted island—at four dollars per day. I find on my desk three letters from you! Evidently there is no lingering doubt in *your* mind as to the pleasure I derive from your correspondence. These letters are undated, but in what I take to be the latest are two passages that require my consideration. You will pardon my candor, dear Flemming, but the conviction forces itself upon me that as your leg grows stronger your head becomes weaker. You ask my advice on a certain point. I will give it. In my opinion you could do nothing more unwise than to address a note to Miss Daw, thanking her for the flower. It would, I am sure, offend her delicacy beyond pardon. She knows you only through me; you are to her an abstraction, a figure in a dream—a dream from which the faintest shock would awaken her. Of course, if you enclose a note to me and insist on its delivery, I shall deliver it; but I advise you not to do so.

You say you are able, with the aid of a cane, to walk about your chamber, and that you purpose to come to The Pines the instant Dillon thinks you strong enough to stand the journey. Again I advise you not to. Do you not see that, every hour you remain away, Marjorie's glamor deepens, and your influence over her increases? You will ruin everything by precipitancy. Wait until you are entirely recovered; in any case, do not come without giving me warning. I fear the effect of your abrupt advent here—under the circumstances.

Miss Daw was evidently glad to see us back again, and gave me both hands in the frankest way. She stopped at the door a moment, this afternoon, in the carriage; she had been over to Rivermouth for her pictures. Unluckily, the photographer had spilt some acid on the plate, and she was obliged to give him another sitting. I have an intuition that something is troubling Marjorie. She had an abstracted air not usual with her. However, it may be only my fancy. . . . I end this, leaving several things unsaid, to accompany my father on one of those long walks which are now his chief medicine—and mine!

XI.—EDWARD DELANEY TO JOHN FLEMMING

August 29

I write in great haste to tell you what has taken place here since my letter of last night. I am in the utmost perplexity. Only one thing is plain—*you* must not dream of coming to The Pines. Marjorie has told her father everything! I saw her for a few minutes, an hour ago, in the garden; and, as near as I could gather from her confused statement, the facts are these: Lieutenant Bradly—that's the naval officer stationed at Rivermouth—has been paying court to Miss Daw for some time past, but not so much to her liking as to that of the colonel, who it seems is an old friend of the young gentleman's father. Yesterday (I knew she was in some trouble when she drove up to our gate) the colonel spoke to Marjorie of Bradly—urged his suit, I infer. Marjorie expressed her dislike for the lieutenant with characteristic frankness, and finally confessed to her father—well, I really do not know what she confessed. It must have been the vaguest of confessions, and must have sufficiently puzzled the colonel. At any rate, it exasperated him. I suppose I am implicated in the matter, and that the colonel feels bitterly towards me. I do not see why: I have carried no messages between you and Miss Daw; I have behaved with the greatest discretion. I can find no flaw anywhere in my proceeding. I do not see that anybody has done anything—except the colonel himself.

It is probable, nevertheless, that the friendly relations between the two houses will be broken off. "A plague o' both your houses," say you. I will keep you informed, as well as I can, of what occurs over the way. We shall remain here until the second week in September. Stay where you are, or, at all events, do not dream of joining me. . . . Colonel Daw is sitting on the piazza looking rather wicked. I have not seen Marjorie since I parted with her in the garden.

XII.—EDWARD DELANEY TO THOMAS DILLON, M.D., MADISON SQUARE, NEW YORK

August 30

My dear Doctor: If you have any influence over Flemming, I beg of you to exert it to prevent his coming to this place at present. There are circumstances, which I will explain to you before long, that make it of the first importance that he should not come into this neighborhood. His appearance here, I speak advisedly, would be disastrous to him. In urging him to remain in New York, or to go to some inland resort, you will be doing him and me a real service. Of course you will not mention my name in this connection. You know me well enough, my dear doctor, to be assured that, in begging your secret cooperation, I have reasons that will meet your entire approval when they are made plain to you. We shall return to town on the 15th of the next month, and my first duty will be to present myself at your hospitable door and satisfy your curiosity, if I have excited it. My father, I am glad to state, has so greatly improved that he can no longer be regarded as an invalid. With great esteem, I am, etc., etc.

XIII.—EDWARD DELANEY TO JOHN FLEMMING

August 31

Your letter, announcing your mad determination to come here, has just reached me. I beseech you to reflect a moment. The step would be fatal to your interests and hers. You would furnish just cause for irritation to R. W. D.; and, though he loves Marjorie tenderly, he is capable of going to any lengths if opposed. You would not like, I am convinced, to be the means of causing him to treat *her* with severity. That would be the result of your presence at The Pines at this juncture. I am annoyed to be obliged to point out these things to you. We are on very delicate ground, Jack; the situation is critical, and the slightest mistake in a move would cost us the game. If you consider it worth the winning, be patient. Trust a little to my sagacity. Wait and see what happens. Moreover, I understand from Dillon that you are in no condition to take so long a journey. He thinks the air of the coast would be the worst thing possible for you; that you ought to go inland, if anywhere. Be advised by me. Be advised by Dillon.

XIV.—TELEGRAMS

September 1

1.—TO EDWARD DELANEY

Letter received. Dillon be hanged. I think I ought to be on the ground.

J. F.

2.—TO JOHN FLEMMING

Stay where you are. You would only complicate matters. Do not move until you hear from me.

E. D.

3.—TO EDWARD DELANEY

My being at The Pines could be kept secret. I must see her.

J. F.

4.—TO JOHN FLEMMING

Do not think of it. It would be useless. R. W. D. has locked M. in her room. You would not be able to effect an interview.

E. D.

5.—TO EDWARD DELANEY

Locked her in her room. Good God. That settles the question. I shall leave by the twelve-fifteen express.

J. F.

XV.—THE ARRIVAL

On the second of September, 187-, as the down express due at 3.40 left the station at Hampton, a young man, leaning on the shoulder of a servant, whom he addressed as Watkins, stepped from the platform into a hack, and requested to be driven to "The Pines." On arriving at the gate of a modest farmhouse, a few miles from the station, the young man descended with difficulty from the carriage, and, casting a hasty glance across the road, seemed much impressed by some peculiarity in the landscape. Again leaning on the shoulder of the person Watkins, he walked to the door of the farmhouse and inquired for Mr. Edward Delaney. He was informed by the aged man who answered his knock, that Mr. Edward Delaney had gone to Boston the day before, but that Mr. Jonas Delaney was within. This information did not appear satisfactory to the stranger who inquired if Mr. Edward Delaney had left any message for Mr. John Flemming. There *was* a letter for Mr. Flemming, if he were that person. After a brief absence the aged man reappeared with a letter.

XVI.—EDWARD DELANEY TO JOHN FLEMMING

September 1

I am horror-stricken at what I have done! When I began this correspondence I had no other purpose than to relieve the tedium of your sick chamber. Dillon told me to cheer you up. I tried to. I thought you entered into the spirit of the thing. I had no idea, until within a few days, that you were taking matters seriously.

What can I say? I am in sackcloth and ashes. I am a pariah, a dog of an outcast. I tried to make a little romance to interest you, something soothing and idyllic, and, by Jove! I have done it only too well! My father doesn't know a word of this, so don't jar the old gentleman any more than you can help. I fly from the wrath to come—when you arrive! For O, dear Jack, there isn't any colonial mansion on the other side of the road, there isn't any piazza, there isn't any hammock—there isn't any Marjorie Daw!!

Reading for Understanding

❑ MAIN IDEA

1. The main idea of the story is that (a) a telegram is better than a letter (b) a friend's good intentions can backfire (c) some people have short tempers (d) a broken leg can be a painful and difficult experience.

❑ DETAILS

2. The "Dresden china shepherdess" is (a) a favorite piece of china (b) a friend of Edward Delaney's (c) the sister of Watkins (d) Marjorie Daw.

3. Delaney cannot send the requested photograph because (a) acid spoiled it (b) it's too precious to steal (c) it doesn't exist (d) Colonel Daw would be furious.

4. Dillon is (a) a doctor (b) Flemming's servant (c) the Daws' gardener (d) Delaney's uncle.

5. When Flemming wrote about coming to The Pines, Delaney (a) sent confusing directions (b) resolved to stay and meet Flemming face to face (c) pleaded with Flemming not to come (d) left to visit him.

❑ INFERENCES

6. Flemming may best be described as (a) impetuous and impulsive (b) calm and meditative (c) bitter and unfriendly (d) realistic and unromantic.

7. Delaney may best be described as (a) dull and uninteresting (b) ingenious and inventive (c) cruel and deceitful (d) sullen and unfriendly.

8. Delaney caught Flemming's interest by his (a) description of the cool weather (b) deep interest in Flemming's medical progress (c) history of the area (d) offhand mention of the young woman.

9. When Delaney tries desperately to play down the "girl across the way," (a) Flemming becomes more infatuated (b) Flemming loses interest in the correspondence (c) the doctor tells Flemming to forget his strange notions (d) Mr. Daw decides to take a hand.

❑ AUTHOR'S PURPOSE

10. The author's purpose in writing the story was to (a) show the dangers of lying (b) entertain with suspense (c) retell a true incident (d) explain a serious misunderstanding.

❑ ORDER OF EVENTS

11. Arrange the items in the order in which they occurred. Use letters only.
    A. John Flemming first tells of his boredom.
    B. Edward Delaney mentions the mysterious girl across the way.
    C. Flemming arrives at the railroad station.
    D. The doctor writes to Delaney to tell of Flemming's condition.
    E. Delaney leaves town.

❑ OUTCOMES

12. Immediately on reading Delaney's last note, Flemming probably (a) thought Delaney wanted Marjorie Daw for himself (b) broke down in tears (c) scolded Delaney's father (d) exploded in rage.

❑ CAUSE AND EFFECT

13. Because of his boredom, we might conclude that Flemming (a) was a good patient (b) enjoyed reading romantic novels (c) was susceptible to Delaney's prank (d) took short trips during his convalescence.

❑ FACT OR OPINION

Tell whether each of the following is a fact or an opinion.

14. Marjorie Daw was a figment of Delaney's imagination.

15. The handsome lieutenant did not exist.

Words in Context

1. "You know how *impetuous* our friend is ordinarily." ***Impetuous*** (153) means (a) moderate (b) talkative (c) adaptable (d) rash.

2. ". . . never content unless he is rushing . . . like a sportive bull at a red shawl; but *amiable withal.*" ***Amiable withal*** (153) means (a) hostile in addition (b) agreeable nevertheless (c) talkative always (d) inquisitive in addition.

3. ". . . to throw at Watkins whenever that *exemplary* serving-man appears with his meals." ***Exemplary*** (153) means (a) admirable (b) tricky (c) trustworthy (d) highly recommended.

4. "Now, if he were a poor man . . . this *irritability and despondency* would be natural enough." ***Irritability and despondency*** (153) means (a) self-pity and anxiety (b) self-concern and lack of interest (c) grouchiness and depression (d) disorganization and anger.

5. "If he continues to give way to his *vagaries* . . . he will end by bringing on an inflammation . . ." ***Vagaries*** (154) means (a) troubles (b) needs (c) friends (d) whims.

6. "Like a certain *personage,* you are not so black and blue as you are painted." ***Personage*** (154) means (a) member of the nobility (b) elected official (c) officer (d) someone important.

7. "It . . . has an *obsequious retinue* of fringed elms and oaks . . ." ***Obsequious retinue*** (155) means (a) surrounding wall (b) obvious decorations (c) stately grove (d) constantly bowing attendants.

8. "But enough of this nonsense, which ill becomes a *sedate* young attorney taking his vacation . . ." ***Sedate*** (155) means (a) popular (b) wealthy (c) ambitious (d) serious.

9. "Young royal Egyptian prince upstairs, snug in his *cerements.*" ***Cerements*** (156) means (a) burial garment (b) plaster cast (c) miseries (d) bed.

10. "Send me a *screed,* Ned, as often as you can . . ." ***Screed*** (156) means (a) picture (b) book (c) card (d) long letter.

11. "If the storyteller becomes *prolix* and *tedious* . . ." ***Prolix . . . tedious*** (156) mean (a) dull . . . sentimental (b) repetitious . . . sarcastic (c) serious . . . careless (d) long-winded . . . boring.

12. "I have a *presentiment,* Jack, that this Daw is a most unusual person!" ***Presentiment*** (157) means (a) clue (b) theory (c) premonition (d) conviction.

13. ". . . the rector was a *pensive* youth, of the *daffydowndilly* sort . . ." ***Pensive . . . daffydowndilly*** (158) mean (a) handsome . . . argumentative (b) intellectual . . . restless (c) thoughtful . . . offbeat (d) sensitive . . . knowledgeable.

14. "I spoke of your *amiability,* of your patience under this severe affliction." ***Amiability*** (158) means (a) fortitude (b) self-pity (c) ingenuity (d) good nature.

15. "I may be all wrong in my *premises* and consequently in my conclusions; but you shall judge." ***Premises*** (160) means (a) assumptions (b) household (c) facts (d) point of view.

Thinking Critically About the Story

1. What makes John Flemming so vulnerable and so easy a prey? What does he have to learn about the fatal combination of illness, convalescence, and emotional reactions? Have you heard or read of others who reached rash decisions during such critical times?

2. Is Edward Delaney aware of the dangerous turns his plan could take? At which point could he have prevented the fatal mistake? When does the ending of the story become inevitable?

3. Is this a story that the reader laughs *with* or laughs *at*? Explain. Was the author's purpose to teach the reader, to reveal basic truths about human beings, or just to make the reader laugh? Explain.

4. In this story a friend feels compelled to create a web of white lies. Are white lies ever justifiable? Is Delaney justified in telling the white lies to his friend? What would you have done in similar circumstances? Explain.

5. What does the story gain by being written in letter form? Would it be more effective if it were told in narrative form from the point of view of only one person? The doctor? Flemming? Why are there so few stories told in this epistolary form?

Stories in Words

Melancholy (page 153) goes back to a medieval belief. It was thought that there were four vital fluids (humors) in the body: black bile, yellow bile, blood, and phlegm. Moods and even personalities were supposedly controlled by these bodily elements. If black bile predominated, the person was *melancholy*. The two parts of the word come from Greek words meaning *black bile*. These are the others.

yellow bile = choleric – short-tempered
blood = sanguine – cheerful, optimistic
phlegm = phlegmatic – slow, unexcitable, full

Chimera (page 161) in ancient Greece was a fire-eating monster, with the body of a goat, the head of a lion, and the tail of a serpent. The word has come into English in a fanciful way: "an illusion, an impossible dream, a creation of the mind." The adjective *chimerical* means "fantastic, visionary, improbable." Thus does the word for an ancient monster broaden its meaning in English, which is always receptive to new, expanded meanings.

Sardonic (page 155) suggests mockery and disdain. Though usually coupled with a word like *laughter* or *smile*, *sardonic* here suggests that spiders are mocking the age and decay of the house. The word is named for a plant growing on the island of Sardinia. Supposedly, a person eating the plant would die in agony, his face contorted into a bitter grimace, a "sardonic smile."

The Lighter Side

Getting Technical

Terms

antihero	farce	surprise ending
coincidence	static character	

Definitions Match each of the above terms with its definition.

1. Accidental concurrence of two or more events
2. Humorous tale depending on exaggerated, improbable events
3. Main character lacking heroic qualities and given the vocation of failure
4. Unexpected turn of fortune or action finishing story
5. One who does not change as the result of plot action

Examples Match each of the following actions with the appropriate term.

1. The butler in this story, despite his newfound wealth, remains the same polite, aloof, self-effacing servant.
2. The Charlie Chaplinesque character finally decides with sadness to leave the city where he has met endless defeats, regardless of his efforts.
3. When I stopped the car at a bus stop, my cousin, whom I had not seen for weeks, was standing right there.
4. The radio in the police car chasing the fleeing bandits suddenly blares the national anthem. The driver tries to stand at attention while the chief hits him over the head to have him sit down.

5. Just before the story ends with the protagonist in disgrace, his true identity is revealed; his wealth and honor are returned, and all is well.
6. The cowhand hero in the white hat appears in most Western tales.
7. Alice is walking her dog and arrives at the corner just as the two speeding cars collide head-on.
8. In the TV movie just as the butler is about to be arrested as the culprit, the widow proves that it was the detective who had committed the murder.

Application Match each of the following events with the appropriate term.

1. The revelation that Marjorie Daw never existed
2. Lord Emsworth with his monomania in "Pig Hoo-o-o-o-ey"
3. Winifred Oglethorpe with her futile attempts to make others happy in "The Aviarian"
4. The bedroom scenes that took place one night in a home in Columbus, Ohio, in "The Night the Bed Fell"
5. The cause of death of the parakeets in "The Aviarian"
6. The grandfather who was still fighting the Civil War in "The Night the Bed Fell"

Thinking Critically About the Stories

1. How does the humor in these four stories compare? Which one tickled your funny bone most? Least? Which one fits closest to your definition of "funny"?
2. Are the protagonists in these stories heroes or antiheroes? Explain.
3. Compare Lord Emsworth's approach to his problem with Lady Constance's, with Mrs. Oglethorpe's, with John Flemming's, with Mr. Pippin's, with your own. Which do you think is most effective? Explain.
4. Compare the devices each author used to create humor. Which one used most variety? Which was most ingenious? Which one is most timeless?
5. Which characters did you find admirable? Less than admirable? Most eccentric? Luckiest? Brightest? Explain.

Writing and Other Activities

1. Using "The Night the Bed Fell" as your model, describe the actions of two or three of the characters you would include in a story about one of the following: (a) Some of the relatives who come to celebrate Grandma's eightieth birthday in absentia because she has eloped to Mexico with her third husband (b) Some of the neighbors who come to the block meeting to honor the school-crossing guard who threatens to resign because she feels unappreciated (c) Some of the students you meet in the school cafeteria, the ones who never let you forget that they are squad members or cheerleaders (d) Some of the TV characters that your friends emulate.

2. Write the plot of a story about one of the following: (a) The time they just misunderstood your good intentions—from their point of view (b) The time your best friend let you down—from your best friend's point of view (c) The time the white lie really worked—from the point of view of the one who benefited (d) The time you were really lucky—from the point of view of one who was not so lucky.

3. Write the setting and inner dialog (talking with one's self) for a short-short story on one of the following: (a) The born loser who wins $5000 in the lottery (b) The class comedian who is being threatened with physical violence by the constant butt of his (her) jokes (c) One who is "out" listening to a member of the "in" group describing how much fun it is to be "in" (d) One who is discovering that she (he) does have a sense of humor and people laugh with, not at, her (him).

4. Write a letter to the local paper on one of the following: (a) A thank-you note for the publicity given in its pages to a school function (b) A request that it include as a regular item a *Letters from the Next Generation* feature open to the students of your school (c) A letter protesting its biased reporting of a sports event in which it favored the rival school (d) A letter suggesting that it include as a regular feature a calendar of coming school events and coverage of newsworthy social events in the school.

5. Write the setting and dialog for the opening of a story on one of the following: (a) Mrs. Oglethorpe tells a new male neighbor about the demise of poor Mr. Pippin and his parakeets (b) Ten years later, John Flemming and Edward Delaney meet for lunch and Marjorie Daw's name comes up (c) The school fat boy who has lost 85 pounds and gained loneliness is in the lunchroom about to break his diet (d) Briggs Beall discusses with the grandfather the major events of the night the bed fell.

Stories in Words: A Review

A. aviarian
B. benevolent
C. chimera
D. crotchet
E. dismally
F. flotsam
G. jigsaw
H. melancholy
I. philosophical
J. phobia
K. preposterous
L. sardonic

Answer the following questions by choosing a word from the list above. Use letters only.

Which of the words above . . .

1. _______ is related to the dance?
2. _______ means *the before coming after*?
3. _______ is derived from the name of a Mediterranean island?
4. _______ is often combined with the word *jetsam*?
5. _______ means *loving wisdom*?
6. _______ contains the root for *bird*?
7. _______ is the name of a fire-eating monster?
8. _______ is based on a theory about the four vital humors in the body?
9. _______ is a word applied to *well-wishers*?
10. _______ is related to a word meaning *hook*?

Many writers have touched upon the loneliness of being and the importance of love in making the loneliness less obvious and more bearable. A glance at any quotation book will show dozens of definitions of love: some ecstatic and some bitter. Love seems to have as many definitions as there are people.

The stories in this unit suggest different varieties of love. The first story is a shocker. A loving family of three are relaxing in the park. All is well. "How good this is," thinks the wife. Then, like a boulder falling into a placid stream, an unexpected incident causes an explosion that suggests the complexities of love.

The second story tells of a close relationship between two sisters-in-law

4

The Many Faces of Love

Love consists in this: that two solitudes protect and touch and greet each other.

Rainer Maria Rilke

and the weekend events that put this relationship to a critical test. The love between the two women is altered, even though nothing spectacular occurs. The third story tells of a pathetic quest for someone to love. The ending suggests that love may come under unexpected circumstances. The heroine of the fourth story is a model of loving—forgiving, undemanding, all-embracing. Yet there is a suggestion that this kind of love is not the ideal.

The stories in this unit explore many aspects of loving and demonstrate that love is both "a many-splendored thing" and an area of surprises and tangled motivations.

Sunday in the Park

BEL KAUFMAN

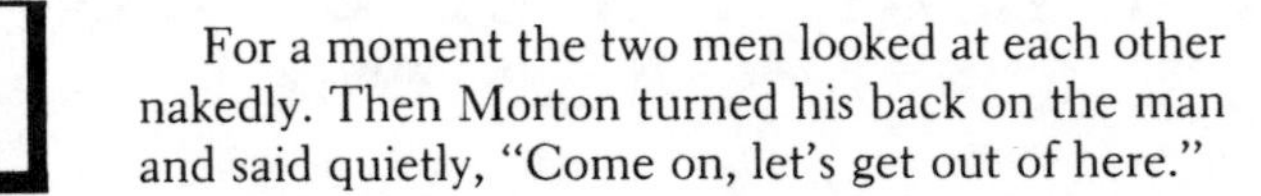

For a moment the two men looked at each other nakedly. Then Morton turned his back on the man and said quietly, "Come on, let's get out of here."

Human relationships tend to be far more complicated than they seem on the surface. Sometimes an incident will awaken the monsters in the deep, bringing to the surface thoughts and emotions repressed by, or unknown to, the persons involved. At such moments, what we say may surprise us. Sometimes those feelings may be best undisturbed. At other times, the naked emotions clear the air and improve relationships. There are no easy answers.

"Sunday in the Park" is a masterpiece in miniature. A frightening incident in the park brings on a confrontation fraught with danger for a mild-mannered college professor. But terrifying as the incident is, it passes without serious overt damage. But the incident triggers an emotional outburst that takes the parents by surprise. Did the incident help or harm the marriage? What do you think?

Sunday in the Park

It was still warm in the late-afternoon sun, and the city noises came muffled through the trees in the park. She put her book down on the bench, removed her sunglasses, and sighed contentedly. Morton was reading the *Times Magazine* section, one arm flung around her shoulder; their three-year-old son, Larry, was playing in the sandbox; a faint breeze fanned her hair softly against her cheek. It was five-thirty of a Sunday afternoon, and the small playground, tucked away in a corner of the park, was all but deserted. The swings and seesaws stood motionless and abandoned, the slides were empty, and only in the sandbox two little boys squatted diligently side by side. *How good this is,* she thought, and almost smiled at her sense of well-being. They must go out in the sun more often; Morton was so city-pale, cooped up all week inside the gray factorylike university. She squeezed his arm affectionately and glanced at Larry, delighting in the pointed little face frowning in concentration over the tunnel he was digging. The other boy suddenly stood up and with a quick, deliberate swing of his chubby arm threw a spadeful of sand at Larry. It just missed his head. Larry continued digging; the boy remained standing, shovel raised, stolid and impassive.

"No, no, little boy." She shook her finger at him, her eyes searching for the child's mother or nurse. "We mustn't throw sand. It may get in someone's eyes and hurt. We must play nicely in the nice sandbox." The boy looked at her in unblinking expectancy. He was about Larry's age but perhaps ten pounds heavier, a husky little boy with none of Larry's quickness and sensitivity in his face. Where was his mother? The only other people left in the playground were two women and a little girl on roller skates leaving now through the gate, and a man on a bench a few feet away. He was a big man, and he seemed to be taking up the whole bench as he held the Sunday comics close to his face. She supposed he was the child's father. He did not look up from his comics, but spat once deftly out of the corner of his mouth. She turned her eyes away.

At that moment, as swiftly as before, the fat little boy threw another spadeful of sand at Larry. This time some of it landed on his hair and forehead. Larry looked up at his mother, his mouth tentative; her expression would tell him whether to cry or not.

Her first instinct was to rush to her son, brush the sand out of his hair, and punish the other child, but she controlled it. She always said that she wanted Larry to learn to fight his own battles.

"Don't *do* that, little boy," she said sharply, leaning forward on the bench. "You mustn't throw sand!"

The man on the bench moved his mouth as if to spit again, but instead he spoke. He did not look at her, but at the boy only.

"You go right ahead, Joe," he said loudly. "Throw all you want. This here is a *public* sandbox."

She felt a sudden weakness in her knees as she glanced at Morton. He had become aware of what was happening. He put his *Times* down carefully on his lap and turned his fine, lean face toward the man, smiling the shy, apologetic smile he might have offered a student in pointing out an error in his thinking. When he spoke to the man, it was with his usual reasonableness.

"You're quite right," he said pleasantly, "but just because this is a public place . . ."

The man lowered his funnies and looked at Morton. He looked at him from head to foot, slowly and deliberately. "Yeah?" His insolent voice was edged with menace. "My kid's got just as good right here as yours, and if he feels like throwing sand, he'll throw it, and if you don't like it, you can take your kid the hell out of here."

The children were listening, their eyes and mouths wide open, their spades forgotten in small fists. She noticed the muscle in Morton's jaw tighten. He was rarely angry; he seldom lost his temper. She was suffused with a tenderness for her husband and an impotent rage against the man for involving him in a situation so alien and so distasteful to him.

"Now, just a minute," Morton said courteously, "you must realize . . ."

"Aw, shut up," said the man.

Her heart began to pound. Morton half rose; the *Times* slid to the ground. Slowly the other man stood up. He took a couple of steps toward Morton, then stopped. He flexed his great arms, waiting. She pressed her trembling knees together. Would there be violence, fighting? How dreadful, how incredible . . . She must do something, stop them, call for help. She wanted to put her hand on her husband's sleeve, to pull him down, but for some reason she didn't.

Morton adjusted his glasses. He was very pale. "This is ridiculous," he said unevenly. "I must ask you . . ."

"Oh, yeah?" said the man. He stood with his legs spread apart, rocking a little, looking at Morton with utter scorn. "You and who else?"

For a moment the two men looked at each other nakedly. Then Morton turned his back on the man and said quietly, "Come on, let's get out of here." He walked awkwardly, almost limping with self-consciousness, to the sandbox. He stooped and lifted Larry and his shovel out.

At once Larry came to life; his face lost its rapt expression and he began to kick and cry. "I don't *want* to go home, I want to play better, I don't *want* any supper, I don't *like* supper. . . ." It became a chant as they walked, pulling their child between them, his feet dragging on the ground. In order to get to the exit gate they had to pass the bench where the man sat sprawling again. She was careful not to look at him. With all the dignity she could summon, she pulled Larry's sandy, perspiring little hand, while Morton pulled the other. Slowly and with head high she walked with her husband and child out of the playground.

Her first feeling was one of relief that a fight had been avoided, that no one was hurt. Yet beneath it there was a layer of something else, something heavy and inescapable. She sensed that it was more than just an unpleasant incident, more than defeat of reason by force. She felt dimly it had something to do with her and Morton, something acutely personal, familiar and important.

Suddenly Morton spoke. "It wouldn't have proved anything."

"What?" she asked.

"A fight. It wouldn't have proved anything beyond the fact that he's bigger than I am."

"Of course," she said.

"The only possible outcome," he continued reasonably, "would have been—what? My glasses broken, perhaps a tooth or two replaced, a couple of days' work missed—and for what? For justice? For truth?"

"Of course," she repeated. She quickened her step. She wanted only to get home and to busy herself with her familiar tasks; perhaps then the feeling, glued like heavy plaster on her heart, would be gone. *Of all the stupid, despicable bullies*, she thought, pulling harder on Larry's hand. The child was still crying. Always before she had felt a tender pity for his defenseless little body, the frail arms, the narrow shoulders with sharp, winglike shoulder blades, the thin and unsure legs, but now her mouth tightened in resentment.

"Stop crying," she said sharply. "I'm ashamed of you!" She felt as if all three of them were tracking mud along the street. The child cried louder.

If there had been an issue involved, she thought, *if there had been something to fight for . . . But what else could he possibly have done? Allow himself to be beaten? Attempt to educate the man? Call a policeman? "Officer, there's a man in the park who won't stop his child from throwing sand on mine. . . ."* The whole thing was as silly as that, and not worth thinking about.

"Can't you keep him quiet, for Pete's sake?" Morton asked irritably.

"What do you suppose I've been trying to do?" she said.

Larry pulled back, dragging his feet.

"If you can't discipline this child, I will," Morton snapped, making a move toward the boy.

But her voice stopped him. She was shocked to hear it, thin and cold and penetrating with contempt. "Indeed?" she heard herself say. "You and who else?"

Reading for Understanding

☐ MAIN IDEA

1. The main idea of the story is that (a) men who bully others shouldn't be allowed in public parks (b) an unpleasant incident may reveal unsuspected tensions (c) children should learn to play together without fighting (d) a sandbox can become a place of terror.

☐ DETAILS

2. The first spadeful of sand (a) missed Larry (b) struck his hair (c) landed at Morton's feet (d) was not seen by the adults.
3. The sand thrower's father (a) was dozing in the sun (b) was reading the *New York Times* (c) was concentrating on the comics (d) apologized for his son's behavior.
4. When the two men faced each other, (a) Morton's wife placed herself between them (b) the sand thrower began to cry (c) the threatening man stepped back (d) Morton backed off.
5. The dispute between the parents at the end of the story was precipitated superficially by (a) the sand in Larry's eye (b) the wife's admiration of the bullying man (c) Larry's crying (d) Morton's broken glasses.

☐ INFERENCES

6. In attempting to stop the little boy from throwing sand, the wife was (a) unfair (b) reasonable (c) too loud (d) tearful.
7. The sand thrower's father can best be characterized as a (a) prizefighter (b) bully (c) gentle father (d) criminal.
8. In refusing battle, Morton was actually being (a) sensible (b) cruel to Larry (c) unfair to his wife (d) furious.
9. The most devastating comment in the entire story is (a) "This here is a *public* sandbox." (b) "You're quite right, but just because this is a public place . . ." (c) "I don't *want* any supper. I don't *like* supper." (d) "Indeed?" she heard herself say. "You and who else?"

☐ TONE OF SELECTION

10. The tone of the story is one of (a) growing tension (b) restrained humor (c) lighthearted conflict (d) unrelieved tragedy.

☐ ORDER OF EVENTS

11. Arrange the items in the order in which they occurred. Use letters only.
    A. The man encourages his son to throw sand.
    B. Morton's wife speaks to him with contempt.
    C. Morton's wife thinks *How good this is.*
    D. Morton refuses a physical contest.
    E. Larry cries out against going home.

☐ OUTCOMES

12. At the conclusion of the story, Morton and his wife (a) have a good cry together (b) severely punish Larry (c) have a serious argument (d) go to dinner to relieve their fatigue.

☐ CAUSE AND EFFECT

13. Which of the following statements might reasonably be made about the story? (a) Larry was an unusually irritating little boy. (b) The problem between Morton and his wife was deeper than the unhappiness over the incident. (c) Because the sand thrower's father had brought things into the open, Morton and his wife thanked him. (d) The sand thrower was punished by his father for causing so much trouble.

☐ FACT OR OPINION

Tell whether each of the following is a fact or an opinion.

14. Morton's wife was extremely unfair in her treatment of him.

15. A physical confrontation between the two men was avoided.

Words in Context

1. "... and only in the sandbox two little boys *squatted diligently.*" ***Squatted diligently*** (179) means (a) shoveled and built sandpiles (b) crouched and worked hard (c) sat on their knees (d) dug furiously.

2. ". . . the boy remained standing, shovel raised, *stolid and impassive.*" ***Stolid and impassive*** (179) means (a) unemotional and calm (b) angry and menacing (c) threatening and sneering (d) massive and tough.

3. "The boy looked at her in *unblinking expectancy.*" The boy looked at her (179) (a) fearful of what was going to happen (b) sorry that he had started something (c) knowing just what would happen soon (d) impatient because of the interruptions.

4. "He did not look up from his comics, but spat once *deftly* out of the corner of his mouth." ***Deftly*** (179) means (a) quickly (b) hurriedly (c) suddenly (d) skillfully.

5. "Larry looked up at his mother, his mouth *tentative*; her expression would tell him whether to cry or not." ***Tentative*** (180) means (a) not firmly set (b) all set to cry (c) set to show his anger (d) twisted in surprise.

6. "She was *suffused with* a tenderness for her husband . . ." ***Suffused with*** (180) means (a) overcome by (b) filled with (c) embarrassed by (d) aware of.

7. ". . . and an *impotent* rage against the man for involving him in a situation so alien and so distasteful to him." ***Impotent*** (180) means (a) overpowering (b) ungovernable (c) ineffective (d) alarming.

8. "At once Larry came to life; his face lost its *rapt* expression and he began to kick and cry." ***Rapt*** (181) means (a) spellbound (b) annoyed (c) enraged (d) timid.

9. "Yet beneath it there was a layer of something else, something *heavy and inescapable.*" ***Heavy and inescapable*** (181) means (a) sad and troubling (b) fatal (c) futile (d) serious and unavoidable.

10. "Of all the stupid, *despicable* bullies . . ." ***Despicable*** (181) means (a) cowardly (b) threatening (c) contemptible (d) unpleasant.

Thinking Critically About the Story

1. Reread or read aloud to the class the first paragraph of the story up to "The other boy suddenly stood up . . ." What mood permeates this opening scene? How does the author attempt to make the reader share it? Why did the author choose this mood as the opener? Explain.

2. "She always said that she wanted Larry to learn to fight his own battles." How does the mother handle the throwing of the first spadeful

of sand? Is she consistent? How do the men handle it? The children? How would you have handled it?

3. The climax of the story is reached in the handling of the second spadeful of sand. How does the author build up to it? How could it have been prevented? Who was at fault? How would you have handled it? Give the reasons for your answer.

4. What is the sequence of reactions of the father of the sand thrower? How does the author make certain that the reader does not side with him? That the reader sides with Morton?

5. Would you characterize Morton as a weakling? A coward? A strong character? Explain. How could his wife have protected him? Who is at fault in the big scenes? Could you admire a person like Morton? Would you be willing to choose him as a friend? A confidant? Explain.

6. From whose point of view is the story told? Would the story be as effective if it were told from the point of view of the husband? The son?

7. In the last scene, why does Morton threaten to discipline Larry? Why does the mother threaten Morton? Does she love her husband? Explain.

Stories in Words

Deliberately (page 180) means "thoughtfully, slowly, unhurriedly." It is derived from the Latin *libra,* "scale." *Libra* is one of the signs of the zodiac. What connection does *scale* have with *thoughtfulness*? When we *deliberate,* we are placing various items in the *scales, weighing* them in our minds.

Rapt (page 181) suggests "wholly absorbed, engrossed." It comes from a Latin root meaning "seize and forcibly remove." It is related to *rapacious* and *rapture.* A *rapt* expression is totally entranced, lost in thought. A person with a rapt expression has been *carried away* from the immediate surroundings. We may also call him *enraptured.*

Discipline (page 181) here means "train by enforcing obedience." The word is, of course, related to *disciple,* "a follower." *Disciple* itself goes back to the Latin *discere,* "to learn." In one sense, the noun *discipline* means "a subject that is taught, a field of study." But its more common use suggests "an orderly prescribed method of behavior." In this sense we hear a frequent comment, "What we need nowadays is more *discipline.*"

Weekend

SHIRLEY HAZZARD

"Oh, Lord! I forgot . . . *Don't*, darling, after all the trouble I took combing it."

"Why is it done differently?" He loosened another strand.

"I don't know—I suppose because Lilian eyes me as though I should Do Something with myself. She makes me feel that I look . . . *married*."

"Scarcely astonishing, in the circumstances."

Two sisters-in-law come together for a weekend in an English home within commuting distance of London. Julie is married to Lilian's brother Ben, but the friendship of the two women has been warmer than the relationship of brother and sister. Julie and Ben have made a choice about the way they will live their lives. Lilian has made hers. The two choices are different, and the story explores the differences subtly and sensitively.

You will find the story especially effective in the understated way in which the two women's feelings are brought out, with understanding and awareness. The three main characters are well drawn; the two neighbors and their dog also come in for perceptive analysis. This is a story to savor, for it implies much more than it says.

Weekend

Lilian, on waking, reached up her arm to pull back the curtain from the window above her bed. The cretonne roses, so recently hung that their folds were still awkward and raw-smelling, tinkled back on brass rings, and sunlight fell around the walls in honey-colored warpings. It was like being under water, she thought, bathed in that delicate light; she had forgotten these contradictions of spring in England—chill, dreary evenings like yesterday's, and bright mornings full of early flowers. She pushed the blankets away and knelt up on the bed to look out the small, paned window. The outer air, the garden glittered; the meadows—for they could hardly be called anything less—unfolded beyond, crowned by a glimpse of the village and the fifteenth-century church. All as suitable, as immaculate as the white windowsill on which her elbows rested.

But the room was, of course, cold, and she sank back into the bedclothes. During the night, she had wakened several times to hear the wind rattling the windowpanes and had pushed herself further down the bed, trying to warm her shoulders. (The little electric radiator had been taken away during the day to dry the baby's washing and had not been returned.) Going to bed last night, she had actually consoled herself with the prospect of departure—that it would be her last night in the house. And tonight, no doubt, back in London, she would wonder about the weekend, and comfort herself by telephoning Julie and by thinking out the long, loving letter she would write when she got back to New York. The letter, in her mind, was already some paragraphs advanced.

Like some desolating childhood disappointment, she thought, this anxiety to get away when she had so longed to come here—so longed to see them, and to see Julie most of all. Because, even though Ben was her own brother, it was to Julie she felt closer; Julie she had missed more in these two years away. Given only this weekend, Lilian felt the need to precipitate confidences—"Are you happy, is this really what you want?" she had almost asked Julie last night, coming upstairs. Which was nonsense, impertinence; one couldn't ask it, and in any case Julie would have laughed and told Ben afterward ("What ever do you think Lilian said to me?").

Married couples always betrayed their friends that way—probably for something to say, being so much together. And Ben, indifferent, would say: "How perfectly extraordinary," or "I'm not in the least surprised," or "Poor old Lilian."

Lilian's room was in the old part of the house—seventeenth-century, Julie had said. Lilian allowed a century either way, for Julie's imprecision and the exaggeration of the estate agent. She lay approving the uneven walls, the heavy beams of the roof, the sturdy irregularities of the window and door. The only furniture other than her bed was a new chest of drawers, a cane chair, and a small, unsteady table. On this table stood a china lamp and *Poets of the Present*, a frayed volume in which Thomas Hardy was heavily represented. The room—in fact, the whole house—looked bare. They needed so many things, Julie had said—practically everything—but for a while nothing more could be done; buying the house had taken every penny. On Friday, when Lilian arrived, Julie had shown her around, walking through the rooms with her hand in the crook of Lilian's arm, separating apologetically at doorways. (All the rooms were at slightly different levels, and there was a step or two at each entrance—sometimes dropping, dangerously, beyond a closed door.) Julie's shy, artless face, lowered so that strands of silky hair drooped on Lilian's shoulder, had seemed tired, frail. Her sweater and skirt were aged, unheeded. Too much for her, Lilian thought, this house, and the baby, though I'm sure it's lovely. "Lovely," she had repeated later, in the nursery, over a mound of blue blanket. In the hallway, it was Lilian who linked their arms again.

She pushed the bedclothes back once more, and lowered her feet to the cold, glossy floor. And Ben, she thought, shivering and resting her elbow on her knee and her chin on her hand. She found it hard to believe in Ben as Julie's husband, Simon's father, a member (as she supposed he must be) of the community, traveling up to London every morning of the week, and at home seeming settled and domestic, reading the evening paper with the air of one who must not be disturbed. She supposed that in his way he must love Julie, but she couldn't really imagine him intimate with anyone. She thought of him as a source of knowledge rather than experience; a good, though not contemporary mind, a person rather than a man.

"I adore you," Ben said, without opening his eyes, "but why are you up so early?"

Julie, at the mirror, uttered a strangled sound. She took a bobby pin from between her teeth and fastened up the last, escaping lock of hair. "I have to take care of Simon until the girl arrives. And think about lunch. . . . And then, there's Lilian."

"What about her?" Ben stretched out into the depression left by Julie's body in the other half of the bed. His eyes, now open, were surprisingly alert. "Come and talk to me."

She came and sat beside him, reaching her arm across his body to rest her hand on the bed. "I just mean I have to think of her—make sure she's not cold or anything."

"Difficult to see how she can be anything else, when we've got both the radiators."

"Oh, Lord! I forgot. . . . *Don't,* darling, after all the trouble I took combing it."

"Why is it done differently?" He loosened another strand.

"I don't know—I suppose because Lilian eyes me as though I should Do Something with myself. She makes me feel that I look . . . *married.*"

"Scarcely astonishing, in the circumstances." He drew her elbow back so that, losing the support of her arm, she collapsed against his chest. She remained there, and he put his arm around her. "'Old, married, and in despair'—is that the idea?"

"Something like that."

"Too soon for that," he observed, encouragingly. "But I know what you mean. Since she's been here I can hardly read the paper without feeling that I've sold my immortal soul."

Julie giggled. "Don't be awful." She drew away from him and put her hands up to her hair, assessing the damage. "Do you think she's happy? I get the feeling she doesn't *want* anything—you know, doesn't know what she should do with her life. . . ." She opened another bobby pin with her teeth and replaced it at the back of her head. "We, at least know where we are."

"'I am between water and stone fruit in India,'" declared Ben, looking up at Lilian over the *Times.* "In eleven letters."

"Any clues?"

"None."

"Pondicherry," Lilian said, after a moment's silence.

Ben wrote. Pleased with herself, Lilian curled her legs up on the sofa and wondered if she should be in the kitchen, helping Julie. There were to be guests for lunch.

"'A secret'—blank—'in the stream.' Tennyson. Nine letters."

"No clues?"

"Begins and ends with 's.'"

"Sweetness," said Julie unexpectedly from the dining room. She appeared for a moment in the doorway and added: "*In Memoriam,*"* polishing a glass with a dish towel.

"Twenty across," Ben resumed, but Lilian got up and followed Julie.

The kitchen smelled of roasting lamb, and of floor polish and mint sauce. What an appalling stove, Lilian thought; surely they'll replace it.

"Do sit down," Julie told her, pulling out a chair by the table. "We'll be five for lunch—some neighbors called Marchant and the three of us. No,

*"*In Memoriam*" a long poem by Alfred Tennyson in memory of his best friend who had died

darling, thank you, there's nothing; everything's done. Unless perhaps you'd like to shell the peas." She turned her attention to the meat. "It's quite efficient, really, this kitchen—though, as you see, we had to put in a new stove."

Lilian began to break pods over a colander. "What are they like, your neighbors?"

"The Marchants? We scarcely know them. They drove over one day, in a Volkswagen, to call—we'd been introduced by the previous owners of the house. And they asked us to dinner last week, but we couldn't leave the baby. Seem all right—a bit dull." Having basted the lamb, Julie slid it back into the oven and straightened up. She plunged the basting spoon into suds in the sink. "Nothing against them, really, apart from the car."

Arriving late in their Volkswagen, the Marchants brought with them a big, restless Dalmatian called Spot. Mr. Marchant was stocky and bald, with heavy glasses and a suit of limp tweed. Mrs. Marchant was slight and ginger-haired, and wore a green pullover and a gray flannel skirt. They stood for some minutes in the hall, commenting on improvements in high, authoritative voices, before they could be induced to enter the living room. Mrs. Marchant did not sit down at once, but moved across the room to stare at a picture before veering sharply away to the window. Rather, Lilian could not help thinking, like a small colored fish in an aquarium. Spot, after a brisk canter around the furniture, flopped down to pant in a corner, where Ben was preparing drinks.

Mrs. Marchant gave Lilian her divided attention. "You've just been—thank you, with a little water—to America?"

"She lives there," Ben said, stepping over the dog. "Out of the way, Fido."

"Spot," corrected Mrs. Marchant, scenting disparagement.

Mr. Marchant, who was a lawyer, produced some formidably documented views on the conduct of government in the United States. Congressional legislation appeared to him as a series of venal disasters—catalogued, Lilian felt, with a certain satisfaction.

Julie was quietly interrogating the dog, now sitting at her feet. "Are you a good doggie?" Spot smiled, but kept his counsel.

Unable to refute Mr. Marchant, and badly situated for conversation with Spot, Lilian kept silent. Perhaps it's a system, something one gets used to again, she told herself—like doing the *Times* crossword puzzle.

Mrs. Marchant was inclined to be tolerant. "The Americans who come over here seem pleasant enough, don't you think?"

"Oh, absolutely," Ben agreed. He put out his cigarette, and added: "A trifle assiduous, perhaps," before lighting another.

Mrs. Marchant persisted. "But I've always got on well with them. We had four in our house—remember, Hugh?—during the war. Well-behaved boys. They read aloud in the evenings." She nodded to reinforce this surprising memory.

"Did they really?" Julie, who had risen, paused at the door of the dining room. "What?"

Mrs. Marchant's approval diminished. "Well, I *was* hoping for Wordsworth, which Daddy would have so loved—my father was living with us then. But instead they read an interminable thing about a whale—a *whale*, I assure you. I thought we'd never see the back of that whale. But mercifully, when the good weather came, they opened the Second Front."

Lilian, glancing up in dismay, was astonished to find Julie's face disarrayed with amusement.

They sat down to lunch, and Ben carved the meat. Spot, having found his way under the table, squeezed back and forth among their legs, his firm, bristly sides heaving with cheerful interest, his tail slapping wildly. Julie looked pained, and once laid down her knife and fork as though she were about to speak—but didn't. At last Mr. Marchant got up from the table, apologizing, and called the dog to the door.

"Out, damned Spot," he said, pointing. Everyone laughed except Mrs. Marchant, who had heard the joke a hundred times. The dog pattered out as if he had intended this all along.

Julie washed the dishes, and Lilian dried them. The Marchants, waving, had disappeared with Spot in their car, shortly after lunch. Ben had gone out to work in the garden ("Before the rain comes," Julie said, although there was no sign of rain). In the sun outside the kitchen window, Simon slept in his pram.

"Is he warm enough there?" Lilian asked.

Julie looked up, her hands in the sink. "Oh, don't you think so?" she asked anxiously, alarming Lilian, who had expected a confident reassurance.

"It's beginning to get chilly," she said. Together, they looked uncertainly at the strip of sunshine on the grass. Their shoulders touched.

"Oh, God!" shouted Ben from the garden. He crossed rapidly in front of the kitchen window and came in at the back door, a bundle of drooping plants in his hands. "Julia," he said, using her full name to emphasize his displeasure. (How infantile men are, Lilian thought.) "Julia, the lupines* are all dug up. Will you please tell those people not to bring their filthy dog here again?"

"Yes, dear," Julie replied seriously, apparently memorizing the message in order to convey it with complete accuracy. "Can't they be replanted?"

He shook his head. "The blighter's chewed them."

Lilian wiped the draining board and hung the wet dish towel on a rod to dry. "I'll bring Simon in, shall I?" she said smoothly, and made her way past Ben into the garden.

"Leave the pram," Julie called. "Ben will bring it."

Outside the kitchen door, the grass was sparse and trampled, and flaked with wood shavings from the recent passage and unpacking of furniture. Beyond, however, it became lavishly green, in need of cutting and scattered with spring flowers. The garden, more delicate than ever in the al-

**lupine* a plant in the pea family

ready dying light, was surrounded by ancient trees and, on one side, by a thick, trim hedge of box.* A memory even as one stands here, Lilian thought, saddened by anticipation of her own nostalgia—and yet pleased all at once to have come out at this moment, to find the scene imposing some sort of misty symmetry on the untidy events of the day. I may cry, she told herself with surprise, as she lifted the sleeping Simon.

Ben, still grasping the ravished lupines, looked at her with interest as he came out of the house.

Lilian gathered up the trailing blanket with her free hand and walked slowly away. He will say: "Poor old Lilian," after I've left, she reminded herself. In the kitchen, she handed Simon over to his mother. "Now I must really go and pack," she said.

Lilian leaned from the window of the train. "I'll telephone you from London," she told Julie.

It will come right again, on the telephone, they assured each other silently.

Julie, suddenly pale and tired, brushed away tears. "It's cold. I should have brought a coat."

"What?"

"It's cold."

"Next time I'll come in the summer."

Crying, Julie laughed. "It'll still be cold. But come back soon."

"Do you have everything you need?" Ben asked, too late for ambiguity, glancing at the magazine stall.

"Yes, thanks. Oh, good-bye." The train drew away. "Good-bye!"

"Good-bye! Lilian . . . good-bye."

They waved, close at last for a moment, before the train ran into the darkness.

The two on the platform stood still for a few seconds, convalescent, before they walked away to their little car. In the clear, black, country air outside the station, Julie shivered again. The wind had risen, as it had the night before. They got into the car without speaking. Only when the engine started, on the third try, did Julie move up against Ben. He put his arm briefly around her, and then withdrew it. The car moved off.

"Poor old Lilian," Julie said.

Reading for Understanding

❑ MAIN IDEA

1. The main point of the story is the (a) hostility between an English family and a neighbor (b) differing perceptions of two old friends

**box* a type of evergreen

at a reunion (c) lack of understanding between husband and wife (d) quaint customs of English country folk.

❑ DETAILS

2. Upon awakening, Lilian (a) disliked the curtains (b) thought first about her New York apartment (c) resolved to tell Julie the truth (d) felt cold.
3. Julie and Lilian hadn't seen each other (a) since the war (b) since childhood (c) in two years (d) in five years.
4. The first person to suggest the correct word for the crossword puzzle was (a) Lilian (b) Julie (c) Ben (d) Simon.
5. The lupines were destroyed by (a) Mr. Marchant (b) Ben (c) Spot (d) Fido.

❑ INFERENCES

6. The quotation that best expresses what Lilian and Julie think of each other is (a) "Is this really what you want?" (b) "What about her?" (c) "Any clues?" (d) "It's beginning to get chilly."
7. Ben's attitude toward Lilian can best be described as (a) bitingly cruel (b) courteous but indifferent (c) warm and loving (d) puzzled and annoyed.
8. Julie and Ben's attitude toward the Marchants can best be described as (a) enthusiastic (b) sarcastic (c) affectionate (d) polite.
9. When Mr. Marchant said, "Out, damned Spot," he was intending to be (a) obstructive (b) cryptic (c) ingratiating (d) funny.

❑ AUTHOR'S ATTITUDE

10. The author's attitude toward the characters is one of (a) sympathetic understanding (b) critical disapproval (c) utter bafflement (d) complete indifference.
11. Of Julie and Lilian it might be said that (a) they were not friendly toward each other (b) their goals and life-styles had diverged (c) both hated dogs (d) they would plan to meet again within a few weeks.

❑ ORDER OF EVENTS

12. Arrange the items in the order in which they occurred. Use letters only.

A. Lilian promises to telephone from London.

B. Julie takes the electric radiator from Lilian's room.
C. Julie shows Lilian the house.
D. The plants are dug up.
E. The Marchants come to lunch.

❑ OUTCOMES

13. After Lilian returns to America, (a) she marries almost immediately (b) Julie flies over for a visit (c) the two women drift farther apart (d) Ben loses his job in London.

❑ CAUSE AND EFFECT

14. At the train station, Julie said, "Poor old Lilian" because (a) Lilian felt the cold (b) Lilian was uncomfortable with the Marchants (c) she pitied her visitor's way of life (d) she thought Lilian disapproved of her brother.

❑ FACT OR OPINION

Tell whether the following is a fact or an opinion.

15. Basically, Lilian was happier than Julie.

Words in Context

1. "The *cretonne roses*, so recently hung that their folds were still awkward and raw-smelling . . ." The ***cretonne roses*** (187) were (a) plantings in window boxes (b) the curtains made of cotton or linen (c) live flowers in a vase (d) artificial flowers around the room.

2. "All as suitable, as *immaculate* as the white windowsill on which her elbows rested." ***Immaculate*** (187) means (a) spick and span (b) guiltless (c) appropriate (d) beautiful.

3. "Like some *desolating* childhood disappointment, she thought, this anxiety to get away when she had so longed to come here . . ." ***Desolating*** (187) means (a) senseless (b) recurring (c) depressing (d) terrifying.

4. "Given only this weekend, Lilian felt the need to *precipitate* confidences . . ." ***Precipitate*** (187) means (a) discover (b) avoid (c) accumulate (d) cause.

5. "What an *appalling* stove, Lilian thought; surely they'll replace it." ***Appalling*** (189) means (a) old-fashioned (b) inefficient (c) conventional (d) dismaying.

6. "They stood for some minutes in the hall, commenting on improvements in high, *authoritative* voices . . ." ***Authoritative*** (190) means (a) flattering (b) decisive (c) meek (d) critical.

7. "Mrs. Marchant . . . moved across the room to stare at a picture before *veering* sharply away to the window." ***Veering*** (190) means (a) ambling (b) sidestepping (c) glancing (d) rushing.

8. "'Spot,' corrected Mrs. Marchant, *scenting disparagement*." ***Scenting disparagement*** (190) means (a) almost automatically (b) amused by the error (c) sensing a put-down (d) forgiving the error.

9. "Congressional legislation appeared to him as a series of *venal* disasters." ***Venal*** (190) means caused by (a) ignorance (b) fate (c) cruelty (d) dishonesty.

10. "Spot smiled, but *kept his counsel*." ***Kept his counsel*** (190) means (a) barked in agreement (b) licked her hand (c) walked away (d) did not exchange opinions.

11. Unable to *refute* Mr. Marchant . . . Lilian kept silent. ***Refute*** (190) means (a) agree with (b) disagree with (c) follow (d) disprove.

12. "But instead, they read an *interminable* thing about a whale . . . I thought we'd never see the back of that whale . . ." ***Interminable*** (191) means (a) incomprehensible (b) boring (c) silly (d) long-winded.

13. "In the sun outside the kitchen window, Simon slept in his *pram*." ***Pram*** (191) means (a) hammock (b) teeter-totter (c) blanket (d) carriage.

14. "Outside the kitchen door, the grass was *sparse* and trampled . . ." ***Sparse*** (191) means (a) uprooted (b) turning brown (c) spotty (d) lush.

15. "A memory even as one stands here, Lilian thought, saddened by anticipation of her own *nostalgia* . . ." ***Nostalgia*** (192) means (a) airsickness (b) yearning to return (c) going back to work (d) uncertainties ahead.

Thinking Critically About the Story

1. This is one of the most subtle stories in the collection. What is the basic conflict? What devices does the author use to bring it into focus? Cite examples.

2. What is Lilian's reaction to the house? Its initial cost? The furnishings? The way of life? How would you have reacted?
3. Select examples—to be read to the class—of descriptive tidbits the author added to give similitude to the story.
4. Give examples of the use of irony in this story. In the relationship of the brother, sister, and wife. In their perception of each other. Whom do you side with? Explain.
5. Julie and Ben have made a choice about the way they will lead their lives. Lilian has made hers. How do the choices differ? Which made the wiser? Which would you choose? Do they resemble people you know?
6. Why does the author include the lunch with the Marchants? And Spot? Does this scene forward the plot, or is it an intrusive irrelevance? Would you omit it?
7. Is there evidence of love in this story? Does Lilian love her brother? Why does she feel closer to Julie, her sister-in-law? Do Julie and Ben love Lilian? Are they jealous of each other? Explain. Whom does the author side with? Justify your answer.

Stories in Words

Cretonne (page 187) is a member of a large family of words derived from place names. A heavy, unglazed cotton cloth, cretonne is often used for curtains. It takes its name from *Creton*, a village in Normandy famous for its cloth since the 16th century. Other words derived from place names are *damask* (Damascus), *cologne*, *copper* (Cyprus), *muslin* (Mosul), *sardine* (Sardinia), *spaniel* (Spain), and *turkey*.

Canter (page 190) refers to the pace of a horse, between a trot and a gallop. The word originated from the pilgrimages of devout worshipers to the shrine of Saint Thomas à Becket at Canterbury. In *The Canterbury Tales*, the great English poet Geoffrey Chaucer told tales of the pilgrims and their experiences on the Old Kent Road. The gait they chose came to be called a *canter*. *Canter* is sometimes called a *clipped word*, because it is derived from a longer word. Other clipped words in English are *phone* (*telephone*), *photo* (*photograph*), *taxi* (*taxicab*), *bike* (*bicycle*), *bus* (*omnibus*), *flu* (*influenza*), *gas* (*gasoline*), and *ad* (*advertisement*).

Nostalgia (page 192) is another name for homesickness, or a longing for another time or place. By derivation from the Greek, *nostos* is a *return* and *algia* is *pain*. *Nostalgia* thus is a somewhat painful, bittersweet yearning to return—to another place or another time. Nostalgia is often the yearning for earlier happier circumstances, though the memory may be faulty. Though *nostos* is an uncommon root in English, *algia* is a bit more common. *Neuralgia* is "nerve pain." An *analgesic* is a drug to avoid pain. If you want to impress your friends, instead of saying you have a *headache*, say you're suffering from *cephalalgia*!

The Magic Barrel

BERNARD MALAMUD

"Here is the one I want." Leo held forth the snapshot.

Salzman slipped on his glasses and took the picture into his trembling hand. He turned ghastly and let out a groan.

"What's the matter?" cried Leo.

"Excuse me. Was an accident this picture. She isn't for you."

In a great many lands around the globe, arranged marriages are the rule. Sometimes parents, usually friends, get together and match their offspring in marriage. Sometimes a marriage broker is used, someone who can match possible partners as modern dating services do.

Leo Finkle calls on a marriage broker for assistance. Pinye Salzman was an obliging broker, trying in desperation to find a bride that the young rabbinical student might find satisfactory. Disappointment follows disappointment; then, quite unexpectedly, events take a surprising turn. Rich discussion arises from the supposed events that might follow the conclusion of the story. The author is saying to his readers, "You decide what happens next."

Many of Pinye's possible marriage partners would be better for Leo than Stella. Why does Leo turn down the others for a possible association with Stella? Is love always unpredictable?

The Magic Barrel

Not long ago there lived in uptown New York, in a small almost meager room, though crowded with books, Leo Finkle, a rabbinical student in the Yeshiva University. Finkle, after six years of study, was to be ordained in June and had been advised by an acquaintance that he might find it easier to win himself a congregation if he were married. Since he had no present prospects of marriage, after two tormented days of turning it over in his mind, he called in Pinye Salzman, a marriage broker whose two-line advertisement he had read in the *Forward.**

The matchmaker appeared one night out of the dark fourth-floor hallway of the graystone rooming house where Finkle lived, grasping a black, strapped portfolio that had been worn thin with use. Salzman, who had been long in the business, was of slight but dignified build, wearing an old hat, and an overcoat too short and tight for him. He smelled frankly of fish, which he loved to eat, and although he was missing a few teeth, his presence was not displeasing, because of an amiable manner curiously contrasted with mournful eyes. His voice, his lips, his wisp of beard, his bony fingers were animated, but give him a moment of repose and his mild blue eyes revealed a depth of sadness, a characteristic that put Leo a little at ease although the situation, for him, was inherently tense.

He at once informed Salzman why he had asked him to come, explaining that his home was in Cleveland, and that but for his parents, who had married comparatively late in life, he was alone in the world. He had for six years devoted himself almost entirely to his studies, as a result of which, understandably, he had found himself without time for a social life and the company of young women. Therefore he thought it the better part of trial and error—of embarrassing fumbling—to call in an experienced person to advise him on these matters. He remarked in passing that the function of the marriage broker was ancient and honorable, highly approved in the Jewish community, because it made practical the necessary without hindering joy. Moreover, his own parents had been brought together by a

*The *Forward* was a popular Yiddish newspaper.

matchmaker. They had made, if not a financially profitable marriage—since neither had possessed any worldly goods to speak of—at least a successful one in the sense of their everlasting devotion to each other. Salzman listened in embarrassed surprise, sensing a sort of apology. Later, however, he experienced a glow of pride in his work, an emotion that had left him years ago, and he heartily approved of Finkle.

The two went to their business. Leo had led Salzman to the only clear place in the room, a table near a window that overlooked the lamp-lit city. He seated himself at the matchmaker's side but facing him, attempting by an act of will to suppress the unpleasant tickle in his throat. Salzman eagerly unstrapped his portfolio and removed a loose rubber band from a thin packet of much-handled cards. As he flipped through them, a gesture and sound that physically hurt Leo, the student pretended not to see and gazed steadfastly out the window. Although it was still February, winter was on its last legs, signs of which he had for the first time in years begun to notice. He now observed the round white moon, moving high in the sky through a cloud menagerie, and watched with half-open mouth as it penetrated a huge hen, and dropped out of her like an egg laying itself. Salzman, though pretending through eyeglasses he had just slipped on to be engaged in scanning the writing on the cards, stole occasional glances at the young man's distinguished face, noting with pleasure the long, severe scholar's nose, brown eyes heavy with learning, sensitive yet ascetic lips, and a certain almost hollow quality of the dark cheeks. He gazed around at shelves upon shelves of books and let out a soft, contented sigh.

When Leo's eyes fell upon the cards, he counted six spread out in Salzman's hand.

"So few?" he asked in disappointment.

"You wouldn't believe me how much cards I got in my office," Salzman replied. "The drawers are already filled to the top, so I keep them now in a barrel, but is every girl good for a new rabbi?"

Leo blushed at this, regretting all he had revealed of himself in a curriculum vitae he had sent to Salzman. He had thought it best to acquaint him with his strict standards and specifications, but in having done so, felt he had told the marriage broker more than was absolutely necessary.

He hesitantly inquired, "Do you keep photographs of your clients on file?"

"First comes family, amount of dowry, also what kind promises," Salzman replied, unbuttoning his tight coat and settling himself in the chair. "After comes pictures, rabbi."

"Call me Mr. Finkle. I'm not yet a rabbi."

Salzman said he would, but instead called him doctor, which he changed to rabbi when Leo was not listening too attentively.

Salzman adjusted his horn-rimmed spectacles, gently cleared his throat and read in an eager voice the contents of the top card:

"Sophie P. Twenty-four years. Widow one year. No children. Educated high school and two years college. Father promises eight thousand dollars.

Has wonderful wholesale business. Also real estate. On the mother's side comes teachers, also one actor. Well known on Second Avenue."

Leo gazed up in surprise. "Did you say a widow?"

"A widow don't mean spoiled, rabbi. She lived with her husband maybe four months. He was a sick boy she made a mistake to marry him."

"Marrying a widow has never entered my mind."

"This is because you have no experience. A widow, especially if she is young and healthy like this girl, is a wonderful person to marry. She will be thankful to you the rest of her life. Believe me, if I was looking now for a bride, I would marry a widow."

Leo reflected, then shook his head.

Salzman hunched his shoulders in an almost imperceptible gesture of disappointment. He placed the card down on the wooden table and began to read another:

"Lily H. High school teacher. Regular. Not a substitute. Has savings and new Dodge car. Lived in Paris one year. Father is successful dentist thirty-five years. Interested in professional man. Well Americanized family. Wonderful opportunity.

"I knew her personally," said Salzman. "I wish you could see this girl. She is a doll. Also very intelligent. All day you could talk to her about books and theater and what not. She also knows current events."

"I don't believe you mentioned her age?"

"Her age?" Salzman said, raising his brows. "Her age is thirty-two years."

Leo said after a while, "I'm afraid that seems a little too old."

Salzman let out a laugh. "So how old are you, rabbi?"

"Twenty-seven."

"So what is the difference, tell me, between twenty-seven and thirty-two? My own wife is seven years older than me. So what did I suffer?—Nothing. If Rothschild's a daughter wants to marry you, would you say on account her age, no?"

"Yes," Leo said dryly.

Salzman shook off the no in the yes. "Five years don't mean a thing. I give you my word that when you will live with her for one week you will forget her age. What does it mean five years—that she lived more and knows more than somebody who is younger? On this girl, God bless her, years are not wasted. Each one that it comes makes better the bargain."

"What subject does she teach in high school?"

"Languages. If you heard the way she speaks French, you will think it is music. I am in the business twenty-five years, and I recommend her with my whole heart. Believe me, I know what I'm talking, rabbi."

"What's on the next card?" Leo said abruptly.

Salzman reluctantly turned up the third card:

"Ruth K. Nineteen years. Honor student. Father offers thirteen thousand cash to the right bridegroom. He is a medical doctor. Stomach specialist with marvelous practice. Brother-in-law owns own garment business. Particular people."

Salzman looked as if he had read his trump card.

"Did you say nineteen?" Leo asked with interest.

"On the dot."

"Is she attractive?" He blushed. "Pretty?"

Salzman kissed his fingertips. "A little doll. On this I give you my word. Let me call the father tonight and you will see what means pretty."

But Leo was troubled. "You're sure she's that young?"

"This I am positive. The father will show you the birth certificate."

"Are you positive there isn't something wrong with her?" Leo insisted.

"Who says there is wrong?"

"I don't understand why an American girl her age should go to a marriage broker."

A smile spread over Salzman's face.

"So for the same reason you went, she comes."

Leo flushed. "I am pressed for time."

Salzman, realizing he had been tactless, quickly explained. "The father came, not her. He wants she should have the best, so he looks around himself. When we will locate the right boy he will introduce him and encourage. This makes a better marriage than if a young girl without experience takes for herself. I don't have to tell you this."

"But don't you think this young girl believes in love?" Leo spoke uneasily.

Salzman was about to guffaw but caught himself and said soberly, "Love comes with the right person, not before."

Leo parted dry lips but did not speak. Noticing that Salzman had snatched a glance at the next card, he cleverly asked, "How is her health?"

"Perfect," Salzman said, breathing with difficulty. "Of course, she is a little lame on her right foot from an auto accident that it happened to her when she was twelve years, but nobody notices on account she is so brilliant and also beautiful."

Leo got up heavily and went to the window. He felt curiously bitter and upbraided himself for having called in the marriage broker. Finally, he shook his head.

"Why not?" Salzman persisted, the pitch of his voice rising.

"Because I detest stomach specialists."

"So what do you care what is his business? After you marry her do you need him? Who says he must come every Friday night to your house?"

Ashamed of the way the talk was going, Leo dismissed Salzman, who went home with heavy, melancholy eyes.

Though he had felt only relief at the marriage broker's departure, Leo was in low spirits the next day. He explained it as arising from Salzman's failure to produce a suitable bride for him. He did not care for his type of clientele. But when Leo found himself hesitating whether to seek out another matchmaker, one more polished than Pinye, he wondered if it could be—his protestations to the contrary, and although he honored his father and mother—that he did not, in essence, care for the matchmaking institution? This thought he quickly put out of mind yet found himself still upset. All day he ran around in the woods—missed an important appointment, forgot to give out his laundry, walked out of a Broadway cafeteria without paying and had to run back with the ticket in his hand; had even not recognized his landlady in the street when she passed with a friend and courteously called out, "A good evening to you, Doctor Finkle." By nightfall, however, he had regained sufficient calm to sink his nose into a book and there found peace from his thoughts.

Almost at once there came a knock on the door. Before Leo could say enter, Salzman, commercial cupid, was standing in the room. His face was gray and meager, his expression hungry, and he looked as if he would expire on his feet. Yet the marriage broker managed, by some trick of the muscles, to display a broad smile.

"So good evening. I am invited?"

Leo nodded, disturbed to see him again, yet unwilling to ask the man to leave.

Beaming still, Salzman laid his portfolio on the table. "Rabbi, I got for you tonight good news."

"I've asked you not to call me rabbi. I'm still a student."

"Your worries are finished. I have for you a first-class bride."

"Leave me in peace concerning this subject." Leo pretended lack of interest.

"The world will dance at your wedding."

"Please, Mr. Salzman, no more."

"But first must come back my strength," Salzman said weakly. He fumbled with the portfolio straps and took out of the leather case an oily paper bag, from which he extracted a hard, seeded roll and a small, smoked white fish. With a quick motion of his hand he stripped the fish out of its skin and began ravenously to chew. "All day in a rush," he muttered.

Leo watched him eat.

"A sliced tomato you have maybe?" Salzman hesitantly inquired.

"No."

The marriage broker shut his eyes and ate. When he had finished he carefully cleaned up the crumbs and rolled up the remains of the fish, in the paper bag. His spectacled eyes roamed the room until he discovered, amid some piles of books, a one-burner gas stove. Lifting his hat he humbly asked, "A glass tea you got, rabbi?"

Conscience-stricken, Leo rose and brewed the tea. He served it with a chunk of lemon and two cubes of lump sugar, delighting Salzman.

After he had drunk his tea, Salzman's strength and good spirits were restored.

"So tell me, rabbi," he said amiably, "you considered some more the three clients I mentioned yesterday?"

"There was no need to consider."

"Why not?"

"None of them suits me."

"What then suits you?"

Leo let it pass because he could give only a confused answer.

Without waiting for a reply, Salzman asked, "You remember this girl I talked to you—the high school teacher?"

"Age thirty-two?"

But, surprisingly, Salzman's face lit in a smile. "Age twenty-nine."

Leo shot him a look. "Reduced from thirty-two?"

"A mistake," Salzman avowed. "I talked today with the dentist. He took me to his safety deposit box and showed me the birth certificate. She was twenty-nine years last August. They made her a party in the mountains where she went for her vacation. When her father spoke to me the first time I forgot to write the age and I told you thirty-two, but now I remember this was a different client, a widow."

"The same one you told me about? I thought she was twenty-four?"

"A different. Am I responsible that the world is filled with widows?"

"No, but I'm not interested in them, nor for that matter, in school teachers."

Salzman pulled his clasped hands to his breast. Looking at the ceiling he devoutly exclaimed, "What can I say to somebody that he is not interested in high school teachers? So what then you are interested?"

Leo flushed but controlled himself.

"In what else will you be interested," Salzman went on, "if you not interested in this fine girl that she speaks four languages and has personally in the bank ten thousand dollars? Also her father guarantees further twelve thousand. Also she has a new car, wonderful clothes, talks on all subjects, and she will give you a first-class home and children. How near do we come in our life to paradise?"

"If she's so wonderful, why hasn't she married ten years ago?"

"Why?" said Salzman with a heavy laugh. "—Why? Because she is *partikiler*. This is why. She wants the *best*."

Leo was silent, amused at how he had entangled himself. But Salzman had aroused his interest in Lily H., and he began seriously to consider calling on her. When the marriage broker observed how intently Leo's mind was at work on the facts he had supplied, he felt certain they would soon come to an agreement.

Late Saturday afternoon, conscious of Salzman, Leo Finkle walked with Lily Hirschorn along Riverside Drive. He walked briskly and erectly, wearing with distinction the black fedora he had that morning taken with trepidation out of the dusty hat box on his closet shelf, and the heavy black Saturday coat he had thoroughly whisked clean. Leo also owned a walking stick, a present from a distant relative, but quickly put temptation aside and did not use it. Lily, petite and not unpretty, had on something signifying the approach of spring. She was au courant, animatedly, with all sorts of subjects, and he weighed her words and found her surprisingly sound—score another for Salzman, whom he uneasily sensed to be somewhere around, hiding perhaps high in a tree along the street, flashing the lady signals with a pocket mirror; or perhaps a cloven-hoofed Pan,* piping nuptial ditties as he danced his invisible way before them, strewing wild buds on the walk and purple grapes in their path, symbolizing fruit of a union, though there was of course still none.

Lily startled Leo by remarking, "I was thinking of Mr. Salzman, a curious figure, wouldn't you say?"

Not certain what to answer, he nodded.

She bravely went on, blushing, "I for one am grateful for his introducing us. Aren't you?"

He courteously replied, "I am."

"I mean," she said with a little laugh—and it was all in good taste, or at least gave the effect of being not in bad—"do you mind that we came together so?"

He was not displeased with her honesty, recognizing that she meant to set the relationship aright, and understanding that it took a certain amount of experience in life, and courage, to want to do it quite that way. One had to have some sort of past to make that kind of beginning.

He said that he did not mind. Salzman's function was traditional and honorable—valuable for what it might achieve, which, he pointed out, was frequently nothing.

Lily agreed with a sigh. They walked on for a while and she said after a long silence, again with a nervous laugh, "Would you mind if I asked you something a little bit personal? Frankly, I find the subject fascinating." Although Leo shrugged, she went on half embarrassedly, "How was it that you came to your calling? I mean was it a sudden passionate inspiration?"

Leo, after a time, slowly replied, "I was always interested in the Law."

"You saw revealed in it the presence of the Highest?"

He nodded and changed the subject. "I understand that you spent a little time in Paris, Miss Hirschorn?"

"Oh, did Mr. Salzman tell you, Rabbi Finkle?" Leo winced but she went on, "It was ages ago and almost forgotten. I remember I had to return for my sister's wedding."

And Lily would not be put off. "When," she asked in a trembly voice, "did you become enamored of religion?"

He stared at her. Then it came to him that she was talking not about Leo Finkle, but of a total stranger, some mystical figure, perhaps even passionate prophet that Salzman had dreamed up for her—no relation to the living or dead. Leo trembled with rage and weakness. The trickster had obviously sold her a bill of goods, just as he had him, who'd expected to become acquainted with a young lady of twenty-nine, only to behold, the moment he laid eyes upon her strained and anxious face, a woman past thirty-five and aging rapidly. Only his self-control had kept him this long in her presence.

**Pan* was a Greek woodland deity.

"I am not," he said gravely, "a talented religious person," and in seeking words to go on, found himself possessed by shame and fear. "I think," he said in a strained manner, "that I came to God not because I loved Him, but because I did not."

This confession he spoke harshly because its unexpectedness shook him.

Lily wilted. Leo saw a profusion of loaves of bread go flying like ducks high over his head, not unlike the winged loaves by which he had counted himself to sleep last night. Mercifully, then, it snowed, which he would not put past Salzman's machinations.

He was infuriated with the marriage broker and swore he would throw him out of the room the minute he reappeared. But Salzman did not come that night, and when Leo's anger had subsided, an unaccountable despair grew in its place. At first he thought this was caused by his disappointment in Lily, but before long it became evident that he had involved himself with Salzman without a true knowledge of his own intent. He gradually realized—with an emptiness that seized him with six hands—that he had called in the broker to find him a bride because he was incapable of doing it himself. This terrifying insight he had derived as a result of his meeting and conversation with Lily Hirschorn. Her probing questions had somehow irritated him into revealing—to himself more than her—the true nature of his relationship to religion, and from that it had come upon him, with shocking force, that apart from his parents, he had never loved anyone. Or perhaps it went the other way, that he did not love religion so well as he might, because he had not loved man. It seemed to Leo that his whole life stood starkly revealed and he saw himself for the first time as he truly was—unloved and loveless. This bitter but somehow not fully unexpected revelation brought him to a point of panic, controlled only by extraordinary effort. He covered his face with his hands and cried.

The week that followed was the worst of his life. He did not eat and lost weight. His beard darkened and grew ragged. He stopped attending seminars and almost never opened a book. He seriously considered leaving the Yeshiva, although he was deeply troubled at the thought of the loss of all his years of study—saw them like pages torn from a book, strewn over the city—and at the devastating effect of this decision upon his parents. But he had lived without knowledge of himself, and never in the Five Books and all the Commentaries*—mea culpa—had the truth been revealed to him. He did not know where to turn, and in all this desolating loneliness there was no *to whom*, although he often thought of Lily but not once could bring himself to go downstairs and make the call. He became touchy and irritable, especially with his landlady, who asked him all manner of personal questions; on the other hand, sensing his own disagreeableness, he waylaid her on the stairs and apologized abjectly, until

*The *Five Books* are the first five books of the Bible contained in the Torah. The *Commentaries* (the Talmud) contains rabbinical explanations for passages in the Bible.

mortified, she ran from him. Out of this, however, he drew the consolation that he was a human being and that a human being suffered. But gradually, as the long and terrible week drew to a close, he regained his composure and some idea of purpose in life: to go on as planned. Although he was imperfect, the ideal was not. As for his quest of a bride, the thought of continuing afflicted him with anxiety and heartburn, yet perhaps with this new knowledge of himself he would be more successful than in the past. Perhaps love would now come to him and a bride to that love. And for this sanctified seeking who needed a Salzman?

The marriage broker, a skeleton with haunted eyes, returned that very night. He looked, withal, the picture of frustrated expectancy—as if he had steadfastly waited the week at Miss Lily Hirschorn's side for a telephone call that never came.

Casually coughing, Salzman came immediately to the point: "So how did you like her?"

Leo's anger rose and he could not refrain from chiding the matchmaker: "Why did you lie to me, Salzman?"

Salzman's pale face went dead white, the world had snowed on him.

"Did you not state that she was twenty-nine?" Leo insisted.

"I give you my word—"

"She was thirty-five, if a day. *At least* thirty-five."

"Of this don't be too sure. Her father told me—"

"Never mind. The worst of it was that you lied to her."

"How did I lie to her, tell me?"

"You told her things about me that weren't true. You made me out to be more, consequently less than I am. She had in mind a totally different person, a sort of semimystical Wonder Rabbi."

"All I said, you was a religious man."

"I can imagine."

Salzman sighed. "This is my weakness that I have," he confessed. "My wife says to me I shouldn't be a salesman, but when I have two fine people that they would be wonderful to be married, I am so happy that I talk too much." He smiled wanly. "This is why Salzman is a poor man."

Leo's anger left him. "Well, Salzman, I'm afraid that's all."

The marriage broker fastened hungry eyes on him.

"You don't want any more a bride?"

"I do," said Leo, "but I have decided to seek her in a different way. I am no longer interested in an arranged marriage. To be frank, I now admit the necessity of premarital love. That is, I want to be in love with the one I marry."

"Love?" said Salzman, astounded. After a moment he remarked, "For us, our love is our life, not for the ladies. In the ghetto they—"

"I know, I know," said Leo. "I've thought of it often. Love, I have said to myself, should be a by-product of living and worship rather than its own end. Yet for myself I find it necessary to establish the level of my need and fulfill it."

Salzman shrugged but answered, "Listen, rabbi, if you want love, this I can find for you also. I have such beautiful clients that you will love them the minute your eyes will see them."

Leo smiled unhappily. "I'm afraid you don't understand."

But Salzman hastily unstrapped his portfolio and withdrew a manila packet from it.

"Pictures," he said, quickly laying the envelope on the table.

Leo called after him to take the pictures away, but as if on the wings of the wind, Salzman had disappeared.

March came. Leo had returned to his regular routine. Although he felt not quite himself yet—lacked energy—he was making plans for a more active social life. Of course it would cost something, but he was an expert in cutting corners; and when there were no corners left he would make circles rounder. All the while Salzman's pictures had lain on the table, gathering dust. Occasionally as Leo sat studying, or enjoying a cup of tea, his eyes fell on the manila envelope, but he never opened it.

The days went by and no social life to speak of developed with a member of the opposite sex—it was difficult, given the circumstances of his situation. One morning Leo toiled up the stairs to his room and stared out the window at the city. Although the day was bright his view of it was dark. For some time he watched the people in the street below hurrying along and then turned with a heavy heart to his little room. On the table was the packet. With a sudden relentless gesture he tore it open. For a half-hour he stood by the table in a state of excitement, examining the photographs of the ladies Salzman had included. Finally, with a deep sigh he put them down. There were six, of varying degrees of attractiveness, but look at them long enough and they all became Lily Hirschorn: all past their prime, all starved behind bright smiles, not a true personality in the lot. Life, despite their frantic yoohooings, had passed them by; they were pictures in a briefcase that stank of fish. After a while, however, as Leo attempted to return the photographs into the envelope, he found in it another, a snapshot of the type taken by a machine for a quarter. He gazed at it a moment and let out a cry.

Her face deeply moved him. Why, he could at first not say. It gave him the impression of youth—spring flowers, yet age—a sense of having been used to the bone, wasted; this came from the eyes, which were hauntingly familiar, yet absolutely strange. He had a vivid impression that he had met her before, but try as he might he could not place her although he could almost recall her name, as if he had read it in her own handwriting. No, this couldn't be; he would have remembered her. It was not, he affirmed, that she had an extraordinary beauty—no, though her face was attractive enough; it was that *something* about her moved him. Feature for feature, even some of the ladies of the photographs could do better; but she leaped forth to his heart—had *lived,* or wanted to—more than just wanted, perhaps regretted how she had lived—had somehow deeply suffered: it could be seen in the depths of those reluctant eyes, and from the way the light enclosed and shone from her, and within her, opening realms of possibility: this was her own. Her he desired. His head ached and eyes narrowed with the intensity of his gazing, then as if an obscure fog had blown up in the mind, he experienced fear of her and was aware that he had received an impression, somehow, of evil. He shuddered, saying softly, "It is thus with us all." Leo brewed some tea in a small pot and sat sipping it without sugar, to calm himself. But before he had finished drinking, again with excitement he examined the face and found it good: good for Leo Finkle. Only such a one could understand him and help him seek whatever he was seeking. She might, perhaps, love him. How she had happened to be among the discards in Salzman's barrel he could never guess, but he knew he must urgently go find her.

Leo rushed downstairs, grabbed up the Bronx telephone book, and searched for Salzman's home address. He was not listed, nor was his office. Neither was he in the Manhattan book. But Leo remembered having written down the address on a slip of paper after he had read Salzman's advertisement in the "personals" column of the *Forward.* He ran up to his room and tore through his papers, without luck. It was exasperating. Just when he needed the matchmaker he was nowhere to be found. Fortunately Leo remembered to look in his wallet. There on a card he found his name written and a Bronx address. No phone number was listed, the reason—Leo now recalled—he had originally communicated with Salzman by letter. He got on his coat, put a hat on and hurried to the subway station. All the way to the far end of the Bronx he sat on the edge of his seat. He was more than once tempted to take out the picture and see if the girl's face was as he remembered it, but he refrained, allowing the snapshot to remain in his inside coat pocket, content to have her so close. When the train pulled into the station he was waiting at the door and bolted out. He quickly located the street Salzman had advertised.

The building he sought was less than a block from the subway, but it was not an office building, nor even a loft, nor a store in which one could rent office space. It was a very old tenement house. Leo found Salzman's name in pencil on a soiled tag under the bell and climbed three dark flights to his apartment. When he knocked, the door was opened by a thin, asthmatic, gray-haired woman, in felt slippers.

"Yes?" she said, expecting nothing. She listened without listening. He could have sworn he had seen her, too, before but he knew it was an illusion.

"Salzman—does he live here? Pinye Salzman," he said, "the matchmaker?"

She stared at him a long minute. "Of course."

He felt embarrassed. "Is he in?"

"No." Her mouth, though left open, offered nothing more.

"The matter is urgent. Can you tell me where his office is?"

"In the air." She pointed upward.

"You mean he has no office?" Leo asked.

"In his socks."

He peered into the apartment. It was sunless and dingy, one large room divided by a half-open curtain, beyond which he could see a sagging metal bed. The near side of a room was crowded with rickety chairs, old bureaus, a three-legged table, racks of cooking utensils, and all the apparatus of a kitchen. But there was no sign of Salzman or his magic barrel, probably also a figment of the imagination. An odor of frying fish made Leo weak to the knees.

"Where is he?" he insisted. "I've got to see your husband."

At length she answered, "So who knows where he is? Every time he thinks a new thought he runs to a different place. Go home, he will find you."

"Tell him Leo Finkle."

She gave no sign she had heard.

He walked downstairs, depressed.

But Salzman, breathless, stood waiting at his door.

Leo was astounded and overjoyed. "How did you get here before me?"

"I rushed."

"Come inside."

They entered. Leo fixed tea, and a sardine sandwich for Salzman. As they were drinking he reached behind him for the packet of pictures and handed them to the marriage broker.

Salzman put down his glass and said expectantly, "You found somebody you like?"

"Not among these."

The marriage broker turned away.

"Here is the one I want." Leo held forth the snapshot.

Salzman slipped on his glasses and took the picture into his trembling hand. He turned ghastly and let out a groan.

"What's the matter?" cried Leo.

"Excuse me. Was an accident this picture. She isn't for you."

Salzman frantically shoved the manila packet into his portfolio. He thrust the snapshot into his pocket and fled down the stairs.

Leo, after momentary paralysis, gave chase and cornered the marriage broker in the vestibule. The landlady made hysterical outcries but neither of them listened.

"Give me back the picture, Salzman."

"No." The pain in his eyes was terrible.

"Tell me who she is then."

"This I can't tell you. Excuse me."

He made to depart, but Leo, forgetting himself, seized the matchmaker by his tight coat and shook him frenziedly.

"Please," sighed Salzman. "*Please.*"

Leo ashamedly let him go. "Tell me who she is," he begged. "It's very important for me to know."

"She is not for you. She is a wild one—wild, without shame. This is not a bride for a rabbi."

"What do you mean wild?"

"Like an animal. Like a dog. For her to be poor was a sin. This is why to me she is dead now."

"In heaven's name, what do you mean?"

"Her I can't introduce to you," Salzman cried.

"Why are you so excited?"

"Why, he asks," Salzman said, bursting into tears. "This is my baby, my Stella, she should burn in hell."

Leo hurried up to bed and hid under the covers. Under the covers he thought his life through. Although he soon fell asleep he could not sleep her out of his mind. He woke, beating his breast. Though he prayed to be rid of her, his prayers went unanswered. Through days of torment he endlessly struggled not to love her; fearing success, he escaped it. He then concluded to convert her to goodness, himself to God. The idea alternately nauseated and exalted him.

He perhaps did not know that he had come to a final decision until he encountered Salzman in a Broadway cafeteria. He was sitting alone at a rear table, sucking the bony remains of a fish. The marriage broker appeared haggard, and transparent to the point of vanishing.

Salzman looked up at first without recognizing him. Leo had grown a pointed beard and his eyes were weighted with wisdom.

"Salzman," he said, "love has at last come to my heart."

"Who can love from a picture?" mocked the marriage broker.

"It is not impossible."

"If you can love her, then you can love anybody. Let me show you some new clients that they just sent me their photographs. One is a little doll."

"Just her I want," Leo murmured.

"Don't be a fool, doctor. Don't bother with her."

"Put me in touch with her, Salzman," Leo said humbly. "Perhaps I can be of service."

Salzman had stopped eating and Leo understood with emotion that it was now arranged.

Leaving the cafeteria, he was, however, afflicted by a tormenting suspicion that Salzman had planned it all to happen this way. Leo was informed by letter that she would meet him on a certain corner, and she was there one spring night, waiting under a street lamp. He appeared, carrying a small bouquet of violets and rosebuds. Stella stood by the lamppost, smoking. She wore white with red shoes, which fitted his expectations, although in a troubled moment he had imagined the dress red, and only the shoes white. She waited uneasily and shyly. From afar he saw that her eyes—clearly her father's—were filled with desperate innocence. He pictured, in her, his own redemption. Violins and lit candles revolved in the sky. Leo ran forward with flowers outthrust.

Around the corner, Salzman, leaning against a wall, chanted prayers for the dead.

Reading for Understanding

❑ MAIN IDEA

1. The main idea of the story is that (a) marriage brokers can do more harm than good (b) some people fail to marry because they are too fussy (c) lonely people should marry (d) no one can predict the ways of the human heart.

❑ DETAILS

2. Finkle rejected Salzman's first prospect because the prospect (a) was too old (b) was partly lame (c) was a widow (d) had no dowry.
3. On his second visit to Finkle, Salzman (a) came uninvited (b) asked for money (c) shouted angrily at Finkle (d) left some pictures behind.
4. The high school teacher's true age was (a) 24 (b) 29 (c) 32 (d) past 35.
5. The person who finally caught Finkle's eye was (a) Lily (b) Stella (c) Salzman's sister (d) none of these.

❑ INFERENCES

6. Finkle's original reason for seeking a bride was tied in with his (a) parents' nagging (b) career (c) romantic nature (d) wish to help Salzman.
7. Salzman can best be characterized as (a) pathetic (b) successful (c) flashy (d) despicable.
8. To put his prospects in a better light, Salzman was (a) scrupulously honest and accurate (b) overbearing (c) inclined to stretch the truth (d) interested above all in the interests of his client.
9. In his feelings toward his daughter, Salzman was (a) inwardly proud (b) outwardly loving (c) unforgiving (d) understanding.
10. Mrs. Salzman's attitude toward her husband was one of (a) vigorous optimism (b) comical appreciation (c) fierce protectiveness (d) weary disillusion.

❑ TONE OF THE SELECTION

11. The tone of the story may be characterized as (a) serious but with many humorous touches (b) unrelentingly grim from beginning to end (c) frivolous and lighthearted (d) sensational and melodramatic.

❑ ORDER OF EVENTS

12. Arrange the items in the order in which they occurred. Use letters only.
    A. Finkle meets Lily.
    B. The matchmaker arrives.
    C. Finkle rushes to meet Stella.
    D. Finkle scolds Salzman after meeting Miss Hirschorn.
    E. Leo finds the photograph of the one who interests him.

❑ OUTCOMES

13. Which sentences suggest that there might be a happy ending to Finkle's romance? (a) Leo was silent, amused at how he had entangled himself. But Salzman had aroused his interest in Lily H., and he began seriously to consider calling on her. (page 204) (b) Conscience-stricken, Leo rose and brewed the tea. He served it with a touch of lemon and two cubes of lump sugar, delighting Salzman. (page 203) (c) He was not displeased with her honesty, recognizing that she meant to set the relationship aright, and understanding that it took a certain amount of experience in life, and courage, to want to do it quite that way. (page 205) (d) She waited uneasily and shyly. From afar he saw that her eyes—clearly her father's—were filled with desperate innocence. (page 211)

❑ CAUSE AND EFFECT

14. Salzman's various strategies (a) made him a successful marriage broker (b) caused Finkle to lose faith in him (c) brought Finkle the woman that Salzman had planned for him (d) were cruel and vicious.

❑ FACT OR OPINION

Tell whether the following is a fact or an opinion.

15. Finkle was an honest, upright, thoroughly reliable rabbinical student.

Words in Context

1. "His voice, his lips, his *wisp* of beard, his bony fingers were *animated* . . ." ***Wisp . . . animated*** (199) mean: (a) abundance . . . passive (b) small amount . . . lively (c) whiteness . . . dramatic (d) contrast . . . startling.

2. "... but give him a moment of *repose* and his mild blue eyes revealed a depth of sadness ..." ***Repose*** (199) means (a) contemplation (b) excitement (c) relaxation (d) anger.

3. "... a characteristic that put Leo a little at ease although the situation, for him, was *inherently* tense." ***Inherently*** (199) means (a) naturally (b) completely (c) partially (d) understandably.

4. "... noting with pleasure ... brown eyes heavy with learning, sensitive yet *ascetic* lips ..." ***Ascetic*** (200) means (a) full (b) self-denying (c) tense (d) smiling.

5. "... regretting all he had revealed of himself in a *curriculum vitae*." ***Curriculum vitae*** (200) means (a) long letter (b) footnote (c) conversation (d) summary of his career.

6. "Salzman hunched his shoulders in an almost *imperceptible* gesture of disappointment." ***Imperceptible*** (201) means (a) obvious (b) theatrical (c) ironic (d) not noticeable.

7. "He felt curiously bitter and *upbraided* himself for having called in the marriage broker." ***Upbraided*** (202) means (a) rebuked (b) pardoned (c) extolled (d) punished.

8. "... wearing with distinction the black fedora he had that morning taken with *trepidation* out of the dusty hat box on his closet shelf." ***Trepidation*** (204) means (a) difficulty (b) bravado (c) uneasiness (d) unwillingness.

9. "She was *au courant, animatedly*, with all sorts of subjects." ***Au courant, animatedly*** (204) mean (a) ... well informed, vivaciously ... (b) ... talkative, humorously ... (c) ... anecdotal, confidently ... (d) ... easygoing, attentively ...

10. "... or perhaps a cloven-hoofed Pan, *piping nuptial ditties* as he danced his invisible way before them ..." ***Piping nuptial ditties*** (205) means (a) shouting words of praise (b) playing wedding songs on his flute (c) singing songs of joy (d) playing woodland music.

11. "'When,' she asked in a trembly voice, 'did you become *enamored of* religion?'" ***Enamored of*** (205) means (a) captivated by (b) interested in (c) acquainted with (d) repulsed by.

12. "Mercifully, then, it snowed, which he would not put past Salzman's *machinations*." ***Machinations*** (206) means (a) imaginings (b) plottings (c) wishful thinking (d) preferences.

13. "But he had lived without knowledge of himself, and never ... *mea culpa*—had the truth been revealed to him." ***Mea culpa*** (206) means (a) because of his conscience (b) because of his innocence (c) through his studies (d) through his own fault.

14. "... he ... apologized *abjectly,* until *mortified,* she ran from him." ***Abjectly ... mortified*** ... (206) mean (a) loudly ... frightened (b) completely ... astonished (c) at great length ... bored (d) humbly ... embarrassed.

15. "But there was no sign of Salzman or his magic barrel, probably also a *figment* of the imagination." ***Figment*** (210) means (a) creator (b) fabrication (c) disaster (d) reaction.

Thinking Critically About the Story

1. "Most of the characters in this story have unlikable qualities, but they have one or more redeemable traits around which the story evolves." To what extent is this true of Leo? Salzman? Stella? What about them is not likable? Is likable? Would you choose any one of them as a close friend? Confidant? Explain.

2. Leo the idealist and Salzman the realist are in sharp contrast. Which one is better prepared to survive in the world of today? Which approach is closer to your own? To that of your best friend? A favorite relative of yours?

3. Would any of Salzman's suggested marriage partners have been a better choice for Leo? Why does he turn down the others for a possible association with Stella? Is love always unpredictable? Explain.

4. What is your opinion of arranged marriages? How do they compare with marriages based on love? Which method has the better chance of leading to a happy marriage? Would you be willing to be involved with a modern dating service? Give the reasons for your answer.

5. The printed story ends at the first formal meeting of Leo and Stella. In your opinion will they continue to see each other? What are their chances of "living together happily thereafter"? Explain.

6. What does Lily Hirschorn come to symbolize in Leo's life? Why? What lesson does he learn from meeting her? Why does the lesson depress him? How does he overcome his "blues"? How does his method compare with your cure for depressed feelings? Your best friend's or a character's in a recent TV drama? Why isn't the cure ever permanent?

Stories in Words

Portfolio (page 200), meaning "carrying case," has a simple derivation. It contains the root *port,* meaning "to carry," and the root *folio,* meaning "leaves." Books and documents once consisted of leaves of paper. Even today we speak of the "leaves" of a book. Other words include *foliage, defoliate,* and *exfoliate.* The *port* root creates a large family of words: *portage, import, export, portable, report, transportation, deport, porter,* and *portmanteau.*

Scholar (page 200) has an unexpected origin. Its immediate origin is not surprising, for it comes from Middle English *scole* and Latin *schola,* both meaning "school." But *schola* came from the Greek *skhole,* meaning "rest, relaxation, leisure." Perhaps you don't think of school as a place of leisure, but the ancient Greeks considered leisure as a time for learning, training, instruction. And so the word has come down to us.

Fascinating (page 205) suggests a link with witchcraft and spellbinding. It goes all the way back to the Latin *fasces,* a bundle of rods. The bundle, together with an ax, was the symbol of authority in ancient Rome. The Italian dictator, Benito Mussolini, chose the same symbol for his authoritarian regime, called *Fascism.* But what is the connection with witchcraft? The word *fascinus* meant "a magical spell." Eric Partridge suggests it referred to "a magical operation in which one tied up the victim." *Fascination* suggests casting a magical spell over someone. If you are *fascinated* by a special television program, it casts a spell over you and binds you to it.

The Darling
ANTON CHEKHOV

> And what was worst of all, she had no opinions of any sort. She saw the objects about her and understood what she saw, but could not form any opinion about them, and did not know what to talk about. And how awful it is not to have any opinions!

Love is a complex emotion often dissected by writers, but no writer can encompass its many dimensions. "The Darling" presents one of those dimensions. The central character, Olenka, is a model wife, concerned and loving. She is undemanding, placid, helpful, pretty. She gives all of herself to a relationship, asking very little in return. This certainly paints a pretty picture, almost perfect in its lack of conflict. Yet Olenka, and those around her, pay a price for those qualities.

One of the world's great short-story writers, Anton Chekhov presents his characters in deceptively simple lights. "The Darling" seems to be a straightforward account of a simple woman's life, but beneath the surface there are rumblings and uncertainties. Olenka is a transparent personality, but there are the complexities that affect the lives of all of us.

One problem with Russian fiction is the use of many names. In "The Darling," for example, *Kukin*, *Vanitchka*, and *Ivan Petrovich* are one and the same. *Vanitchka* is a pet name for *Ivan*. *Petrovich* indicates that Kukin's father was *Peter*. *Semyonovna* indicates that Olga (Olenka) is the daughter of *Semyon*. *Ovich* and *ovna* (called *patronymics*) are suffixes identifying parentage. When you are in doubt, pay close attention to the context. This will show you, for example, that *Pustovalov*, *Vassitchka*, and *Vassily Andreitch* are one and the same.

The insights gained are worth the effort.

The Darling

Olenka, the daughter of the retired collegiate assessor, Plemvanniakov, was sitting in her back porch, lost in thought. It was hot, the flies were persistent and teasing, and it was pleasant to reflect that it would soon be evening. Dark rainclouds were gathering from the east, and bringing from time to time a breath of moisture in the air.

Kukin, who was the manager of an open-air theater called the Tivoli, and who lived in the lodge, was standing in the middle of the garden looking at the sky.

"Again!" he observed despairingly. "It's going to rain again! Rain every day, as though to spite me. I might as well hang myself! It's ruin! Fearful losses every day."

He flung up his hands, and went on, addressing Olenka:

"There! that's the life we lead, Olga Semyonovna. It's enough to make one cry. One works and does one's utmost, one wears oneself out, getting no sleep at night, and racks one's brain what to do for the best. And then what happens? To begin with, one's public is ignorant, boorish. I give them the very best operetta, a dainty masque,* first rate music-hall artists. But do you suppose that's what they want! They don't understand anything of that sort. They want a clown; what they ask for is vulgarity. And then look at the weather! Almost every evening it rains. It started on the tenth of May, and it's kept it up all May and June. It's simply awful! The public doesn't come, but I've to pay the rent just the same, and pay the artists."

The next evening the clouds would gather again, and Kukin would say with an hysterical laugh:

"Well, rain away, then! Flood the garden, drown me! Damn my luck in this world and the next! Let the artists have me up! Send me to prison!—to Siberia!—the scaffold! Ha, ha, ha!"

And next day the same thing.

Olenka listened to Kukin with silent gravity, and sometimes tears came into her eyes. In the end his misfortunes touched her; she grew to love

**masque* medieval drama

him. He was a small thin man, with a yellow face, and curls combed forward on his forehead. He spoke in a thin tenor; as he talked his mouth worked on one side, and there was always an expression of despair on his face; yet he aroused a deep and genuine affection in her. She was always fond of some one, and could not exist without loving. In earlier days she had loved her papa, who now sat in a darkened room, breathing with difficulty; she had loved her aunt who used to come every other year from Bryansk; and before that, when she was at school, she had loved her French master. She was a gentle, soft-hearted, compassionate girl, with mild, tender eyes and very good health. At the sight of her full rosy cheeks, her soft white neck with a little dark mole on it, and the kind, naïve smile, which came into her face when she listened to anything pleasant, men thought, "Yes, not half bad," and smiled too, while lady visitors could not refrain from seizing her hand in the middle of a conversation, exclaiming in a gush of delight, "You darling!"

The house in which she had lived from her birth upwards, and which was left her in her father's will, was at the extreme end of the town, not far from the Tivoli. In the evenings and at night she could hear the band playing, and the crackling and banging of fireworks, and it seemed to her that it was Kukin struggling with his destiny, storming the entrenchments of his chief foe, the indifferent public; there was a sweet thrill at her heart, she had no desire to sleep, and when he returned home at daybreak, she tapped softly at her bedroom window, and showing him only her face and one shoulder through the curtain, she gave him a friendly smile. . . .

He proposed to her, and they were married. And when he had a closer view of her neck and her plump, fine shoulders, he threw up his hands, and said:

"You darling!"

He was happy, but as it rained on the day and night of his wedding, his face still retained an expression of despair.

They got on very well together. She used to sit in his office, to look after things in the Tivoli, to put down the accounts and pay the wages. And her rosy cheeks, her sweet, naïve, radiant smile, were to be seen now at the office window, now in the refreshment bar or behind the scenes of the theater. And already she used to say to her acquaintances that the theater was the chief and most important thing in life, and that it was only through the drama that one could derive true enjoyment and become cultivated and humane.

"But do you suppose the public understands that?" she used to say. "What they want is a clown. Yesterday we gave 'Faust Inside Out,' and almost all the boxes were empty; but if Vanitchka and I had been producing some vulgar thing, I assure you the theater would have been packed. Tomorrow Vanitchka and I are doing 'Orpheus in Hell.'* Do come."

And what Kukin said about the theater and the actors she repeated.

**Orpheus in Hell* French operetta by Jacques Offenbach

Like him she despised the public for their ignorance and their indifference to art; she took part in the rehearsals, she corrected the actors, she kept an eye on the behavior of the musicians, and when there was an unfavorable notice in the local paper, she shed tears, and then went to the editor's office to set things right.

The actors were fond of her and used to call her "Vanitchka and I," and "the darling"; she was sorry for them and used to lend them small sums of money, and if they deceived her, she used to shed a few tears in private, but did not complain to her husband.

They got on well in the winter too. They took the theater in the town for the whole winter, and let it for short terms to a little Russian company, or to a conjurer, or to a local dramatic society. Olenka grew stouter, and was always beaming with satisfaction, while Kukin grew thinner and yellower, and continually complained of their terrible losses, although he had not done badly all the winter. He used to cough at night, and she used to give him hot raspberry tea or limeflower water, to rub him with eau-de-Cologne and to wrap him in her warm shawls.

"You're such a sweet pet!" she used to say with perfect sincerity, stroking his hair. "You're such a pretty dear!"

Towards Lent he went to Moscow to collect a new troupe, and without him she could not sleep, but sat all night at her window, looking at the stars, and she compared herself with the hens, who are awake all night and uneasy when the cock is not in the henhouse. Kukin was detained in Moscow, and wrote that he would be back at Easter, adding some instructions about the Tivoli. But on the Sunday before Easter, late in the evening, came a sudden ominous knock at the gate; someone was hammering on the gate as though on a barrel—boom, boom, boom! The drowsy cook went flopping with her bare feet through the puddles, as she ran to open the gate.

"Please open," said some one outside in a thick bass. "There is a telegram for you."

Olenka had received telegrams from her husband before, but this time for some reason she felt numb with terror. With shaking hands she opened the telegram and read as follows:

"Ivan Petrovich died suddenly to-day. Awaiting immate instructions fufuneral Tuesday."

That was how it was written in the telegram—"fufuneral," and the utterly incomprehensible word "immate." It was signed by the stage manager of the operatic company.

"My darling!" sobbed Olenka. "Vanitchka, my precious, my darling! Why did I ever meet you! Why did I know you and love you! Your poor heartbroken Olenka is all alone without you!"

Kukin's funeral took place on Tuesday in Moscow, Olenka returned home on Wednesday, and as soon as she got indoors she threw herself on her bed and sobbed so loudly that it could be heard next door, and in the street.

"Poor darling!" the neighbors said, as they crossed themselves. "Olga Semyonovna, poor darling! How she does take on!"

Three months later Olenka was coming home from mass, melancholy and in deep mourning. It happened that one of her neighbors, Vassily Andreitch Pustovalov returning home from church, walked back beside her. He was the manager at Babakayev's, the timber merchant's. He wore a straw hat, a white waistcoat, and a gold watch chain, and looked more like a country gentleman than a man in trade.

"Everything happens as it is ordained, Olga Semyonovna," he said gravely, with a sympathetic note in his voice; "and if any of our dear ones die, it must be because it is the will of God, so we ought to have fortitude and bear it submissively."

After seeing Olenka to her gate, he said good-bye and went on. All day afterwards she heard his sedately dignified voice, and whenever she shut her eyes she saw his dark beard. She liked him very much. And apparently she had made an impression on him too, for not long afterwards an elderly lady, with whom she was only slightly acquainted, came to drink coffee with her, and as soon as she was seated at table began to talk about Pustovalov, saying that he was an excellent man whom one could thoroughly depend upon, and that any girl would be glad to marry him. Three days later Pustovalov came himself. He did not stay long, only about ten minutes, and he did not say much, but when he left, Olenka loved him—loved him so much that she lay awake all night in a perfect fever, and in the morning she sent for the elderly lady. The match was quickly arranged, and then came the wedding.

Pustovalov and Olenka got on very well together when they were married.

Usually he sat in the office till dinnertime, then he went out on business, while Olenka took his place, and sat in the office till evening, making up accounts and booking orders.

"Timber gets dearer every year; the price rises twenty per cent," she would say to her customers and friends. "Only fancy we used to sell local timber, and now Vassitchka always has to go for wood to the Mogilev district. And the freight!" she would add, covering her cheeks with her hands in horror. "The freight!"

It seemed to her that she had been in the timber trade for ages and ages, and that the most important and necessary thing in life was timber; and there was something intimate and touching to her in the very sound of words such as "balk," "post," "beam," "pole," "scantling," "batten," "lath," "plank," etc.

At night when she was asleep she dreamed of perfect mountains of planks and boards, and long strings of wagons, carting timber somewhere far away. She dreamed that a whole regiment of six-inch beams forty feet high, standing on end, was marching upon the timberyard; that logs, beams, and boards knocked together with the resounding crash of dry wood, kept falling and getting up again, piling themselves on each other. Olenka cried out in her sleep, and Pustovalov said to her tenderly: "Olenka, what's the matter, darling? Cross yourself!"

Her husband's ideas were hers. If he thought the room was too hot, or that business was slack, she thought the same. Her husband did not care for entertainments, and on holidays he stayed at home. She did likewise.

"You are always at home or in the office," her friends said to her. "You should go to the theater, darling, or to the circus."

"Vassitchka and I have no time to go to theaters," she would answer sedately. "We have no time for nonsense. What's the use of these theaters?"

On Saturdays Pustovalov and she used to go to the evening service; on holidays to early mass, and they walked side by side with softened faces as they came home from church. There was a pleasant fragrance about them both, and her silk dress rustled agreeably. At home they drank tea, with fancy bread and jams of various kinds, and afterwards they ate pie. Every day at twelve o'clock there was a savory smell of beet-root soup and of mutton or duck in their yard, and on fastdays of fish, and no one could pass the gate without feeling hungry. In the office the samovar was always boiling, and customers were regaled with tea and cracknels. Once a week the couple went to the baths and returned side by side, both red in the face.

"Yes, we have nothing to complain of, thank God," Olenka used to say to her acquaintances. "I wish every one were as well off as Vassitchka and I."

When Pustovalov went away to buy wood in the Mogilev district, she missed him dreadfully, lay awake and cried. A young veterinary surgeon in the army, called Smirnin, to whom they had let their lodge, used sometimes to come in in the evening. He used to talk to her and play cards with her, and this entertained her in her husband's absence. She was particularly interested in what he told her of his home life. He was married and had a little boy, but was separated from his wife because she had been unfaithful to him, and now he hated her and used to send her forty rubles a month for the maintenance of their son. And hearing of all this, Olenka sighed and shook her head. She was sorry for him.

"Well, God keep you," she used to say to him at parting, as she lighted him down the stairs with a candle. "Thank you for coming to cheer me up, and may the Mother of God give you health."

And she always expressed herself with the same sedateness and dignity, the same reasonableness, in imitation of her husband. As the veterinary surgeon was disappearing behind the door below, she would say:

"You know, Vladimir Platonitch, you'd better make it up with your wife. You should forgive her for the sake of your son. You may be sure the little fellow understands."

And when Pustovalov came back, she told him in a low voice about the veterinary surgeon and his unhappy home life, and both sighed and shook their heads and talked about the boy, who, no doubt, missed his father, and by some strange connection of ideas, they went up to the holy icons, bowed to the ground before them and prayed that God would give them children.

And so the Pustovalovs lived for six years quietly and peaceably in love and complete harmony.

But behold! one winter day after drinking hot tea in the office, Vassily Andreitch went out into the yard without his cap on to see about sending off some timber, caught cold and was taken ill. He had the best doctors, but he grew worse and died after four months' illness. And Olenka was a widow once more.

"I've nobody, now you've left me, my darling," she sobbed, after her husband's funeral. "How can I live without you, in wretchedness and misery! Pity me, good people, all alone in the world!"

She went about dressed in black with long "weepers,"* and gave up wearing hat and gloves for good. She hardly ever went out, except to church, or to her husband's grave, and led the life of a nun. It was not till six months later that she took off the weepers and opened the shutters of the windows. She was sometimes seen in the morning, going with her cook to market for provisions, but what went on in her house and how she lived now could only be surmised. People guessed, from seeing her drinking tea in her garden with the veterinary surgeon, who read the newspaper aloud to her, and from the fact that, meeting a lady she knew at the post office, she said to her:

"There is no proper veterinary inspection in our town, and that's the cause of all sorts of epidemics. One is always hearing of people's getting infection from the milk supply, or catching diseases from horses and cows. The health of domestic animals ought to be as well cared for as the health of human beings."

She repeated the veterinary surgeon's words, and was of the same opinion as he about everything. It was evident that she could not live a year without some attachment, and had found new happiness in the lodge. In anyone else this would have been censured, but no one could think ill of Olenka; everything she did was so natural. Neither she nor the veterinary surgeon said anything to other people of the change in their relations, and tried, indeed, to conceal it, but without success, for Olenka could not keep a secret. When he had visitors, men serving in his regiment, and she poured out tea or served the supper, she would begin talking of the cattle plague, of the foot and mouth disease, and of the municipal slaughterhouses. He was dreadfully embarrassed, and when the guests had gone, he would seize her by the hand and hiss angrily:

"I've asked you before not to talk about what you don't understand.

**weepers* black streamers worn as a sign of mourning

When we veterinary surgeons are talking among ourselves, please don't put your word in. It's really annoying."

And she would look at him with astonishment and dismay, and ask him in alarm: "But, Voloditchka, what *am* I to talk about?"

And with tears in her eyes she would embrace him, begging him not to be angry, and they were both happy.

But this happiness did not last long. The veterinary surgeon departed, departed forever with his regiment, when it was transferred to a distant place—to Siberia, it may be. And Olenka was left alone.

Now she was absolutely alone. Her father had long been dead, and his armchair lay in the attic, covered with dust and lame of one leg. She got thinner and plainer, and when people met her in the street they did not look at her as they used to, and did not smile to her; evidently her best years were over and left behind, and now a new sort of life had begun for her, which did not bear thinking about. In the evening Olenka sat in the porch, and heard the band playing and the fireworks popping in the Tivoli, but now the sound stirred no response. She looked into her yard without interest, thought of nothing, wished for nothing, and afterwards, when night came on she went to bed and dreamed of her empty yard. She ate and drank as it were unwillingly.

And what was worst of all, she had no opinions of any sort. She saw the objects about her and understood what she saw, but could not form any opinion about them, and did not know what to talk about. And how awful it is not to have any opinions! One sees a bottle, for instance, or the rain, or a peasant driving in his cart, but what the bottle is for, or the rain, or the peasant, and what is the meaning of it, one can't say, and could not even for a thousand rubles. When she had Kukin, or Pustovalov, or the veterinary surgeon, Olenka could explain everything, and give her opinion about anything you like, but now there was the same emptiness in her brain and in her heart as there was in her yard outside. And it was as harsh and as bitter as wormwood* in the mouth.

Little by little the town grew in all directions. The road became a street, and where the Tivoli and the timberyard had been, there were new turnings and houses. How rapidly time passes! Olenka's house grew dingy, the roof got rusty, the shed sank on one side, and the whole yard was overgrown with docks and stinging nettles. Olenka herself had grown plain and elderly; in summer she sat in the porch, and her soul, as before, was empty and dreary and full of bitterness. In winter she sat at her window and looked at the snow. When she caught the scent of spring, or heard the chime of the church bells, a sudden rush of memories from the past came over her, there was a tender ache in her heart, and her eyes brimmed over with tears; but this was only for a minute, and then came emptiness again and the sense of the futility of life. The black kitten, Briska, rubbed against her and purred softly, but Olenka was not touched by these feline caresses.

*_wormwood_ a bitter herb

That was not what she needed. She wanted a love that would absorb her whole being, her whole soul and reason—that would give her ideas and an object in life, and would warm her old blood. And she would shake the kitten off her skirt and say with vexation:

"Get along; I don't want you!"

And so it was, day after day and year after year, and no joy, and no opinions. Whatever Mavra, the cook, said she accepted.

One hot July day, towards evening, just as the cattle were being driven away, and the whole yard was full of dust, someone suddenly knocked at the gate. Olenka went to open it herself and was dumbfounded when she looked out: she saw Smirnin, the veterinary surgeon, greyheaded, and dressed as a civilian. She suddenly remembered everything. She could not help crying and letting her head fall on his breast without uttering a word, and in the violence of her feelings she did not notice how they both walked into the house and sat down to tea.

"My dear Vladimir Platonitch! What fate has brought you?" she muttered, trembling with joy.

"I want to settle here for good, Olga Semyonovna," he told her. "I have resigned my post, and have come to settle down and try my luck on my own account. Besides, it's time for my boy to go to school. He's a big boy. I am reconciled with my wife, you know."

"Where is she?" asked Olenka.

"She's at the hotel with the boy, and I'm looking for lodgings."

"Good gracious, my dear soul! Lodgings? Why not have my house? Why shouldn't that suit you? Why, my goodness, I wouldn't take any rent!" cried Olenka in a flutter, beginning to cry again. "You live here, and the lodge will do nicely for me. Oh dear! how glad I am!"

Next day the roof was painted and the walls were whitewashed, and Olenka, with her arms akimbo, walked about the yard giving directions. Her face was beaming with her old smile, and she was brisk and alert as though she had waked from a long sleep. The veterinary's wife arrived—a thin, plain lady, with short hair and a peevish expression. With her was her little Sasha, a boy of ten, small for his age, blue-eyed, chubby, with dimples in his cheeks. And scarcely had the boy walked into the yard when he ran after the cat, and at once there was the sound of his gay, joyous laugh.

"Is that your puss, auntie?" he asked Olenka. "When she has little ones, do give us a kitten. Mamma is awfully afraid of mice."

Olenka talked to him, and gave him tea. Her heart warmed and there was a sweet ache in her bosom, as though the boy had been her own child. And when he sat at the table in the evening, going over his lessons, she looked at him with deep tenderness and pity as she murmured to herself:

"You pretty pet! . . . my precious! . . . Such a fair little thing, and so clever."

"'An island is a piece of land which is entirely surrounded by water,'" he read aloud.

"An island is a piece of land," she repeated, and this was the first opinion to which she gave utterance with positive conviction after so many years of silence and dearth of ideas.

Now she had opinions of her own, and at supper she talked to Sasha's parents, saying how difficult the lessons were at the high schools, but that yet the high school was better than a commercial one, since with a high-school education all careers were open to one, such as being a doctor or an engineer.

Sasha began going to the high school. His mother departed to Harkov to her sister's and did not return; his father used to go off every day to inspect cattle, and would often be away from home for three days together, and it seemed to Olenka as though Sasha was entirely abandoned, that he was not wanted at home, that he was being starved, and she carried him off to her lodge and gave him a little room there.

And for six months Sasha had lived in the lodge with her. Every morning Olenka came into his bedroom and found him fast asleep, sleeping noiselessly with his hand under his cheek. She was sorry to wake him.

"Sashenka," she would say mournfully, "get up, darling. It's time for school."

He would get up, dress and say his prayers, and then sit down to breakfast, drink three glasses of tea, and eat two large cracknels and a half a buttered roll. All this time he was hardly awake and a little ill-humored in consequence.

"You don't quite know your fable, Sashenka," Olenka would say, looking at him as though he were about to set off on a long journey. "What a lot of trouble I have with you! You must work and do your best, darling, and obey your teachers."

"Oh, do leave me alone!" Sasha would say.

Then he would go down the street to school, a little figure, wearing a big cap and carrying a satchel on his shoulder. Olenka would follow him noiselessly.

"Sashenka!" she would call after him, and she would pop into his hand a date or a caramel. When he reached the street where the school was, he would feel ashamed of being followed by a tall, stout woman; he would turn round and say:

"You'd better go home, auntie. I can go the rest of the way alone."

She would stand still and look after him fixedly till he had disappeared at the school gate.

Ah, how she loved him! Of her former attachments not one had been so deep; never had her soul surrendered to any feeling so spontaneously, so disinterestedly, and so joyously as now that her maternal instincts were aroused. For this little boy with the dimple in his cheek and the big school cap, she would have given her whole life, she would have given it with joy and tears of tenderness. Why? Who can tell why?

When she had seen the last of Sasha, she returned home, contented and serene, brimming over with love; her face, which had grown younger during the last six months, smiled and beamed; people meeting her looked at her with pleasure.

"Good morning, Olga Semyonovna, darling. How are you, darling?"

"The lessons at the high school are very difficult now," she would relate at the market. "It's too much; in the first class yesterday they gave him a fable to learn by heart, and a Latin translation and a problem. You know it's too much for a little chap."

And she would begin talking about the teachers, the lessons, and the school books, saying just what Sasha said.

At three o'clock they had dinner together: in the evening they learned their lessons together and cried. When she put him to bed, she would stay a long time making the Cross over him and murmuring a prayer; then she would go to bed and dream of that far-away misty future when Sasha would finish his studies and become a doctor or an engineer, would have a big house of his own with horses and a carriage, would get married and have children. . . . She would fall asleep still thinking of the same thing, and tears would run down her cheeks from her closed eyes, while the black cat lay purring beside her: "Mrr, mrr, mrr."

Suddenly there would come a loud knock at the gate.

Olenka would wake up breathless with alarm, her heart throbbing. Half a minute later would come another knock.

"It must be a telegram from Harkov," she would think, beginning to tremble from head to foot. "Sasha's mother is sending for him from Harkov. . . . Oh, mercy on us!"

She was in despair. Her head, her hands, and her feet would turn chill, and she would feel that she was the most unhappy woman in the world. But another minute would pass, voices would be heard: it would turn out to be the veterinary surgeon coming home from the club.

"Well, thank God!" she would think.

And gradually the load in her heart would pass off, and she would feel at ease. She would go back to bed thinking of Sasha, who lay sound asleep in the next room, sometimes crying out in his sleep:

"I'll give it you! Get away! Shut up!"

Reading for Understanding

❑ MAIN IDEA

1. The main point of the story can best be summed up in which of the following sentences? (a) "She was always fond of someone, and could not exist without loving." (b) "And so the Pustovalovs lived for six years quietly and peaceably in love and complete harmony." (c) "She was particularly interested in what he told her of his home life." (d) "Olenka could not keep a secret."

❑ DETAILS

2. Olenka's first husband (a) was a veterinarian (b) managed an open-air theater (c) was a soldier (d) was cruel to her.
3. Vanitchka (a) returned to Olenka after many years (b) was a skilled actor (c) died in Moscow (d) replaced Kukin in Olenka's affections.
4. Smirnin (a) was a brother of Kukin's (b) was Olenka's third husband (c) was in the timber trade (d) was the father of Sasha.
5. Sasha was (a) a friend of Kukin's (b) Olenka's dead father (c) a schoolboy (d) a schoolteacher.

❑ INFERENCES

6. *Vanitchka* and *Vassitchka* (a) are pet names (b) were the names of two brothers (c) refer to officials in Olenka's village (d) were names used in the voting registers.
7. After Olenka married her second husband, she (a) scorned the profession of her first husband (b) learned to manage the theater (c) disagreed with him on several key issues (d) soon began to dislike him.
8. Olenka's opinions were always (a) original (b) disagreeable (c) those of the people she loved (d) based on her own experiences.
9. Sasha probably (a) intended to follow in his father's footsteps (b) found Olenka's attentions overwhelming (c) wanted to marry a person just like Olenka (d) especially enjoyed his Latin lessons.

❑ FIGURE OF SPEECH

10. The best image to describe Olenka is a (a) hammer (b) mirror (c) snake (d) panther.

❑ AUTHOR'S ATTITUDE

11. The author's attitude toward Olenka can best be characterized as (a) bitterly antagonistic (b) totally opposed in all respects (c) sympathetic but disapproving (d) amused.

❑ ORDER OF EVENTS

12. Arrange the items in the order in which they occurred. Use letters only.

    A. Olenka takes care of Sasha.
    B. Kukin goes to Moscow.

C. Smirnin's regiment is transferred.
D. Olenka marries Kukin.
E. Smirnin returns as a civilian.

❑ OUTCOMES

13. In time, Sasha will probably (a) become a famous veterinary surgeon (b) go into the timber business (c) become a teacher (d) abandon Olenka.

❑ CAUSE AND EFFECT

14. One reason for Olenka's popularity in town is her (a) basic sweetness (b) courageous fight for human rights (c) refusal to smother others with her love (d) descent from famous forebears.

❑ FACT OR OPINION

Tell whether the following is a fact or an opinion.

15. The veterinarian wanted to settle down in Olenka's village.

Words in Context

1. "One works and does one's utmost . . . and *racks one's brain* what to do for the best. And then what happens?" ***Racks one's brain*** (218) means (a) succeeds handsomely in planning (b) gets nowhere in planning (c) just breaks even in planning (d) strains with great effort in planning.
2. "To begin with, one's public is ignorant, *boorish*." ***Boorish*** (218) means (a) economy-minded (b) backward (c) unrefined (d) timid.
3. "Olenka listened to Kukin with silent *gravity*, and sometimes tears came into her eyes." ***Gravity*** (218) means (a) understanding (b) seriousness (c) sympathy (d) attention.
4. "She was a gentle, soft-hearted, *compassionate* girl, with mild, tender eyes and very good health." ***Compassionate*** (219) means (a) beautiful (b) intelligent (c) humane (d) tense.
5. ". . . it seemed to her that it was Kukin struggling with his destiny, storming the *entrenchments* of his chief foe, the *indifferent* public." ***Entrenchments . . . indifferent*** (219) mean (a) fortifications . . . unconcerned (b) vanities . . . fickle (c) prejudices . . . frugal (d) dislikes . . . stolid.

6. "But on the Sunday before Easter, late in the afternoon, came a sudden *ominous* knock at the gate ..." ***Ominous*** (220) means (a) thundering (b) foreboding (c) unexpected (d) sharp.

7. "Everything happens as it is *ordained,* Olga Semyonovna, ... it must be because it is the will of God ..." ***Ordained*** (221) means (a) destined (b) worshiped (c) conjectured (d) hoped for.

8. "... so we ought to have *fortitude* and bear it *submissively.*" ***Fortitude* ... *submissively*** ... (221) mean (a) faith ... sensitively (b) strength ... intelligently (c) insight ... with moderation (d) courage ... meekly.

9. "All day afterwards she heard his *sedately* dignified voice ..." ***Sedately*** (221) means (a) obviously (b) levelheadedly (c) subtly (d) conspicuously.

10. "Every day at twelve o'clock there was a *savory* smell of beet-root soup and of mutton or duck in their yard ..." ***Savory*** (222) means (a) heavy (b) distinctive (c) recognizable (d) appetizing.

11. "In the office the *samovar* was always boiling, and customers were *regaled* with tea and *cracknels.*" ***Samovar* ... *regaled* ... *cracknels*** ... (222) mean (a) ... water ... fed ... pieces of cake (b) ... tea urn ... entertained ... hard biscuits (c) ... coffeepot ... overfed ... small sandwiches (d) ... gossip ... humored ... pointed anecdotes.

12. "... but what went on in her house and how she lived now could only be *surmised.*" ***Surmised*** (223) means (a) inferred (b) narrated (c) disapproved (d) pitied.

13. "In anyone else this would have been *censured,* but no one could think ill of Olenka ..." ***Censured*** (223) means (a) acceptable (b) disquieting (c) denounced (d) understandable.

14. "... and Olenka, with her *arms akimbo,* walked about the yard giving directions." ***Arms akimbo*** (225) means (a) with hands held high (b) with palms up (c) with palms pressed together (d) with hands on hips.

15. "... to which she gave utterance with positive conviction after so many years of silence and *dearth* of ideas." ***Dearth*** (226) means (a) oversupply (b) richness (c) scarcity (d) sufficiency.

Thinking Critically About the Story

1. Be prepared to evaluate Olenka's definition of love. "She wanted a love that would absorb her whole being, her whole soul and reason—that

would give her ideas and an object in life." To what extent do you agree with her? Disagree? Give the reasons for your answer.

2. Is Olenka a dynamic character, being molded by circumstances?

3. How do the men in Olenka's years of maturity compare with each other? Are they "typical men"? How do they compare with the men you know as relatives? Parents' friends? TV soap opera characters? Would you set them as "good examples" for your brother (cousin, best friend) to follow?

4. Why did so many people who know Olenka call her "darling"? Would a feminist, one who advocates equality of men and women, call her a darling? Would you call her a darling? Would you use her as a model for the formation of your own or your sister's (cousin's) character? Give the reasons for your answer.

5. To what extent do you agree with the following statement?

   "The Darling" is told by an omniscient author who takes the reader at will from the consciousness of one character to that of another."

   Would the story have been more effective if it had been told solely from the point of view of Olenka or of one of the men in her life? Explain.

6. In introducing characters Chekhov often develops a detailed objective statement that gives the reader a brief sketch of the lives they have been leading. Be prepared to read to the class the capsule that you found most effective. Give the reasons for your choice. What did Chekhov achieve by using this method? Advantages? Disadvantages?

Stories in Words

Compassionate (219) and *sympathetic* (221) have many elements in common. In both words the root word means "to suffer." Originally, *passion* was "suffering," as in *The Passion Play*. Both *patient* and *patience* were connected with the idea of suffering. A *compassionate* person is one who "suffers with" another. Coincidentally, a *sympathetic* person, by derivation, is also one who "suffers with" another. The *path* root also appears in *pathetic* and *pathology*. Though the Latin root is *pass* and the Greek *path*, they were probably linked in early Indo-European languages.

Epidemic (223) has two common Greek elements: *epi*—"upon" and *dem*—"people." An *epidemic* is a disease that is visited *upon the people*. *Epi* appears in *epitaph* (on a tomb), as well as many other words. *Dem* appears in *democracy* (rule of the *people*) and *demagogue* (a false leader of the *people*).

Journey (226) is an example of a word that has expanded its meaning. It is derived from the French word *jour* (day), which is itself derived from the Latin *dies*. A *journey* was apparently a *day's* travel, but now the word has expanded to mean a trip of any duration. The word *journal* also has the idea of *day*—a record of *day-to-day* events. An *adjourned* meeting will assemble at another *day*. *Sojourn* meant a stay as a temporary resident, perhaps a *day* at a time. Not all words expand in meaning, however. *Meat*, for example, has contracted. In *meat and drink*, *meat* once meant any solid food. Some words go uphill. A *marshal* was once a servant in charge of horses. Some go downhill. A *villain* was once just a villager.

The Many Faces of Love

Getting Technical

Terms

dynamic character	protagonist	verisimilitude
irony	sentimental	

Definitions Match each of the above terms with its definition.

1. Acceptable presentation of reality
2. Hero; person around whom the plot evolves
3. Resulting from excessive feeling rather than from reason or thought
4. Incongruity between words and their meaning, between appearance and reality, or between actions and results
5. One who changes as the result of plot action

Examples Match each of the following actions with the appropriate term.

1. With the years she became wiser and more tolerant of the weaknesses of others.
2. His love of humanity was so great that he wept freely on reading of the fate of the villain.
3. The description had the sense of probability, of a photograph that has not been touched up.
4. Because of his fatal illness, he never learned of his final victory.

5. The master criminal outwitted the forces of justice on TV every Friday night for three years.
6. "'Tis love and love alone that rules the world."
7. Because of the nightmare, Scrooge's attitude toward the people and the world around him altered dramatically.
8. He was so meticulous in his painting that many times viewers stopped to clear the lipstick smudge off the rim of the cup the model was holding.

Application Match each of the following quotations with the appropriate term.

1. For this little boy with the dimple in his cheek and the big school cap, she would have given her whole life, she would have given it with joy and tears of tenderness. Why? Who can tell why? ("The Darling")
2. "Poor old Lilian," Julie said. ("Weekend")
3. She waited uneasily and shyly. From afar he saw that her eyes—clearly her father's—were filled with desperate innocence. ("The Magic Barrel")
4. Lilian's room was in the old part of the house—seventeenth century, Julie had said. Lilian allowed a century either way, for Julie's imprecision and the exaggeration of the estate agent. ("Weekend")
5. But her voice stopped him . . . "Indeed?" she heard herself say. "You and who else?" ("Sunday in the Park")
6. With a quick motion of his hand he stripped the fish out of its skin and began ravenously to chew. ("The Magic Barrel")

Thinking Critically About the Stories

1. Compare the attitude of each of the following toward love.

   Group One Olenka in "The Darling"
   The wife in "Sunday in the Park"
   Julie, the wife in "Weekend"
   Group Two Kukin in "The Darling"
   Leo Finkle in "The Magic Barrel"
   Ben, the husband in "Weekend"

   Which one comes closest to your own attitude? Which one differs most sharply from that of your favorite relative? Which one has an attitude that leads best toward marital happiness?

2. Which of the following characters seems to you to be the most mature? Refer to the incidents in the story to support your reasoning.

   Group One Leo Finkle in the "Magic Barrel"
   Morton in "Sunday in the Park"
   Pustovalov in "The Darling"
   Group Two Lilian in "Weekend"
   The mother in "Sunday in the Park"
   Stella in "The Magic Barrel"

3. Compare Morton of "Sunday in the Park" with Pinye Salzman in "The Magic Barrel." Why are they survivors? Which one would make a better friend? How do they compare with your grown-up relatives?

4. The stories in this unit have a wide range of approaches to life and to love. Which one gave you most to think about? Which one revealed most about human nature? Which one will you remember longest? Justify your choices.

5. Compare the use of dialog in each of these stories. Which author proved to be most skillful in letting the characters talk the plot? Be prepared to read to the class excerpts to prove your statements.

Writing and Other Activities

1. Using the Chekhov thumbnail sketches as your model, write a paragraph that will introduce to the reader each of the following characters.
   a. Jill has broken off for the fourth time with her steady. She meets Alan on the school cafeteria line. She is going to accept Alan's date offer.
   b. Harold's parents have just told him that they are planning to separate. Harold is devastated and leaves for a walk to clear his head. He meets the basketball coach, and they will discuss Harold's choices.
   c. Paula has just dented two fenders on the family car. The accident was most likely her fault. But no one was hurt. How is she to handle the problem with her parents? On the scene comes her older sister, Francie. They will discuss.
   d. Herb has decided to quit the basketball team because he was not elected captain. He is going to open his heart to cousin Penny.

2. Use Malamud's technique of building through dialog and action as your model. (A good example begins on page 200 when Salzman begins to read his cards.) Develop one of the following scenes for a few pages:
   a. Older Brother is trying to con nimble Younger Brother into lending him a prized possession or into trading chores.

b. The wily door-to-door salesman delivers half-truths to Sarah, who is not gullible enough to fall for them.
c. Candidate for office is heckled into defeat by well-informed members of the audience.
d. Marge has been going steady with Alvie for almost two months. She finds him too self-centered. Marge has decided on a firm, polite confrontation—and quits. They are sitting outside on a delightful summer evening.

3. Lead a roundtable discussion on one of the following topics:
   a. Puppy Love, Infatuation, and the Real Thing. Is there a difference? Is there a litmus test to reveal this difference? Can soap operas act as reliable guides?
   b. Going Steady and College Plans. Is there a sensible mixture? How can both be handled without anyone's getting hurt?
   c. Is College for Everyone? What is college for, anyway? Can you safely delay going to college for a year or so? Is it sensible for a capable girl (boy) to avoid the college experience? Is a two-year college experience better than no taste at all? Cite people you know about to support your point of view.
   d. Careers and Career Planning. So many adults we know drift into careers without ever setting their sights on a desired goal and then striving to reach it. What is the most sensible way of deciding on a career? Is selection and success in it just a matter of chance? Should girls have career plans?

4. Write an editorial for the class or grade bulletin on one of the following topics:
   a. What is the role of women in our generation in the family setup of the future? Will there be two breadwinners? Whose career should be given priority?
   b. With all this talk about women's rights, what should be the role in the family of the man of the future? Explain.
   c. "Handling the Sword of Damocles." In your opinion, how should members of our generation deal with:

      Poverty in Our Country
      Poverty Anywhere in the World
      Famine in Distressed Countries
      Lack of Medical Attention Among the Deprived

   d. Are You Your Brother's and Sister's Keeper? To what extent should our generation be held responsible for lives without education in this country? Throughout the world?

5. Write a telephone monolog for one of the following calls:
   a. To the local-store manager who is destroying the business through his (her) mishandling of the customers and employees.

b. To the friend who is so intent on revealing his (her) keen sense of humor that he (she) doesn't care who gets hurt.
c. To the relative who insists on telling the truth to all just as she (he) sees it without realizing the damage being committed.
d. The boy (girl) on the block who has so low an estimate of his (her) ability and worth that he (she) doesn't even try to succeed.

Stories in Words: A Review

A. canter	E. discipline	I. nostalgia
B. compassionate	F. epidemic	J. portfolio
C. cretonne	G. fascinating	K. rapt
D. deliberately	H. journey	L. scholar

Answer the following questions by choosing a word from the list above. Use letters only.

Which of the words above . . .

1. ______ contains the idea of *suffering?*
2. ______ is based on a root meaning "leisure?"
3. ______ is derived from the name of a famous English shrine?
4. ______ is based on the root meaning "to learn"?
5. ______ contains the idea of *weighing?*
6. ______ has something to do with a *magical spell?*
7. ______ is something visited *on the people?*
8. ______ is derived from a word meaning "day"?
9. ______ has the basic root meaning "carry"?
10. ______ comes from the name of a Normandy village?

Both fantasy and science fiction (pages 431ff) stretch our imaginations and depend upon wonder for much of their appeal. But there is a striking difference. Science fiction takes current events and knowledge and extrapolates them. Extrapolation has been defined as the projection of known data into an area not yet known or experienced. Fantasy is different.

In fantasy, anything can happen. Natural laws as we understand them are suspended. Miraculous events occur without explanation. It is enough that they happen. Ours is not to reason why.

Fantasy is a major ingredient of the stories of childhood. Clicking shoes together will never send a person to Oz. Talking engines do not occur in the real world. Wolves don't swallow grandmothers only to disgorge the grandmothers in good health. Children find these stories irresistible.

5

The Willing Suspension of Disbelief

Fantasy—what reality becomes when we ask enough questions of it.

John Ciardi

So, in a way, do adults. Adult fantasy resembles the fantasies of childhood, though the stories are more sophisticated, as in this unit. Cats don't actually speak. Magicians don't counter each others' mystical powers. No one can "stop the world." A supernatural wish does not play a part in the life of an ordinary couple.

In recent years, both the movies and television have tapped the adult interest in fantasy. As we grow older, most of us never quite lose that sense of awe, an interest in things as they can never be. When we read fantasy, we make a contract with the author to accept the unbelievable. We undergo "a willing suspension of disbelief." Suspend your disbelief for a little while. Enjoy this excursion into the world of wonder.

The Witch's Cat

MANLY WADE WELLMAN

Jael Bettiss was mystified, for once in her relationship with Gib. She took the thing from him, turned it over, and saw a reflection.

She screamed.

Though the word *Gib,* short for *Gilbert,* was a common name for a cat, Gib in this story is no ordinary cat. Like all cats, Gib has an instinctive love of a place, a loyalty to a house, an emotion that goes beyond an attachment to people. Gib is a good cat, a moral cat, but when his connection with his beloved house is threatened, Gib shows quite another side.

A modern story about witches is difficult to carry off. The witches of history have often been pathetic old women who were condemned for irrelevant reasons. The witches of fiction, like those in *Macbeth,* have often been instruments of evil. Jael Bettiss, in "The Witch's Cat," is unashamedly evil.

The story is remarkable for several reasons. It is written with a sly touch of humor. It provides honest suspense and a sense of tension. It depicts a fascinatingly malevolent old woman. Most important, it humanizes a cat and makes him the protagonist. The reader cannot resist cheering Gib on to the fateful resolution.

The Witch's Cat

Old Jael Bettiss, who lived in the hollow among the cypresses, was not a real witch.

It makes no difference that folk thought she was, and walked fearfully wide of her shadow. Nothing can be proved by the fact that she was as disgustingly ugly without as she was wicked within. It is quite irrelevant that evil was her study and profession and pleasure. She was no witch; she only pretended to be.

Jael Bettiss knew that all laws providing for the punishment of witches had been repealed, or at the least forgotten. As to being feared and hated, that was meat and drink to Jael Bettiss, living secretly alone in the hollow.

The house and the hollow belonged to a kindly old villager, who had been elected marshal and was too busy to look after his property. Because he was easygoing and perhaps a little daunted, he let Jael Bettiss live there rent-free. The house was no longer snug; the back of its roof was broken in, the eaves drooped slackly. At some time or other the place had been painted brown, before that with ivory black. Now both coats of color peeled away in huge flakes, making the clapboards seem scrofulous. The windows had been broken in every small, grubby pane, and mended with coarse brown paper, so that they were like cast and blurred eyes. Behind was the muddy, bramble-choked backyard, and behind that yawned the old quarry, now abandoned and full of black water. As for the inside—but few ever saw it.

Jael Bettiss did not like people to come into her house. She always met callers on the old cracked doorstep, draped in a cloak of shadowy black, with gray hair straggling, her nose as hooked and sharp as the beak of a buzzard, her eyes filmy and sore-looking, her wrinkle-bordered mouth always grinning and showing her yellow, chisel-shaped teeth.

The nearby village was an old-fashioned place, with stone flags instead of concrete for pavements, and the villagers were the simplest of men and women. From them Jael Bettiss made a fair living, by selling love philters, or herbs to cure sickness, or charms to ward off bad luck. When she wanted extra money, she would wrap her old black cloak about her and, tramping along a country road, would stop at a cowpen and ask the farmer what he would do if his cows went dry. The farmer, worried, usually came at dawn next day to her hollow and bought a good-luck charm. Occasionally the cows would go dry anyway, by accident of nature, and their owner would pay more and more, until their milk returned to them.

Now and then, when Jael Bettiss came to the door, there came with her the gaunt black cat, Gib.

Gib was not truly black, any more than Jael Bettiss was truly a witch. He had been born with white markings at muzzle, chest, and forepaws, so that he looked to be in full evening dress. Left alone, he would have grown fat and fluffy. But Jael Bettiss, who wanted a fearsome pet, kept all his white spots smeared with thick soot, and underfed him to make him look rakish and lean.

On the night of the full moon, she would drive poor Gib from her door. He would wander to the village in search of food, and would wail mournfully in the yards. Awakened householders would angrily throw boots or pans or sticks of kindling. Often Gib was hit, and his cries were sharpened by pain. When that happened, Jael Bettiss took care to be seen next morning with a bandage on head or wrist. Some of the simplest villagers thought that Gib was really the old woman, magically transformed. Her reputation grew, as did Gib's unpopularity. But Gib did not deserve mistrust—like all cats, he was a practical philosopher, who wanted to be comfortable and quiet and dignified. At bottom, he was amiable. Like all cats, too, he loved his home above all else; and the house in the hollow, be it ever so humble and often cruel, was home. It was unthinkable to him that he might live elsewhere.

In the village he had two friends—black-eyed John Frey, the storekeeper's son, who brought the mail to and from the county seat, and Ivy Hill, pretty blonde daughter of the town marshal, the same town marshal who owned the hollow and let Jael Bettiss live in the old house. John Frey and Ivy Hill were so much in love with each other that they loved everything else, even black-stained, hungry Gib. He was grateful; if he had been able, he would have loved them in return. But his little heart had room for one devotion only, and that was given to the house in the hollow.

One day, Jael Bettiss slouched darkly into old Mr. Frey's store, and up to the counter that served as a post office. Leering, she gave John Frey a letter. It was directed to a certain little-known publisher, asking for a certain little-known book. Several days later, she appeared again, received a parcel, and bore it to her home.

In her gloomy, secret parlor, she unwrapped her purchase. It was a small, drab volume, with no title on cover or back. Sitting at the rickety table, she began to read. All evening and most of the night she read, forgetting to give Gib his supper, though he sat hungrily at her feet.

At length, an hour before dawn, she finished. Laughing loudly and briefly, she turned her beak-nose toward the kerosene lamp on the table.

From the book she read aloud two words. The lamp went out, though she had not blown at it. Jael Bettiss spoke one commanding word more, and the lamp flamed alight again.

"At last!" she cried out in shrill exultation, and grinned down at Gib. Her lips drew back from her yellow chisels of teeth. "At last!" she crowed again. "Why don't you speak to me, you little brute? . . . Why don't you, indeed?"

She asked that final question as though she had been suddenly inspired. Quickly she glanced through the back part of the book, howled with laughter over something she found there, then sprang up and scuttled like a big, filthy crab into the dark, windowless cell that was her kitchen. There she mingled salt and malt in the palm of her skinny right hand. After that, she rummaged out a bundle of dried herbs, chewed them fine, and spat them into the mixture. Stirring again with her forefinger, she returned to the parlor. Scanning the book to refresh her memory, she muttered a nasty little rhyme. Finally she dashed the mess suddenly upon Gib.

He retreated, shaking himself, outraged and startled. In a corner he sat down, and bent his head to lick the smeared fragments of the mixture away. But they revolted his tongue and palate, and he paused in the midst of this chore, so important to cats; and meanwhile Jael Bettiss yelled, "Speak!"

Gib crouched and blinked, feeling sick. His tongue came out and steadied his lips. Finally he said: "I want something to eat."

His voice was small and high, like a little child's, but entirely understandable. Jael Bettiss was so delighted that she laughed and clapped her bony knees with her hands, in self-applause.

"It worked!" she cried. "No more humbug about me, you understand? I'm a real witch at last, and not a fraud!"

Gib found himself able to understand all this, more clearly than he had ever understood human affairs before. "I want something to eat," he said again, more definitely than before. "I didn't have any supper, and it's nearly—"

"Oh, stow your gab!" snapped his mistress. "It's this book, crammed with knowledge and strength, that made me able to do it. I'll never be without it again, and it'll teach me all the things I've only guessed at and mumbled about. I'm a real witch now, I say. And if you don't think I'll make those ignorant sheep of villagers realize it—"

Once more she went off into gales of wild, cracked mirth, and threw a dish at Gib. He darted away into a corner just in time, and the missile crashed into blue-and-white china fragments against the wall. But Jael Bettiss read aloud from her book an impressive gibberish, and the dish reformed itself on the floor; the bits crept together and joined and the cracks disappeared, as trickling drops of water form into a pool. And finally, when the witch's twiglike forefinger beckoned, the dish floated upward like a leaf in a breeze and set itself gently back on the table. Gib watched warily.

"That's small to what I shall do hereafter," swore Jael Bettiss.

When next the mail was distributed at the general store, a dazzling stranger appeared.

She wore a cloak, an old-fashioned black coat, but its drapery did not conceal the tall perfection of her form. As for her face, it would have stirred interest and admiration in larger and more sophisticated gatherings than the knot of letter-seeking villagers. Its beauty was scornful but inviting, classic but warm, with something in it of Grecian sculpture and Oriental allure. If the nose was cruel, it was straight; if the lips were sullen, they were full; if the forehead was a suspicion low, it was white and smooth. Thick, thunder-black hair swept up from that forehead, and backward to a knot at the neck. The eyes glowed with strange, hot lights, and wherever they turned they pierced and captivated.

People moved away to let her have a clear, sweeping pathway forward to the counter. Until this stranger had entered, Ivy Hill was the loveliest person present; now she looked only modest and fresh and blonde in her starched gingham, and worried to boot. As a matter of fact, Ivy Hill's insides felt cold and topsy-turvy, because she saw how fascinated was the sudden attention of John Frey.

"Is there," asked the newcomer in a deep, creamy voice, "any mail for me?"

"Wh-what name, ma'am?" asked John Frey, his brown young cheeks turning full crimson.

"Bettiss. Jael Bettiss."

He began to fumble through the sheaf of envelopes, with hands that shook. "Are you," he asked, "any relation to the old lady of that name, the one who lives in the hollow?"

"Yes, of a sort." She smiled a slow, conquering smile. "She's my—aunt. Yes. Perhaps you see the family resemblance?" Wider and wider grew the smile with which she assaulted John Frey. "If there isn't any mail," she went on, "I would like a stamp. A one-cent stamp."

Turning to his little metal box on the shelf behind, John Frey tore a single green stamp from the sheet. His hand shook still more as he gave it to the customer and received in exchange a copper cent.

There was really nothing exceptional about the appearance of that copper cent. It looked brown and a little worn, with Lincoln's head on it, and a date—1957. But John Frey felt a sudden glow in the hand that took it, a glow that shot along his arm and into his heart. He gazed at the coin as if he had never seen its like before. And he put it slowly into his pocket, a different pocket from the one in which he usually kept change, and placed another coin in the till to pay for the stamp. Poor Ivy Hill's blue eyes grew round and downright miserable. Plainly he meant to keep that copper piece as a souvenir. But John Frey gazed only at the stranger, raptly, as though he were suddenly stunned or hypnotized.

The dark, sullen beauty drew her cloak more tightly around her and moved regally out of the store and away toward the edge of town.

As she turned up the brush-hidden trail to the hollow, a change came.

Not that her step was less young and free, her figure less queenly, her eyes dimmer, or her beauty short of perfect. All these were as they had been; but her expression became set and grim, her body tense, and her head high and truculent. It was as though, beneath that young loveliness, lurked an old and evil heart, which was precisely what did lurk there, it does not boot to conceal. But none saw except Gib, the black cat with soot-covered white spots, who sat on the doorstep of the ugly cottage. Jael Bettiss thrust him aside with her foot and entered.

In the kitchen she filled a tin basin from a wooden bucket, and threw into the water a pinch of coarse green powder with an unpleasant smell. As she stirred it in with her hands, they seemed to grow skinny and harsh. Then she threw great palmfuls of the liquid into her face and over her head, and other changes came. . . .

The woman who returned to the front door, where Gib watched with a cat's apprehensive interest, was hideous old Jael Bettiss, whom all the village knew and avoided.

"He's trapped," she shrilled triumphantly. "That penny, the one I soaked for three hours in a love philter, trapped him the moment he touched it!" She stumped to the table, and patted the book as though it were a living, lovable thing.

"You taught me," she crooned to it. "You're winning me the love of John Frey!" She paused, and her voice grew harsh again. "Why not? I'm old and ugly and strange, but I can love, and John Frey is the handsomest man in the village!"

The next day she went to the store again, in her new and dazzling person as a dark, beautiful girl. Gib, left alone in the hollow, turned over in his mind the things that he had heard. The new gift of human speech had brought with it, of necessity, a human quality of reasoning; but his viewpoint and his logic were as strongly feline as ever.

Jael Bettiss's dark love that lured John Frey promised no good to Gib. There would be plenty of trouble, he was inclined to think, and trouble was something that all sensible cats avoided. He was wise now, but he was weak. What could he do against danger? And his desires, as they had been since kittenhood, were food and warmth and a cozy sleeping place, and a little respectful affection. Just now he was getting none of the four.

He thought also of Ivy Hill. She liked Gib, and often had shown it. If she won John Frey despite the witch's plan, the two would build a house all full of creature comforts—cushions, open fires, probably fish and chopped liver. Gib's tongue caressed his soot-stained lips at the savory thought. It would be good to have a home with Ivy Hill and John Frey, if once he was quit of Jael Bettiss. . . .

But he put the thought from him. The witch had never held his love and loyalty. That went to the house in the hollow, his home since the month that he was born. Even magic had not taught him how to be rid of that cat-instinctive obsession for his own proper dwelling place. The sinister, strife-sodden hovel would always call and claim him, would draw him back from the warmest fire, the softest bed, the most savory food in the world. Only John Howard Payne could have appreciated Gib's yearnings to the full, and he died long ago, in exile from the home he loved.

When Jael Bettiss returned, she was in a fine trembling rage. Her real self shone through the glamor of her disguise, like murky fire through a thin porcelain screen.

Gib was on the doorstep again and tried to dodge away as she came up, but her enchantments, or something else, had made Jael Bettiss too quick even for a cat. She darted out a hand and caught him by the scruff of the neck.

"Listen to me," she said, in a voice as deadly as the trickle of poisoned water. "You understand human words. You can talk, and you can hear what I say. You can do what I say, too." She shook him, by way of emphasis. "Can't you do what I say?"

"Yes," said Gib weakly, convulsed with fear.

"All right, I have a job for you. And mind you do it well, or else—" She broke off and shook him again, letting him imagine what would happen if he disobeyed.

"Yes," said Gib again, panting for breath in her tight grip. "What's it about?"

"It's about that little fool, Ivy Hill. She's not quite out of his heart. Go to the village tonight," ordered Jael Bettiss, "and to the house of the marshal. Steal something that belongs to Ivy Hill."

"Steal something?"

"Don't echo me, as if you were a silly parrot." She let go of him, and hurried back to the book that was her constant study. "Bring me something that Ivy Hill owns and touches—and be back here with it before dawn."

Gib carried out her orders. Shortly after sundown he crept through the deepened dusk to the home of Marshal Hill. Doubly black with the soot habitually smeared upon him by Jael Bettiss, he would have been almost invisible, even had anyone been on guard against his coming. But nobody watched; the genial old man sat on the front steps, talking to his daughter.

"Say," the father teased, "isn't young Johnny Frey coming over here tonight, as usual?"

"I don't know, daddy," said Ivy Hill wretchedly.

"What's that, daughter?" The marshal sounded surprised. "Is there anything gone wrong between you two young 'uns?"

"Perhaps not, but—oh, daddy, there's a new girl come to town—"

And Ivy Hill burst into tears, groping dolefully on the step beside her for her little wadded handkerchief. But she could not find it.

For Gib, stealing near, had caught it up in his mouth and was scampering away toward the edge of town, and beyond to the house in the hollow.

Meanwhile, Jael Bettiss worked hard at a certain project of wax modeling. Any witch, or student of witchcraft, would have known at once why she did this.

After several tries, she achieved something quite interesting and even clever—a little female figure, that actually resembled Ivy Hill.

Jael Bettiss used the wax of three candles to give it enough substance and proportion. To make it more realistic, she got some fresh, pale-gold hemp, and of this made hair, like the wig of a blonde doll, for the wax head. Drops of blue ink served for eyes, and a blob of berry juice for the red mouth. All the while she worked, Jael Bettiss was muttering and mumbling words and phrases she had gleaned from the rearward pages of her book.

When Gib brought in the handkerchief, Jael Bettiss snatched it from his mouth, with a grunt by way of thanks. With rusty scissors and coarse white thread, she fashioned for the wax figure a little dress. It happened that the handkerchief was of gingham, and so the garment made all the more striking the puppet's resemblance to Ivy Hill.

"You're a fine one!" twittered the witch, propping her finished figure against the lamp. "You'd better be scared!"

For it happened that she had worked into the waxen face an expression of terror. The blue ink of the eyes made wide round blotches, a stare of agonized fear; and the berry-juice mouth seemed to tremble, to plead shakily for mercy.

Again Jael Bettiss refreshed her memory of gothic spells by poring over the back of the book, and after that she dug from the bottom of an old pasteboard box a handful of rusty pins. She chuckled over them, so that one would think triumph already hers. Laying the puppet on its back, so that the lamplight fell full upon it, she began to recite a spell.

"I have made my wish before," she said in measured tones. "I will make it now. And there was never a day that I did not see my wish fulfilled." Simple, vague—but how many have died because those words were spoken in a certain way over images of them?

The witch thrust a pin into the breast of the little wax figure and drove it all the way in, with a murderous pressure of her thumb. Another pin she pushed into the head, another into an arm, another into a leg; and so on, until the gingham-clad puppet was fairly studded with transfixing pins.

"Now," she said, "we shall see what we shall see."

Morning dawned, as clear and golden as though wickedness had never been born into the world. The mysterious new paragon of beauty—not a young man of the village but mooned over her, even though she was the reputed niece and namesake of that unsavory old vagabond, Jael Bettiss—walked into the general store to make purchases. One delicate pink ear turned to the gossip of the housewives.

Wasn't it awful, they were agreeing, how poor little Ivy Hill was suddenly sick almost to death; she didn't seem to know her father or her friends. Not even Doctor Melcher could find out what was the matter with her. Strange that John Frey was not interested in her troubles; but John Frey sat behind the counter, slumped on his stool like a mud idol, and his eyes lighted up only when they spied lovely young Jael Bettiss with her market basket.

When she had heard enough, the witch left the store and went straight to the town marshal's house. There she spoke gravely and sorrowfully about how she feared for the sick girl, and was allowed to visit Ivy Hill in her bedroom. To the father and the doctor, it seemed that the patient grew stronger and felt less pain while Jael Bettiss remained to wish her a quick recovery; but, not long after this new acquaintance departed, Ivy Hill grew worse. She fainted, and recovered only to vomit.

And she vomited—pins, rusty pins. Something like that happened in old Salem Village, and earlier still in Scotland, before the grisly cult of North Berwick was literally burned out. But Doctor Melcher, a more modern scholar, had never seen or heard of anything remotely resembling Ivy Hill's disorder.

So it went, for three full days. Gib, too, heard the doleful gossip as he slunk around the village to hunt for food and to avoid Jael Bettiss, who did not like him near when she did magic. Ivy Hill was dying, and he mourned her, as for the boons of fish and fire and cushions and petting that might have been his. He knew, too, that he was responsible for her doom and his loss—that handkerchief that he had stolen had helped Jael Bettiss to direct her spells.

But philosophy came again to his aid. If Ivy Hill died, she died. Anyway, he had never been given the chance to live as her pensioner and pet. He was not even sure that he would have taken the chance—thinking of it, he felt strong, accustomed clamps upon his heart. The house in the hollow was his home forever. Elsewhere he'd be an exile.

Nothing would ever root it out of his feline soul.

On the evening of the third day, witch and cat faced each other across the tabletop in the old house in the hollow.

"They've talked loud enough to make his dull ears hear," grumbled the fearful old woman—with none but Gib to see her, she had washed away the disguising enchantment that, though so full of lure, seemed to be a burden upon her. "John Frey has agreed to take Ivy Hill out in his automobile. The doctor thinks that the fresh air, and John Frey's company, will make her feel better—but it won't. It's too late. She'll never return from that drive."

She took up the pin-pierced wax image of her rival, rose, and started toward the kitchen.

"What are you going to do?" Gib forced himself to ask.

"Do?" repeated Jael Bettiss, smiling murderously. "I'm going to put an end to that baby-faced chit, but why are you so curious? Get out, with your prying!"

And, snarling curses and striking with her clawlike hands, she made him spring down from his chair and run out of the house. The door slammed, and he crouched in some brambles and watched. No sound, and at the half-blinded windows no movement; but, after a time, smoke began to coil upward from the chimney. Its first puffs were dark and greasy-looking. Then it turned dull gray, then white, then blue as indigo. Finally it vanished altogether.

When Jael Bettiss opened the door and came out, she was once more in the semblance of a beautiful dark girl. Yet Gib recognized a greater terror about her than ever before.

"You be gone from here when I get back," she said to him.

"Gone?" stammered Gib, his little heart turning cold. "What do you mean?"

She stooped above him, like a threatening bird of prey.

"You be gone," she repeated. "If I ever see you again, I'll kill you—or I'll make my new husband kill you."

He still could not believe her. He shrank back, and his eyes turned mournfully to the old house that was the only thing he loved.

"You're the only witness to the things I've done," Jael Bettiss continued. "Nobody would believe their ears if a cat started telling tales, but anyway, I don't want any trace of you around. If you leave, they'll forget that I used to be a witch. So run!"

She turned away. Her mutterings were now only her thoughts aloud:

If my magic works—and it always works—that car will find itself idling around through the hill road to the other side of the quarry. John Frey will stop there. And so will Ivy Hill—forever.

Drawing her cloak around her, she stalked purposefully toward the old quarry behind the house.

Left by himself, Gib lowered his lids and let his yellow eyes grow dim and deep with thought. His shrewd beast's mind pawed and probed at this final wonder and danger that faced him and John Frey and Ivy Hill.

He must run away if he would live. The witch's house in the hollow, which had never welcomed him, now threatened him. No more basking on the doorstep, no more ambushing woodmice among the brambles, no more dozing by the kitchen fire. Nothing for Gib henceforth but strange, forbidding wilderness, and scavenger's food, and no shelter, not on the coldest night. The village? But his only two friends, John Frey and Ivy Hill, were being taken from him by the magic of Jael Bettiss and her book. . . .

That book had done this. That book must undo it. There was no time to lose.

The door was not quite latched, and he nosed it open, despite the groans of its hinges. Hurrying in, he sprang up on the table.

It was gloomy in that tree-invested house, even for Gib's sharp eyes. Therefore, in a trembling fear almost too big for his little body, he spoke a word that Jael Bettiss had spoken, on her first night of power. As had happened then, so it happened now; the dark lamp glowed alight.

Gib pawed at the closed book, and contrived to lift its cover. Pressing it open with one front foot, with the other he painstakingly turned leaves, more leaves, and more yet. Finally he came to the page he wanted.

Not that he could read; and, in any case, the characters were strange in their shapes and combinations. Yet, if one looked long enough and levelly enough—even though one were a cat, and afraid—they made sense, conveyed intelligence.

And so into the mind of Gib, beating down his fears, there stole a phrase: *Beware of mirrors . . .*

So that was why Jael Bettiss never kept a mirror—not even now, when she could assume such dazzling beauty.

Beware of mirrors, the book said to Gib, *for they declare the truth, and truth is fatal to sorcery. Beware also, of crosses, which defeat all spells.*

That was definite inspiration. He moved back from the book, and let it snap shut. Then, pushing with head and paws, he coaxed it to the edge of the table and let it fall. Jumping down after it, he caught a corner of the book in his teeth and dragged it to the door, more like a retriever than a cat. When he got it into the yard, into a place where the earth was soft, he dug furiously until he had made a hole big enough to contain the volume. Then, thrusting it in, he covered it up.

Nor was that all his effort, so far as the book was concerned. He trotted a little way off to where lay some dry, tough twigs under the cypress trees. To the little grave he bore first one, then another of these, and laid them across each other, in the form of an X. He pressed them well into the earth, so that they would be hard to disturb. Perhaps he would keep an eye on that spot henceforth, after he had done the rest of the things in his mind, to see that the cross remained. And, though he acted thus only by chance reasoning, all the demonologists, even the Reverend Montague Summers, would have nodded approval. Is this not the way to foil the black wisdom of the *Grand Albert*? Did not Prospero thus inter his grimoires, in the fifth act of *The Tempest*?

Now back to the house once more and into the kitchen. It was even darker than the parlor, but Gib could make out a basin on a stool by the moldy wall, and smelled an ugly pungency: Jael Bettiss had left her mixture of powdered water after last washing away her burden of false beauty.

Gib's feline nature rebelled at a wetting; his experience of witchcraft bade him be wary, but he rose on his hind legs and with his forepaws dragged at the basin's edge. It tipped and toppled. The noisome fluid drenched him. Wheeling, he ran back into the parlor, but paused on the doorstep. He spoke two more words that he remembered from Jael Bettiss. The lamp went out again.

And now he dashed around the house and through the brambles and to the quarry beyond.

It lay amid uninhabited wooded hills, a wide excavation from which had once been quarried all the stones for the village houses and pavements. Now it was full of water, from many thaws and torrents. Almost at its lip was parked John Frey's touring car, with the top down, and beside it he lolled, slack-faced and dreamy. At his side, cloak-draped and enigmatically queenly, was Jael Bettiss, her back to the quarry, never more terrible or handsome. John Frey's eyes were fixed dreamily upon her, and her eyes were fixed commandingly on the figure in the front seat of the car—a slumped, defeated figure, hard to recognize as poor sick Ivy Hill.

"Can you think of no way to end all this pain, Miss Ivy?" the witch was asking. Though she did not stir, or glance behind her, it was as though she had gestured toward the great quarry pit, full to unknown depths with black, still water. The sun, at the very point of setting, made angry red lights on the surface of that stagnant pond.

"Go away," sobbed Ivy Hill, afraid without knowing why. "Please, please!"

"I'm only trying to help," said Jael Bettiss. "Isn't that so, John?"

"That's so, Ivy," agreed John, like a little boy who is prompted to an unfamiliar recitation. "She's only trying to help."

Gib, moving silently as fate, crept to the back of the car. None of the three human beings, so intent upon each other, saw him.

"Get out of the car," persisted Jael Bettiss. "Get out, and look into the water. You will forget your pain."

"Yes, yes," chimed in John Frey mechanically. "You will forget your pain."

Gib scrambled stealthily to the running board, then over the side of the car and into the rear seat. He found what he had hoped to find. Ivy Hill's purse—and open.

He pushed his nose into it. Tucked into a little side pocket was a hard, flat rectangle, about the size and shape of a visiting card. All normal girls carry mirrors in their purses; all mirrors show the truth. Gib clamped the edge with his mouth, and struggled to drag the thing free.

"Miss Ivy," Jael Bettiss was commanding, "get out of this car, and come and look into the water of the quarry."

No doubt what would happen if once Ivy Hill should gaze into that shiny black abyss; but she bowed her head, in agreement or defeat, and began slowly to push aside the catch of the door.

Now or never, thought Gib. He made a little noise in his throat, and sprang up on the side of the car next to Jael Bettiss. His black-stained face and yellow eyes were not a foot from her.

She alone saw him; Ivy Hill was too sick, John Frey too dull. "What are you doing here?" she snarled, like a bigger and fiercer cat than he; but he moved closer still, holding up the oblong in his teeth. Its back was uppermost, covered with imitation leather, and hid the real nature of it. Jael Bettiss was mystified, for once in her relationship with Gib. She took the thing from him, turned it over, and saw a reflection.

She screamed.

The other two looked up, horrified through their stupor. The scream that Jael Bettiss uttered was not deep and rich and young; it was the wild, cracked cry of a terrified old woman.

"I don't look like that," she choked out, and drew back from the car. "Not old—ugly—"

Gib sprang at her face. With all four claw-bristling feet he seized and clung to her. Again Jael Bettiss screamed, flung up her hands, and tore him away from his hold; but his soggy fur had smeared the powdered water upon her face and head.

Though he fell to earth, Gib twisted in midair and landed upright. He had one glimpse of his enemy. Jael Bettiss, no mistake—but a Jael Bettiss with hooked beak, rheumy eyes, hideous wry mouth and yellow chisel teeth—Jael Bettiss exposed for what she was, stripped of her lying mask of beauty!

And she drew back a whole staggering step. Rocks were just behind her. Gib saw, and flung himself. Like a flash he clawed his way up her cloak, and with both forepaws ripped at the ugliness he had betrayed. He struck for his home that was forbidden him—Marco Bozzaris never strove harder for Greece, or Stonewall Jackson for Virginia.

Jael Bettiss screamed yet again, a scream loud and full of horror. Her feet had slipped on the edge of the abyss. She flung out her arms, the cloak flapped from them like frantic wings. She fell, and Gib fell with her, still tearing and fighting.

The waters of the quarry closed over them both.

Gib thought that it was a long way back to the surface and a longer way to shore. But he got there, and scrambled out with the help of projecting rocks. He shook his drenched body, climbed back into the car and sat upon the rear seat. At least Jael Bettiss would no longer drive him from the home he loved. He'd find food some way, and take it back there each day to eat. . . .

With tongue and paws he began to rearrange his sodden fur.

John Frey, clear-eyed and wide awake, was leaning in and talking to Ivy Hill. As for her, she sat up straight, as though she had never known a moment of sickness.

"But just what did happen?" she was asking.

John Frey shook his head, though all the stupidity was gone from his face and manner. "I don't quite remember. I seem to have wakened from a dream. But are you all right, darling?"

"Yes, I'm all right." She gazed toward the quarry, and the black water that had already subsided above what it had swallowed. Her eyes were puzzled, but not frightened. "I was dreaming, too," she said. "Let's not bother about it."

She lifted her gaze, and cried out with joy. "There's that old house that daddy owns. Isn't it interesting?"

John Frey looked, too. "Yes. The old witch has gone away—I seem to have heard she did."

Ivy Hill was smiling with excitement. "Then I have an inspiration. Let's get daddy to give it to us. And we'll paint it over and fix it up, and then—" she broke off, with a cry of delight. "I declare, there's a cat in the car with me!"

It was the first she had known of Gib's presencc.

John Frey stared at Gib. He seemed to have wakened only the moment before. "Yes, and isn't he a thin one? But he'll be pretty when he gets through cleaning himself. I think I see a white shirt front."

Ivy Hill put out a hand and scratched Gib behind the ear. "He's bringing us good luck, I think. John, let's take him to live with us when we have the house fixed up and move in."

"Why not?" asked her lover. He was gazing at Gib. "He looks as if he was getting ready to speak."

But Gib was not getting ready to speak. The power of speech was gone from him, along with Jael Bettiss and her enchantments. But he understood, in a measure, what was being said about him and the house in the hollow. There would be new life there, joyful and friendly this time. And he would be a part of it, forever, and of his loved home.

He could only purr to show his relief and gratitude.

Reading for Understanding

❑ MAIN IDEA

1. The main point of the story is (a) the course of true love (b) fashions in magical spells (c) the power of a cat's instincts (d) how cats differ from other animals.

❑ DETAILS

2. Jael's house was actually owned by (a) the postmaster (b) a farmer (c) another witch (d) the marshal.

3. Jael kept Gib all black to (a) make him look scary (b) match her own clothing (c) please John Frey (d) find him another home.

4. Jael's magical spells came from (a) a lifetime of experience (b) a small book (c) Gib's ancient knowledge (d) Ivy Hill.

5. For the success of her magical spell, Jael used (a) water from the storekeeper's well (b) a hatchet (c) a handkerchief (d) a hat.

☐ INFERENCES

6. Sometimes the villagers bought philters and charms because (a) they were afraid of Jael (b) they felt sorry for her (c) they wanted to do each other harm (d) the charms made attractive souvenirs.
7. Jael wanted the villagers to think that she (a) sometimes took the form of a cat (b) was innocent of any magic spells (c) had a great fondness for Ivy (d) was in reality a beautiful woman.
8. The first words that Gib spoke dealt with his (a) appearance (b) bed (c) affection for Jael (d) hunger.
9. The reason for John Frey's new infatuation was (a) anger at Ivy (b) enchantment (c) a meeting with the woman several years earlier (d) an opportunity for financial gain.

☐ IMAGERY

10. "She always met callers on the old cracked doorstep, draped in a cloak of shadowy black, with gray hair straggling, her nose as hooked and sharp as the beak of a buzzard, her eyes filmy and sore-looking, her wrinkle-bordered mouth always grinning and showing her yellow, chisel-shaped teeth."
    An example of simile is (a) "with gray hair straggling" (b) "as hooked and sharp as the beak of a buzzard" (c) "showing her yellow, chisel-shaped teeth" (d) "draped in a cloak of shadowy black."

☐ AUTHOR'S ATTITUDE

11. The author's attitude toward Gib is one of (a) unconcealed disapproval (b) complete indifference (c) unexpected anger (d) fond sympathy.

☐ ORDER OF EVENTS

12. Arrange the items in the order in which they occurred. Use letters only.
    A. Gib speaks for the first time.
    B. Jael sends for the magic book.
    C. Jael falls into the quarry.
    D. Jael begins to capture the attention of John Frey.
    E. John and Ivy resolve to adopt Gib.

❑ OUTCOMES

13. At the conclusion of the story (a) Jael returns to plague the lovers (b) John decides to leave Ivy (c) John and Ivy move into Jael's old house (d) Gib talks frequently.

❑ CAUSE AND EFFECT

14. Jael was "feared and hated" because (a) she wanted to be (b) the villagers were cruel (c) she showed undue affection for her cat (d) she had injured the marshal after a disagreement.

❑ FACT OR OPINION

Tell whether the following is a fact or an opinion.

15. Gib defeated the evil plans of Jael Bettiss.

Words in Context

1. "It is quite *irrelevant* that evil was her study and profession and pleasure. She was no witch . . ." ***Irrelevant*** (241) means (a) obvious (b) well-known (c) nonpertinent (d) well-proved.
2. "Because he was easygoing and perhaps a little *daunted,* he let Jael Bettiss live there rent-free." ***Daunted*** (241) means (a) intimidated (b) foolish (c) not too bright (d) concerned.
3. "Now and then, when Jael Bettiss came to the door, there came with her the *gaunt* black cat, Gib." ***Gaunt*** (242) means (a) handsome (b) chubby (c) purring (d) emaciated.
4. "But Jael Bettiss, who wanted a fearsome pet, kept all his white spots smeared with thick soot . . . to make him look *rakish* and lean." ***Rakish*** (242) means (a) fierce (b) devilish (c) powerful (d) mysterious.
5. "Quickly she glanced through the back part of the book, howled with laughter over something she found there . . . and *scuttled* like a big, filthy crab into . . . her kitchen." ***Scuttled*** (243) means (a) limped (b) crawled (c) tripped (d) scurried.
6. "'It worked!' she cried. 'No more *humbug* about me, you understand? I'm a real witch at last, and not a fraud!'" ***Humbug*** (243) means (a) sham (b) magic (c) concern (d) slander.
7. ". . . the dish floated upward like a leaf in a breeze and set itself gently back on the table. Gib watched *warily.*" ***Warily*** (243) means

(a) with much fear (b) joyously (c) very knowingly (d) unconcernedly.

8. "Its beauty was scornful but inviting, classic but warm, with something in it of Grecian sculpture and Oriental *allure*." ***Allure*** (244) means (a) cruelty (b) heaviness (c) charm (d) mysticism.

9. "The woman who returned to the front door, where Gib watched with a cat's *apprehensive* interest, was hideous old Jael Bettiss, whom all the village knew and avoided." ***Apprehensive*** (245) means (a) intelligent (b) solicitous (c) loving (d) uneasy.

10. "Even magic had not taught him to be rid of that cat-instinctive *obsession* for his own proper dwelling place." ***Obsession*** (245) means (a) sharp distaste (b) utter unconcern (c) ruling passion (d) deep fears.

11. ". . . Jael Bettiss was muttering and mumbling words and phrases she had *gleaned* from the rearward pages of her book." ***Gleaned*** (247) means (a) memorized (b) accumulated (c) cut out (d) developed.

12. "Something like that happened in old Salem Village, and earlier still in Scotland, before the *grisly cult* of North Berwick was literally burned out." ***Grisly cult*** (248) means (a) merciless killers (b) secret organization (c) fanatical outlaws (d) loathsome sect.

13. "When Jael Bettiss opened the door and came out, she was once more in the *semblance* of a beautiful dark girl." ***Semblance*** (249) means (a) clothing (b) likeness (c) thoughts (d) incantations.

14. "At his side, cloak-draped and *enigmatically* queenly, was Jael Bettiss . . . never more terrible or handsome." ***Enigmatically*** (251) means (a) fearsomely (b) quietly (c) mysteriously (d) proudly.

15. "She gazed toward the quarry, and the black water that had already *subsided* above what it had swallowed." ***Subsided*** (252) means (a) risen (b) swirled (c) bubbled (d) settled down.

Thinking Critically About the Story

1. To what extent is the following statement valid for Jael Bettis:

> ". . . she was as disgustingly ugly without as she was wicked within . . . evil was her study and profession and pleasure."

Are there people like Jael in the real world, people who are malevolent to the core—or are they found only in storyland? How can society protect itself from such people? What makes these "bad" characters so fascinating that even if they never existed, we would have to invent them?

2. To what extent is the following statement valid?

   "Gib has no sense of evil or of good. He fights successfully against evil and for the good on other than a moral plane."

   Is this lack of moral judgments typical of animal pets? Give examples from fiction or real life to support your contention. Does morality separate human beings from the rest of the animal world? Explain. Gib willingly does evil for an evil witch; he even kills. Yet we accept him as a sympathetic character. How does the author bring this about?

3. By referring to specific incidents in the story, prove the truth of the following statement.

   "'The Witch's Cat' is written with a sly touch of humor."

   Why is sly humor usually absent in stories of witchcraft? How does sly humor differ from black humor or the laugh of the villain enjoying the plight of his hapless victims? Does the humor in this story add to reader enjoyment, or is it a distraction?

4. With the instruction book at her command, what are the potential limits to Jael's power? What limits does she set for herself? Given the instruction book, what would you seek? What did Jael place before wealth and power? What was the key to her behavior? Once you know that key, do you then condone her behavior?

5. Be prepared to tell the class your favorite cat story. How do cats compare with other animals as house pets? Why do some people prefer them? Does Gib deserve inclusion in the list of "Famous Cats of History"?

Stories in Words

Amiable (242) is a doublet for *amicable.* Doublets are word pairs that are derived from the same source. They survive in different spellings and usually have different meanings. Common doublets include *regal* and *royal, legal* and *loyal, army* and *armada, papyrus* and *paper, shriek* and *screech.* Both *amiable* and *amicable* can be traced to the Latin root *amare,* "to love," as can the word *enamored.* The Latin word *amicus,* "friend," is itself derived from *amare.* A friend is someone to *love.* Someone or something *unfriendly,* hostile, is *inimical.*

Gibberish (243) is one of an interesting class of words derived from the sounds they make. *Gibber* means "to speak rapidly, unclearly, and often foolishly." If you say the word aloud several times, you will have an idea of the meaning of *gibber*. Words like these are called imitative, echoic, onomatopoeic. Here's a sample: *crash, bang, buzz, hiss, whisper, murmur, whoosh, zoom, crackle, pop, whiz, moo, meow*. See also *murmur*, page 448.

Feline (245) is derived from the Latin *felis*, "cat." It can mean "relating to cats." It can also take on a secondary meaning from qualities associated with cats: *graceful, sly, treacherous, stealthy*. A number of other words are derived in the same way from the Latin words for animals. Interestingly, they also have secondary meanings. *Bovine*, derived from the word for *cow*, can also mean "sluggish, patient, slow, dull, stupid, stolid." *Serpentine*, from the Latin word for *snake*, can also mean "wily, winding, twisting, turning." *Porcine*, from the Latin word for *pig*, can also mean "obese."

Tricky Customers

JAMES CHATTO

It was stifling, an almost tangible pressure. And then the whole world exploded . . . Well, not the world of course, but the enormous plate glass windows of the shop. There was an actual detonation and the air was suddenly lethal with showering glass.

The conflict of good and evil is one of the oldest themes in religion, folklore, and literature. The Faust legend, for example, shows what happens when a man sells his soul to the devil for earthly gain. In a modern version, "The Devil and Daniel Webster," Daniel Webster successfully battles the Satanic Mr. Scratch for the soul of Jabez Stone, a New Hampshire farmer. In "The Killers" (pages 372–386), the forces of evil prevail.

"Tricky Customers" rings some new changes on the ancient theme. The setting is an unpretentious bookstore. The proprietor and his assistant are menaced by an unexpected force. Major Jonathan Galloway is an imposing physical presence, but there is more to him, an aura that terrifies. When all looks bleak, help comes from an unexpected source. There is always a satisfaction in seeing a mild-mannered opponent standing up courageously to a domineering bully.

There is an inner logic in stories of fantasy. Except for the occasional disruption of natural law, cause and effect do operate. In "Tricky Customers," for example, James and the proprietor act perfectly naturally and realistically. Not all questions are specifically answered, however. Much is left to the imagination, and the reader must fill in the gaps. What happens at the end of the story?

Tricky Customers

There is something about a good bookshop that lures eccentrics; it beckons and draws them as a conjurer does children, offering enchanted diversion. When the bookshop is small and erudite its attraction is doubled, and if it should also happen to be located in a part of London with a large resident lunatic fringe, as was the place where I once worked, the patronage of the socially abnormal can amount to infestation.

We were called Michael Adam Ltd and we occupied an old two-story building, with low, sagging ceilings and a big display window, in a backstreet between Fulham and Knightsbridge. The premises were too small, really, for the enormous variety of our stock, but they contributed to the tranquil, dusty atmosphere that our clientele found so tempting. Downstairs we kept the books that sold, the new biographies, fiction, art and history, atlases, cooking and travel; upstairs, crowded by the paperbacks, were the more arcane categories: philosophy, religion, the occult, musicology, antiques, crafts and poetry. The majority of our customers, people who actually wanted to buy a book, rarely climbed the narrow stairs into this den, but the eccentrics made a beeline for it. Solitary figures, they came to browse, resenting any intrusion, some using the room like a library, most just seeking sanctuary from the bustle walking in off the streets for an hour or so as people used to into a church.

At least, that is what I reckoned during my first few days in the job: I put our popularity down to the ambience, but it soon became clear that the real reason had much more to do with my employer, Michael Adam, a man of charm and infallible literary expertise, with the most beautiful manners in the world. Difficult old ladies melted at his smile; furious women with twenty carrier bags and a parking ticket were soothed within minutes by his subtly distracting small talk. When I tried to imitate him I became merely obsequious or cheeky, but Michael had the ability to delight them without even trying. He made foolish people seem clever, giving them things to say about the latest fashionable *Collected Letters*; and clever people listened attentively to his more profound opinions, expressed so casually that no one ever felt challenged by his knowledge. The secret, I suppose, was his endless patience, and the fact that he genuinely liked his fellow man as much as he liked books, and enjoyed bringing the two together.

That he prospered as a result did not displease him. He made a reasonable living from the wealthy gentry who shopped and gossiped downstairs, and they enjoyed the sight of the odd Bohemian as he edged past the shelves towards the staircase, feeling themselves in touch with the poetical and the avant-garde. As for the eccentrics themselves, they idolized Michael, sharing with him the grievances and triumphs of their peculiar little worlds. They would have defended our shop with their lives, and all because he took them seriously.

He was even kind to Señor Petche. The Señor was one of our dottier regulars and to me his habits were deeply irritating. At six o'clock, just as we were closing, his wrinkled, monkey head would loom out of the darkness and peer in hopelessly through the window. Sometimes I pretended to ignore him, but more often we would sigh and gather smiles from our tired faces and turn the lights back on upstairs. Then he would come in, bobbing a bow, a hesitant grin trembling on his thin ascetic lips. He always wore black—a suit and tie and a trim overcoat with an astrakhan collar, and black leather gloves that clutched a miniature umbrella. Dapper, wistful and five feet tall, he would hover by the door until Michael went forward to greet him.

It was no good my feigning a welcome. Whenever I spoke to him he looked away and stepped back surreptitiously, whispering something in his querulous, accented falsetto, too quietly for me to hear. Only Michael could penetrate his acute shyness and over the years he had refined this maneuver to an art. While Señor Petche darted agonized glances at me, Michael drew his attention inexorably into the twin securities of his pet subjects, bibliography and metaphysics. It was like trying to light a fire with damp straw, but sooner or later the smoke began to rise. My presence was forgotten, as was the rest of the world, and Señor Petche would lay down his umbrella, lick his lips and frown down at some title page, his chin lifted to the light.

"He's rather good on Jung,"* Michael might suggest. A small apologetic cough from the Señor, perhaps the echo of a coy giggle.

"Yes, indeed, largely, indeed, but you know I heard him lecture in Prague in 1959 and you will forgive me Michael but he showed so small an understanding of the Jungian interest in alchemy that one is permitted to wonder . . ." And he was off.

How Petche coped outside the shop is a mystery. His nerves discouraged him from going out until dusk, but I gathered from overheard remarks that his own library was extensive and no doubt he could function

**Jung* Swiss psychiatrist

there. Among books he suddenly became cool and self-assured, even masterful; beyond them he was nothing. I think Michael was his only friend—confessor, Samaritan, confidant—as he was to so many others.

Then, in the early spring of 1983, we were blessed with the patronage of another, very different bizarre.

It was a cold, bright morning and I was busy unpacking orders in the tiny office at the back of the shop when I heard the bell on the door. I looked through the spyhole but could see no one. Turning back, I nearly touched a man who was suddenly standing behind me. He was obviously delighted at my terrified start and his handsome face—Errol Flynn with a hint of Charles the Second—broke into a grin.

"Is Michael here?" he purred.

I explained that he had gone out for a moment but would soon be back.

"I'll wait upstairs."

He disappeared up to the den and I breathed again. Even if he hadn't scared me like that I think his appearance would have proved affecting. It was calculated to be so. He must have been six foot six, in his forties and clearly very fit, and he wore a floor-length brown kaftan with a Russian collar, drawn in at the waist by a monk's cord, and heavy riding boots. Hearing him clump about upstairs I wondered how on earth he had moved so silently and so fast from the shop door to the office. And there was a smell in the air, very faint, of patchouli.

When Michael came in I told him there was someone to see him and he called out a cheerful hello. We heard an answering "Ah!" and the footsteps crossing the room and then the kaftan appeared. Beside me Michael inhaled sharply. I looked round at him. His calm, urbane face was scowling. Then our customer's head ducked under the arch of the staircase and Michael managed to assume his usual expression.

"Hello Michael," drawled Kaftan. "I gave your boy here a bit of a turn. How are you? Coining it?"

"Not bad . . ."

Kaftan had turned away without waiting for an answer. "Same old crap on your shelves. Don't suppose you've anything for me."

"Probably not."

I found it hard not to stare at Michael. I had never heard him so cold. Kaftan picked up a book from the central display, glanced at it and dropped it back onto the pile. Then he sniffed, grotesquely, as if he were taking snuff.

"I'll dictate a list of books for you to get for me," he said. "Fetch a pen, Bunter."

I tried to look haughty as I obeyed him, but I was unconvincing. The list was long and consisted of ponderous titles to do with magic and natural philosophy. I recognized none of them.

Michael had stood to one side as I wrote. "I'll drop you a card if we can find any," he said.

"No. I'll be in and out. I'm staying in town for a couple of months."

The man's eyes wandered briefly round the shop, his mouth set in a sneer. Then he suddenly stared at me. "Boo!" he shouted, and with a swish of his robe he strode out into the street and away.

"God! Who was that?"

Michael looked troubled. "That was Major Jonathan Galloway. He used to come in here a lot, once upon a time."

"Does he always wear that outfit?"

"Mmm."

"What does he do?"

Michael was looking at the list glumly. He glanced up. "What? Sorry?"

"I wondered what he does?"

He shrugged. "I really don't know. I've known him for years. He went to my school in fact. He was a vindictive little chap in those days. And about ten years ago he ruined someone I was very fond of. Nothing was proved but he did it all right." He paused by the office entrance. "He told me once he was a warlock."

Major Galloway returned a week later. Michael and I were both busy with Lady N, helping her decide what to give her many friends for Easter and trying to stop her dachshunds from dirtying the stock. Whether he saw the dogs or not I do not know, but as he strode through us, the Major contrived to punt one of them clear across the floor, into the side of the box where we keep the Michelin guides. Lady N screamed, as did the dachshund—the other one started to scamper about yapping—and somehow a pile of books slipped off a table. Major Galloway just stamped upstairs. A moment later we heard him laughing.

Michael calmed Lady N down while she keened over her hysterical but undamaged dog. I carried her books out to her car. As she drove away she shot me a look of profound reproach.

When I got back to the shop Galloway was downstairs again, and apparently in an ugly mood.

We had done our best with his list, but if a book is out of print there is little that a shop like ours, selling only new publications, can do to acquire it. All but two of Galloway's were no longer available, and those two had to be ordered from the States.

He swung round as I came in.

"I suppose you set this oaf on the job," he said. The sneer I had noticed before was back. "Really Michael, there's more to running a bookshop than selling memoirs to the parish dowagers. If my requirements are too high-brow you should have said so instead of wasting my time. The only reason I came here at all was because of the old connection."

Michael's lips were dry and pulled back from his teeth. He paused for a moment before responding.

"The things you asked for are all rather obscure—obviously you know that. I'll get you the two I can and, if you like, I'll put an advertisement in *The Clique* for the others."

"That I could have done for myself!"

"Yup. Well I think you should. Or there are other shops specializing . . ."

"I am aware of the other shops!"

"Well perhaps you'd be better off looking there?"

"Or perhaps you could pull your thumb out a bit, eh? Do it yourself instead of palming the work off on your help."

Michael smiled. "There's nothing I could do that James didn't."

"I dare say."

"Really, I think you should try the occult bookshops."

"Oh you do." He exhaled noisily. "Look. You've got a week. I can't wait forever."

"No, you don't understand. What I'm saying is I don't want your custom."

Galloway narrowed his eyes and stared. "Say again?"

"I don't want your custom."

The Major let it sink in, then he suddenly threw back his head and roared with laughter. It was a harsh, mirthless noise, so loud that it hurt my ears.

"You don't want my custom! You stupid little man." He took a step towards Michael, towering over him, fists balled and white-knuckled. "You stupid little fool. Don't you dare try and tell me where I can or can't shop!"

I was cringing, sick and useless, but somehow Michael kept his ground and his temper.

"Get out," he said quietly.

I was sure Galloway was going to hit him, but he didn't. Instead he just stood there, his muscles so tense that he seemed to quiver, his breathing clearly audible. He appeared to be having some sort of apoplectic fit. The veins at his temples throbbed and his eyes bulged, unfocused—the room was full of his anger. It was stifling, an almost tangible pressure. And then the whole world exploded . . . Well, not the world of course, but the enormous plate glass windows of the shop. There was an actual detonation and the air was suddenly lethal with showering glass. I threw myself down onto the floor while razor-sharp debris crashed about me and I am sure I heard the Major mutter *Damn You* as he swept past. When I looked up he was gone.

Michael clambered slowly to his feet. There was glass everywhere, even in our clothes. Splinters had cut our faces and hands and another shard had torn my trousers at the knee and cut me there. Blades of the stuff stuck out of books, embedded in their spines and jackets; the display in the window was ruined. The traffic up on the Brompton Road seemed very loud.

Michael is a methodical man. I wanted to stand and gape and discuss what had happened there and then, but he made it clear as we bandaged our wounds from the first aid kit in the office that the shop must come before my curiosity. So while I swept up the wreckage and moved lacerated stock down into the basement he phoned about for a glazier capable of repairing our window that afternoon. It was not until work was under way, just after three, that he showed any signs of relaxing.

"It was magic, wasn't it," was my proposition. Michael shrugged wearily, but I persisted. "Mind over matter. A psychic blow. That's what magic means isn't it: material change wrought by mental energies?"

"You could say the same about an influential book."

"How did he do it, though?"

"Honestly, I haven't the faintest idea."

"And what exactly did he do?"

Michael was staring at me. The bandage on his nose gave him an irritable look.

"I don't think either of us are even qualified to guess, James, do you? Why not take the afternoon off. I'll stay and see to the work."

"Well okay, if you're sure . . . Thanks! He really is a warlock, though, wouldn't you say? I mean he really is."

I did not expect to see Major Galloway again, but a week later to the day, he breezed in in his chocolate-colored kaftan and stood before me, grinning. Michael was out at lunch and there was no one else in the shop. It occurred to me that I ought to tell him to leave, but I decided against it. He just stood there, enjoying my discomfiture. Then a piece of paper fluttered from his hand, coming to rest on a boxed set of the new Proust.

"Settling my account," he said. He widened his eyes dramatically and turned to go. "And I shall continue to do business here," he added at the door.

The paper was a check for five hundred pounds.

Michael scowled when he returned and I told him what had happened. He asked me to look at the credit book and nodded when I reported that the Major had no debts to his name. I took the book back into the office. When I came back, Michael had torn up the check and dropped it into the wastebasket. Later I heard him typing—a letter to Galloway, telling him to keep his distance.

For weeks after that a sort of gloom hung over us. We both believed that the warlock would return for a confrontation, not wanting to leave the last word with us. As dusk fell each evening and he still had not arrived our relief was enormous, but each morning resharpened the Damoclean sword.* The last thing I wanted was to have to delay our locking-up at night, therefore, but I had forgotten the habits of the other loonie, Señor Petche. One Wednesday evening, prompt as ever at six, he materialized in the twilight, scratching at the new window.

Michael let him in. In a way he was something of a tonic, with his whispered gratitude and harmless self-absorption, darting shy affection at Michael. For the first time I felt myself warming to him and perhaps he detected it, for I was suddenly included in the conversation.

**Damoclean sword* sword held by a single hair over one's head, a constant threat of instant death

Michael had been telling him about Galloway's exhibition and he was keenly aroused by the story, nodding and frowning at each detail. I was listening at a distance great enough to avoid worrying him, when he turned and looked up at me.

"You also were abused?" he piped, with a little moue of sympathy.

"Yes I was!"

"But you heard no actual incantation. He fumed in silence."

"He just stood there."

"And then the window . . . I see. How very interesting. Such power. I would like to meet this warlock of yours." He began to murmur about poltergeists, blinking rapidly, then his head twitched. "There is something pertinent, as it happens, in one of the books upstairs. May I fetch it?"

"Of course."

"One wonders about the extent of the control a man of his temper could exert over the subtle energies . . ." He peered at Michael. "But here I am hypothesizing over what is to you a very personal predicament. Forgive me. I am distressed and may I say enraged by such treatment of a friend." He dithered, wishing, I think, to say more, and then remembered the book upstairs. "Two minutes!"

As the old man climbed out of sight I made a face at Michael. He smiled, looking down at his watch.

"You might as well go home."

"Are you sure?"

"Yup. Go on."

Well it was already past time. I went into the office for my coat. The light in there was off but enough spilled in from the shop for me to see Major Galloway, motionless, impossibly tall, pressed against the wall in the deep shadows. His eyes were open and he was leering down at me.

I made a sort of strangled whimper and the skin on my head and neck prickled with terror. His eyes rolled insanely and returned to mine. I started to shiver, dumb and rooted. Then I heard Michael's voice: "Hang on for a second will you, James, I'm just going to bring the car round." I heard the shop door open and close, I heard my heart pounding, and then, like a clarion of heaven, a tiny cough from upstairs—Señor Petche reminding us that he was still there.

A hiss escaped the Major. Very slowly, his gaze never wavering, he detached himself from the wall.

"I shall finish what I began," he muttered.

He stepped out into the light of the shop, gliding towards the staircase. To my shame, I did nothing. I didn't even move. The darkness in the office was a blanket to hide under. His boots were heavy on the stairs, on the floorboards above.

Only then did I creep a little way, just to the archway of the office, still half in shadow. I heard Galloway speak.

"You were asking after me, sir."

Something inaudible from Señor Petche . . . I edged a pace closer to the bottom of the stairs.

"And on what do you base this presumption?"

More murmuring.

"I do as I please! I was insulted in this place and I shall enjoy my revenge."

Then I heard Señor Petche. He was asking Galloway to leave his friend alone.

"Are you threatening me?" boomed the Major. "Are you? Very well then."

Petche spoke again, again too softly for me to catch a word. There was a terrible peel of laughter, like the braying of a mule. And then silence.

I should have gone up. I wanted to run away. But that awful silence precluded any movement. Once I thought I heard a tiny creak, like a riding boot or a shoe, but it could have been my own taut neck. When the bell on the door went ping I felt as though I'd been punched in the stomach.

It was Michael. He looked tired and started to apologize for keeping me waiting. Then he noticed my expression.

"He's up there," I croaked, "with Petche."

Michael winced as if in pain, but he did not hesitate. His foot was already on the bottom step when the Señor appeared above him. We both fell back.

Señor Petche was smiling, almost glowing. His descent was superb in its dignity. Neither of us said a thing.

"I took the liberty of introducing myself to your friend," he murmured demurely, when he had joined us. "And of criticizing his manners."

I was staring past him up the stairs.

"Major Galloway is no longer up there. I was correct about that book, Michael, and my consultation of it was, in fact, rather timely. However I already possess a copy. I would like to buy this instead. It does not appear to be priced."

He held out a book. It was heavy and large and bound in chocolate-colored cloth.

I reached out automatically, but Michael put a hand on my arm.

"Please take it as a gift."

Señor Petche smiled again. "Thank you. It will fill a gap in my collection. A work of vigor and some style, but without any real sense of direction."

"What did you do?" I asked, unable to bear it any longer. The Señor looked decidedly embarrassed. He seemed to be searching for words.

"Bibliopegy?" he suggested at last. "You see, I take issue with the adage: a book usually can be judged by its binding."

He said goodnight and left, his new volume under his arm.

A little later Michael and I went upstairs. There was no sign of a struggle, nothing strange at all. We tidied the stacks for a while in silence. It was only when I finally turned to follow Michael down that I thought I detected something—just the merest hint of patchouli in the air. The fancy lingered for weeks.

Reading for Understanding

❑ MAIN IDEA

1. The main point of the story is that (a) a gentle, mild-mannered person may be more than a match for a domineering intimidator (b) bookstores can be the setting for crime (c) reading is fun (d) old friends are the best friends.

❑ DETAILS

2. An item to be found in the upstairs section is (a) atlases (b) philosophy (c) fiction (d) new biographies.
3. Señor Petche might be described as (a) wealthy gentry (b) an expert on art (c) a dotty regular (d) a force for evil.
4. The year of Major Galloway's visit is (a) 1980 (b) 1983 (c) 1986 (d) not given.
5. Most of the books on Galloway's list were (a) on literature (b) available in the United States (c) written by Michael Adams (d) unavailable.

❑ INFERENCES

6. The narrator regarded the "large resident lunatic fringe" with (a) mild annoyance (b) more affection than did Michael (c) terror (d) great affection because of his skill in handling the patrons.
7. We are prepared for Señor Petche's attack on Galloway because of the Señor's interest in (a) crafts and poetry (b) musicology and art (c) art and history (d) bibliography and metaphysics.
8. "Beside me Michael inhaled sharply." This sentence suggests that Michael was (a) clearly delighted (b) surprisingly inattentive (c) unhappily surprised (d) forcefully assertive.
9. Michael tore up Galloway's check because (a) he didn't need the money (b) he knew it wouldn't clear (c) he wanted nothing to do with Galloway (d) Galloway requested him to.

❑ AUTHOR'S ATTITUDE

10. The author's attitude toward Michael Adams is one of (a) admiration and affection (b) ill-concealed hostility (c) studied indifference (d) pity for his shortcomings.

❑ IRONY

11. An example of irony is contained in which of the following sentences? (a) Then, in the early spring of 1983, we were blessed with the patronage of another, very different bizarre. (b) He disappeared up to the den and I breathed again. (c) That he prospered as a result did not displease him. (d) I was sure Galloway was going to hit him, but he didn't.

❑ ORDER OF EVENTS

12. Arrange the items in the order in which they occurred. Use letters only.
    A. Señor Petche confronts Galloway.
    B. Major Galloway shatters the plate glass.
    C. Michael and Señor Petche talk about Jung.
    D. Major Galloway enters for the first time.
    E. Major Galloway disappears for good.

❑ OUTCOMES

13. At the conclusion of the story, (a) Michael closes the bookstore (b) Galloway breaks more windows from afar (c) the narrator gains greater respect for Señor Petche (d) Michael fires the narrator.

❑ CAUSE AND EFFECT

14. Señor Petche came out on top because (a) Major Galloway was not as cruel as he seemed (b) he knew more than the Major (c) Michael stood at his side in the struggle (d) the Major had left his book of spells behind.

❑ FACT OR OPINION

Tell whether the following is a fact or an opinion.

15. Michael Adams was the pleasantest bookseller in his neighborhood.

Words in Context

1. ". . . it beckons and draws them as a *conjurer* does children, offering enchanted *diversion*." ***Conjurer* . . . *diversion*** (260) means (a) clown . . . entertainment (b) swindler . . . profits (c) prophet . . . future awards (d) magician . . . amusement.

2. "When the bookshop is small and *erudite* its attraction is doubled." ***Erudite*** (260) means (a) scholarly (b) well-advertised (c) inexpensive (d) exclusive.

3. ". . . I put our popularity down to the *ambience*, but it soon became clear that the real reason had much more to do with my employer . . ." ***Ambience*** (260) means (a) clientele (b) atmosphere (c) collections (d) advertising.

4. ". . . and they enjoyed the sight of the odd *Bohemian* . . . feeling themselves in touch with the poetical and the *avant-garde*." ***Bohemian . . . avant-garde*** (261) mean (a) nonconformist . . . trendsetters (b) yuppy . . . professionals (c) intellectual . . . wealthy (d) innovator . . . creators.

5. ". . . Michael drew his attention *inexorably* into the twin securities of his pet subjects . . ." ***Inexorably*** (261) means (a) slowly (b) relentlessly (c) frequently (d) patiently.

6. "The list was long and consisted of *ponderous* titles to do with magic and natural philosophy." ***Ponderous*** (262) means (a) obscure (b) massive (c) unusual (d) foreign.

7. "As she drove away she shot me a look of *profound reproach*." ***Profound reproach*** (263) means (a) deep sorrow (b) sorrowful regret (c) keenly felt reprimand (d) justifiable resentment.

8. "There was an actual *detonation* and the air was suddenly *lethal* with showering glass." ***Detonation . . . lethal . . .*** (264) mean (a) explosion . . . deadly . . . (b) discharge . . . sparkling . . . (c) outburst . . . crackling . . . (d) clap of thunder . . . overfilled.

9. "He just stood there, enjoying my *discomfiture*." ***Discomfiture*** (265) causes a feeling of (a) rage and belligerence (b) pride and disgust (c) embarrassment and frustration (d) helplessness and terror.

10. "'You also were abused?' he piped, with a little *moue* of sympathy." ***Moue*** (266) means (a) glance (b) pout (c) hand movement (d) shrug.

11. "But you heard no actual *incantation*." ***Incantation*** (266) means (a) command (b) spirit (c) spell (d) response.

12. "But here I am *hypothesizing over* what is to you a very personal predicament . . ." ***Hypothesizing over*** (266) means (a) talking about (b) making light of (c) theorizing about (d) thinking aloud about.

13. "But that awful silence *precluded* any movement." ***Precluded*** (267) means (a) encouraged (b) anticipated (c) ruled out (d) delayed.

14. "'*Bibliopegy?*' he suggested at last. 'You see, I take issue with the *adage:* a book usually can be judged by its binding.'" ***Bibliopegy*** . . . ***adage*** . . . (267) means (a) book collecting . . . proverb (b) magic . . . saying (c) writing . . . maxim (d) bookbinding . . . traditional saying.

15. ". . . I thought I detected something—just the merest hint of *patchouli* in the air." ***Patchouli*** (267) means (a) brimstone (b) smoke (c) garlic (d) heavy perfume.

Thinking Critically About the Story

1. What accepted truths must be suspended temporarily for the enjoyment of this story? Refer to specific details to substantiate your statement. Can the story please the reader who refuses to release his grasp on reality? Explain. What groups of stories make this demand? Why are they called escape literature? Is there any danger to the reader who so indulges himself? Why do some people resist these stories and find no sense in them? What do they miss? How do you react to stories and TV programs of the escape variety?

2. What traits make Michael Adams a successful shopkeeper? Refer to specific incidents in the story. How does he rate when compared with the workers in the stores you patronize? Why does the author stress these prosaic qualities in one of his main characters?

3. Whom would you classify as an eccentric in this story?

Señor Petche	the narrator
Michael Adam	Major Jonathan Galloway

Who are some of your favorite TV eccentrics? Have you met any in real life? Do you react the same way to real-life and storyland eccentrics? What makes people become eccentrics? Are they all amusing? All sad? All anything?

4. Why is Michael—who is normally a confessor, a good Samaritan, a confidant to the eccentrics—gruff and cold to the Major from the start? What does the Major do to make certain that he will be treated in that way? Why does the Major act that way? Are there people in real life who insist on "rubbing others the wrong way"? Do you know any? Why do they do it?

5. How does the author use foreshadowing to prepare us for the final confrontation? Is Señor Petche justified? Does Michael condone the action? Explain. Does the author condone murder?

Stories in Words

Eccentric (260) is derived from Greek through Latin. The roots literally mean "out of center, off center." An eccentric person deviates from accepted modes of conduct. He or she is "off center." The term is also used in physics for a disk not centered on a shaft. It converts the circular motion of the shaft into back-and-forth motion of the attached rod.

Astrakhan (261) is a kind of curled wool from a city in Russia. Like many other places, Astrakhan has given its name to a product now spelled without a capital letter. Other common examples include *currant* (Corinth), *bayonet* (Bayonne), *champagne*, *hamburger* (Hamburg), *frankfurter* (Frankfurt), *jersey*, *limerick*, and *tuxedo*.

Damoclean sword (265) is derived from a lovely old legend. In the fifth century B.C., Dionysius, the Elder of Syracuse, was annoyed by a courtier, Damocles. The courtier irritated the ruler by his flattering references to the ruler's great power and supposed happiness. Dionysius decided to teach the flatterer a lesson. He invited Damocles to a sumptuous banquet, which the guest enjoyed . . . until he looked up and noticed a sword above his head. It was suspended by a single hair and pointed directly at his head. The sight took away the joy of the meal and taught Damocles the threats, fears, and worries that beset the powerful. The current expression, *sword of Damocles*, suggests the fears of impending disaster. The expression *hang by a thread* has also been derived from the legend—to suggest imminent danger. In *Henry IV, Part II*, Shakespeare expresses the same thought: "Uneasy lies the head that wears a crown."

The Man Who Could Work Miracles

H. G. WELLS

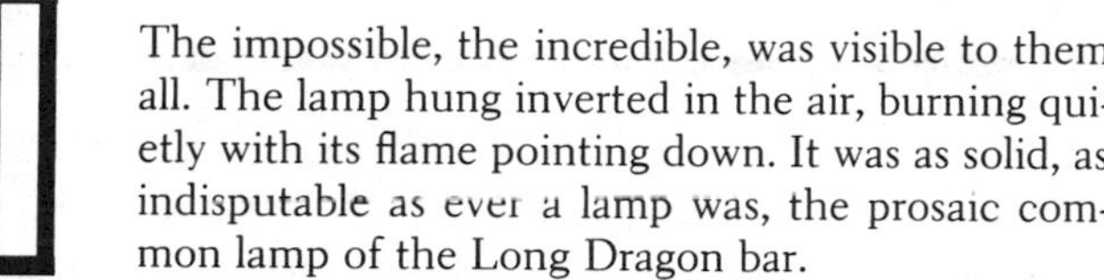

The impossible, the incredible, was visible to them all. The lamp hung inverted in the air, burning quietly with its flame pointing down. It was as solid, as indisputable as ever a lamp was, the prosaic common lamp of the Long Dragon bar.

George Bernard Shaw once said, "There are two tragedies in life. One is to lose your heart's desire. The other is to gain it." Shaw loved to shock; yet the quip, stated in contradictory form, may express a sound truth. It may be the journey, not the destination, that makes life worth living.

Benjamin Franklin expressed a similar thought. "If a man could have half his wishes, he would double his trouble."

Suppose you had every wish granted. Would the gift make you happier than you are now? George McWhirter Fotheringay was a man who discovered he had unusual powers. He could indeed work miracles, without number. If he wanted a third egg for breakfast, he merely had to wish for it. If he wanted to get rid of an annoying person, he could send him to Hades . . . or San Francisco. But then, at the urging of an enthusiastic friend, he makes the ultimate wish. What happens surprises Mr. Fotheringay . . . and the reader.

Did it all really happen? How can we ever be sure?

The Man Who Could Work Miracles

It is doubtful whether the gift was innate. For my own part, I think it came to him suddenly. Indeed, until he was thirty he was a skeptic, and did not believe in miraculous powers. And here, since it is the most convenient place, I must mention that he was a little man, and had eyes of a hot brown, very erect red hair, a mustache with ends that he twisted up, and freckles. His name was George McWhirter Fotheringay—not the sort of name by any means to lead to any expectation of miracles—and he was a clerk at Gomshott's. He was greatly addicted to assertive argument. It was while he was asserting the impossibility of miracles that he had his first intimation of his extraordinary powers. This particular argument was being held in the bar of the Long Dragon, and Toddy Beamish was conducting the opposition by a monotonous but effective "So *you* say," that drove Mr. Fotheringay to the very limit of his patience.

There were present, besides these two, a very dusty cyclist, landlord Cox, and Miss Maybridge, the perfectly respectable and rather portly barmaid of the Dragon. Miss Maybridge was standing with her back to Mr. Fotheringay, washing glasses; the others were watching him, more or less amused by the present ineffectiveness of the assertive method. Goaded by the overaggressive tactics of Mr. Beamish, Mr. Fotheringay determined to make an unusual rhetorical effort. "Looky here, Mr. Beamish," said Mr. Fotheringay. "Let us clearly understand what a miracle is. It's something contrariwise to the course of nature done by power or Will, something what couldn't happen without being specially willed."

"So *you* say," said Mr. Beamish, repulsing him.

Mr. Fotheringay appealed to the cyclist, who had hitherto been a silent auditor, and received his assent—given with a hesitating cough and a glance at Mr. Beamish. The landlord would express no opinion, and Mr. Fotheringay, returning to Mr. Beamish, received the unexpected concession of a qualified assent to his definition of a miracle.

"For instance," said Mr. Fotheringay, greatly encouraged. "Here would be a miracle. That lamp, in the natural course of nature, couldn't burn like that upsy-down, could it, Beamish?"

"*You* say it couldn't," said Beamish.

"And you?" said Fotheringay. "You don't mean to say—eh?"

"No," said Beamish reluctantly. "No, it couldn't."

"Very well," said Mr. Fotheringay. "Then here comes someone, as it might be me, along here, and stands as it might be here, and says to that lamp, as I might do, collecting all my will—'Turn upsy-down without breaking, and go on burning steady,' and—Hullo!"

It was enough to make anyone say "Hullo!" The impossible, the incredible, was visible to them all. The lamp hung inverted in the air, burning quietly with its flame pointing down. It was as solid, as indisputable as ever a lamp was, the prosaic common lamp of the Long Dragon bar.

Mr. Fotheringay stood with an extended forefinger and the knitted brows of one anticipating a catastrophic smash. The cyclist, who was sitting next the lamp, ducked and jumped across the bar. Everybody jumped, more or less. Miss Maybridge turned and screamed. For nearly three seconds the lamp remained still. A faint cry of mental distress came from Mr. Fotheringay. "I can't keep it up," he said, "any longer." He staggered back, and the inverted lamp suddenly flared, fell against the corner of the bar, bounced aside, smashed upon the floor, and went out.

It was lucky it had a metal receiver, or the whole place would have been in a blaze. Mr. Cox was the first to speak, and his remark, shorn of needless excrescences, was to the effect that Fotheringay was a fool. Fotheringay was beyond disputing even so fundamental a proposition as that! He was astonished beyond measure at the thing that had occurred. The subsequent conversation threw absolutely no light on the matter so far as Fotheringay was concerned; the general opinion not only followed Mr. Cox very closely but very vehemently. Everyone accused Fotheringay of a silly trick, and presented him to himself as a foolish destroyer of comfort and security. His mind was a tornado of perplexity, he was himself inclined to agree with them, and he made a remarkably ineffectual opposition to the proposal of his departure.

He went home flushed and heated, coat collar crumpled, eyes smarting, and ears red. He watched each of the ten street lamps nervously as he passed it. It was only when he found himself alone in his little bedroom in Church Row that he was able to grapple seriously with his memories of the occurrence, and ask, "What on earth happened?"

He had removed his coat and boots, and was sitting on the bed with his hands in his pockets repeating the text of his defense for the seventeenth time, "*I* didn't want the confounded thing to upset," when it occurred to him that at the precise moment he had said the commanding words he had inadvertently willed the thing he said, and that when he had seen the lamp in the air he had felt that it depended on him to maintain it there without being clear how this was to be done. He had not a particularly complex mind, or he might have stuck for a time at that "inadvertently willed," embracing, as it does, the abstrusest problems of voluntary action; but as it was, the idea came to him with a quite acceptable haziness. And from that, following, as I must admit, no clear logical path, he came to the test of experiment.

He pointed resolutely to his candle and collected his mind, though he felt he did a foolish thing. "Be raised up," he said. But in a second that feeling vanished. The candle was raised, hung in the air one giddy moment, and as Mr. Fotheringay gasped, fell with a smash on his dressing-table, leaving him in darkness save for the expiring glow of its wick.

For a time Mr. Fotheringay sat in the darkness, perfectly still. "It did happen, after all," he said. "And 'ow I'm to explain it I *don't* know." He sighed heavily, and began feeling in his pockets for a match. He could find none, and he rose and groped about the dressing-table. "I wish I had a match," he said. He resorted to his coat, and there were none there, and then it dawned upon him that miracles were possible even with matches. He extended a hand and scowled at it in the dark. "Let there be a match in that hand," he said. He felt some light object fall across his palm, and his fingers closed upon a match.

After several ineffectual attempts to light this, he discovered it was a safety match. He threw it down, and then it occurred to him that he might have willed it lit. He did, and perceived it burning in the midst of his dressing-table mat. He caught it up hastily, and it went out. His perception of possibilities enlarged, and he felt for and replaced the candle in its candlestick. "Here! *you* be lit," said Mr. Fotheringay, and forthwith the candle was flaring, and he saw a little black hole in the tablecover, with a wisp of smoke rising from it. For a time he stared from this to the little flame and back, and then looked up and met his own gaze in the looking-glass. By this help he communed with himself in silence for a time.

"How about miracles now?" said Mr. Fotheringay at last, addressing his reflection.

The subsequent meditations of Mr. Fotheringay were of a severe but confused description. So far as he could see, it was a case of pure willing with him. The nature of his first experiences disinclined him for any further experiments except of the most cautious type. But he lifted a sheet of paper, and turned a glass of water pink and then green, and he created a snail, which he miraculously annihilated, and got himself a miraculous new toothbrush. Somewhere in the small hours he had reached the fact that his willpower must be of a particularly rare and pungent quality, a fact of which he had certainly had inklings before, but no certain assurance. The scare and perplexity of his first discovery were now qualified by pride in this evidence of singularity and by vague intimations of advantage. He became aware that the church clock was striking one, and as it did not occur to him that his daily duties at Gomshott's might be miraculously dispensed with, he resumed undressing, in order to get to bed without further delay. As he struggled to get his shirt over his head he was struck with a brilliant idea. "Let me be in bed," he said, and found himself so. "Undressed," he stipulated; and, finding the sheets cold, added hastily, "and in my nightshirt—no, in a nice soft woollen nightshirt. Ah!" he said with immense enjoyment. "And now let me be comfortably asleep . . ."

He awoke at his usual hour and was pensive all through breakfast-time, wondering whether his overnight experience might not be a particularly vivid dream. At length his mind turned again to cautious experiments. For instance, he had three eggs for breakfast; two his landlady had supplied, good, but strong flavored, and one was a delicious fresh goose-egg, laid, cooked, and served by his extraordinary will. He hurried off to Gomshott's in a state of profound but carefully concealed excitement, and only remembered the shell of the third egg when his landlady spoke of it that night. All day he could do no work because of this astonishing new self-knowledge, but this caused him no inconvenience, because he made up for it miraculously in his last ten minutes.

As the day wore on his state of mind passed from wonder to elation, albeit the circumstances of his dismissal from the Long Dragon were still disagreeable to recall, and a garbled account of the matter that had reached his colleagues led to some badinage. It was evident he must be careful how he lifted frangible articles, but in other ways his gift promised more and more as he turned it over in his mind. He intended among other things to increase his personal property by unostentatious acts of creation. He called into existence a pair of very splendid diamond cuff links, and hastily annihilated them again as young Gomshott came across the counting-house to his desk. He was afraid young Gomshott might wonder how he came by them. He saw quite clearly the gift required caution and watchfulness in its exercise, but so far as he could judge the difficulties attending its mastery would be no greater than those he had already faced in the study of cycling. It was that analogy, perhaps, quite as much as the feeling that he would be unwelcome in the Long Dragon, that drove him out after supper into the lane beyond the gas-works, to rehearse a few miracles in private.

There was possibly a certain want of originality in his attempts, for apart from his willpower Mr. Fotheringay was not a very exceptional man. The miracle of Moses' rod came to his mind, but the night was dark and unfavorable to the proper control of large miraculous snakes. Then he recollected the story of "Tannhäuser" that he had read on the back of the Philharmonic program. That seemed to him singularly attractive and harmless. He stuck his cane—a very nice Poona-Penang lawyer*—into the turf that edged the footpath, and commanded the dry wood to blossom. The air was immediately full of the scent of roses, and by means of a

**Poona* type of hard wood *Penang lawyer* cane with bulbous head match he saw for himself that this beautiful miracle was indeed accomplished. His satisfaction was ended by advancing footsteps. Afraid of a premature discovery of his powers, he addressed the blossoming cane hastily: "Go back." What he meant was "Change back"; but of course he was confused. The cane receded at a considerable velocity, and suddenly came a cry of anger and a bad word from the approaching person. "Who are you throwing brambles at, you fool?" cried a voice. "That got me on the shin."

"I'm sorry, old chap," said Mr. Fotheringay, and then, realizing the awkward nature of the explanation, caught nervously at his mustache. He saw Winch, one of the three Immering constables, advancing.

"What d'yer mean by it?" asked the constable. "Hullo! It's you, is it? The gent that broke the lamp at the Long Dragon!"

"I don't mean anything by it," said Mr. Fotheringay. "Nothing at all."

"What d'yer do it for then?"

"Oh, bother!" said Mr. Fotheringay.

"Bother, indeed? D'yer know that stick hurt? What d'yer do it for, eh?"

For the moment Mr. Fotheringay could not think what he had done it for. His silence seemed to irritate Mr. Winch. "You've been assaulting the police, young man, this time. That's what *you* done!"

"Look here, Mr. Winch," said Mr. Fotheringay, annoyed and confused, "I've very sorry. The fact is—"

"Well!"

He could think of no way but the truth. "I was working a miracle." He tried to speak in an offhand way, but try as he would he couldn't.

"Working a—! 'Ere, don't you talk rot. Working a miracle, indeed! Miracle! Well, that's downright funny! Why, you's the chap that don't believe in miracles . . . Fact is, this is another of your silly conjuring tricks—that's what this is. Now, I tell you—"

But Mr. Fotheringay never heard what Mr. Winch was going to tell him. He realized he had given himself away, flung his valuable secret to all the winds of heaven. A violent gust of irritation swept him to action. He turned on the constable swiftly and fiercely. "Here," he said, "I've had enough of this, I have! I'll show you a silly conjuring trick, I will. Go to Hades! Go, now!"

He was alone!

Mr. Fotheringay performed no more miracles that night nor did he trouble to see what had become of his flowering stick. He returned to the town, scared and very quiet, and went to his bedroom. "Lord!" he said, "it's a powerful gift—an extremely powerful gift! I didn't hardly mean as much as that. Not really . . . I wonder what Hades is like!"

He sat on the bed taking off his boots. Struck by a happy thought he transferred the constable to San Francisco, and without any more interference with normal causation went soberly to bed. In the night he dreamt of the anger of Winch.

The next day Mr. Fotheringay heard two interesting items of news. Someone had planted a most beautiful climbing rose against the elder Mr.

Gomshott's private house in the Lullaborough Road, and the river as far as Rawling's Mill was to be dragged for Constable Winch.

Mr. Fotheringay was abstracted and thoughtful all that day, and performed no miracles except certain provisions for Winch, and the miracle of completing his day's work with punctual perfection in spite of all the bee-swarm of thoughts that hummed through his mind. And the extraordinary abstraction and meekness of his manner was remarked by several people, and made a matter for jesting. For the most part he was thinking of Winch.

On Sunday evening he went to chapel, and oddly enough, Mr. Maydig, who took a certain interest in occult matters, preached about "things that are not lawful." Mr. Fotheringay was not a regular chapel goer, but the system of assertive skepticism, to which I have already alluded, was now very much shaken. The tenor of the sermon threw an entirely new light on these novel gifts, and he suddenly decided to consult Mr. Maydig immediately after the service. So soon as that was determined, he found himself wondering why he had not done so before.

Mr. Maydig, a lean, excitable man with quite remarkably long wrists and neck, was gratified at a request for a private conversation from a young man whose carelessness in religious matters was a subject for general remark in the town. After a few necessary delays, he conducted him to the study of the Manse, which was contiguous to the chapel, seated him comfortably, and, standing in front of a cheerful fire—his legs threw a Rhodian arch* of shadow on the opposite wall—requested Mr. Fotheringay to state his business.

At first Mr. Fotheringay was a little abashed, and found some difficulty in opening the matter. "You will scarcely believe me, Mr. Maydig, I am afraid"—and so forth for some time. He tried a question at last, and asked Mr. Maydig his opinion of miracles.

Mr. Maydig was still saying "Well" in an extremely judicial tone, when Mr. Fotheringay interrupted again: "You don't believe, I suppose, that some common sort of person—like myself, for instance—as it might be sitting here now, might have some sort of twist inside him that made him able to do things by his will."

"It's possible," said Mr. Maydig. "Something of the sort, perhaps, is possible."

"If I might make free with something here, I think I might show you a sort of experiment," said Mr. Fotheringay. "Now, take that tobacco jar on the table, for instance. What I want to know is whether what I am going to do with it is a miracle or not. Just half a minute, Mr. Maydig, please."

He knitted his brows, pointed to the tobacco jar and said: "Be a bowl of vi'lets."

The tobacco jar did as it was ordered.

Mr. Maydig started violently at the change, and stood looking from the

***Rhodian arch* base of massive ancient statue, one of the Seven Wonders

thaumaturgist to the bowl of flowers. He said nothing. Presently he ventured to lean over the table and smell the violets; they were fresh-picked and very fine ones. Then he stared at Mr. Fotheringay again.

"How did you do that?" he asked.

Mr. Fotheringay pulled his mustache. "Just told it—and there you are. Is that a miracle, or is it black art, or what is it? And what do you think's the matter with me? That's what I want to ask."

"It's a most extraordinary occurrence."

"And this day last week I knew no more that I could do things like that than you did. It came quite sudden. It's something odd about my will, I suppose, and that's as far as I can see."

"Is *that*—the only thing? Could you do other things besides that?"

"Lord, yes!" said Mr. Fotheringay. "Just anything." He thought, and suddenly recalled a conjuring entertainment he had seen. "Here!" He pointed. "Change into a bowl of fish—no, not that—change into a glass bowl full of water with goldfish swimming in it. That's better! You see that, Mr. Maydig?"

"It's astonishing. It's incredible. You are either a most extraordinary . . . But no—"

"I could change it into anything," said Mr. Fotheringay. "Just anything. Here! be a pigeon, will you?"

In another moment a blue pigeon was fluttering round the room and making Mr. Maydig duck every time it came near him. "Stop there, will you," said Mr. Fotheringay; and the pigeon hung motionless in the air. "I could change it back to a bowl of flowers," he said, and after replacing the pigeon on the table worked that miracle. "I expect you will want your pipe in a bit," he said, and restored the tobacco jar.

Mr. Maydig had followed all these later changes in a sort of explosive silence. He stared at Mr. Fotheringay and, in a very gingerly manner, picked up the tobacco jar, examined it, replaced it on the table, "*Well!*" was the only expression of his feelings.

"Now, after that it's easier to explain what I came about," said Mr. Fotheringay; and proceeded to a lengthy and involved narrative of his strange experiences, beginning with the affair of the lamp in the Long Dragon and complicated by persistent allusions to Winch. As he went on, the transient pride Mr. Maydig's consternation had caused passed away; he became the very ordinary Mr. Fotheringay of everyday conversation again. Mr. Maydig listened intently, the tobacco jar in his hand, and his bearing changed also with the course of the narrative. Presently, while Mr. Fotheringay was dealing with the miracle of the third egg, the minister interrupted with a fluttering extended hand—

"It is possible," he said. "It is credible. It is amazing, of course, but it reconciles a number of difficulties. The power to work miracles is a gift—a peculiar quality like genius or second sight—hitherto it has come very rarely and to exceptional people. But in this case . . . I have always wondered at the miracles of Mahomet, and at Yogi's miracles, and the miracles of Madame Blavatsky.* But, of course! Yes, it is simply a gift! It carries out so beautifully the arguments of that great thinker"—Mr. Maydig's voice sank—"his Grace the Duke of Argyll. Here we plumb some profounder law—deeper than the ordinary laws of nature. Yes—yes. Go on. Go on!"

Mr. Fotheringay proceeded to tell of his misadventure with Winch, and Mr. Maydig, no longer overawed or scared, began to jerk his limbs about and interject astonishment. "It's this what troubled me most," proceeded Mr. Fotheringay; "it's this I'm most in want of advice for; of course he's at San Francisco—wherever San Francisco may be—but of course it's awkward for both of us, as you'll see, Mr. Maydig. I don't see how he can understand what has happened, and I dare say he's scared and exasperated something tremendous, and trying to get at me. I dare say he keeps on starting off to come here. I send him back, by a miracle every few hours, when I think of it. And of course, that's a thing he won't be able to understand, and it's bound to annoy him; and, of course, if he takes a ticket every time it will cost him a lot of money. I done the best I could for him, but of course it's difficult for him to put himself in my place. I thought afterwards that his clothes might have got scorched, you know—if Hades is all it's supposed to be—before I shifted him. In that case I suppose they'd have locked him up in San Francisco. Of course I willed him a new suit of clothes on him directly I thought of it. But, you see, I'm already in a deuce of a tangle—"

Mr. Maydig looked serious. "I see you are in a tangle. Yes, it's a difficult position. How you are to end it . . ." He became diffuse and inconclusive.

"However, we'll leave Winch for a little and discuss the larger question. I don't think this is a case of the black art or anything of the sort. I don't think there is any taint of criminality about it at all, Mr. Fotheringay—none whatever, unless you are suppressing material facts. No, it's miracles—pure miracles—miracles, if I may say so, of the very highest class."

He began to pace the hearthrug and gesticulate, while Mr. Fotheringay sat with his arm on the table and his head on his arm, looking worried. "I don't see how I'm to manage about Winch," he said.

"A gift of working miracles—apparently a very powerful gift," said Mr. Maydig, "will find a way about Winch—never fear. My dear sir, you are a most important man—a man of the most astonishing possibilities. As evidence, for example! And in other ways, the things you may do. . . ."

"Yes, *I've* thought of a thing or two," said Mr. Fotheringay. "But—some of the things came a bit twisty. You saw that fish at first? Wrong sort of bowl and wrong sort of fish. And I thought I'd ask someone."

"A proper course," said Mr. Maydig, "a very proper course—altogether the proper course." He stopped and looked at Mr. Fotheringay. "It's practically an unlimited gift. Let us test your powers, for instance. If they really are . . . If they really *are* all they seem to be."

And so, incredible as it may seem, in the study of the little house behind

**Mahomet* Muhammad *Yogi* Hindu mystic *Madame Blavatsky* Russian mystic

the Congregational Chapel, on the evening of Sunday, Nov. 10, 1896, Mr. Fotheringay, egged on and inspired by Mr. Maydig, began to work miracles. The reader's attention is specially and definitely called to that date. He will object, probably has already objected, that certain points in this story are improbable, that if any things of the sort already described had indeed occurred, they would have been in all the papers a year ago. The details immediately following he will find particularly hard to accept, because among other things they involve the conclusion that he or she, the reader in question, must have been killed in a violent and unprecedented manner more than a year ago. Now a miracle is nothing if not improbable, and as a matter of fact the reader *was* killed in a violent and unprecedented manner a year ago. In the subsequent course of this story it will become perfectly clear and credible, as every right-minded and reasonable reader will admit. But this is not the place for the end of the story, being but little beyond the hither side of the middle. And at first the miracles worked by Mr. Fotheringay were timid little miracles—little things with the cups and living-room knickknacks, as feeble as the miracles of Theosophists,* and, feeble as they were, they were received with awe by his collaborator. He would have preferred to settle the Winch business out of hand, but Mr. Maydig would not let him. But after they had worked a dozen of these domestic trivialities, their sense of power grew, their imagination began to show signs of stimulation, and their ambition enlarged. Their first larger enterprise was due to hunger and the negligence of Mrs. Minchin, Mr. Maydig's housekeeper. The meal to which the minister conducted Mr. Fotheringay was certainly ill-laid and uninviting as refreshment for two industrious miracle workers; but they were seated, and Mr. Maydig was descanting in sorrow rather than in anger upon his housekeeper's shortcomings, before it occurred to Mr. Fotheringay that an opportunity lay before him. "Don't you think, Mr. Maydig," he said, "if it isn't a liberty, I—"

"My dear Mr. Fotheringay! Of course! No—I didn't think."

Mr. Fotheringay waved his hand. "What shall we have?" he said, in a large, inclusive spirit, and, at Mr. Maydig's order, revised the supper very thoroughly. "As for me," he said, eyeing Mr. Maydig's selection, "I am always particularly fond of a tankard of stout and a nice Welsh rarebit, and I'll order that. I ain't much given to Burgundy," and forthwith stout and Welsh rarebit promptly appeared at his command. They sat long at their supper, talking like equals, as Mr. Fotheringay, presently perceived with a glow of surprise and gratification, of all the miracles they would presently do. "And, by the bye, Mr. Maydig," said Mr. Fotheringay, "I might perhaps be able to help you—in a domestic way."

"Don't quite follow," said Mr. Maydig, pouring out a glass of miraculous old Burgundy.

Mr. Fotheringay helped himself to a second Welsh rarebit out of vacancy, and took a mouthful. "I was thinking," he said, "I might be able

**Theosophists* members of a mystical cult

(*chum, chum*) to work (*chum, chum*) a miracle with Mrs. Minchin (*chum, chum*)—make her a better woman."

Mr. Maydig put down the glass and looked doubtful. "She's—She strongly objects to interference, you know, Mr. Fotheringay. And—as a matter of fact—it's well past eleven and she's probably in bed and asleep. Do you think, on the whole—"

Mr. Fotheringay considered these objections. "I don't see that it shouldn't be done in her sleep."

For a time Mr. Maydig opposed the idea, and then he yielded. Mr. Fotheringay issued his orders, and a little less at their ease, perhaps, the two gentlemen proceeded with their repast. Mr. Maydig was enlarging on the changes he might expect in his housekeeper next day, with an optimism that seemed even to Mr. Fotheringay's supper senses a little forced and hectic, when a series of confused noises from upstairs began. Their eyes exchanged interrogations, and Mr. Maydig left the room hastily. Mr. Fotheringay heard him calling up to his housekeeper and then his footsteps going softly up to her.

In a minute or so the minister returned, his step light, his facc radiant. "Wonderful!" he said, "and touching! Most touching!"

He began pacing the hearthrug. "A repentance—a most touching repentance—through the crack of the door. Poor woman! A most wonderful change! She had got up. She must have got up at once. She had got up out of her sleep to smash a private bottle of brandy in her box. And to confess it, too! . . . But this gives us—it opens—a most amazing vista of possibilities. If we can work this miraculous change in *her* . . ."

"The thing's unlimited seemingly," said Mr. Fotheringay. "And about Mr. Winch—"

"Altogether unlimited." And from the hearthrug Mr. Maydig, waving the Winch difficulty aside, unfolded a series of wonderful proposals—proposals he invented as he went along.

Now what those proposals were does not concern the essentials of this story. Suffice it that they were designed in a spirit of infinite benevolence, the sort of benevolence that used to be called postprandial. Suffice it, too, that the problem of Winch remained unsolved. Nor is it necessary to describe how far that series got to its fulfillment. There were astonishing changes. The small hours found Mr. Maydig and Mr. Fotheringay careering across the chilly market-square under the still moon, in a sort of ecstasy of thaumaturgy, Mr. Maydig all flap and gesture, Mr. Fotheringay short and bristling, and no longer abashed at his greatness. They had reformed every drunkard in the Parliamentary division, changed all the beer and alcohol to water (Mr. Maydig had overruled Mr. Fotheringay on this point), they had, further, greatly improved the railway communication of the place, drained Flinder's swamp, improved the soil of One Tree Hill, and cured the Vicar's wart. And they were going to see what could be done with the injured pier at South Bridge. "The place," gasped Mr. Maydig, "won't be the same place tomorrow. How surprised and thankful everyone will be!" And just at that moment the church clock struck three.

" I say," said Mr. Fotheringay, "that's three o'clock! I must be getting back. I've got to be at business by eight. And besides, Mrs. Wimms—"

"We're only beginning," said Mr. Maydig, full of the sweetness of unlimited power. "We're only beginning. Think of all the good we're doing. When people wake—"

"But—" said Mr. Fotheringay.

Mr. Maydig gripped his arm suddenly. His eyes were bright and wild. "My dear chap," he said, "there's no hurry. Look"—he pointed to the moon at the zenith—"Joshua!"

"Joshua?" said Mr. Fotheringay.

"Joshua," said Mr. Maydig. "Why not? Stop it."

Mr. Fotheringay looked at the moon.

"That's a bit tall," he said after a pause.

"Why not?" said Mr. Maydig. "Of course it doesn't stop. You stop the rotation of the earth, you know. Time stops. It isn't as if we were doing harm."

"H'm!" said Mr. Fotheringay. "Well." He sighed. "I'll try. Here—"

He buttoned up his jacket and addressed himself to the habitable globe, with as good an assumption of confidence as lay in his power. "Jest stop rotating, will you?" said Mr. Fotheringay.

Completely out of control he was flying head over heels through the air at the rate of dozens of miles a minute. In spite of the innumerable circles he was describing per second, he thought; for thought is wonderful—sometimes as sluggish as flowing pitch, sometimes as instantaneous as light. He thought in a second, and willed. "Let me come down safe and sound. Whatever else happens, let me down safe and sound."

He willed it only just in time, for his clothes, heated by his rapid flight through the air, were already beginning to singe. He came down with a forcible but by no means injurious bump in what appeared to be a mound of fresh-turned earth. A large mass of metal and masonry, extraordinarily like the clock tower in the middle of the market square, hit the earth near him, ricochetted over him, and flew into stonework, bricks, and masonry, like a bursting bomb. A hurtling cow hit one of the larger blocks and smashed like an egg. There was a crash that made all the most violent crashes of his past life seem like the sound of falling dust, and this was followed by a descending series of lesser crashes. A vast wind roared throughout earth and heaven, so that he could scarcely lift his head to look. For a while he was too breathless and astonished even to see where he was or what had happened. And his first movement was to feel his head and reassure himself that his streaming hair was still his own.

"Lord!" gasped Mr. Fotheringay, scarce able to speak for the gale. "I've had a squeak! What's gone wrong? Storms and thunder. And only a minute ago a fine night. It's Maydig set me on to this sort of thing. *What* a wind! If I go on fooling in this way I'm bound to have a thundering accident!

"Where's Maydig?

"What a confounded mess everything's in!"

He looked about him so far as his flapping jacket would permit. The appearance of things was really extremely strange. "The sky's all right anyhow," said Mr. Fotheringay. "And that's about all that is all right. And even there it looks like a terrific gale coming up. But there's the moon overhead. Just as it was just now. Bright as midday. But as for the rest—Where's the village? Where's—where's anything? And what on earth set this wind a-blowing?*I* didn't order no wind."

Mr. Fotheringay struggled to get to his feet in vain, and after one failure, remained on all fours, holding on. He surveyed the moonlit world to leeward, with the tails of his jacket streaming over his head. "There's something seriously wrong," said Mr. Fotheringay. "And what it is—goodness knows."

Far and wide nothing was visible in the white glare through the haze of dust that drove before a screaming gale but tumbled masses of earth and heaps of inchoate ruins, no trees, no houses, no familiar shapes, only a wilderness of disorder vanishing at last into the darkness beneath the whirling columns and streamers, the lightnings and thunderings of a swiftly rising storm. Near him in the livid glare was something that might once have been an elm tree, a smashed mass of splinters, shivered from boughs to base, and further a twisted mass of iron girders—only too evidently the viaduct—rose out of the piled confusion.

You see, when Mr. Fotheringay had arrested the rotation of the solid globe, he had made no stipulation concerning the trifling movables upon its surface. And the earth spins so fast that the surface at its equator is traveling at rather more than a thousand miles an hour, and in these latitudes at more than half that pace. So that the village, and Mr. Maydig, and Mr. Fotheringay, and everybody and everything had been jerked violently forward at about nine miles per second—that is to say, much more violently than if they had been fired out of a cannon. And every human being, every living creature, every house, and every tree—all the world as we know it—had been so yanked and smashed and utterly destroyed. That was all.

These things Mr. Fotheringay did not, of course, fully appreciate. But he perceived that his miracle had miscarried, and with that a great disgust of miracles came upon him. He was in darkness now, for the clouds had swept together and blotted out his momentary glimpse of the moon, and the air was full of fitful struggling tortured wraiths of hail. A great roaring of wind and waters filled earth and sky, and, peering under his hand through the dust and sleet to windward, he saw by the play of the lightnings a vast wall of water pouring towards him.

"Maydig!" screamed Mr. Fotheringay's feeble voice amid the elemental uproar. "Here!—Maydig!"

"Stop!" cried Mr. Fotheringay to the advancing water. "Oh, for goodness' sake, stop!

"Just a moment," said Mr. Fotheringay to the lightnings and thunder. "Stop jest a moment while I collect my thoughts . . . And now what shall I do?" he said. "What *shall* I do? Lord! I wish Maydig was about.

"I know," said Mr. Fotheringay. "And for goodness' sake let's have it right *this* time."

He remained on all fours, leaning against the wind, very intent to have everything right.

"Ah!" he said. "Let nothing what I'm going to order happen until I say 'Off' . . . Lord! I wish I'd thought of that before!"

He lifted his little voice against the whirlwind, shouting louder and louder in the vain desire to hear himself speak. "Now then!—here goes! Mind about that what I said just now. In the first place, when all I've got to say is done, let me lose my miraculous power, let my will become just like anybody else's will, and all these dangerous miracles be stopped. I don't like them. I'd rather I didn't work 'em. Ever so much. That's the first thing. And the second is—let me be back just before the miracles begin; let everything be just as it was before that blessed lamp turned up. It's a big job, but it's the last. Have you got it? No more miracles, everything as it was—me back in the Long Dragon just before I drank my half-pint. That's it! Yes."

He dug his fingers into the mold, closed his eyes, and said "Off!"

Everything became perfectly still. He perceived that he was standing erect.

"So *you* say," said a voice.

He opened his eyes. He was in the bar of the Long Dragon, arguing about miracles with Toddy Beamish. He had a vague sense of some great thing forgotten that instantaneously passed. You see, except for the loss of his miraculous power, everything was back as it had been; his mind and memory therefore were now just as they had been at the time when this story began. So that he knew absolutely nothing of all that is told here, knows nothing of all that is told here to this day. And among other things, of course, he still did not believe in miracles.

"I tell you that miracles, properly speaking, can't possibly happen," he said, "whatever you like to hold. And I'm prepared to prove it up to the hilt."

"That's what *you* think," said Toddy Beamish, and "Prove it if you can."

"Looky here, Mr. Beamish," said Mr. Fotheringay. "Let us clearly understand what a miracle is. It's something contrariwise to the course of nature done by power of Will. . . ."

Reading for Understanding

❑ MAIN IDEA

1. The theme of the story is that (a) some people show off to impress others (b) having wishes without end is dangerous (c) miracles are always in accordance with natural law (d) skepticism is always unjustified.

❑ DETAILS

2. The annoying speaker of "So *you* say" was (a) Miss Maybridge (b) the dusty cyclist (c) the landlord Cox (d) Toddy Beamish.

3. Fotheringay performed his second miracle with (a) a lamp (b) a candle (c) Gomshott (d) Winch.

4. Winch was (a) a lawyer (b) a minister (c) a constable (d) the housekeeper's husband.

5. A project of Maydig and Fotheringay was (a) reforming drunkards (b) betting on the races (c) removing traffic snarls (d) running for Parliament.

❑ INFERENCES

6. We may assume that the dusty cyclist is (a) extremely shy (b) unusually assertive (c) slightly paranoid (d) boisterous.

7. Fotheringay soon gets into trouble because (a) he wishes for evil things (b) other people counter his wishes (c) people are immediately terrified of him (d) his wishes are taken literally.

8. Mr. Maydig's attitude toward Fotheringay's marvelous gift is one of (a) disapproval (b) indifference (c) enthusiasm (d) bitterness.

9. The story suggests that Fotheringay (a) by his actions, contradicts his own assertiveness about miracles (b) is basically an evil character (c) wants most of all to impress Miss Maybridge (d) dislikes Mr. Maydig intensely.

❑ FIGURE OF SPEECH

10. An oxymoron is an expression combining contradictory ideas, as in *wise fool, sweet sorrow, honest thief, cruel kindness.* Which of the following contains an oxymoron? (a) He was a little man, and had eyes of a hot brown, very erect red hair, a mustache with ends that he twisted up, and freckles. (b) He pointed resolutely to his candle and collected his mind, though he felt he did a foolish thing. (c) In a minute or so the minister returned, his step light, his face radiant. (d) Mr. Maydig had followed all these later changes in a sort of explosive silence.

❑ AUTHOR'S STYLE

11. The style of the author may be characterized as (a) ponderous and serious (b) light and whimsical (c) halting and repetitive (d) breathless and staccato.

❑ ORDER OF EVENTS

12. Arrange the items in the order in which they occurred. Use letters only.
    A. Fotheringay sends Winch to San Francisco.
    B. Beamish first derides the ideas of Fotheringay.
    C. Fotheringay confides in Maydig.
    D. Fotheringay renounces his magical powers.
    E. The constable questions Fotheringay.

❑ OUTCOMES

13. At the conclusion of the story, (a) Maydig asks Fotheringay to perform more miracles (b) Winch arrives by boat from San Francisco (c) Fotheringay still expresses skepticism about miracles (d) Fotheringay pays for the lamp he broke.

❑ CAUSE AND EFFECT

14. According to the logic of the story, stopping the earth's rotation was (a) impossible (b) an improvement (c) a disaster (d) first suggested by Toddy Beamish.

❑ FACT OR OPINION

Tell whether the following is a fact or an opinion.

15. Fotheringay was a person of fine character.

Words in Context

1. "It is doubtful whether the gift was *innate*." ***Innate*** (274) means (a) intentional (b) inborn (c) accidental (d) moralistic.
2. "It was as solid, as indisputable as ever a lamp was, the *prosaic* common lamp of the Long Dragon bar." ***Prosaic*** (275) means (a) inexpensive (b) brassy (c) polished (d) run-of-the-mill.
3. "Mr. Cox was the first to speak, and his remark, *shorn of needless excrescences*, was . . . that Fotheringay was a fool." ***Shorn of needless excrescences*** (275) means (a) very clearly and distinctly (b) filled with fear and anger (c) without excess outbursts (d) lacking praise and astonishment.
4. "'Here! you be lit,' said Fotheringay, and *forthwith* the candle was flaring." ***Forthwith*** (276) means (a) in a short while (b) quietly (c) immediately (d) with a swish.

5. "By this help he *communed with* himself in silence for a time." ***Communed with*** (276) means (a) conferred with (b) argued with (c) analyzed (d) took stock of.

6. "The scare and perplexity . . . were now qualified by pride in this evidence of *singularity* and by vague *intimations* of advantage." ***Singularity*** . . . ***intimations*** . . . (276) mean (a) fame . . . realizations (b) loneliness . . . dreaming (c) uniqueness . . . hinting at (d) trickery . . . fears

7. ". . . a *garbled* account of the matter that had reached his *colleagues* led to some *badinage*." ***Garbled*** . . . ***colleagues*** . . . ***badinage*** (277) mean (a) preliminary . . . employers . . . ridicule (b) distorted . . . fellow workers . . . playful teasing (c) exaggerated . . . employers . . . eyebrow raising (d) partial . . . customers . . . sneering.

8. "He intended among other things to increase his personal property by *unostentatious* acts of creation." ***Unostentatious*** (277) means (a) rapid (b) repeated (c) inconspicuous (d) well-planned.

9. "The *tenor* of the sermon threw an entirely new light on these *novel* gifts, and he suddenly decided to consult Mr. Maydig immediately after the service." ***Tenor*** . . . ***novel*** (279) mean (a) singer . . . dangerous (b) general direction . . . uncommon (c) moral . . . literary (d) sound . . . unique.

10. "After a few necessary delays, he conducted him to the study of the *Manse,* which was *contiguous to* the chapel." ***Manse*** . . . ***contiguous to*** (279) mean (a) university . . . not far from (b) dining hall . . . part of (c) dormitory . . . alongside (d) minister's house . . . adjoining.

11. "As he went on, the *transient* pride Mr. Maydig's *consternation* had caused passed away . . ." ***Transient*** . . . ***consternation*** . . . (280) mean (a) momentary . . . shock (b) intense . . . anxiety (c) modest . . . astonishment (d) natural . . . bewilderment.

12. "'Yes, it is a difficult position. How are you to end it . . .' He became *diffuse and inconclusive.*" ***Diffuse and inconclusive*** (281) means (a) deliberate and puzzling (b) argumentative and opinionated (c) oratorical and vague (d) long-winded and indefinite.

13. "Mr. Maydig was *descanting* in sorrow rather than in anger upon his housekeeper's shortcomings. . ." ***Descanting*** (282) means (a) meditating (b) drawing (c) commenting (d) dwelling.

14. "Far and wide nothing was visible . . .but tumbled masses of earth and heaps of *inchoate* ruins . . . a wilderness of disorder." ***Inchoate*** (285) means (a) smoldering (b) formless (c) lifeless (d) endless.

15. "He was in darkness now . . . and the air was full of *fitful* struggling tortured *wraiths* of hail." ***Fitful*** . . . ***wraiths*** . . . (285) mean

(a) incessant . . . masses (b) frightening . . . storms (c) deafening . . . torrents (d) intermittent . . . apparitions.

Thinking Critically About the Story

1. What type of person is Fotheringay? Would you choose him as a friend?
2. How does H. G. Wells make certain from the very beginning that the reader is sympathetic toward Fotheringay? What is the author's reaction to Fotheringay? Cite specific incidents to support your statement.
3. Prove the validity of the following statement by referring to specific incidents in the story. "H. G. Wells was fond of irony, perhaps overfond."
4. Is "The Man Who Could Work Miracles":

   A tall tale?
   A tale of terror?
   Just a series of practical jokes?
   A plausible story?

   Under what circumstances would you label it as realistic? How do Fotheringay's adventures compare with the daydream accomplishments of most people? When are such deeds dangerous? Should we resist daydreaming? Justify your answer.
5. George McWhirter Fotheringay suddenly discovers that he can work miracles without end. His every wish is granted. How do his wishes compare with ones you would consider making—if you had the same power? Does the gift bring him happiness? If you had the gift would it make you happier than you are now?

Stories in Words

Prosaic (275) is derived from *prose* and then from the Latin *prosa*, "straightforward." Because prose is often contrasted with poetry, the word *prosaic* has come to mean "factual," then "dull" and "unimaginative." The word *prosy* is synonymous. There is a famous line in Molière's *Le Bourgeois Gentilhomme*. Monsieur Jourdain is pleased and gratified at one of his unsuspected accomplishments. He says, "For more than forty years I have been talking prose without knowing it." Per-

haps the qualitative label often attached to prose is unfair. There is much excellent prose and much awful poetry!

Rhodian arch (279) is a clever reference to one of the Seven Wonders of the Ancient World. The Colossus of Rhodes, a huge statue at the harbor's mouth, greeted incoming ships. One legend calls for a statue so huge, ships could sail beneath the legs. The truth is less dramatic. Still the statue was tall enough to be a beloved landmark of the area. In the story, Mr. Maydig is standing in front of a fire. "His legs threw a Rhodian arch of shadow on the opposite wall." By this dramatic description, he is compared with the famous statue. For another ancient Wonder, see *mausoleum,* page 80.

Infinite (283) comes from the Latin *finis,* "limit" or "boundary of a field." The associated meaning, "end," has provided English with a host of words, all containing within them the idea of "end" or "limit." The prefix *in* suggests that *infinite* means "without end, limitless." The noun *infinity* is often linked with eternity to suggest endless space and endless time. Other words derived from the same root include *final, finale, finish, infinitesimal, define,* and *confine.* An *infinitive* is a verb without *limitations* of tense.

Desire

JAMES STEPHENS

I did not ask to live forever, or any of that nonsense, for I saw that to live forever is to be condemned to a misery of boredom more dreadful than anything else the mind can conceive of. But, while I do live, I wish to live competently, and so I asked to be allowed to stay at the age of forty-eight years with all the equipment of my present state unimpaired.

One of the oldest themes in folklore is the granting of wishes. A fisherman releases a genie from a bottle and has every wish satisfied, but there are inevitably conditions. In some legends, the last wish is to return to the situation as before. In modern times, people who play the state lotteries are seeking wish fulfillment. Yet lottery winners soon discover that suddenly getting large amounts of cash doesn't solve all life's problems. The desire, however, is ancient and universal. "If only . . ." is a common theme in daydreams.

Wishes are sometimes taken too literally. In "The Man Who Could Work Miracles" (pages 273–286), wish fulfillment brings unexpected results. When Fotheringay wishes that the constable would go to Hades, he doesn't expect the wish to be taken literally. Like a computer, the granter of wishes interprets the requests exactly as stated.

One of the most unusual wish-fulfillment stories is James Stephens's "Desire." Here the wish theme is combined with a dream sequence worthy of classic horror stories. The gentle, serene beginning of the story lulls the reader. Then the pace picks up, and the story suddenly changes its character. We experience, with the wife, a heart-stopping nightmare. And then—the ending has a strange logic all its own.

Desire

He was excited, and as he leaned forward in his chair and told this story to his wife he revealed to her a degree or a species of credulity of which she could not have believed him capable.

He was a levelheaded man, and habitually conducted his affairs on hardheaded principles. He had conducted his courtship, his matrimonial and domestic affairs in a manner which she should not have termed reckless or romantic. When, therefore, she found him excited, and over such a story, she did not know how just to take the matter.

She compromised by agreeing with him, not because her reason was satisfied or even touched, but simply because he was excited, and a woman can welcome anything which varies the dull round and will bathe in exclamations if she gets the chance.

This was what he told her.

As he was walking to lunch a motor car came down the street at a speed much too dangerous for the narrow and congested thoroughfare. A man was walking in front of him, and, just as the car came behind, this man stepped off the path with a view to crossing the road. He did not even look behind as he stepped off. Her husband stretched a ready arm that swept the man back to the pavement one second before the car went blaring and buzzing by.

"If I had not been there," said her husband, who liked slang, "you would have got it where the chicken got the axe."

The two men grinned at each other; her husband smiling with good-fellowship, the other crinkling with amusement and gratitude.

They walked down the street and, on the strength of that adventure, they had lunch together.

They had sat for a long time after lunch, making each other's acquaintance, smoking innumerable cigarettes, and engaged in a conversation which she could never have believed her husband would have shared in for ten minutes; and they had parted with a wish, from her husband, that they should meet again on the following day, and a wordless smile from the man.

He had neither ratified nor negatived the arrangement.

"I hope he'll turn up," said her husband.

This conversation had excited her man, for it had drawn him into an atmosphere to which he was a stranger, and he had found himself moving there with such pleasure that he wished to get back to it with as little delay as possible.

Briefly, as he explained it to her, the atmosphere was religious; and while it was entirely intellectual it was more heady and exhilarating than the emotional religion to which he had been accustomed, and from which he had silently lapsed.

He tried to describe his companion; but had such ill success in the description that she could not remember afterward whether he was tall or short; fat or thin; fair or dark.

It was the man's eyes only that he succeeded in emphasizing; and these, it appeared, were eyes such as he had never before seen in a human face.

That also, he amended, was a wrong way of putting it; for his eyes were exactly like everybody else's. It was the way he looked through them that was different. Something, very steady, very ardent, very quiet and powerful, was using these eyes for purposes of vision. He had never met anyone who looked at him so . . . comprehendingly; so agreeably.

"You are in love," said she with a laugh.

After this her husband's explanations became more explanatory but not less confused, until she found that they were both, with curious unconsciousness, in the middle of a fairy-tale.

"He asked me," said her husband, "what was the thing I wished for beyond all things."

"That was the most difficult question I have ever been invited to answer," he went on; "and for nearly half an hour we sat thinking it out, and discussing magnificences and possibilities."

"I had all the usual thoughts; and, of course, the first of them was wealth. We are more dominated by proverbial phrases than we conceive of, and, such a question being posed, the words 'healthy, wealthy, and wise' will come, unbidden, to answer it. To be alive is to be acquisitive, and so I mentioned wealth, tentatively, as a possibility; and he agreed that it was worth considering. But after a while I knew that I did not want money."

"One always has need of money," said his wife.

"In a way, that is true," he replied, "but not in this way; for, as I thought it over, I remembered that we have no children; and that our relatively few desires, or fancies, can be readily satisfied by the money we already have. Also we are fairly well off; we have enough in the stocking to last our time even if I ceased from business, which I am not going to do; and, in short, I discovered that money or its purchasing power had not any particular advantages to offer."

"All the same!" she murmured; and halted with her eyes fixed on purchasings far away in time and space.

"All the same!" he agreed with a smile.

"I could not think of anything worth wishing for," he continued. "I mentioned health and wisdom, and we considered these; but, judging myself by the standard of the world in which we move, I concluded that both my health and knowledge were as good as the next man's; and I thought also that if I elected to become wiser than my contemporaries I might be a very lonely person for the rest of my days."

"Yes," said she thoughtfully, "I am glad you did not ask to be made wise, unless you could have asked it for both of us."

"I asked him in the end what he would advise me to demand, but he replied that he could not advise me at all. 'Behind everything stands desire,' said he, 'and you must find out your desire.'"

"I asked him then, if the conditions were reversed and if the opportunity had come to him instead of me, what he should have asked for; not, as I explained to him, in order that I might copy his wish, but from sheer curiosity. He replied that he should not ask for anything. This reply astonished, almost alarmed me at first, but most curiously satisfied me on considering it, and I was about to adopt that attitude—"

"Oh," said his wife.

"When an idea came to me. 'Here I am,' I said to myself, 'forty-eight years of age: rich enough; sound enough in wind and limb; and as wise as I can afford to be. What is there now belonging to me, absolutely mine, but from which I must part, and which I should like to keep?' And I saw that the thing which was leaving me day by day; second by second; irretrievably and inevitably; was my forty-eighth year. I thought I should like to continue at the age of forty-eight until my time was up."

"I did not ask to live forever, or any of that nonsense, for I saw that to live forever is to be condemned to a misery of boredom more dreadful than anything else the mind can conceive of. But, while I do live, I wish to live competently, and so I asked to be allowed to stay at the age of forty-eight years with all the equipment of my present state unimpaired."

"You should not have asked for such a thing," said his wife, a little angrily. "It is not fair to me," she explained. "You are older than I am now, but in a few years this will mean that I shall be needlessly older than you. I think it was not a loyal wish."

"I thought of that objection," said he, "and I also thought that I was past the age at which certain things matter; and that both temperamentally and in the matter of years I am proof against sensual or such-like attractions. It seemed to me to be right; so I just registered my wish with him."

"What did he say?" she queried.

"He did not say anything; he just nodded; and began to talk again of other matters—religion, life, death, mind; a host of things, which, for all the diversity they seem to have when I enumerate them, were yet one single theme."

"I feel a more contented man tonight than I have ever felt," he continued, "and I feel in some curious way a different person from the man I was yesterday."

Here his wife awakened from the conversation and began to laugh.

"You are a foolish man," said she, "and I am just as bad. If anyone were to hear us talking this solemn silliness they would have a right to mock at us."

He laughed heartily with her, and after a light supper they went to bed.

During the night his wife had a dream.

She dreamed that a ship set away for the Polar Seas on an expedition in which she was not sufficiently interested to find out its reason. The ship departed with her on board. All that she knew or cared was that she was greatly concerned with baggage, and with counting and going over the various articles that she had brought against arctic weather.

She had thick woolen stockings. She had skin boots all hairy inside, all pliable and wrinkled without. She had a great skin cap shaped like a helmet and fitting down in a cape over her shoulders. She had, and they did not astonish her, a pair of very baggy fur trousers. She had a sleeping sack.

She had an enormous quantity of things; and everybody in the expedition was equipped, if not with the same things, at least similarly.

These traps were a continuous subject of conversation aboard, and, although days and weeks passed, the talk of the ship hovered about and fell continually into the subject of warm clothing.

There came a day when the weather was perceptibly colder; so cold that she was tempted to draw on these wonderful breeches, and to fit her head into that most comfortable hat. But she did not do so for, and everybody on the ship explained it to her, it was necessary that she should accustom herself to the feeling, the experience, of cold; and, she was further assured, that the chill which she was now resenting was nothing to the freezing she should presently have to bear.

It seemed good advice; and she decided that as long as she could bear the cold she would do so, and would not put on any protective covering; thus, when the cold became really intense, she would be in some measure inured to it, and would not suffer so much.

But steadily, and day by day, the weather grew colder.

For now they were in wild and whirling seas wherein great green and white icebergs went sailing by; and all about the ship little hummocks of ice bobbed and surged, and went under and came up; and the gray water slashed and hissed against and on top of these small hillocks.

Her hands were so cold that she had to put them under her armpits to keep any warmth in them; and her feet were in a worse condition. They had begun to pain her; so she decided that on the morrow she would put on her winter equipment, and would not mind what anybody said to the contrary.

"It is cold enough," said she, "for my arctic trousers, for my warm soft boots, and my great furry gloves. I will put them on in the morning," for it was then almost night and she meant to go to bed at once.

She did go to bed; and she lay there in a very misery of cold.

In the morning, she was yet colder; and immediately on rising she looked for the winter clothing which she had laid ready by the side of her bunk the night before; but she could not find them. She was forced to dress in her usual rather thin clothes; and, having done so, she went on deck.

When she got to the side of the vessel she found that the world about her had changed.

The sea had disappeared. Far as the eye could peer was a level plain of ice, not white, but dull gray; and over it there lowered a sky, gray as itself and of almost the same dullness.

Across this waste there blew a bitter, a piercing wind that her eyes winced from, and that caused her ears to tingle and sting.

Not a soul was moving on the ship, and the dead silence which brooded on the ice lay heavy and almost solid on the vessel.

She ran to the other side, and found that the whole ship's company had landed, and were staring at her from a little distance of the ship. And these people were as silent as the frozen air, as the frozen ship. They stared at her; they made no move; they made no sound.

She noticed that they were all dressed in their winter furs; and, while she stood, ice began to creep into her veins.

One of the ship's company strode forward a few paces and held up a bundle in his mittened hand. She was amazed to see that the bundle contained her clothes; her broad furry trousers; her great cozy helmet and gloves.

To get from the ship to the ice was painful but not impossible. A rope ladder was hanging against the side, and she went down this. The rungs felt hard as iron, for they were frozen stiff; and the touch of those glassy surfaces bit into her tender hand like fire. But she got to the ice and went across it toward her companions.

Then, to her dismay, to her terror, all these, suddenly, with one unexpressed accord, turned and began to run away from her; and she, with a heart that shook once and could scarcely beat again, took after them.

Every few paces she fell, for her shoes could not grip on the ice; and each time that she fell those monsters stood and turned and watched her, and the man who had her clothes waved the bundle at her and danced grotesquely, silently.

She continued running, sliding, falling, picking herself up, until her breath went, and she came to a halt, unable to move a limb further and scarcely able to breathe; and this time they did not stay to look at her.

They continued running, but now with great and greater speed, with the very speed of madmen; and she saw them become black specks away on the white distance; and she saw them disappear; and she saw that there was nothing where she stared but the long white miles, and the terrible silence, and the cold.

How cold it was!

And with that there arose a noiseless wind, keen as a razor.

It stung into her face; it swirled about her ankles like a lash; it stabbed under her armpits like a dagger.

"I am cold," she murmured.

She looked backward whence she had come, but the ship was no longer in sight, and she could not remember from what direction she had come.

Then she began to run in any direction.

Indeed she ran in every direction to find the ship; for when she had taken an hundred steps in one way she thought, frantically, "this is not the way," and at once she began to run on the opposite road. But run as she might she could not get warm; it was colder she got. And then, on a steel-gray plane, she slipped, and slipped again, and went sliding down a hollow, faster and faster; she came to the brink of a cleft, and swished over this, and down into a hole of ice and there she lay.

"I shall die!" she said. "I shall fall asleep here and die. . . ."

Then she awakened.

She opened her eyes directly on the window and saw the ghost of dawn struggling with the ghoul of darkness. A grayish perceptibility framed the window without, but could not daunt the obscurity within; and she lay for a moment terrified at that grotesque adventure, and thanking God that it had only been a dream.

In another second she felt that she was cold. She pulled the clothes more tightly about her, and she spoke to her husband.

"How miserably cold it is!" she said.

She turned in the bed and snuggled against him for warmth; and she found that an atrocity of cold came from him; that he was icy.

She leaped from the bed with a scream. She switched on the light, and bent over her husband—

He was stone dead. He was stone cold. And she stood by him, shivering and whimpering.

Reading for Understanding

❑ MAIN IDEA

1. The point of the story may perhaps be best expressed by the following advice. (a) Never help a stranger. (b) If you have to make an important decision, consult your wife first. (c) Be careful what you wish. The wish may be granted. (d) Don't go to bed too soon after supper.

❑ DETAILS

2. The husband saved a person's life (a) on the street (b) at the shore (c) on the Polar Seas (d) in his imagination.

3. The husband was especially struck by the stranger's (a) slender hands (b) bushy eyebrows (c) teeth (d) eyes.

4. Of possible wishes, the wife thought most fondly of (a) health (b) children (c) fame (d) money.

5. The most terrible part of the wife's dream was (a) the loud noises (b) her cold isolation (c) the captain's cruelty (d) the mysterious figure in black.

❑ INFERENCES

6. The husband apparently had (a) a streak of cruelty (b) an insensitivity toward his wife (c) a lack of gratitude (d) a minimum of education.

7. The stranger "neither ratified nor negatived the arrangement" (having lunch the next day) because he probably knew the husband (a) would be dead (b) had a bad memory (c) wasn't listening (d) would retell the story all wrong.

8. The stranger's comment "that he should not ask for anything" (a) did not surprise the husband (b) irritated the wife (c) started an argument (d) should have warned the husband.

9. The wife's objection to the husband's wish was based on her desire (a) to ask the stranger for a wish (b) to take a trip with her husband to the Arctic (c) not to grow older than he (d) to give up housework for a lifetime.

10. The cold in the wife's dream was probably triggered by (a) a draft (b) an open window (c) her husband's death (d) finding the covers on the floor.

11. The husband really thought that his wish was (a) excessive (b) reasonable (c) hasty (d) suggested by the stranger.

❑ AUTHOR'S PURPOSE

12. The author's purpose is to (a) warn against casual conversations (b) suggest what a trip to the Arctic might be like (c) tell us to be careful what we wish for (d) show what middle-class English life is like.

❑ CAUSE AND EFFECT

13. When the husband expressed his wish, (a) he was gratified by the granting (b) it was granted (c) the stranger said it was not possible (d) the wife said that she was sorry he ever met the stranger.

❑ FACT OR OPINION

Tell whether each of the following is a fact or an opinion.

14. The stranger was vindictive and cruel.

15. The husband had lunch with the stranger.

Words in Context

1. ". . . he revealed to her a degree or a species of *credulity* of which she could not have believed him capable." ***Credulity*** (293) means (a) insensitivity (b) overreadiness to believe (c) illogical thinking (d) guile.

2. ". . . a motor car came down the street at a speed much too dangerous for the narrow and congested *thoroughfare*." ***Thoroughfare*** (293) means (a) neighborhood (b) crossroad (c) street corner (d) avenue.

3. ". . . the atmosphere was religious; and . . . it was more *heady and exhilarating* than the emotional religion . . ." ***Heady and exhilarating*** (294) means (a) exciting and stimulating (b) intellectual and humorous (c) moving and elusive (d) revealing and believable.

4. "Something, very steady, very *ardent*, very quiet and powerful, was using these eyes for purposes of vision." ***Ardent*** (294) means (a) persuasive (b) intense (c) knowledgeable (d) wealthy.

5. "We are more dominated by *proverbial* phrases than we conceive of . . ." ***Proverbial*** (294) means (a) deceptive (b) basic (c) axiomatic (d) romantic.

6. "To be alive is to be *acquisitive*, and so I mentioned wealth, tentatively, as a possibility . . ." ***Acquisitive*** (294) means (a) energetic (b) cautious (c) hardworking (d) covetous.

7. ". . . if I elected to become wiser than my *contemporaries* I might be a very lonely person for the rest of my days." ***Contemporaries*** (295) means those who (a) work together (b) live together (c) live at the same time (d) are born.

8. "But, while I do live, I wish to live *competently* . . . with all the equipment of my present state *unimpaired*." ***Competently . . . unimpaired*** (295) mean (a) in conformity . . . increased (b) proficiently . . . not decreased (c) without worries . . . indifferent (d) highly admired . . . never dulled.

9. ". . . and I also thought . . . that both temperamentally and in the matter of years I am proof against *sensual* or such-like attractions." ***Sensual*** (295) means (a) tempting (b) earthy (c) sensational (d) unrealistic.

10. ". . . a host of things, which, for all the *diversity* they seem to have when I *enumerate* them, were yet one single theme." ***Diversity . . . enumerate*** (295) mean (a) variance . . . count (b) depth . . . classify (c) consistency . . . suggest (d) profundity . . . recall.

11. "There came a day when the weather was *perceptibly* colder . . ." ***Perceptibly*** (296) means (a) increasingly (b) quietly (c) suddenly (d) noticeably.

12. ". . . thus, when the cold became really intense, she would be in some measure *inured to* it . . ." ***Inured to*** (296) means (a) habituated to (b) unaware of (c) desirous of (d) not frightened by.

13. ". . . and all about the ship little *hummocks* of ice bobbed and surged, . . ." ***Hummocks*** (296) means (a) blocks (b) mounds (c) globs (d) icicles.

14. "Across this waste there blew a bitter, a piercing wind that her eyes *winced* from . . ." ***Winced*** (297) means (a) learned from (b) feared (c) recoiled (d) avoided.

15. ". . . the man . . . waved the bundle at her and danced *grotesquely*, silently." ***Grotesquely*** (297) means (a) wildly (b) delicately (c) stiffly (d) bizarrely.

Thinking Critically About the Story

1. At what point is the willing suspension of disbelief necessary? Is it as the story is evolving, or after the action on the last page? Explain.

2. How does James Stephens use foreshadowing to make the ending have the force of plausible logic? Support your statement with specific references to the text of the story.

3. The story begins *in medias res* (in the midst of ongoing events). In a flashback the events are brought into their proper time sequence. Would the story have been more effective if it had been told in strict chronological order? Explain.

4. What is ironic about the fate of the husband? What would the wife have wanted as his wish? How did you evaluate the one wish that the husband finally made? If you had had one wish, as a child, what might it have been? Would your one wish today be the same one? How would you word the wish, now that you have read this story?

5. To what extent do you agree with the stranger's statement:

   "Behind everything stands desire, . . . and you must find out your desire."

   How appropriate is the title? What attitude toward desire is brought into focus in this story? Do you agree with it? Explain.

Stories in Words

Exhilarating (294) can be traced to the Latin *hilarus*, "cheerful." Something exhilarating makes us feel cheerful, excited, stimulated, refreshed. A situation that is *hilarious* makes us happy. *Hilarity* is a pleasant state of merriment. The name *Hilary* is traceable to the same root.

Arctic (296) is derived from the Greek word *arktos*, "bear." What connection does the Arctic have with a bear? Think a moment of the constellation that circles about the North Pole. Though we call it the *Big Dipper*, to the ancient Greeks it was the *Great Bear—Ursa Major* in its Latin form. The area at the other pole is called the *Antarctic*. The star Arcturus, the guardian of the Bear, is found by following out the curve of the Bear's tail.

Grotesquely (297) is related to the word *grotto*, "cave." The phrase was originally, in Latin, *grottesca pittura*, literally *cave picture*. This was a reference to designs found in Roman caves. Then, by a process common in language growth, the meaning subtly changed, little by little. The word *grotesque* referred to a style of painting and sculpture using fantastic or bizarre designs. The word then broadened its meaning to include anything with distortions or incongruities. Now the word has the general meaning of "strange, eccentric, ridiculous, absurd." If we go far enough back, we come upon the Greek root that gives us *crypt*, "something hidden."

The Willing Suspension of Disbelief

Getting Technical

Terms

contrived	poetic justice	willing suspension of disbelief
eccentrics	tall tale	

Definitions Match each of the above terms with its definition.

1. An outcome in which vice is punished appropriately and virtue is justly rewarded
2. A story that is extravagant, outlandish, or highly improbable
3. Characters deviating, usually harmlessly, from the norm, especially in manner of dress, behavior, actions
4. Attitude of the reader who accepts the premises—however fanciful—upon which the story is based
5. Not probable; brought about to meet author's needs; not a logical result; forced

Examples Match each of the following actions with the appropriate term.

1. The villain dies in the final gun battle, and the hero and heroine kiss as the curtain goes down.

2. As the TV drama approaches the time for the last commercials, the bullets that have been missing their mark all along suddenly put an end to the three villains.

3. The story is of the ingenious cave dweller who unintentionally stretched the giraffe's neck permanently.

4. Jasper must at all costs interrupt the flow of the conversation with puns, and Alicia never takes off her flowered hat—even when she goes to sleep.

5. I eagerly await the rest of the story after reading the first lines in which we meet an earthling hurtling backward through time to recover a lost formula.

6. The reader is introduced to a new character, who can prove the heroine's innocence since she is her twin.

Application Choose the statement that best completes each of the following statements.

1. Poetic justice is at work when (a) Jael Bettiss transforms herself into a beautiful woman (b) John Frey befriends Gib (c) Ivy Hill becomes deathly ill (d) Gib goes to live with Ivy and John.

2. Willing suspension of disbelief is in evidence when (a) Toddy Beamish repeats, "So *you* say!" (b) Cox, the landlord, says nothing (c) Mr. Fotheringay turns the lamp upside down (d) Miss Maybridge washes the glasses.

3. In "Desire" poetic justice works in reverse for the (a) wife (b) husband (c) stranger (d) driver of the car.

4. The number of tall stories in this unit is (a) one (b) two (c) three (d) four.

5. In "Tricky Customers" the one character who is not eccentric is (a) the narrator (b) Señor Petche (c) Major Jonathan Galloway (d) the odd Bohemian.

6. The label *tall tale* belongs to (a) the smell of patchouli in "Tricky Customers" (b) Gib's ability to swim (c) the wife's dream in "Desire" (d) the end of the world in the H. G. Wells story.

Thinking Critically About the Stories

1. To what extent is poetic justice in evidence in each of the stories in this unit? Is poetic justice a universal force at work in our world or only in some works of fiction? Explain.

2. Is the ending the logical outgrowth of forces at work in each of these stories, or is it contrived to surprise or amuse the reader? Cite specific incidents to prove your contentions.

3. Compare the main characters in the four stories. Whom would you consider most mature? Most capable? The clearest thinker? Closest to your image of yourself? Least plausible as a human being? Support your point of view with references to the stories.

4. How do these stories compare with children's fairy tales? Fables? Tall tales? Would the stories be more effective if they began with "Once upon a time . . ."?

5. Compare each of the following pairs for similarities and differences:

   Jael Bettiss and Major Jonathan Galloway
   Señor Petche and the husband in "Desire"
   Michael Adam and John Frey
   Ivy Hill and the wife in "Desire"

Writing and Other Activities

1. Write the setting and dialog for a wish-fulfilling scene when:
   a. A student with no musical training listens to a piano recital in the local museum.
   b. The student who works many hours after school passes through the gym while the varsity basketball team is practicing.
   c. A new student in the school, while doing science homework, hears a local health official describe how researchers have helped the sick and suffering.
   d. The senior dance is imminent, and Leslie walks home alone, watching some of the paired couples amble on ahead.

2. Use Señor Petche and his shyness or Major Galloway and his aggressiveness as your model. Describe—from real life or from your imagination—a plausible eccentric with a basis in one of the following areas:

Fear of being greedy	Need to be always right
Need for praise	Fear of being exceptional
Fear of poverty	Fear of success

3. Lead a panel discussion in class on one of the following:

   Logic and the daydream world
   Profiting from daydreams
   Desires and the road to happiness
   Is fate malevolent? Is fate a real entity?

4. Early in a story, the author will often set the mood by describing a building or a scene. For superb examples, reread the description of the house in "The Witch's Cat" and of the bookstore in "Tricky Customers." Then write the description of a place or building for one of the following:
   a. Sitting in a busy doctor's waiting room, the narrator reaches her (his) career decision to work in the medical profession.
   b. The day of the big game has arrived. The school gymnasium is filling up with spectators and contestants. The state championship will be decided.
   c. The students are entering the classroom. It is the day of the big test. The main character—not having studied—is ill-prepared for the ordeal ahead.
   d. It is the night of the Senior Prom. The orchestra is ready. Couples are drifting toward the dance area. Properly dressed, with suitable escort, the main character looks forward to taking this giant step toward maturity.

5. Write two or three brief vignettes as contributions to "Irony Corner" in the school newspaper. The following are merely suggestions and direction givers.
   a. Henry graciously and pompously gives little pointers to one of the lesser competitors in a debating contest. The lesser competitor wins.
   b. By the time Marion is able to afford it, he (she) is unable to enjoy its use.
   c. Leslie plans elaborately and carefully to arrive at the bank on time, but doesn't know it closes early on Mondays.

Stories in Words: A Review

A. amiable	E. eccentrics	I. grotesquely
B. arctic	F. exhilarating	J. infinite
C. astrakhan	G. feline	K. prosaic
D. Damoclean sword	H. gibberish	L. Rhodian arch

Answer the following questions by choosing a word from the list above. Use letters only.

Which of the words above . . .

1. ______ has the same root as *inimical*?
2. ______ is named for a colossal ancient statue?
3. ______ contains the root for *bear*?

4. ________ contains the idea of boundaries?
5. ________ is used both for people and for drive shafts?
6. ________ may mean "treacherous" and "stealthy"?
7. ________ originated in the word for *cave*?
8. ________ is often opposed to *poetic*?
9. ________ is an imitative word?
10. ________ is named for a courtier to Dionysius?

The stories of childhood tend to be simple. Red Riding Hood is simple goodness; the wolf is unabashed evil. The beautiful princess and the handsome prince are as simple as cardboard cutouts, as are the witch, the genie, and the evil stepmother. Even as adults, we enjoy such stories. James Bond, for example, is unquestionably a hero, and the villains he meets, like Dr. No and Goldfinger, are irredeemably evil. But there are other kinds of stories, stories that mirror the complexity of human emotions. In such stories, life is never simple. There are no easy solutions, no magic formulas, no pat heroes and villains, no incantations ending in "They lived happily ever after."

The stories in this unit abound with complexities. There is no straight

6

Mixed Motivations

Life is like playing a violin in public and learning the instrument as one goes on.

Samuel Butler

line from A to Z, for there are all the complicating letters in between. In the first story, a father and son somehow try to express their love for each other, but such expressions come with difficulty, sometimes only indirectly. A parent-child relationship illuminates story two. Like the stories in Unit 1, this takes us across the generations and enriches our lives during the journey. Story three, with its pictures of many positive kinds of love, contrasts with four, which shows the reverse side of love. It is hard to imagine that the narrator of three and the narrator of four can inhabit the same planet.

There are no easy answers, no pat directions. Life is an intricate business. Stories like these can help deepen understanding.

Wild Men of Borneo

SUSAN M. DODD

"I always wanted to see Borneo when I was a boy," he said. "Borneo. Imagine."

"Why Borneo?"

"'The Wild Men of Borneo.' In those days, all the circuses and carnivals had them." He seemed to study me speculatively for a moment, taking my measure.

"Before your time," he said.

A man and his son are meeting, perhaps for the last time. The father is old, and the separation may last for many years. It may be the last time for the two men to communicate with each other face to face. There are so many things that might be said, but communication on a deep personal level is never easy.

Though there are only two persons in the dialog, there are really four people in the story. The missing two play an important part in the thoughts of the two characters as they try to express their love for each other. All four people are sharply drawn, even though the son's divorced wife is mentioned only briefly. In that brief description, we can sense reasons for a failed relationship.

This is a story on many levels. The obvious level is not the most important. The unusual title has many possible explanations.

Wild Men of Borneo

My father, seventy-nine, squats in a square of morning light. His hands, removing snails from a jade plant, look naked, shamed in the glare of the California sun. These hands never meant to live so long, their fingers pared down to nothing. Yet they move rapidly, plucking the snails with surgical steadiness. The family fortune: my father's hands.

"You're looking good, Pa," I say.

He doesn't look up from the cluster of deep green leaves, cushy as the pads of children's thumbs. "So you said. Last night."

He picked me up at the airport himself, crawling through Los Angeles at rush hour, locked behind tinted windows in the Buick's conditioned air. He was an hour early for my arrival. I, his son, didn't take my eyes off my watch during landing. The flight was already twenty minutes late as we started our descent: I was keeping the old man waiting. Even in retirement, he remains a surgeon. I imagined him in the airport's sordid men's room, scrubbing up, watching the clock.

"Guess the climate agrees with you," I say. Lame: the physician's son.

He looks up. "*I* agree with *it*," he tells me smoothly. "Why fight it?"

My father turns from me and raises his eyes to the piercingly clear sky. The light is like that in a hospital amphitheater, uncomplaisant and antiseptic. He smiles grimly, a man perfectly accustomed to prolonging life beyond the point of diminishing marginal returns.

My father and I have much in common. We lack for nothing but wives. We are both in positions to see to our own comforts. We admire, on strictly-timed visits, one another's amenities, for we are men who appreciate comfortable lives. Born to a tradition of tact, we delete references to the wives who abandoned us. My father managed to keep his for thirty-three years. I could hold onto mine for only five.

We speak of "my mother," of course. But somehow, in death, she has divided like an amoeba. "My mother" is another woman, not my father's wife. When she died of cancer of the colon, my father, savior of lives, could not help but take it as a personal affront. Her death humiliated him. Now when he speaks of "your mother," his tones of sorrow are tokens of affection for me. His wife is another case entirely, a strictly forbidden topic, a buried mistake.

My father told me a year or so ago of a predatory, gabby widow he met at a cocktail party. She plied him with questions about his past and prospects. "What about your late wife?" she said.

"My wife," my father told her, "has never been late."

Now I do not believe my father actually said this. He is a helplessly courteous man. But he *wanted* to say it, which is more to the point. I suspect him of secretly worshipping a recollection of a dim creature who was always on time. However, he does not speak of her, nor have her in mind, when he says to me, "your mother."

He knows I am about to leave him. He understands that I have come to California to tell him so. My last visit is not long enough past to justify this one. Besides, it is April, and my usual journeys are dictated by the fiscal year. My father knows I have come to take my leave.

He will not deign to inquire. He will not permit me to wedge the announcement easily into our conversation if he can help it. But he is waiting for me to hammer it home, I can tell.

He takes me out to lunch. We sit at a chrome and oak table, separated from Balboa Bay by a wall of amber glass. My father eats a club sandwich, impressing me still with his capable hands, his own teeth. He wears his gardening clothes—a yellow porkpie hat, plaid pants, a red cardigan. I admire the jauntiness he has acquired in retirement, a bold adaptation to this unnatural habitat. Perhaps he has cultivated brazen visibility as a means of survival. Now that he can no longer play golf, he seems to take pains to look as if he does.

"Your mother loved it here," he says.

"The Yacht Club?"

"California. She said it made her think the world wasn't so old, after all."

I smile.

"She couldn't get over the fruits and vegetables in winter. I thought avocadoes and kiwi fruit would start sprouting from my ears. And she'd bring the damnedest-looking squash home from the Safeway. . . ."

I see my opening. "You miss her, Pa," I say.

My father sets the mangled triangle of his sandwich firmly on the edge of his plate. When he looks at me, his light gray eyes are steely. I imagine this is the expression he used to buck up patients who must be made to accept bad news. "Your mother had a great deal of . . . zest," he says.

He is not about to brook a second opinion.

The fact is, my mother was frail. In her opinions, more than her person. She fell in love with my father the year she lost her own. I, by the time I was twelve, could convince her of anything, provided my father left me to my own devices. My mother, my father's wife, was a woman weakened by respect for men. She laid her fragile doubts to rest in a warm cradle of affection and regard, and bridled her own enthusiasms. My father and I could come and go as we pleased. She always waited for us.

Sometimes my mother cried in the afternoons. But she always swore she didn't. The days must have been long for her. Waiting. Some days I would come home late from school to find her sitting in the darkened living room, on the edge of the piano bench, at the bass end of the keyboard. There would be no sheet music in sight, and my mother never could play from memory. I would switch on the old brass floor lamp, and the silk shade would cast a false golden glow over her face, her auburn hair, her narrow shoulders.

"You're home," she'd say, as if I'd done something miraculous. The lids of her eyes would be rosy and swollen.

At a certain age, I was not too cautious to ask if she'd been crying. She always denied it with a girlish laugh. In time, perhaps to forestall my indelicate question, she moved from the piano bench to the crewelwork wingback chair beside the fireplace. She would hold a book in her lap, and listen for the door to open so she could switch on a lamp before I reached the room.

"Have you been crying, Mom?"

"A sad book, lovey. I'm a silly old sob sister." I permitted her laugh to convince me. She became an admirer of Anne Morrow Lindbergh and other brave lady-writers who had outlived their children.

I never told my father that his wife, my mother, wept behind his back. I expected him to know it, just as she expected me to guard her secret. My father was a brilliant doctor, with a gift for diagnostics. At the very least, he should have seen the days were bound to be long for her.

Two and a half years ago, after my mother's funeral, I did not look at her husband to see if he cried when her cushioned, polished casket was cradled in the sandy California ground. I was afraid for a moment I might hate him either way, despise his strength or his weakness. I edged closer to him and kept my eyes on my ex-wife, Linda, who stood with the minor mourners on the opposite side of the grave. Linda and my mother had been very fond of each other. I distracted myself from my father by wondering if my wife had ever been reduced to tears by the unbearable weight of a long afternoon.

Although they had courted me for several years, I accepted a position with the World Bank only after my father and I had lost our wives. I could not leave my whereabouts to chance, knowing women waited for me. Linda might have come along wherever I went, of course, and we had no children. But each time I considered the prospect of a foreign post, there arose a pathetic picture of my wife languishing in a hammock in Karachi or Calcutta with the sun still high in the sky. I heard her soft, desperate voice struggling to confide in some Swahili-speaking houseboy, or haggling over a piece of stringy meat at a stall in the Casbah. I toyed with such scraps of imagination until I froze fast to them, like a child's tongue stuck to a metal fencepost in winter. I tore myself away from exotic ambitions, claimed the World Bank was a poor risk: some parts of the world are not fit to be seen by a man with dependents.

I neglected, however, to extrapolate my theories to McClean, Virginia. I hastened to my office at the Brookings Institution each morning and never paused to ask how my wife spent her days. She mistook my conscientiousness for passion, my confidence for disregard. When she left me, I found her, for the first time, stunning. Not long ago she married a linguist from Georgetown and moved to Peru without batting an eye. Like my mother, Linda was sadly underestimated.

When the World Bank tendered what I felt would be its final offer, I discussed it with my father. I could not calculate the precise effect my whereabouts might have on him.

"They could send me to some pretty out-of-the-way places," I said.

"You're young," he told me, as if that answered everything.

"For two- or three-year hitches," I said.

"It's your decision, son."

"But what about you?"

He gazed past my shoulder toward an oil portrait of my mother, the oddly incongruous gift his colleagues had commissioned to mark his retirement from the staff of Sloan-Kettering. "I always wanted to see Borneo when I was a boy," he said. "Borneo. Imagine."

"Why Borneo?"

"'The Wild Men of Borneo.' In those days, all the circuses and carnivals had them." He seemed to study me speculatively for a moment, taking my measure. "Before your time," he said.

I waited for him to continue, but he didn't. "I guess that settles it, then," I said foolishly.

My father nodded, his expression solemn and innocent, sealing a bargain without logic. The lack of irony in his eyes aged him in mine.

That was two years ago. I have yet to see Borneo, but I have traveled to South America, Africa, the Far East. I have explored the economic ruins of world powers, the fiscal jungles of developing nations. I have kept a sharp eye on deficits, gross national products, and per capita incomes while governments toppled. At the World Bank, as at Brookings, I have earned a reputation as a "troubleshooter," a cool correspondent of currency wars. I, however, prefer to regard myself as merely a chip off the old block—a man with a gift for diagnostics.

Now I am to be rewarded for the slim margin of error in my second guesses: Tokyo. The assignment is something of a plum. I have been promised a host of benefits: administrative autonomy, car with driver, the opportunity to sway world markets. My flight departs from Dulles one week from tomorrow. I have come to take leave of my father. He knows, without being told. He waits through the long afternoon.

"What time is your plane on Sunday?" It is Friday.

"Early. Seven-thirty."

He nods. "No traffic problems, then."

"Why don't I just get a limousine?"

I am dismissed with a gesture, a wave of his still-competent hand. "How about some Mexican food tonight?" he says. "There's this place Nixon loved in San Juan Capistrano. . . ."

I give the old man credit: he has managed to work the evils of politics and the perils of foreign travel into a single proposition. He is a master of the suggestive remark.

"Sure. I could go for some chiles rellenos."

"And margaritas. We'll make a night of it."

He is waiting.

"Pa—."

"So, where's it going to be?"

"The place in San Juan Capistrano sounds fine," I say.

His laugh is brutally abbreviated, like the bark of a dog with a choke-chain clutching its throat. I remember him telling me once, long ago, "The first incision's always the hardest to make . . . but it shouldn't be. That's rarely the one a patient dies from."

"Tokyo, Pa. Next week."

"For how long?"

My fingers curl, tighten, as if I am holding a scalpel. I relax them, force my own hand to hold firm. "For a couple of years, anyway."

"Tokyo . . . sounds like you're moving up pretty fast, boy."

I shrug. It wouldn't do, now, to tell him about the living allowance, influence on exchange rates, a waiting driver, the balance of trade.

"Tokyo." He shakes his head. "Not exactly Borneo, is it?"

The restaurant is crowded. Even with a reservation, we have to wait twenty minutes for a table. My father and I, two independent men, stand side by side at the blue and white tiled bar, drinking margaritas. A swag of plastic peppers festoons a mirrored arch, the bartender's proscenium. Absurdly young and beautiful, he performs with the staccato precision of a picador among the lustrous glasses and whirring chrome machines.

The old man plays host, drawing me out about world gold prices, the Federal Reserve. He has put on a navy blue blazer, a vague nautical insignia on its breast pocket. His handkerchief is paisley silk. Coarse salt glimmers at the corners of his mouth.

I catch myself stumbling, losing the strength of my convictions under my father's merciless charm. Then there is the inevitable lull. He lets me off the hook.

"Sorry about the wait, son."

"Friday nights," I say.

"Funny . . . time always seems so much longer when you're waiting for something." He sets his thick-lipped greenish glass on the bar and spreads his hands on either side of it. He stares in mild astonishment at how they betray him. "I'm beginning to understand what your mother . . . what Claire . . . meant."

Speechless, I touch my father's sleeve.

"She'd use that expression, 'Time hangs heavy on your hands.' I never understood her."

Beneath my fingers, my father's bent elbow twitches, once, as if he is trying to shake me off. "She was always waiting for something, your mother."

"We all are, Pa."

"I suppose so."

In the next room, a mariachi band is playing "Vaya con Dios."

"Don't get me wrong," my father says, "but I wish sometimes you'd been a girl."

Indescribable pain fills my chest, suffocating me. My father observes, making a swift, sure diagnosis.

"It just might be easier, son."

"How?"

"If you were a daughter, maybe I could ask you not to go."

"What if I went anyway?"

My father looks away, through the archway into the crowded, noisy dining room. He tilts his head to one side, seems to be listening to the music, inhaling the over-spiced air. There is a twisted smile on his salty lips.

"Tonight I'd dance with you," he says.

A waitress in an embroidered blouse approaches us. There is a string of veined turquoise beads around her neck. She has the coarse-grained, unfinished look of a primitive madonna. "Your table is ready, sir." She addresses me, not my father.

My old man lifts his glass. "To Tokyo," he says.

"To Borneo," I correct him, gently touching my glass to his.

He takes my arm and allows me to lead him into the next room.

Reading for Understanding

❑ MAIN IDEA

1. The main point of the story is the (a) unquenchable lure of exotic, faraway places (b) callousness of surgeons after seeing so much

suffering (c) effort of two persons to express to each other their deepest feelings (d) difficulties of taking a job that takes the workers to distant assignments.

☐ DETAILS

2. The narrator (a) is a widower (b) never married (c) is divorced (d) has remarried.
3. The narrator's mother (a) loved California (b) sometimes disputed the father (c) divorced the father (d) died 33 years ago.
4. Linda (a) disliked the mother (b) was the father's wife (c) did not attend the funeral (d) went to Peru.
5. The narrator was leaving for (a) Calcutta (b) Tokyo (c) Karachi (d) Borneo.

☐ INFERENCES

6. The father's comment about the weather, "*I* agree with *it*," suggests (a) a morbid interest in the weather (b) flabby thinking and weak character (c) a keen sense of humor and some frivolity (d) a desire to make an impression on his wife.
7. About both men it might justly be said that they (a) agreed on every major or minor point (b) misunderstood their wives (c) would have enjoyed living together (d) were careless about their manner of talking.
8. To the mother, the narrator's father probably represented a kind of (a) second son (b) teacher of the arts (c) dependable acquaintance (d) father figure.
9. Irony suggests that reality is quite different from appearances. Which of the following best expresses irony? (a) Not long ago she married a linguist from Georgetown and moved to Peru without batting an eye. (b) My father knows I have come to take my leave. (c) We sit at a chrome and oak table, separated from Balboa Bay by a wall of amber glass. (d) The old man plays host, drawing me out about world gold prices, the Federal Reserve.
10. The father betrays some of his deepest emotions when he says, (a) "Sorry about the wait, son." (b) "No traffic problems, then." (c) "I wish sometimes you'd been a girl." (d) "What time is your plane on Sunday?"

☐ TONE OF SELECTION

11. The tone of the story is one of (a) restrained optimism (b) studied indifference (c) grievous antagonism (d) sadness and regret.

☐ ORDER OF EVENTS

12. Arrange the items in the order in which they occurred. Use letters only.
    A. The mother dies.
    B. The father picks up the narrator at the airport.
    C. The narrator leaves for Tokyo.
    D. The two men go to dinner.
    E. A widow asks about the father's "late wife."

☐ OUTCOMES

13. After the departure of the narrator, the father probably (a) remarries (b) misses him grievously (c) goes back to the East Coast (d) returns to his surgery.

☐ CAUSE AND EFFECT

14. The father's career and manner of living (a) wasted the family fortune (b) made his wife unhappy (c) attracted Linda to the family (d) encouraged the son's divorce.

☐ FACT OR OPINION

Tell whether the following is a fact or an opinion.

15. The father loved his career more than he loved his wife.

Words in Context

1. "I imagined him in the airport's *sordid* men's room, scrubbing up, watching the clock." ***Sordid*** (311) means (a) bright (b) unclean (c) desolate (d) small.
2. "The light is like that in a *hospital amphitheater, uncomplaisant* and *antiseptic.*" ***Hospital amphitheater*** . . . ***uncomplaisant*** . . . ***antiseptic*** (311) mean (a) garage . . . dazzling . . . medicinal (b) entrance way . . . overcrowded . . . curative (c) room with a gallery . . . not obliging . . . germ-free (d) reception area . . . fragrant . . . healthful.
3. "We admire, on strictly-timed visits, one another's *amenities,* for we are men who appreciate comfortable lives." ***Amenities*** (311) means (a) successes (b) ways of thinking (c) scale of living (d) pleasant social acts.

4. "When she died of cancer . . . my father, savior of lives, could not help but take it as a personal *affront*." ***Affront*** (312) means (a) insult (b) defeat (c) tragedy (d) responsibility.

5. "My father told me a year or so ago of a *predatory*, gabby widow he met at a cocktail party." ***Predatory*** (312) means (a) fierce (b) gossipy (c) humorless (d) insensitive.

6. "I admire the *jauntiness* he has acquired in retirement, a bold adaptation to this unnatural habitat." ***Jauntiness*** (312) means (a) calmness (b) lightheartedness (c) melancholy (d) sense of responsibility.

7. "Perhaps he has cultivated *brazen* visibility as a means of survival." ***Brazen*** (312) means (a) polite (b) modest (c) shameless (d) protective.

8. "He is not about to *brook* a second opinion." ***Brook*** (312) means (a) request (b) require (c) deliver (d) tolerate.

9. "She laid her fragile doubts to rest in a warm cradle of affection and regard, and *bridled* her own enthusiasms." ***Bridled*** (313) means (a) cultivated (b) expressed (c) curbed (d) obeyed.

10. "In time, perhaps to *forestall* my *indelicate* question, she moved from the piano bench . . ." ***Forestall*** . . . ***indelicate*** . . . (313) mean (a) answer . . . cruel . . . (b) provoke . . . expected . . . (c) ward off . . . indiscreet . . . (d) counter . . . logical . . .

11. ". . . there arose a pathetic picture of my wife *languishing* in a hammock in Karachi or Calcutta . . ." ***Languishing*** (314) means (a) swinging (b) sleeping (c) forced to remain (d) wilting.

12. "*I neglected, however, to extrapolate my theories to McClean, Virginia*." The sentence means that he failed to (a) get all the details (b) discuss the problem with his father (c) apply his insights to his home life (d) make his refusal definite.

13. "He gazed past my shoulder toward an oil portrait of my mother, the oddly *incongruous* gift his colleagues had commissioned to mark his retirement from the staff of Sloan-Kettering." ***Incongruous*** (314) means (a) sad (b) fitting (c) inappropriate (d) placed.

14. "I have been promised a host of benefits: *administrative autonomy* . . ." ***Administrative autonomy*** (315) means (a) sufficient assistance (b) ample funds (c) limited hours (d) freedom from interference.

15. "Absurdly young and beautiful, he performs with the *staccato* precision of a *picador* . . ." ***Staccato*** . . . ***picador*** (315) mean (a) abrupt . . . bullfighter's assistant (b) deadly . . . matador (c) remarkable . . . surgeon (d) trained . . . toreador.

Thinking Critically About the Story

1. What is the father's definition of success? How does it compare with his son's definition? How does it compare with yours? What price did they have to pay to achieve success in their careers? Was it worth it? Would you be willing to pay that price to achieve success on their level?

2. What is the accepted role of the husband in this family? Of the wife? Why did the mother not rebel? Why did the son's wife rebel? Did the men love their wives? Cite incidents to prove your statements. Were the men aware of the unhappiness of the women? Would you accept such a relationship? How could they have prevented the unhappiness?

3. The author makes frequent use of understatement in this story. Find an example and be prepared to read it to the class and to discuss what was really being said.

4. What, in your opinion, should be the relationship between careers and marriage? Which should be given precedence in a one-career family? In a two-career family? At which point would you be willing to give one up for the other? Cite examples, in real life or in fiction, of people who had to make the choice.

5. What is ironic about:
   (a) The father's not wanting his son to leave and the son's reaction to his father's feelings?
   (b) The father's wishing he had a daughter instead of a son?
   (c) The title of the story?

6. Do you feel sorry for or envy the father? The mother? The son? The son's wife? What is the basic conflict? Is the same problem in evidence among the members of your family? How do the successful members of your family handle it? How do you feel about the way they handle it?

Stories in Words

April (page 312) has a disputed origin, but the most romantic explanation derives the word from the Latin verb *aperio*, "to uncover, open." April is the month when flower buds open. The word *aperture*, "opening," is related. At the time of the French Revolution, a new calendar was introduced. The calendar year began on September 22, the day of the autumnal equinox. Names of the months were lovely, associated with natural events. Thus, the month beginning in December was *Nivose*, "snowy." The month beginning in March was *Germinal*, "seed." Appropriately, the following month, beginning in April, was *Florial*, "flower."

Calculate (page 314), as used in the text, has very little to do with counting. Here it is roughly synonymous with *sense, determine, conjecture.* Yet the word primarily means "to count, to determine by using mathematics." The Romans borrowed the *abax*, or "counting board," from the Greeks. Although this device is the ancestor of the abacus, originally it was divided into compartments, with pebbles that were moved from compartment to compartment as the count progressed. The Latin word for *pebble* is *calculus.* Though calculus is an advanced mathematical procedure, the word derives from the simple word for *pebble.*

Carnival (page 314) has an interesting history. By derivation, the word means "flesh, farewell." The carnival was a period of feasting and revelry just before the restrictions of Lent. It led to the Mardi Gras, literally "fat Tuesday," the day before the leaner days of Lent. In ancient Paris, a fat ox was actually paraded through the streets as a reminder that meat should not be eaten during the following 40 days. The Mardi Gras in New Orleans and in Rio de Janeiro are descendants of that pre-Lent gaiety. The word *carnival* has broadened to include traveling sideshows and organized sports programs.

Winterblossom Garden

DAVID LOW

"Next time, I'll take you uptown to see a movie," I say as we step outside.

"Radio City?" my father asks.

"They don't show movies there now," my mother reminds him.

"I'll cook dinner for you at my apartment."

My father laughs.

"We'll eat out," my mother suggests.

"Winterblossom Garden" is an example of another type of short story that is an acquired taste. What it doesn't do is easily recognized. It has no surprise ending. The three people we meet are not of heroic mold; they make no supreme effort, nor do they reach great heights of human emotions. We see them in the seemingly quiet ebb and flow of daily living. The end of the story comes so casually, like the twilight turning to night or a stream flowing into a river.

It begins with a young man visiting his parents, his father at the family restaurant, his mother at home. Let this gentle story reveal its universal appeal. Given its chance, it will bring you into the inner core of three lives, so different from, yet so similar to, yours and those of the members of your own family.

Winterblossom Garden

I

I have no photographs of my father. One hot Saturday in June, my camera slung over my shoulder, I take the subway from Greenwich Village to Chinatown. I switch to the M local which becomes an elevated train after it crosses the Williamsburg Bridge. I am going to Ridgewood, Queens, where I spent my childhood. I sit in a car that is almost empty; I feel the loud rumble of the whole train through the hard seat. Someday, I think, wiping the sweat from my face, they'll tear this el down, as they've torn down the others.

I get off at Fresh Pond Road and walk the five blocks from the station to my parents' restaurant. At the back of the store in the kitchen, I find my father packing an order: white cartons of food fit neatly into a brown paper bag. As the workers chatter in Cantonese, I smell the food cooking: spareribs, chicken lo mein, sweet and pungent pork, won ton soup. My father, who has just turned seventy-three, wears a wrinkled white short-sleeve shirt and a cheap maroon tie, even in this weather. He dabs his face with a handkerchief.

"Do you need money?" he asks in Chinese, as he takes the order to the front of the store. I notice that he walks slower than usual. Not that his walk is ever very fast; he usually walks with quiet assurance, a man who knows who he is and where he is going. Other people will just have to wait until he gets there.

"Not this time," I answer in English. I laugh. I haven't borrowed money from him in years but he still asks. My father and I have almost always spoken different languages.

"I want to take your picture, Dad."

"Not now, too busy." He hands the customer the order and rings the cash register.

"It will only take a minute."

He stands reluctantly beneath the green awning in front of the store, next to the gold-painted letters on the window:

WINTERBLOSSOM GARDEN
CHINESE-AMERICAN RESTAURANT
WE SERVE THE FINEST FOOD

I look through the camera viewfinder.

"Smile," I say.

Instead my father holds his left hand with the crooked pinky on his stomach. I have often wondered about that pinky; is it a souvenir of some street fight in his youth? He wears a jade ring on his index finger. His hair, streaked with gray, is greased down as usual; his face looks a little pale. Most of the day, he remains at the restaurant. I snap the shutter.

"Go see your mother," he says slowly in English.

According to my mother, in 1929 my father entered this country illegally by jumping off the boat as it neared Ellis Island and swimming to Hoboken, New Jersey; there he managed to board a train to New York, even though he knew no English and had not one American cent in his pockets. Whether or not the story is true, I like to imagine my father hiding in the washroom on the train, dripping wet with fatigue and feeling triumphant. Now he was in America, where anything could happen. He found a job scooping ice cream at a dance hall in Chinatown. My mother claims that before he married her, he liked to gamble his nights away and drink with scandalous women. After two years in this country, he opened his restaurant with money he had borrowed from friends in Chinatown who already ran their own businesses. My father chose Ridgewood for the store's location because he mistook the community's name for "Richwood." In such a lucky place, he told my mother, his restaurant was sure to succeed.

When I was growing up, my parents spent most of their days in Winterblossom Garden. Before going home after school, I would stop at the restaurant. The walls then were a hideous pale green with red numbers painted in Chinese characters and Roman numerals above the side booths. In days of warm weather huge fans whirred from the ceiling. My mother would sit at a table in the back where she would make egg rolls. She began by placing generous handfuls of meat-and-cabbage filling on squares of thin white dough. Then she delicately folded up each piece of dough, checking to make sure the filling was totally sealed inside, like a mummy wrapped in bandages. Finally, with a small brush she spread beaten eggs on the outside of each white roll. As I watched her steadily produce a tray of these uncooked creations, she never asked me about school; she was more concerned that my shirt was sticking out of my pants or that my hair was disheveled.

"Are you hungry?" my mother would ask in English. Although my parents had agreed to speak only Chinese in my presence, she often broke this rule when my father wasn't in the same room. Whether I wanted to eat or not, I was sent into the kitchen where my father would repeat my mother's question. Then without waiting for an answer, he would prepare for me a bowl of beef with snow peas or a small portion of steamed fish. My parents assumed that as long as I ate well, everything in my life would be fine. If I said "Hello" or "Thank you" in Chinese, I was allowed to choose whatever dish I liked; often I ordered a hot turkey sandwich. I liked the taste of burnt rice soaked in tea.

I would wait an hour or so for my mother to walk home with me. During that time, I would go to the front of the store, put a dime in the jukebox and press the buttons for a currently popular song. It might be D3: "Bye-Bye, Love." Then I would lean on the back of the bench where customers waited for take-outs; I would stare out the large window that faced the street. The world outside seemed vast, hostile, and often sad.

Across the way, I could see Rosa's Italian Bakery, the Western Union office and Von Ronn's soda fountain. Why didn't we live in Chinatown? I wondered. Or San Francisco? In a neighborhood that was predominantly German, I had no Chinese friends. No matter how many bottles of Coca-Cola I drank, I would still be different from the others. They were fond of calling me "Skinny Chink" when I won games of stoopball. I wanted to have blond curly hair and blue eyes; I didn't understand why my father didn't have a ranch like the rugged cowboys on television.

Now Winterblossom Garden has wood-paneling on the walls, formica tables, and aluminum Roman numerals over the mock-leather booths. Several years ago, when the ceiling was lowered, the whirring fans were removed; a huge air-conditioning unit was installed. The jukebox has been replaced by Muzak. My mother no longer makes the egg rolls; my father hires enough help to do that.

Some things remain the same. My father has made few changes in the menu, except for the prices; the steady customers know they can always have the combination plates. In a glass case near the cash register, cardboard boxes overflow with bags of fortune cookies and almond candies that my father gives away free to children. The first dollar bill my parents ever made hangs framed on the wall above the register. Next to that dollar, a picture of my parents taken twenty years ago recalls a time when they were raising four children at once, paying mortgages and putting in the bank every cent that didn't go toward bills. Although it was a hard time for them, my mother's face is radiant, as if she has just won the top prize at a beauty pageant; she wears a flower-print dress with a large white collar. My father has on a suit with wide lapels that was tailored in Chinatown; he is smiling a rare smile.

My parents have a small brick house set apart from the other buildings on the block. Most of their neighbors have lived in Ridgewood all their lives. As I ring the bell and wait for my mother to answer, I notice that the maple tree in front of the house has died. All that is left is a gray ghost; bare branches lie in the gutter. If I took a picture of this tree, I think, the printed image would resemble a negative.

"The gas man killed it when they tore up the street," my mother says.

She watches television as she lies back on the gold sofa like a queen, her head resting against a pillow. A documentary about wildlife in Africa is on the screen; gazelles dance across a dusty plain. My mother likes soap operas but they aren't shown on weekends. In the evenings she will watch almost anything except news specials and police melodramas.

"Why don't you get a new tree planted?"

"We would have to get a permit," she answers. "The sidewalk belongs to the city. Then we would have to pay for the tree."

"It would be worth it," I say. "Doesn't it bother you, seeing a dead tree everyday? You should find someone to cut it down."

My mother does not answer. She has fallen asleep. These days she can doze off almost as soon as her head touches the pillow. Six years ago she had a nervous breakdown. When she came home from the hospital she needed to take naps in the afternoon. Soon the naps became a permanent refuge, a way to forget her loneliness for an hour or two. She no longer needed to work in the store. Three of her children were married. I was away at art school and planned to live on my own when I graduated.

"I have never felt at home in America," my mother once told me.

Now as she lies there, I wonder if she is dreaming. I would like her to tell me her darkest dream. Although we speak the same language, there has always been an ocean between us. She does not wish to know what I think alone at night, what I see of the world with my camera.

My mother pours two cups of tea from the porcelain teapot that has always been in its wicker basket on the kitchen table. On the sides of the teapot, a maiden dressed in a jade-green gown visits a bearded emperor at his palace near the sky. The maiden waves a vermillion fan.

"I bet you still don't know how to cook," my mother says. She places a plate of steamed roast pork buns before me.

"Mom, I'm not hungry."

"If you don't eat more, you will get sick."

I take a bun from the plate but it is too hot. My mother hands me a napkin so I can put the bun down. Then she peels a banana in front of me.

"I'm not obsessed with food like you," I say.

"What's wrong with eating?"

She looks at me as she takes a big bite of the banana.

"I'm going to have a photography show at the end of the summer."

"Are you still taking pictures of old buildings falling down? How ugly! Why don't you take happier pictures?"

"I thought you would want to come," I answer. "It's not easy to get a gallery."

"If you were married," she says, her voice becoming unusually soft, "you would take better pictures. You would be happy."

"I don't know what you mean. Why do you think getting married will make me happy?"

My mother looks at me as if I have spoken in Serbo-Croatian. She always gives me this look when I say something she does not want to hear. She finishes the banana; then she puts the plate of food away. Soon she stands at the sink, turns on the hot water and washes dishes. My mother learned long ago that silence has a power of its own.

She takes out a blue cookie tin from the dining room cabinet. Inside this tin, my mother keeps her favorite photographs. Whenever I am ready to leave, my mother brings it to the living room and opens it on the coffee table. She knows I cannot resist looking at these pictures again; I will sit down next to her on the sofa for at least another hour. Besides the portraits of the family, my mother has images of people I have never met: her father who owned a poultry store on Pell Street and didn't get a chance to return to China before he died; my father's younger sister who still runs a pharmacy in Rio de Janeiro (she sends the family an annual supply of cough drops); my mother's cousin Kay who died at thirty, a year after she came to New York from Hong Kong. Although my mother has a story to tell for each photograph, she refuses to speak about Kay, as if the mere mention of her name will bring back her ghost to haunt us all.

My mother always manages to find a picture I have not seen before; suddenly I discover I have a relative who is a mortician in Vancouver. I pick up a portrait of Uncle Lao-Hu, a silver-haired man with a goatee who owned a curio shop on Mott Street until he retired last year and moved to Hawaii. In a color print, he stands in the doorway of his store, holding a bamboo Moon Man in front of him, as if it were a bowling trophy. The statue, which is actually two feet tall, has a staff in its left hand, while its right palm balances a peach, a sign of long life. The top of the Moon Man's head protrudes in the shape of an eggplant; my mother believes that such a head contains an endless wealth of wisdom.

"Your Uncle Lao-Hu is a wise man, too," my mother says, "except when he's in love. When he still owned the store, he fell in love with his women customers all the time. He was always losing money because he gave away his merchandise to any woman who smiled at him."

I see my uncle's generous arms full of gifts: a silver Buddha, an ivory dragon, a pair of emerald chopsticks.

"These women confused him," she adds. "That's what happens when a Chinese man doesn't get married."

My mother shakes her head and sighs.

"In his last letter, Lao-Hu invited me to visit him in Honolulu. Your father refuses to leave the store."

"Why don't you go anyway?"

"I can't leave your father alone." She stares at the pictures scattered on the coffee table.

"Mom, why don't you do something for yourself? I thought you were going to start taking English lessons."

"Your father thinks it would be a waste of time."

While my mother puts the cookie tin away, I stand up to stretch my legs. I gaze at a photograph that hangs on the wall above the sofa: my parents' wedding picture. My mother was matched to my father; she claims that if her own father had been able to repay the money that Dad spent to bring her to America, she might never have married him at all. In the wedding picture she wears a stunned expression. She is dressed in a luminous gown of ruffles and lace; the train spirals at her feet. As she clutches a bouquet tightly against her stomach, she might be asking, "What am I doing? Who is this man?" My father's face is thinner than it is now. His tuxedo is too small for him; the flower in his lapel droops. He hides his hand with the crooked pinky behind his back.

I have never been sure if my parents really love each other. I have only seen them kiss at their children's weddings. They never touch each other in public. When I was little, I often thought they went to sleep in the clothes they wore to work.

Before I leave, my mother asks me to take her picture. Unlike my father she likes to pose for photographs as much as possible. When her children still lived at home, she would leave snapshots of herself all around the house; we could not forget her, no matter how hard we tried.

She changes her blouse, combs her hair and redoes her eyebrows. Then I follow her out the back door into the garden where she kneels down next to the rosebush. She touches one of the yellow roses.

"Why don't you sit on the front steps?" I ask, as I peer through the viewfinder. "It will be more natural."

"No," she says firmly. "Take the picture now."

She smiles without opening her mouth. I see for the first time that she has put on a pair of dangling gold earrings. Her face has grown round as the moon with the years. She has developed wrinkles under the eyes, but like my father, she hardly shows her age. For the past ten years, she has been fifty-one. Everyone needs a fantasy to help them stay alive: my mother believes she is perpetually beautiful, even if my father has not complimented her in years.

After I snap the shutter, she plucks a rose.

As we enter the kitchen through the back door, I can hear my father's voice from the next room.

"Who's he talking to?" I ask.

"He's talking to the goldfish," she answers. "I have to live with this man."

My father walks in, carrying a tiny can of fish food.

"You want a girlfriend?" he asks, out of nowhere. "My friend has a nice daughter. She knows how to cook Chinese food."

"Dad, she sounds perfect for you."

"She likes to stay home," my mother adds. "She went to college and reads books like you."

"I'll see you next year," I say.

That evening in the darkroom at my apartment, I develop and print my parents' portraits. I hang the pictures side by side to dry on a clothesline in the bathroom. As I feel my parents' eyes staring at me, I turn away. Their faces look unfamiliar in the fluorescent light.

II

At the beginning of July my mother calls me at work.

"Do you think you can take off next Monday morning?" she asks.

"Why?"

"Your father has to go to the hospital for some tests. He looks awful."

We sit in the back of a taxi on the way to a hospital in Forest Hills. I am sandwiched between my mother and father. The skin of my father's face is pale yellow. During the past few weeks he has lost fifteen pounds; his wrinkled suit is baggy around the waist. My mother sleeps with her head tilted to one side until the taxi hits a bump on the road. She wakes up startled, as if afraid she has missed a stop on the train.

"Don't worry," my father says weakly. He squints as he turns his head toward the window. "The doctors will give me pills. Everything will be fine."

"Don't say anything," my mother says. "Too much talk will bring bad luck."

My father takes two crumpled dollar bills from his jacket and places them in my hand.

"For the movies," he says. I smile, without mentioning it costs more to go to a film these days.

My mother opens her handbag and takes out a compact. She has forgotten to put on her lipstick.

The hospital waiting room has beige walls. My mother and I follow my father as he makes his way slowly to a row of seats near an open window.

"Fresh air is important," he used to remind me on a sunny day when I would read a book in bed. Now after we sit down, he keeps quiet. I hear the sound of plates clattering from the coffee shop in the next room.

"Does anyone want some breakfast?" I ask.

"Your father can't eat anything before the tests," my mother warns.

"What about you?"

"I'm not hungry," she says.

"My father reaches over to take my hand in his. He considers my palm.

"Very, very lucky," he says. "You will have lots of money."

I laugh. "You've been saying that ever since I was born."

He puts on his glasses crookedly and touches a curved line near the top of my palm.

"Be patient," he says.

My mother rises suddenly.

"Why are they making us wait so long? Do you think they forgot us?"

While she walks over to speak to a nurse at the reception desk, my father leans toward me.

"Remember to take care of your mother."

The doctors discover that my father has stomach cancer. They decide to operate immediately. According to them, my father has already lost so much blood that it is a miracle he is still alive.

The week of my father's operation, I sleep at my parents' house. My mother has kept my bedroom on the second floor the way it was before I moved out. A square room, it gets the afternoon light. Dust covers the top of my old bookcase. The first night I stay over I find a pinhole camera on a shelf in the closet; I made it when I was twelve from a cylindrical Quaker Oats box. When I lie back on the yellow comforter that covers my bed, I see the crack in the ceiling that I once called the Yangtze River, the highway for tea merchants and vagabonds.

At night I help my mother close the restaurant. I do what she and my father have done together for the past forty-three years. At ten o'clock I turn off the illuminated white sign above the front entrance. After all the customers leave and the last waiter says good-bye, I lock the front door and flip over the sign that says "Closed." Then I shut off the radio and the back lights. While I refill the glass case with bottles of duck sauce and packs of cigarettes, my mother empties the cash register. She puts all the money in white cartons and packs them in brown paper bags. My father thought up that idea long ago.

In the past when they have walked the three blocks home, they have given the appearance of carrying bags of food. The one time my father was attacked by three teenagers, my mother was sick in bed. My father scared the kids off by pretending he knew kung fu. When he got home, he showed me his swollen left hand and smiled.

"Don't tell your mother."

On the second night we walk home together, my mother says:

"I could never run the restaurant alone. I would have to sell it. I have four children and no one wants it."

I say nothing, unwilling to start an argument.

Later my mother and I eat jello in the kitchen. A cool breeze blows through the window.

"Maybe I will sleep tonight," my mother says. She walks out to the back porch to sit on one of the two folding chairs. My bedroom is right above the porch; as a child I used to hear my parents talking late into the night, their paper fans rustling.

After reading a while in the living room, I go upstairs to take a shower. When I am finished, I hear my mother calling my name from downstairs.

I find her dressed in her bathrobe, opening the dining-room cabinet.

"Someone has stolen the money," she says. She walks nervously into the living room and looks under the lamp table.

"What are you talking about?" I ask.

"Maybe we should call the police," she suggests. "I can't find the money we brought home tonight."

She starts to pick up the phone.

"Wait. Have you checked everywhere? Where do you usually put it?"

"I thought I locked it in your father's closet but it isn't there."

"I'll look around," I say. "Why don't you go back to sleep?"

She lies back on the sofa.

"How can I sleep?" she asks. "I told your father a long time ago to sell the restaurant but he wouldn't listen."

I search the first floor. I look in the shoe closet, behind the television, underneath the dining-room table, in the clothes hamper. Finally after examining all the kitchen cupboards without any luck, I open the refrigerator to take out something to drink. The three cartons of money are on the second shelf, next to the mayonnaise and the strawberry jam.

When I bring the cartons to the living room, my mother sits up on the sofa, amazed.

"Well," she says, "how did they ever get *there*?"

She opens one of them. The crisp dollar bills inside are cold as ice.

The next day I talk on the telephone to my father's physician. He informs me that the doctors have succeeded in removing the malignancy before it has spread. My father will remain in intensive care for at least a week.

In the kitchen my mother irons a tablecloth.

"The doctors are impressed by Dad's willpower, considering his age," I tell her.

"A fortune-teller on East Broadway told him that he will live to be a hundred," she says.

That night I dream that I am standing at the entrance to Winterblossom Garden. A taxi stops in front of the store. My father jumps out, dressed in a bathrobe and slippers.

"I'm almost all better," he tells me. "I want to see how the business is doing without me."

In a month my father is ready to come home. My sister Elizabeth, the oldest child, picks him up at the hospital. At the house the whole family waits for him.

When Elizabeth's car arrives my mother and I are already standing on the front steps. My sister walks around the car to open my father's door. He cannot get out by himself. My sister offers him a hand but as he reaches out to grab it, he misses and falls back in his seat.

Finally my sister helps him stand up, his back a little stooped. While my mother remains on the steps, I run to give a hand.

My father does not fight our help. His skin is dry and pale but no longer yellow. As he walks forward, staring at his feet, I feel his whole body shaking against mine. Only now, as he leans his weight on my arm, do I begin to understand how easily my father might have died. He seems light as a sparrow.

When we reach the front steps, my father raises his head to look at my mother. She stares at him a minute, then turns away to open the door. Soon my sister and I are leading him to the living-room sofa, where we help him lie back. My mother has a pillow and a blanket ready. She sits down on the coffee table in front of him. I watch them hold each other's hands.

III

At the beginning of September my photography exhibit opens at a cooperative gallery on West 13th Street. I have chosen to hang only a dozen pictures, not much to show for ten years of work. About sixty people come to the opening, more than I expected; I watch them from a corner of the room, now and then overhearing a conversation I would like to ignore.

After an hour I decide I have stayed too long. As I walk around the gallery, hunting for a telephone, I see my parents across the room. My father calls out my name in Chinese; he has gained back all his weight and appears to be in better shape than many of the people around him. As I make my way toward my parents, I hear him talking loudly in bad English to a short young woman who stares at one of my portraits.

"That's my wife," he says. "If you like it, you should buy it."

"Maybe I will," the young woman says. She points to another photograph. "Isn't that you?"

My father laughs. "No, that's my brother."

My mother hands me a brown paper bag.

"Leftover from dinner," she tells me. "You didn't tell me you were going to show my picture. It's the best one in the show."

I take my parents for a personal tour.

"Who is that?" my father asks. He stops at a photograph of a naked woman covered from the waist down by a pile of leaves as she sits in the middle of a forest.

"She's a professional model," I lie.

"She needs to gain some weight," my mother says.

A few weeks after my show has closed, I have lunch with my parents at the restaurant. After we finish our meal, my father walks into the kitchen to scoop ice cream for dessert. My mother opens her handbag. She takes out a worn manila envelope and hands it to me across the table.

"I found this in a box while I was cleaning the house," she says. "I want you to have it."

Inside the envelope, I find a portrait of my father, taken when he was still a young man. He does not smile but his eyes shine like wet black marbles. He wears a polka-dot tie; a plaid handkerchief hangs out of the front pocket of his suit jacket. My father has never cared about his clothes matching. Even when he was young, he liked to grease down his hair with brilliantine.

"Your father's cousin was a doctor in Hong Kong," my mother tells me. "After my eighteenth birthday, he came to my parents' house and showed them this picture. He said your father would make the perfect husband because he was handsome and very smart. Grandma gave me the picture before I got on the boat to America."

"I'll have it framed right away."

My father returns with three dishes of chocolate ice cream balanced on a silver tray.

"You want to work here?" he asks me.

"Your father wants to sell the business next year," my mother says. "He feels too old to run a restaurant."

"I'd just lose money," I say. "Besides, Dad, you're not old."

He does not join us for dessert. Instead, he dips his napkin in a glass of water and starts to wipe the table. I watch his dish of ice cream melt.

When I am ready to leave, my parents walk me to the door.

"Next time, I'll take you uptown to see a movie," I say as we step outside.

"Radio City?" my father asks.

"They don't show movies there now," my mother reminds him.

"I'll cook dinner for you at my apartment."

My father laughs.

"We'll eat out," my mother suggests.

My parents wait in front of Winterblossom Garden until I reach the end of the block. I turn and wave. With her heels on, my mother is the same height as my father. She waves back for both of them. I would like to take their picture, but I forgot to bring my camera.

Reading for Understanding

❑ MAIN IDEA

1. Which of the following quotations best expresses the main idea of the story? (a) "She does not wish to know what I think alone at night, what I see of the world with my camera." (b) "No matter how many bottles of Coca-Cola I drank, I would still be different from the others." (c) "I would like to take their picture, but I forgot to bring my camera." (d) "Although we speak the same language, there has been an ocean between us."

❑ DETAILS

2. The story opens when the son (a) takes his weekly trip to see his parents (b) learns of his father's illness (c) is invited to dine with his parents (d) brings his camera to the restaurant.

3. The story takes place mainly in (a) Hong Kong (b) Canton (c) San Francisco (d) Queens.

4. Which of the following is true of the father? (a) He came into this country under the Chinese quota. (b) He earned the right to marry the mother by paying for her passage from China. (c) He worked hard and long enough to save money to open the restaurant. (d) He fell in love with the mother when he met her in China.

5. Which of the following is true of the mother? (a) She dislikes working in the store. (b) Each night, while the children were growing up, she helped them with their homework after the store was closed. (c) She has strong personal ambitions. (d) She does what is expected of her.

6. The father's illness was diagnosed as (a) influenza (b) emphysema (c) cancer (d) stroke.

❑ INFERENCES

7. The son does not work in the family restaurant because (a) his parents want to control the business themselves (b) he lacks ability (c) he lacks intelligence (d) he is uninterested.

8. The son's attitude toward his parents was one of (a) love and compassion (b) thinly veiled hostility (c) irritability and impatience (d) indifference.

9. The father may be characterized as (a) selfish and quick to judge (b) quirky but strong (c) incompetent but lucky (d) thoughtless and unresourceful.

10. The parents showed the depth of their love for their son by (a) not feeding him (b) suggesting that he marry (c) letting him find his own path (d) arguing with him.

❑ TONE OF SELECTION

11. The tone of this story is (a) angry and sad (b) disproportionately resentful (c) straightforward and accepting (d) callously mocking.

❑ ORDER OF EVENTS

12. Arrange the items in the order in which they occurred. Use letters only.

A. The son helps his mother run the restaurant.
B. The father requires an operation.
C. The son exhibits some of his photographs at a gallery.
D. The parents hold hands.
E. The mother is hospitalized.

❑ OUTCOMES

13. After the father's illness, (a) the restaurant goes bankrupt (b) the son gives up photography (c) the son takes over the business permanently (d) nothing changes.

❑ CAUSE AND EFFECT

14. The mother refuses to visit relatives in Hawaii without her husband because she feels that (a) the trip would be too expensive (b) she really does not want to visit relatives (c) the business would suffer (d) her duty is to be with her husband.

❑ FACT OR OPINION

Tell whether the following is a fact or an opinion.

15. The son feels that the selling of the restaurant would leave his parents unhappy, with too much time on their hands.

Words in Context

1. "I smell the food cooking . . . sweet and *pungent* pork . . ." ***Pungent*** (323) means (a) plentiful (b) sharp (c) colorful (d) tasty.
2. "In a neighborhood that was *predominantly* German . . ." ***Predominantly*** (325) means (a) partially (b) completely (c) mainly (d) noticeably.
3. " . . . have a ranch like the *rugged* cowboys on television." ***Rugged*** (325) means (a) traditional (b) Western (c) tough (d) popular.
4. " . . . *gazelles* dance across the plain." ***Gazelles*** (326) means (a) camels (b) dust storms (c) sandstorms (d) small antelopes.
5. ". . . the porcelain teapot that has always been in its *wicker* basket on the kitchen table." ***Wicker*** (326) means made of (a) stainless steel (b) cotton cloth (c) woven twigs (d) painted glass.
6. "The maiden waves a *vermillion* fan." ***Vermillion*** (326) means (a) delicate (b) bamboo (c) bright red (d) large.

7. "... a silver-haired man ... who owned a *curio* shop ..." A ***curio*** shop (327) contains (a) art objects (b) food (c) old coins (d) antiques.

8. "The top of the Moon Man's head *protrudes* in the shape of an eggplant ..." ***Protrudes*** (327) means (a) sticks out (b) is portrayed (c) is hidden (d) is seen.

9. "She is dressed in a *luminous* gown ..." ***Luminous*** (328) means (a) expensive (b) simple (c) traditional (d) shining.

10. "... the doctors have succeeded in removing the *malignancy* before it has spread." ***Malignancy*** (331) means (a) difficulty (b) source (c) cancer (d) obstruction.

Thinking Critically About the Story

1. The author has made effective use of symbols in this story. How appropriate is the title for this story? For the restaurant? What is the symbolism in the dead tree in front of the house? What other examples of symbolism can you cite?

2. What is the conflict involving the business? Are the parents justified? Is the son justified? What would you do if you had to make the decision?

3. What do we learn about the parents in their handling their son and his decisions? About the son in his handling their crises? How do their definitions of love and family obligations compare with yours? How would you handle the son if you were the parents? How would your parents have handled the son?

4. What attitude did the other children in the neighborhood have toward the narrator when he was growing up? Does the same attitude toward those of your generation who are different prevail in your neighborhood today?

5. What does the author mean by "My father and I have almost always spoken different languages"? How do the son's values differ from his father's? Is such a difference true of your family? In TV dramas?

Stories in Words

Camera (323) The earliest recorded use of the word *camera* as an English word is 1688. At that time it came into the language along with another Latin word. A *camera obscura,* literally a "dark room," was a room or box with a tiny hole through which a light could pass. Shortened, *camera* refers to a box used to take pictures. The idea of *room* persists in other expressions. If a committee meets *in camera,* it meets secretly, in a secret *room.* The English word *chamber,* meaning "room," is derived from the Latin *camera.* A *chamberlain* was once the bedchamber attendant of a ruler or lord.

Greenwich Village (323), once the artists' quarters in New York City, has one too many villages in its name. The second part of *Greenwich* is the old Latin root *vic,* for *village.* Thus *wich* and *village* say the same thing: "Greenvillage Village!" The original Greenwich is the place in England that is the center from which the time zones of the world radiate. Other town names with the *vic* root are *Norwich, Sandwich, Berwick,* and *Warwick.* The root also appears in *vicinity.* The Latin root is itself related to the Greek *oikos,* "house," from which we derive *economics, ecology,* and *ecosystem.*

Resist (327) *Resist* is one of a multitude of English words derived from the Latin verb *stare,* "to stand." As an irregular verb, its principal parts are radically different from one another: *stare, steti, statum.* Each of these parts has innumerable offspring: *standard, obstacle, state, destitute, circumstance, constant, constituent, constitution, instant, stable, stationary, static, statue, status,* among others. A related root *sist* gives us *insist, desist, insistent, consistent, exist,* and *persist. Resist* literally means "stand firmly against."

The Patterns of Love

WILLIAM MAXWELL

Everywhere they go, he thought, they leave tracks behind them, like people walking in the snow. Paths crisscrossing, lines that are perpetually meeting: the mother's loving pursuit of her youngest, the man's love for his daughter, the dog's love for the man, the two boys' preoccupation with each other.

Love tends to be a by-product of the interactions between people. "The Patterns of Love" dissects such interactions and suggests how activities breed love that in turn brings forth other activities in a continuing chain. The Talbots are a closely knit family, and each personality impinges on the others, with generally happy results.

The Talbots themselves do not overtly realize the treasure they possess. They are too busy living. It takes an outsider, the narrator, to put the situation into perspective. What he describes, in a few pages, are real people, not cardboard characters.

Many philosophies suggest that we try to live more in the present, since it is the only reality. Looking to the future and recalling the past are useful activities only if they do not dominate us. Thomas La Mance once said, "Life is what happens to us while we are making other plans." The Talbots are so busy that they cannot help living in the golden present. Life is indeed happening to them.

The Patterns of Love

Kate Talbot's bantam rooster, awakened by the sudden appearance of the moon from behind a cloud on a white June night, began to crow. There were three bantams—a cock and two hens—and their roost was in a tree just outside the guest room windows. The guest room was on the first floor and the Talbots' guest that weekend was a young man by the name of Arnold, a rather light sleeper. He got up and closed the windows and went back to bed. In the sealed room he slept, but was awakened at frequent intervals until daylight Saturday morning.

Arnold had been coming to the Talbots' place in Wilton sometime during the spring or early summer for a number of years. His visits were, for the children, one of a thousand seasonal events that could be counted on, less exciting than the appearance of the first robin or the arrival of violets in the marsh at the foot of the Talbots' hill but akin to them. Sometimes Duncan, the Talbots' older boy, who for a long time was under the impression that Arnold came to see *him*, slept in the guest room when Arnold was there. Last year, George, Duncan's younger brother, had been given that privilege. This time, Mrs. Talbot, knowing how talkative the boys were when they awoke in the morning, had left Arnold to himself.

When he came out of his room, Mrs. Talbot and George, the apple of her eye, were still at breakfast. George was six, small and delicate and very blond, not really interested in food at any time, and certainly not now, when there was a guest in the house. He was in his pajamas and a pink quilted bathrobe. He smiled at Arnold with his large and very gentle eyes and said, "Did you miss me?"

"Yes, of course," Arnold said. "I woke up and there was the other bed, flat and empty. Nobody to talk to while I looked at the ceiling. Nobody to watch me shave."

George was very pleased that his absence had been felt. "What is your favorite color?" he asked.

"Red," Arnold said, without having to consider.

"Mine, too," George said, and his face became so illuminated with pleasure at this coincidence that for a moment he looked angelic.

"No matter how much we disagree about other things," Arnold said, "we'll always have that in common, won't we?"

"Yes," George said.

"You'd both better eat your cereal," Mrs. Talbot said.

Arnold looked at her while she was pouring his coffee and wondered if there wasn't something back of her remark—jealousy, perhaps. Mrs. Talbot was a very softhearted woman, but for some reason she seemed to be ashamed—or perhaps afraid—to let other people know it. She took refuge continually behind a dry humor. There was probably very little likelihood that George would be as fond of anyone else as he was of his mother, Arnold decided, for many years to come. There was no real reason for her to be jealous.

"Did the bantams keep you awake?" she asked.

Arnold shook his head.

"Something tells me you're lying," Mrs. Talbot said. "John didn't wake up, but he felt his responsibilities as a host even so. He cried 'Oh!' in his sleep every time a bantam crowed. You'll have to put up with them on Kate's account. She loves them more than her life."

Excluded from the conversation of the grown-ups, George finished his cereal and ate part of a soft-boiled egg. Then he asked to be excused and, with pillows and pads which had been brought in from the garden furniture the night before, he made a train right across the dining room floor. The cook had to step over it when she brought a fresh pot of coffee, and Mrs. Talbot and Arnold had to do likewise when they went out through the dining-room door to look at the bantams. There were only two—the cock and one hen—walking around under the Japanese cherry tree on the terrace. Kate was leaning out of an upstairs window, watching them fondly.

"Have you made your bed?" Mrs. Talbot asked.

The head withdrew.

"Kate is going to a house party," Mrs. Talbot said, looking at the bantams. "A sort of house party. She's going to stay all night at Mary Sherman's house and there are going to be some boys and they're going to dance to the record player."

"How old is she, for heaven's sake?" Arnold asked.

"Thirteen," Mrs. Talbot said. "She had her hair cut yesterday and it's too short. It doesn't look right, so I have to do something about it."

"White of egg?" Arnold asked.

"How did you know that?" Mrs. Talbot asked in surprise.

"I remembered it from the last time," Arnold said. "I remembered it because it sounded so drastic."

"It only works with blonds," Mrs. Talbot said. "Will you be able to entertain yourself for a while?"

"Easily," Arnold said. "I saw 'Anna Karenina' in the library and I think I'll take that and go up to the little house."

"Maybe I'd better come with you," Mrs. Talbot said.

The little house was a one-room studio halfway up the hill, about a hundred feet from the big house, with casement windows on two sides and a Franklin stove.* It had been built several years before, after Mrs. Talbot had read "A Room of One's Own," and by now it had a slightly musty odor which included lingering traces of wood smoke.

"Hear the wood thrush?" Arnold asked, as Mrs. Talbot threw open the windows for him. They both listened.

"No," she said. "All birds sound alike to me."

"Listen," he said.

This time there was no mistaking it—the liquid notes up and then down the same scale.

"Oh, that," she said. "Yes, I love that," and went off to wash Kate's hair.

From time to time Arnold raised his head from the book he was reading and heard not only the wood thrush but also Duncan and George, quarreling in the meadow. George's voice was shrill and unhappy and sounded as if he were on the verge of tears. Both boys appeared at the window eventually and asked for permission to come in. The little house was out of bounds to them. Arnold nodded. Duncan, who was nine, crawled in without much difficulty, but George had to be hoisted. No sooner were they inside than they began to fight over a wooden gun which had been broken and mended and was rightly George's, it seemed, though Duncan had it and refused to give it up. He refused to give it up one moment, and the next moment, after a sudden change of heart, pressed it upon George—*forced* George to take it, actually, for by that time George was more concerned about the Talbots' dog, who also wanted to come in.

The dog was a Great Dane, very mild but also very enormous. He answered to the name of Satan. Once Satan was admitted to the little house, it became quite full and rather noisy, but John Talbot appeared and sent the dog out and made the children leave Arnold in peace. They left as they had come, by the window. Arnold watched them and was touched by the way Duncan turned and helped George, who was too small to jump. Also by the way George accepted this help. It was as if their hostility had two faces and one of them was the face of love. Cain and Abel, Arnold thought, and the wood thrush. All immortal.

John Talbot lingered outside the little house. Something had been burrowing in the lily of the valley bed, he said, and had also uprooted several lady slippers. Arnold suggested that it might be moles.

"More likely a rat," John Talbot said, and his eyes wandered to a two-

**Franklin stove* metal, portable fireplace with chimney

foot espaliered pear tree. "That pear tree," he said, "we put in over a year ago."

Mrs. Talbot joined them. She had shampooed not only Kate's hair but her own as well.

"It's still alive," John Talbot said, staring at the pear tree, "but it doesn't put out any leaves."

"I should think it would be a shock to a pear tree to be espaliered," Mrs. Talbot said. "Kate's ready to go."

They all piled into the station wagon and took Kate to her party. Her too-short blond hair looked quite satisfactory after the egg shampoo, and Mrs. Talbot had made a boutonnière out of a pink geranium and some little blue and white flowers for Kate to wear on her coat. She got out of the car with her suitcase and waved at them from the front steps of the house.

"I hope she has a good time," John Talbot said uneasily as he shifted gears. "It's her first dance with boys. It would be terrible if she didn't have any partners." In his eyes there was a vague threat toward the boys who, in their young callowness, might not appreciate his daughter.

"Kate always has a good time," Mrs. Talbot said. "By the way, have you seen both of the bantam hens today?"

"No," John Talbot said.

"One of them is missing," Mrs. Talbot said.

One of the things that impressed Arnold whenever he stayed with the Talbots was the number and variety of animals they had. Their place was not a farm, after all, but merely a big white brick house in the country, and yet they usually had a dog and a cat, kittens, rabbits, and chickens, all actively involved in the family life. This summer the Talbots weren't able to go in and out by the front door, because a phoebe had built a nest in the porch light. They used the dining-room door instead, and were careful not to leave the porch light on more than a minute or two, lest the eggs be cooked. Arnold came upon some turtle food in his room, and when he asked about it, Mrs. Talbot informed him that there were turtles in the guest room, too. He never came upon the turtles.

The bantams were new this year, and so were the two very small ducklings that at night were put in a paper carton in the sewing room, with an electric light bulb to keep them warm. In the daytime they hopped in and out of a saucer of milk on the terrace. One of them was called Mr. Rochester because of his distinguished air. The other had no name.

All the while that Mrs. Talbot was making conversation with Arnold, after lunch, she kept her eyes on the dog, who, she explained, was jealous of the ducklings. Once his great head swooped down and he pretended to take a nip at them. A nip would have been enough. Mrs. Talbot spoke to him sharply and he turned his head away in shame.

"They probably smell the way George did when he first came home from the hospital," she said.

"What did George smell like?" Arnold asked.

"Sweetish, actually. Actually awful."

"Was Satan jealous of George when he was a baby?"

"Frightfully," Mrs. Talbot said. "Call Satan!" she shouted to her husband, who was up by the little house. He had found a rat hole near the ravaged lady slippers and was setting a trap. He called the dog, and the dog went bounding off, devotion in every leap.

While Mrs. Talbot was telling Arnold how they found Satan at the baby's crib one night, Duncan, who was playing only a few yards away with George, suddenly, and for no apparent reason, made his younger brother cry. Mrs. Talbot got up and separated them.

"I wouldn't be surprised if it wasn't time for your nap, George," she said, but he was not willing to let go of even a small part of the day. He wiped his tears away with his fist and ran from her. She ran after him, laughing, and caught him at the foot of the terrace.

Duncan wandered off into a solitary world of his own, and Arnold, after yawning twice, got up and went into the house. Stretched out on the bed in his room, with the venetian blinds closed, he began to compare the life of the Talbots with his own well-ordered but childless and animalless life in town. Everywhere they go, he thought, they leave tracks behind them, like people walking in the snow. Paths crisscrossing, lines that are perpetually meeting: the mother's loving pursuit of her youngest, the man's love for his daughter, the dog's love for the man, the two boys' preoccupation with each other. Wheels and diagrams, Arnold said to himself. The patterns of love.

That night Arnold was much less bothered by the crowing, which came to him dimly, through dreams. When he awoke finally and was fully awake, he was conscious of the silence and the sun shining in his eyes. His watch had stopped and it was later than he thought. The Talbots had finished breakfast and the Sunday *Times* was waiting beside his place at the table. While he was eating, John Talbot came in and sat down for a minute, across the table. He had been out early that morning, he said, and had found a chipmunk in the rat trap and also a nest with three bantam eggs in it. The eggs were cold.

He was usually a very quiet, self-contained man. This was the first time Arnold had ever seen him disturbed about anything. "I don't know how we're going to tell Kate," he said. "She'll be very upset."

Kate came home sooner than they expected her, on the bus. She came up the driveway, lugging her suitcase.

"Did you have a good time?" Mrs. Talbot called to her from the terrace.

"Yes," she said; "I had a beautiful time."

Arnold looked at the two boys, expecting them to blurt out the tragedy as soon as Kate put down her suitcase, but they didn't. It was her father who told her, in such a roundabout way that she didn't seem to understand at all what he was saying. Mrs. Talbot interrupted him with the flat facts; the bantam hen was not on her nest and therefore, in all probability, had been killed, maybe by the rat.

Kate went into the house. The others remained on the terrace. The dog didn't snap at the ducklings, though his mind was on them still, and the two boys didn't quarrel. In spite of the patterns on which they seem so intent, Arnold thought, what happens to one of them happens to all. They are helplessly involved in Kate's loss.

At noon other guests arrived, two families with children. There was a picnic, with hot dogs and bowls of salad, cake, and wine, out under the grape arbor. When the guests departed, toward the end of the afternoon, the family came together again on the terrace. Kate was lying on the ground, on her stomach, with her face resting on her arms, her head practically in the ducklings' saucer of milk. Mrs. Talbot, who had stretched out on the garden chaise longue, discovered suddenly that Mr. Rochester was missing. She sat up in alarm and cried, "Where is he?"

"Down my neck," Kate said.

The duck emerged from her crossed arms. He crawled around them and climbed up on the back of her neck. Kate smiled. The sight of the duck's tiny downy head among her pale ash-blond curls made them all burst out laughing. The cloud that had been hanging over the household evaporated into bright sunshine, and Arnold seized that moment to glance surreptitiously at his watch.

They all went to the train with him, including the dog. At the last moment Mrs. Talbot, out of a sudden perception of his lonely life, tried to give him some radishes, but he refused them. When he stepped out of the car at the station, the boys were arguing and were with difficulty persuaded to say good-bye to him. He watched the station wagon drive away and then stood listening for the sound of the wood thrush. But, of course, in the center of South Norwalk there was no such sound.

Reading for Understanding

❑ MAIN IDEA

1. Which of the following best expresses the main idea of the story? (a) A weekend in the country is beneficial for health and a source of relaxation. (b) Children who have pets should be encouraged to take good care of them. (c) In a large family, love can express itself in a variety of ways. (d) The comfort of a guest should be the first consideration of any host or hostess.

❑ DETAILS

2. The oldest child in the Talbot family was (a) Duncan (b) George (c) Kate (d) John.

3. *Satan* was the name of (a) the favorite bantam rooster (b) one of the turtles (c) the favorite duckling (d) the dog.

4. The bantams were most loved by (a) Duncan (b) George (c) Kate (d) Arnold.

5. Mary Sherman was (a) a nurse (b) Mrs. Talbot's sister (c) Kate's friend (d) a cousin of the Talbots'.

❑ INFERENCES

6. The bantam rooster was tricked into crowing by (a) Arnold (b) the moon (c) a bantam hen (d) the sound of the wood thrush.

7. Arnold was (a) liked by George and Duncan (b) secretly in love with Mrs. Talbot (c) an excellent sleeper (d) an animal expert.

8. When Mrs. Talbot said, "All birds sound alike to me," she (a) showed a deep insensitivity (b) intended to be humorous (c) tried to discourage Arnold from his nature notes (d) was being friendly.

9. When Arnold thought, "It was as if their hostility had two faces," he was suggesting (a) the cruelty of young boys (b) the annoyances of childhood (c) the blindness of a bachelor (d) the complexities of love.

10. When Arnold "began to compare the life of the Talbots with his own well-ordered but childless and animalless life," his mood was probably (a) irritable (b) cheerful (c) sad (d) bitterly angry.

❑ AUTHOR'S STYLE

11. The pace of the story can best be described as (a) rapid-fire (b) monotonous (c) leisurely and sensitive (d) blunt and vigorous.

❑ ORDER OF EVENTS

12. Arrange the items in the order in which they occurred. Use letters only.
    A. Mr. Talbot discovers cold eggs in the nest.
    B. Arnold is awakened in the middle of the night by the bantam rooster.
    C. Arnold goes to the little house to read.
    D. Kate goes to the party.
    E. The little duck walks around Kate's neck.

❑ OUTCOMES

13. After Arnold steps out of the car, (a) he will turn around and come back from the station, (b) the Talbots will begin the bitter fighting concealed during the visit, (c) he will vow never to return (d) he will probably visit again the next year.

☐ CAUSE AND EFFECT

14. The tragedy of the lost hen (a) brought the family closer together (b) increased George's hostility toward Duncan (c) caused Arnold to go out and buy another one (d) scarred Kate forever.

☐ FACT OR OPINION

Tell whether the following is a fact or an opinion.

15. The Talbot family members were on good behavior during Arnold's visit.

Words in Context

1. "His visits were . . . less exciting than the appearance of the first robin or the arrival of violets . . . but *akin to them.*" ***Akin to them*** (339) means (a) much different from them (b) of the same stock (c) reflective of them (d) just as effective.
2. "There were only two . . . walking around under the Japanese cherry tree on the *terrace.*" The definition of ***terrace*** (340) appropriate for its use in the sentence is (a) open platform (b) strip of park (c) narrow plain bordering a stream (d) level planted area adjoining a building.
3. "I saw '*Anna Karenina*' in the library and I think I'll take that and go up to the little house." The "***Anna Karenina***" (341) Arnold referred to is a (a) long drink (b) delicacy (c) neighbor's pet (d) novel.
4. "The little house was a one-room studio. . . with *casement* windows on two sides. . . " ***Casement*** (341) means (a) containing stained glass (b) having hinged opening (c) having storm sash (d) screened.
5. ". . . by now it had a slightly *musty* odor which included lingering traces of wood smoke." ***Musty*** (341) means (a) moldy (b) woodsy (c) acrid (d) old-fashioned.
6. "George's voice was shrill . . . and sounded as if he were *on the verge of tears.*" ***On the verge of tears*** (341) means (a) pretending to cry (b) getting over a crying spell (c) controlling an urge to cry (d) at the point of crying.
7. ". . . and his eyes wandered to a two-foot *espaliered* pear tree." ***Espaliered*** (342) means (a) stunted (b) forced to bloom (c) trained to grow flat (d) stripped bare of fruit.

8. ". . . Mrs. Talbot had made a *boutonnière* out of a pink geranium and some little blue and white flowers for Kate to wear on her coat." ***Boutonnière*** (342) means (a) corsage (b) lapel ornament (c) identification tag (d) bouquet.

9. "In his eyes there was a vague threat toward the boys who, in their young *callowness*, might not appreciate his daughter." ***Callowness*** (342) means (a) inexperience (b) enthusiasm (c) insensitivity (d) boisterousness.

10. "He had found a rat hole near the *ravaged* lady slippers and was setting a trap." ***Ravaged*** (343) means (a) newly planted (b) laid waste (c) overgrown (d) trampled on.

11. "Paths crisscrossing, lines that are perpetually meeting . . . the two boys' *preoccupation with* each other." ***Preoccupation with*** (343) means (a) complete absorption in (b) lack of concern for (c) dislike for (d) unwilling acceptance of.

12. "He was usually a very quiet, *self-contained* man." ***Self-contained*** (343) means (a) informal (b) reserved (c) well-dressed (d) outgoing.

13. "There was a picnic. . . out under the grape *arbor*." ***Arbor*** (344) means (a) trellis (b) leaves (c) press (d) bower.

14. ". . . Arnold seized that moment to glance *surreptitiously* at his watch." ***Surreptitiously*** (344) means (a) stealthily (b) openly (c) guiltily (d) in astonishment.

15. ". . . Mrs. Talbot, out of a sudden *perception* of his lonely life, tried to give him some radishes, but he refused them." ***Perception*** (344) means (a) acceptance (b) rejection (c) impulsive fear (d) awareness.

Thinking Critically About the Story

1. In this story the author accents the positive. What formula for family happiness is exemplified here? Would this formula work for your family? For the TV families you usually watch?

2. What is the pattern of love between Duncan, age 9, and George, age 6? How does it compare with sibling reactions in your family? How do they handle sibling rivalry? How is it handled in your family? Among your friends?

3. How significant is the family menagerie? What is the advantage of having pet animals in and around the house? What is lacking if there are

none? What are the disadvantages? What did you learn by having pet animals around? Should every family have them?

4. What was Mrs. Talbot's role in the family configuration? Mr. Talbot's role? Is this formula possible in a two-career family? In a household where mother or father spends long hours on the job? Where father has two jobs? In a home split by divorce?

5. What did the thrush symbolize? "He watched the station wagon drive away and then stood listening for the sound of the wood thrush. But, of course, in the center of South Norwalk there was no such sound." Do thrushes sing in inner-cities? In underprivileged areas? In towns? In suburbia? Only for the well-to-do?

Stories in Words

Fondly (340) demonstrates a tendency in language for a word to upgrade its meaning. *Fond* once meant "foolish" from the Middle English *fonne,* "fool." Then the word meant "foolishly adoring," but the "silly" meaning began to disappear. Now the word means "affectionate and loving" without the idea of foolishness. Not all words go up in meaning. Some go downhill. *Knave,* for example, once meant just "boy." A *villain* was once just a "poor, honest serf," without any suggestion of evil. A *boor* was just a "farmer."

Geranium (342) links the flower with a colorful bird, the crane. The ancient Greeks thought the beaked seed pods of the flower resembled the head and beak of a crane, and so they gave the flower the name, *geranos,* " crane." Strangely enough, the florist plant called a *geranium* is of a different species, the *Pelargonium.* But this word is also related to a bird, the stork, so named for the shape of its fruit. This Greek word for crane also is an ancestor of the word *pedigree,* by definition the footprint of a crane. If you've ever seen a pedigree listing a line of descent, you may remember the pattern that looks like a bird's footprint.

Chaise longue (344) is frequently mispronounced and confused with another word. It comes from French and literally means "long chair." But it has been influenced by the English word *lounge,* of unknown origin. Most people call the object of furniture "chaise lounge," despite all efforts to keep the original distinction.

A Poetics for Bullies

STANLEY ELKIN

John Williams mourns for me. He grieves his gamy grief. No one has everything—not even John Williams. He doesn't have *me*. He'll never have me, I think. If my life were only to deny him that, it would almost be enough.

You will find "A Poetics for Bullies" most unusual. It is apparently a tale of evil told from the viewpoint of the scoundrel. Push, the narrator, reveals all. He doesn't spare himself. The revelations are as open and honest as if he were providing an ordinary autobiography. He is even scrupulously honest in describing his archenemy, the boy who is his own antithesis.

The story begins with some keen self-revelations and develops conflicts as the new boy makes Push's little evils irrelevant. The last sentence of the story restates the first and provides a glimpse of hopelessness. There are clues to the origins of Push's all-around nastiness, but understanding is difficult. Is it possible to sympathize with Push's seemingly unreconstructed hatred? What do you think?

Though the story is told in the first person, it puts into the mouth and mind of Push a kind of articulateness and self-awareness that would be beyond him. This is a kind of poetic license often indulged in by writers. *Poetics* has several dictionary definitions: "a treatise on poetry or esthetics; poetic theory or practice; poetic feelings or expressions." Why do you think the author chose this particular word for this confession?

A Poetics for Bullies*

I'm Push the bully, and what I hate are new kids and sissies, dumb kids and smart, rich kids, poor kids, kids who wear glasses, talk funny, show off, patrol boys and wise guys and kids who pass pencils and water the plants—and cripples, *especially* cripples. I love nobody loved.

One time I was pushing this red-haired kid (I'm a pusher, no hitter, no belter; an aggressor of marginal violence, I hate *real* force) and his mother stuck her head out the window and shouted something I've never forgotten. "*Push,*" she yelled. "*You, Push.* You pick on him because you wish you had his red hair!" It's true; I *did* wish I had his red hair. I wish I were tall, or fat, or thin. I wish I had different eyes, different hands, a mother in the supermarket. I wish I were a man, a small boy, a girl in the choir. I'm a coveter casing the world. Endlessly I covet and case. (Do you know what makes me cry? The Declaration of Independence. "All men are created equal." That's beautiful.)

If you're a bully like me, you use your head. Toughness isn't enough. You beat them up, they report you. Then where are you? I'm not even particularly strong. (I used to be strong. I used to do exercise, work out, but strength implicates you, and often isn't an advantage anyway—read the judo ads. Besides, your big bullies aren't bullies at all—they're *athletes*. With them, beating guys up is a sport.) But what I lose in size and strength I make up in courage. I'm very brave. That's a lie about bullies being cowards underneath. If you're a coward, get out of the business.

I'm best at torment.

A kid has a toy bow, toy arrows. "Let Push look," I tell him.

He's suspicious, he knows me. "Go way, Push," he says, this mama-warned Push doubter.

"Come on," I say, "come on."

*In the fourth century B.C., Aristotle wrote *Poetics,* a treatise on poetry. In the twentieth century A.D., Elkin wrote "A Poetics for Bullies," a treatise on modern bullies.

"No, Push. I can't. My mother said I can't."

I raise my arms, I spread them. I'm a bird—slow, powerful, easy, free. I move my head offering profile like something beaked. I'm the Thunderbird.* "In the school where I go I have a teacher who teaches me magic," I say. "Arnold Salamancy, give Push your arrows. Give him one, he gives back two. Push is the God of the Neighborhood."

"Go way, Push," the kid says, uncertain.

"Right," Push says, himself again. "Right. I'll disappear. First the fingers." My fingers ball to fists. "My forearms next." They jackknife into my upper arms. "The arms." Quick as bird-blink they snap behind my back, fit between the shoulder blades like a small knapsack. (I am double-jointed, protean.) "My head," I say.

"No, Push," the kid says, terrified. I shudder and everything comes back, falls into place from the stem of self like a shaken puppet.

"The arrow, the arrow. Two where was one." He hands me an arrow.

"*Trouble, trouble, double rubble!*" I snap it and give back the pieces.

Well, sure. There *is* no magic. If there were I would learn it. I would find out the words, the slow turns and strange passes, drain the bloods and get the herbs, do the fires like a vestal. I would look for the main chants. *Then* I'd change things. *Push* would!

But there's only casuistical trick. Sleight-of-mouth, the bully's poetics.

You know the formulas:

"Did you ever see a match burn twice?" you ask. Strike. Extinguish. Jab his flesh with the hot stub.

"Play 'Gestapo'?" †

"How do you play?"

"What's your name?"

"It's Morton."

I slap him. "You're lying."

"Adam and Eve and Pinch Me Hard went down to the lake for a swim. Adam and Eve fell in. Who was left?"

"Pinch Me Hard."

I do.

Physical puns, conundrums. Push the punisher, the conundrummer!

But there has to be more than tricks in a bag of tricks.

I don't know what it is. Sometimes I think *I'm* the only new kid. In a room, the school, the playground, the neighborhood, I get the feeling I've just moved in, no one knows me. You know what I like? To stand in crowds. To wait with them at the airport to meet a plane. Someone asks what time it is. I'm the first to answer. Or at the ballpark when the vendor comes. He passes the hot dog down the long row. I want *my* hands on it, too. On the dollar going up, the change coming down.

I am ingenious, I am patient.

**Thunderbird* mythical bird believed by American Indians to cause lightning and thunder
†*Gestapo* secret police known for terrorist methods

A kid is going downtown on the elevated train. He's got his little suit on, his shoes are shined, he wears a cap. This is a kid going to the travel bureaus, the foreign tourist offices to get brochures, maps, pictures of the mountains for a unit at his school—a kid looking for extra credit. I follow him. He comes out of the Italian Tourist Information Center. His arms are full. I move from my place at the window. I follow for two blocks and bump into him as he steps from a curb. It's a *collision*—The pamphlets fall from his arms. Pretending confusion, I walk on his paper Florence. I grind my heel in his Riviera. I climb Vesuvius and sack his Rome and dance on the Isle of Capri.

The Industrial Museum is a good place to find children. I cut somebody's five- or six-year-old kid brother out of the herd of eleven- and twelve-year-olds he's come with. "*Quick*," I say. I pull him along the corridors, up the stairs, through the halls, down to a mezzanine landing. Breathless, I pause for a minute. "I've got some gum. Do you want a stick?" He nods; I stick him. I rush him into an auditorium and abandon him. He'll be lost for hours.

I sidle up to a kid at the movies. "You smacked my brother," I tell him. "After the show—I'll be outside."

I break up games. I hold the ball above my head. "You want it? Take it."

I go into barbershops. There's a kid waiting. "I'm next," I tell him, "understand?"

One day Eugene Kraft rang my bell. Eugene is afraid of me, so he helps me. He's fifteen and there's something wrong with his saliva glands and he drools. His chin is always chapped. I tell him he has to drink a lot because he loses so much water.

"Push? Push," he says. He's wiping his chin with his tissues. "Push, there's this kid—"

"Better get a glass of water, Eugene."

"No, Push, no fooling, there's this new kid—he just moved in. You've got to see this kid."

"Eugene, get some water, please. You're drying up. I've never seen you so bad. There are deserts in you, Eugene."

"All right, Push, but then you've got to see—"

"Swallow, Eugene. You better swallow."

He gulps hard.

"Push, this is a kid and a half. Wait, you'll see."

"I'm very concerned about you, Eugene. You're dying of thirst, Eugene. Come into the kitchen with me."

I push him through the door. He's very excited. I've never seen him so excited. He talks at me over his shoulder, his mouth flooding, his teeth like the little stone pebbles at the bottom of a fishbowl. "He's got this sport coat, with a patch over the heart. Like a king, Push. No kidding."

"Be careful of the carpet, Eugene."

I turn on the taps in the sink. I mix in hot water. "Use your tissues, Eugene. Wipe your chin."

He wipes himself and puts the Kleenex in his pocket. All of Eugene's pockets bulge. He looks, with his bulging pockets, like a clumsy smuggler.

"Wipe, Eugene. Swallow, you're drowning."

"He's got this funny accent—you could die." Excited, he tamps at his mouth like a diner, a tubercular.

"Drink some water, Eugene."

"No, Push. I'm not thirsty—really."

"Don't be foolish, kid. That's because your mouth's so wet. Inside where it counts you're drying up. It stands to reason. Drink some water."

"He has this crazy haircut."

"*Drink*," I command. I shake him. "*Drink*!"

"Push, I've got no glass. Give me a glass at least."

"I can't do that, Eugene. You've got a terrible sickness. How could I let you use our drinking glasses? Lean under the tap and open your mouth."

He knows he'll have to do it, that I won't listen to him until he does. He bends into the sink.

"Push, it's *hot*." he complains. The water splashes into his nose, it gets on his glasses and for a moment his eyes are magnified, enormous. He pulls away and scrapes his forehead on the faucet.

"Eugene, you touched it. Watch out, please. You're too close to the tap. Lean your head deeper into the sink."

"It's *hot*, Push."

"Warm water evaporates better. With your affliction you've got to evaporate fluids before they get into your glands."

He feeds again from the tap.

"Do you think that's enough?" I ask after a while.

"I do, Push, I really do," he says. He is breathless.

"Eugene," I say seriously, "I think you'd better get yourself a canteen."

"A canteen, Push?"

"That's right. Then you'll always have water when you need it. Get one of those Boy Scout models. The two-quart kind with a canvas strap."

"But you hate the Boy Scouts, Push."

"They make very good canteens, Eugene. *And wear it!* I never want to see you without it. Buy it today."

"All right, Push."

"Promise!"

"All right, Push."

"Say it out."

He made the formal promise that I like to hear.

"Well, then," I said, "let's go see this new kid of yours."

He took me to the schoolyard. "Wait," he said, "you'll see." He skipped ahead.

"Eugene," I said, calling him back. "Let's understand something. No matter what this new kid is like, nothing changes as far as you and I are concerned."

"Aw, Push," he said.

"Nothing, Eugene. I mean it. You don't get out from under me."

"Sure, Push, I know that."

There were some kids in the far corner of the yard, sitting on the ground, leaning up against the wire fence. Bats and gloves and balls lay scattered around them.

"There. See? Do you see him?" Eugene, despite himself, seemed hoarse.

"Be quiet," I said, checking him, freezing as a hunter might. I stared.

He was a *prince*, I tell you.

He was tall, tall, even sitting down. His long legs comfortable in expensive wool, the trousers of a boy who had been on ships, jets; who owned a horse, perhaps; who knew Latin—what *didn't* he know?—somebody made up, like a kid in a play with a beautiful mother and a handsome father; who took his breakfast from a sideboard, and picked, even at fourteen and fifteen and sixteen, his mail from a silver plate. He would have hobbies—stamps, stars, things lovely dead. He wore a sport coat, brown as wood, thick as heavy bark. The buttons were leather buds. His shoes seemed carved from horses' saddles, gunstocks. His clothes had once grown in nature. *What it must feel like inside those clothes,* I thought.

I looked at his face, his clear skin, and guessed at the bones, white as beached wood. His eyes had skies in them. His yellow hair swirled on his head like a crayoned sun.

"Look, look at him," Eugene said. "The sissy. Get him, Push."

He was talking to them and I moved closer to hear his voice. It was clear, beautiful, but faintly foreign—like herb-seasoned meat.

When he saw me he paused, smiling. He waved. The others didn't look at me.

"Hello there," he called. "Come over if you'd like. I've been telling the boys about tigers."

"Tigers," I said.

"Give him the 'match burn twice,' Push," Eugene whispered.

"Tigers, is it?" I said. "What do you know about tigers?" My voice was high.

"*The 'match burn twice,' Push.*"

"Not so much as a Master *Tugjah*. I was telling the boys. In India there are men of high caste—*Tugjahs,* they're called. I was apprenticed to one once in the Southern Plains and might perhaps have earned my mastership, but the Red Chinese attacked the northern frontier and . . . well, let's just say I had to leave. At any rate, these *Tugjahs* are as intimate with the tiger as you are with dogs. I don't mean they keep them as pets. The relationship goes deeper. Your dog is a service animal, as is your elephant."

"Did you ever see a match burn twice?" I asked suddenly.

"Why no, can you do that? Is it a special match you use?"

"No," Eugene said, "it's an ordinary match. He used an ordinary match."

"Can you do it with one of mine, do you think?"

He took a matchbook from his pocket and handed it to me. The cover was exactly the material of his jacket, and in the center was a patch with a coat of arms identical to the one he wore over his heart.

I held the matchbook for a moment and then gave it back to him. "I don't feel like it," I said.

"Then some other time, perhaps," he said.

Eugene whispered to me. "His accent, Push, his funny *accent.*"

"Some other time, perhaps," I said. I am a good mimic. I can duplicate a particular kid's lisp, his stutter, a thickness in his throat. There were two or three here whom I had brought close to tears by holding up my mirror to their voices. I can parody their their limps, their waddles, their girlish runs, their clumsy jumps. I can throw as they throw, catch as they catch. I looked around. "Some other time, perhaps," I said again. No one would look at me.

"I'm *so* sorry," the new one said, "we don't know each other's names. You are?"

"I'm so sorry," I said. "You arc?"

He seemed puzzled. Then he looked sad, disappointed. No one said anything.

"It don't sound the same," Eugene whispered.

It was true. I sounded nothing like him. I could imitate only defects, only flaws.

A kid giggled.

"Shh," the prince said. He put one finger to his lips.

"Look at that," Eugene said under his breath. "He's a sissy."

He had begun to talk to them again. I squatted, a few feet away. I ran gravel through my loose fists, one bowl in an hourglass feeding another.

He spoke of jungles, of deserts. He told of ancient trade routes traveled by strange beasts. He described lost cities and a lake deeper than the deepest level of the sea. There was a story about a boy who had been captured by bandits. A woman in the story—it wasn't clear whether she was the boy's mother—had been tortured. His eyes clouded for a moment when he came to this part and he had to pause before continuing. Then he told how the boy escaped—it was cleverly done—and found help, mountain tribesmen riding elephants. The elephants charged the cave in which the mo—*the woman*—was still a prisoner. It might have collapsed and killed her, but one old bull rushed in and, shielding her with his body, took the weight of the crashing rocks. Your elephant is a service animal.

I let a piece of gravel rest on my thumb and flicked it in a high arc above his head. Some of the others who had seen me stared, but the boy kept on talking. Gradually I reduced the range, allowing the chunks of gravel to come closer to his head.

"You see?" Eugene said quietly. "He's afraid. He pretends not to notice."

The arcs continued to diminish. The gravel went faster, straighter. No one was listening to him now, but he kept talking.

"—of magic," he said, "what occidentals call 'a witch doctor.' There are spices that induce these effects. The *Bogdovii* was actually able to stimulate the growth of rocks with the powder. The Dutch traders were ready to go to war for the formula. Well, you can see what it could mean for the

Low Countries. Without accessible quarries they've never been able to construct a permanent system of dikes. But with the *Bogdovii's* powder"—he reached out and casually caught the speeding chip as if it had been a Ping-Pong ball—"they could turn a grain of sand into a pebble, use the pebbles to grow stones, the stones to grow rocks. This little piece of gravel, for example, could be changed into a mountain." He dipped his thumb into his palm as I had and balanced the gravel on his nail. He flicked it; it rose from his nail like a missile, and climbed an impossible arc. It disappeared. "The *Bogdovii* never revealed how it was done."

I stood up. Eugene tried to follow me.

"Listen," he said, "you'll get him."

"Swallow," I told him. "Swallow, you pig!"

I have lived my life in pursuit of the vulnerable: Push the chink seeker, wheeler dealer in the flawed cement of the personality, a collapse maker. But what isn't vulnerable, *who* isn't? There is that which is unspeakable, so I speak it, that which is unthinkable, which I think. Me and the devil, we do nature's dirty work, after all.

I went home after I left him. I turned once at the gate, and the boys were around him still. The useless Eugene had moved closer. *He* made room for him against the fence.

I ran into Frank the fat boy. He made a move to cross the street, but I had seen him and he went through a clumsy retractive motion. I could tell he thought I would get him for that, but I moved by, indifferent to a grossness in which I had once delighted. As I passed he seemed puzzled, a little hurt, a little—this was astonishing—guilty. *Sure* guilty. Why *not* guilty? The forgiven tire of their exemption. Nothing could ever be forgiven, and I forgave nothing. I held them to the mark. Who else cared about the fatties, about the dummies and slobs and clowns, about the gimps and squares and oafs and fools the kids with a mouthful of mush, all those shut-ins of the mind and heart, all those losers? Frank the fat boy knew, and passed me shyly. His wide, fat body, stiffened, forced jokishly martial when he saw me, had already become flaccid as he moved by, had already made one more forgiven surrender. Who cared?

The streets were full of failure. Let them. Let them be. There was a paragon, a paragon loose. What could he be doing here, why had he come, what did he want? It was impossible that this hero from India and everywhere had made his home here; that he lived, as Frank the fat boy did, as Eugene did, as *I* did, in an apartment; that he shared our lives.

In the afternoon I looked for Eugene. He was in the park, in a tree. There was a book in his lap. He leaned against the thick trunk.

"Eugene," I called up to him.

"Push, they're closed. It's Sunday, Push. The stores are closed. I looked for the canteen. The stores are closed."

"Where is he?"

"Who, Push? What do you want, Push?"

"*Him.* Your pal. The prince. Where? Tell me, Eugene, or I'll shake you out of that tree. I'll burn you down. I swear it. Where is he?"

"No, Push. I was wrong about that guy. He's nice. He's really nice. Push, he told me about a doctor who could help me. Leave him alone, Push."

"Where, Eugene? *Where?* I count to three."

Eugene shrugged and came down the tree.

I found the name Eugene gave me—funny, foreign—over the bell in the outer hall. The buzzer sounded and I pushed open the door. I stood inside and looked up the carpeted stairs, the angled banisters.

"What is it?" She sounded old, worried.

"The new kid," I called, "the new kid."

"It's for you," I heard her say.

"Yes?" His voice, the one I couldn't mimic. I mounted the first stair. I leaned back against the wall and looked up through the high, boxy banister poles. It was like standing inside a pipe organ.

"Yes?"

From where I stood at the bottom of the stairs I could see only a boot. He was wearing boots.

"Yes? What is it, please?"

"*You,*" I roared. "Glass of fashion, model of form, it's me! It's Push the bully!"

I heard his soft, rapid footsteps coming down the stairs—a springy, spongy urgency. He jingled. He had coins—I could see them: rough, golden, imperfectly round; raised, massively gowned goddesses, their heads fingered smooth, their arms gone—and keys to strange boxes, thick doors. I saw his boots. I backed away.

"I brought you down," I said.

"Be quiet, please. There's a woman who's ill. A boy who must study. There's a man with bad bones. An old man needs sleep."

"He'll get it," I said.

"We'll go outside," he said.

"No. Do you live here? What do you do? Will you be in our school? Were you telling the truth?"

"Shh. Please. You're very excited."

"Tell me your name," I said. It could be my campaign, I thought. His *name.* Scratched in new sidewalk, chalked onto walls, written on papers dropped in the street. To leave it behind like so many clues, to give him a fame, to take it away, to slash and cross out, to erase and to smear—my kid's witchcraft. "Tell me your name."

"It's John," he said softly.

"What?"

"It's John."

"John what? Come on now. I'm Push the bully."

"John Williams," he said.

"John Williams? John Williams? Only that? Only John Williams?"

He smiled.

"Who's that on the bell? The name on the box?"

"She needs me," he said.

"Cut it out."

"I help her," he said.

"You stop that."

"There's a man that's in pain. A woman who's old. A husband that's worried. A wife that despairs."

"You're the bully," I said. "Your John Williams is a service animal," I yelled in the hall.

He turned and began to climb the stairs. His calves bloomed in their leather sheathing.

"Good-deeder," I whispered to him.

He turned to me at the landing. He shook his head sadly.

"We'll see," I said.

"We'll see what we'll see," he said.

That night I painted his name on the side of the gymnasium in enormous letters. In the morning it was still there, but it wasn't what I meant. There was nothing incantatory in the huge letters, no scream, no curse. I had never traveled with a gang, there had been no togetherness in my tearing, but this thing on the wall seemed the act of vandals, the low production of ruffians. When you looked at it you were surprised they had gotten the spelling right.

Astonishingly, it was allowed to remain. And each day there was something more celebrational in the giant name, something of increased hospitality, lavish welcome. John Williams might have been a football hero, or someone back from the kidnapers. Finally I had to take it off myself.

Something had changed.

Eugene was not wearing his canteen. Boys didn't break off their conversations when I came up to them. One afternoon a girl winked at me. (Push has never picked on girls. *Their* submissiveness is part of their nature. They are ornamental. Don't get me wrong, please. There is a way in which they function as part of the landscape, like flowers at a funeral. They have a strange cheerfulness. They are the organizers of pep rallies and dances. They put out the Year Book. They are *born* Gray Ladies.* I can't bully them.)

John Williams was in the school, but except for brief glimpses in the hall I never saw him. Teachers would repeat the things he had said in their other classes. They read from his papers. In the gym the coach described plays he had made, set shots he had taken. Everyone talked about him, and girls made a reference to him a sort of love signal. If it was suggested that he had smiled at one of them, the girl referred to would blush or, what was worse, look aloofly mysterious. (*Then* I could have punished her, *then* I could.) Gradually his name began to appear on all their notebooks,

***Gray Ladies* volunteer nonprofessional hospital helpers, workers for the Red Cross

in the margins of their texts. (It annoyed me to remember what *I* had done on the wall.) The big canvas books, with their careful, elaborate J's and W's, took on the appearance of ancient, illuminated fables. It was the unconscious embroidery of love, hope's bright doodle. Even the administration was aware of him. In Assembly the principal announced that John Williams had broken all existing records in the school's charity drives. She had never seen good citizenship like his before, she said.

It's one thing to live with a bully, another to live with a hero.

Everyone's hatred I understand, no one's love; everyone's grievance, no one's content.

I saw Mimmer. Mimmer should have graduated years ago. I saw Mimmer the dummy.

"Mimmer," I said, "you're in his class."

"He's very smart."

"Yes, but is it fair? You work harder. I've seen you study. You spend hours. Nothing comes. He was born knowing. You could have used just a little of what he's got so much of. It's not fair."

"He's very clever. It's wonderful," Mimmer says.

Slud is crippled. He wears a shoe with a built-up heel to balance himself.

"Ah, Slud," I say, "I've seen him run."

"He has beaten the horses in the park. It's very beautiful," Slud says.

"He's handsome, isn't he, Clob?" Clob looks contagious, radioactive. He has severe acne. He is ugly *under* his acne.

"He gets the girls," Clob says.

He gets *everything*, I think. But I'm alone in my envy, awash in my lust. It's as if I were a prophet to the deaf. Schnooks, schnooks, I want to scream, dopes and settlers. What good does his smile do you, of what use is his good heart?

The other day I did something stupid. I went to the cafeteria and shoved a boy out of the way and took his place in the line. It was foolish, but their fear is almost all gone and I felt I had to show the flag. The boy only grinned and let me pass. Then someone called my name. It was *him*. I turned to face him. "Push," he said, "you forgot your silver." He handed it to a girl in front of him and she gave it to the boy in front of her and it came to me down the long line.

I plot, I scheme. Snares, I think; tricks and traps. I remember the old days when there were ways to snap fingers, crush toes, ways to pull noses, twist heads and punch arms—the old-timey Flinch Law I used to impose, the gone bully magic of deceit. But nothing works against him, I think. How does he know so much? He is bully-prepared, that one, not to be trusted.

It is worse and worse.

In the cafeteria he eats with Frank. "You don't want those potatoes," he tells him. "Not the ice cream, Frank. One sandwich, remember. You lost three pounds last week." The fat boy smiles his fat love at him. John Williams puts his arm around him. He seems to squeeze him thin.

He's helping Mimmer to study. He goes over his lessons and teaches him tricks, short cuts. "I want you up there with me on the Honor Roll, Mimmer."

I see him with Slud the cripple. They go to the gym. I watch from the balcony. "Let's develop those arms, my friend." They work out with weights. Slud's muscles grow, they bloom from his bones.

I lean over the rail. I shout down, "He can bend iron bars. Can he pedal a bike? Can he walk on rough ground? Can he climb up a hill? Can he wait on a line? Can he dance with a girl? Can he go up a ladder or jump from a chair?"

Beneath me the rapt Slud sits on a bench and raises a weight. He holds it at arm's length, level with his chest. He moves it high, higher. It rises above his shoulders, his throat, his head. He bends back his neck to see what he's done. If the weight should fall now it would crush his throat. I stare down into his smile.

I see Eugene in the halls. I stop him. "Eugene, what's he done for you?" I ask. He smiles—he never did this—and I see his mouth's flood. "High tide," I say with satisfaction.

Williams has introduced Clob to a girl. They have double-dated.

A *week ago John Williams came to my house to see me!* I wouldn't let him in.

"Please open the door, Push. I'd like to chat with you. Will you open the door? Push? I think we ought to talk. I think I can help you to be happier."

I was furious. I didn't know what to say to him. "I don't want to be happier. Go way." It was what little kids used to say to me.

"*Please* let me help you."

"*Please* let me—" I begin to echo. "Please let me alone."

"We ought to be friends, Push."

"No deals." I am choking, I am close to tears. What can I do? *What?* I want to kill him.

I double-lock the door and retreat to my room. He is still out there. I have tried to live my life so that I could keep always the lamb from my door.

He has gone too far this time; and I think sadly, I will have to fight him, I will have to fight him. Push pushed. I think sadly of the pain. Push pushed. I will have to fight him. Not to preserve honor but its opposite. Each time I see him I will have to fight him. And then I think—*of course.* And *I* smile. He has done *me* a favor. I know it at once. If he fights me he fails. He fails if he fights me. *Push pushed pushes!* It's physics! Natural law! I know he'll beat me, but I won't prepare, I won't train, I won't use the tricks I know. It's strength against strength, and my strength is as the strength of ten because my jaw is glass! *He doesn't know everything, not everything he doesn't.* And I think, I could go out now, he's still there, I could hit him in the hall, but I think, No, I want them to see, I want *them* to see!

The next day I am very excited. I look for Williams. He's not in the halls. I miss him in the cafeteria. Afterward I look for him in the schoolyard where I first saw him. (He has them organized now. He teaches them games of Tibet, games of Japan; he gets them to play lost sports of the dead.) He does not disappoint me. He is there in the yard, a circle around him, a ring of the loyal.

I join the ring. I shove in between two kids I have known. They try to change places; they murmur and fret.

Williams sees me and waves. His smile could grow flowers. "Boys," he says, "boys, make room for Push. Join hands, boys." They welcome me to the circle. One takes my hand, then another. I give to each calmly.

I wait. *He doesn't know everything.*

"Boys," he begins, "today we're going to learn a game that the knights of the lords and kings of old France used to play in another century. Now you may not realize it, boys, because today when we think of a knight we think, too, of his fine charger, but the fact is that a horse was a rare animal—not a domestic European animal at all, but Asian. In western Europe, for example, there was no such thing as a workhorse until the eighth century. Your horse was just too expensive to be put to heavy labor in the fields. (This explains, incidentally, the prevalence of famine in western Europe, whereas famine is unrecorded in Asia until the ninth century, when Euro-Asian horse trading was at its height.) It wasn't only expensive to purchase a horse, it was expensive to keep one. A cheap fodder wasn't developed in Europe until the tenth century. Then, of course, when you consider the terrific risks that the warrior horse of a knight naturally had to run, you begin to appreciate how expensive it would have been for the lord—unless he was extremely rich—to provide all his knights with horses. He'd want to make pretty certain that the knights who got them knew how to handle a horse. (Only your knights errant—an elite, crack corps—ever had horses. We don't realize that most knights were *home* knights; *chevalier chez* they were called.)

"This game, then, was devised to let the lord, or king, see which of his knights had the skill and strength in his hands to control a horse. Without moving your feet, you must try to jerk the one next to you off balance. Each man has two opponents, so it's very difficult. If a man falls, or if his knee touches the ground, he's out. The circle is diminished but must close up again immediately. Now, once for practice only—"

"Just a minute," I interrupt.

"Yes, Push?"

I leave the circle and walk forward and hit him as hard as I can in the face.

He stumbles backward. The boys groan. He recovers. He rubs his jaw and smiles. I think he is going to let me hit him again. I am prepared for this. He knows what I'm up to and will use his passivity. Either way I win, but I am determined he shall hit me. I am ready to kick him, but as my foot comes up he grabs my ankle and turns it forcefully. I spin in the air. He lets go and I fall heavily on my back. I am surprised at how easy it was, but am content if they understand. I get up and am walking away, but there is an arm on my shoulder. He pulls me around roughly. He hits me.

"*Sic semper tyrannus,*"* he exults.

"Where's your other cheek?" I ask, falling backward.

"One cheek for tyrants," he shouts. He pounces on me and raises his fist and I cringe. His anger is terrific. I do not want to be hit again.

"You see? You see?" I scream at the kids, but I have lost the train of my former reasoning. I have in no way beaten him. I can't remember now what I had intended.

He lowers his fist and gets off my chest and they cheer. "Hurrah," they yell. "Hurrah, hurrah." The word seems funny to me.

He offers his hand when I try to rise. It is so difficult to know what to do. It is so difficult to know which gesture is the right one. I don't even know this. He knows everything, and I don't know this. I am a fool on the ground, one hand behind me pushing up, the other not yet extended but itching in the palm where the need is. It is better to give than receive, surely. It is best not to need at all.

Appalled, guessing what I miss, I rise alone.

"Friends?" he asks. He offers to shake.

"Take it, Push." It's Eugene's voice.

"Go ahead, Push." Slud limps forward.

"Push, hatred's so ugly," Clob says, his face shining.

"You'll feel better, Push," Frank, thinner, taller, urges softly.

"Push, don't be foolish," Mimmer says.

I shake my head. I may be wrong. I am probably wrong. All I know at last is what feels good. "Nothing doing," I growl. "No deals." I begin to talk, to spray my hatred at them. They are not an easy target even now. "Only your knights errant—your crack corps—ever have horses. Slud may dance and Clob may kiss but they'll never be good at it. *Push is no service animal.* No. *No.* Can you hear that, Williams? There isn't any magic, but your no is still stronger than your yes, and distrust is where I put my faith." I turn to the boys. "What have you settled for? Only your knights errant ever have horses. *What have you settled for*? Will Mimmer do sums in his head? How do you like your lousy hunger, thin boy? Slud, you can break me but you can't catch me. And Clob will never shave without pain, and ugly, let me tell you, is *still* in the eye of the beholder!"

John Williams mourns for me. He grieves his gamy grief. No one has everything—not even John Williams. He doesn't have *me*. He'll never have me, I think. If my life were only to deny him that, it would almost be enough. I could do his voice now if I wanted. His corruption began when he lost me. "You," I shout, rubbing it in, "*indulger*, dispense me no dispensations. Push the bully hates your heart!"

"Shut him up, somebody," Eugene cries. His saliva spills from his mouth when he speaks.

**Sic semper tyrannus* Latin: Thus ever to tyrants

"Swallow! *Pig, swallow!*"

He rushes toward me.

Suddenly I raise my arms and he stops. I feel a power in me. I am Push, Push the bully, God of the Neighborhood, its incarnation of envy and jealousy and need. I vie, strive, emulate, compete, a contender in every event there is. I didn't make myself. I probably can't save myself, but maybe that's the only need I don't have. I taste my lack and that's how I win—by having nothing to lose. It's not good enough! I want and I want and I will die wanting, but first I will have something. This time I will have something. I say it aloud. "This time I will have something." I step toward them. The power makes me dizzy. It is enormous. They feel it. They back away. They crouch in the shadow of my outstretched wings. It isn't deceit this time but the real magic at last, the genuine thing: the cabala* of my hate, of my irreconcilableness.

Logic is nothing. Desire is stronger.

I move toward Eugene. "*I will have something,*" I roar.

"Stand back," he shrieks, "I'll spit in your eye."

"*I will have something.* I will have terror. I will have drought. I bring the dearth. Famine's contagious. Also is thirst. Privation, privation, barrenness, void. I dry up your glands, I poison your well."

He is choking, gasping, chewing furiously. He opens his mouth. It is dry. His throat is parched. There is sand on his tongue.

They moan. They are terrified, but they move up to see. We are thrown together. Slud, Frank, Clob, Mimmer, the others, John Williams, myself. I will not be reconciled, or halve my hate. *It's* what I have, all I can keep. My bully's sour solace. It's enough, I'll make do.

I can't stand them near me. I move against them. I shove them away. I force them off. I press them, thrust them aside. *I push through.*

Reading for Understanding

❑ MAIN IDEA

1. The major idea of the story is that (a) childhood can be a difficult time, especially for the weak (b) a young person needs friends (c) superficially at least, good cannot always overcome evil (d) most bullies have hearts of gold.

❑ DETAILS

2. When the young child finally gives Push an arrow, Push (a) uses it to shoot at a distant target (b) gives it back with an expression of thanks (c) strikes the child (d) snaps the arrow.

**cabala* system of magical powers or beliefs

3. All the following were Push's acts of cruelty EXCEPT (a) knocking papers out of a boy's hands (b) getting a little child lost (c) breaking up ballgames (d) burning a child's schoolbooks.
4. Push's favorite dupe was named (a) Eugene (b) John (c) Frank (d) Clob.
5. An offer of friendship is made to Push by (a) Mimmer (b) Slud (c) John (d) Frank.
6. The expression "I love nobody loved" suggests that (a) Push considers himself unloved (b) Push really likes the people he seems to despise (c) underneath the rough surface, Push has a heart of gold (d) basically John Williams and Push are similar in attitude.

❑ INFERENCES

7. A surprising element in Push's feelings toward the new boy is (a) love (b) admiration (c) indifference (d) humor.
8. The anger of John Williams is a terrible thing to see, but it is (a) a source of contempt by the other children (b) disliked by John himself (c) intentionally quieted by Push (d) feigned.
9. Push's actions toward the new boy result in (a) a complete break between Push and Eugene (b) a reconciliation between the two (c) a loss in Eugene's admiration for John (d) a change in Push's pointless hatred.
10. In the battle between John and Push, (a) nobody wins (b) both win (c) Push wins (d) John wins.
11. The author's attitude toward Push is one of (a) awed fascination (b) utter rejection (c) grudging acceptance (d) insensitivity.

❑ ORDER OF EVENTS

12. Arrange the items in the order in which they occurred. Use letters only.
    A. Push strikes John.
    B. John goes to Push's house.
    C. Eugene tells Push about the new boy.
    D. Push gets a little brother lost.
    E. John tells the group about tigers.

❑ OUTCOMES

13. After the story, Push will probably (a) turn over a new leaf (b) move to another state (c) beg John's forgiveness (d) continue to be an outcast.

❑ CAUSE AND EFFECT

14. John's arrival (a) made Push a better person (b) had a positive impact on most of the children (c) was timed by him for maximum dramatic effect (d) was actually cheered by Push.

❑ FACT OR OPINION

Tell whether the following is a fact or an opinion.

15. Push had many good impulses which had been submerged by a sad childhood.

Words in Context

1. "I am a *coveter* casing the world." ***Coveter*** (350) means an (a) outlaw (b) intellectual outcast (c) alibi maker (d) envier.
2. "I used to exercise, work out, but strength *implicates* you, and often isn't an advantage anyway . . ." ***Implicates*** (350) means (a) weakens (b) involves (c) destroys (d) betrays.
3. "But there's only *casuistical* trick. Sleight-of-mouth, the bully's *poetics*." ***Casuistical*** . . . ***poetics*** . . . (351) mean (a) vicious . . . cruelties (b) incidental . . . exaggerations (c) theatrical . . . weaponry (d) clever but false . . . manual of operation.
4. "I climb Vesuvius and *sack* his Rome and dance on the Isle of Capri." ***Sack*** (352) means (a) sit on (b) lay waste (c) wrap up (d) entrap.
5. "I pull him along the corridors, up the stairs, through the halls, down to a *mezzanine* landing." ***Mezzanine*** (352) means (a) isolated (b) theatrical (c) distant (d) between two floors.
6. "I can *parody* their limps, their waddles, their girlish runs, their clumsy jumps." ***Parody*** (355) means (a) exaggerate (b) quickly bring about (c) describe precisely (d) imitate humorously.
7. "There are spices that *induce* these effects." ***Induce*** (355) means (a) bring about (b) exaggerate (c) counteract (d) prolong.
8. "I have lived my life in pursuit of the *vulnerable* . . . wheeler dealer in the flawed cement of the personality . . ." ***Vulnerable*** (356) means those who are (a) capable of being hurt (b) cowardly (c) willing to fight back (d) unable to take orders.
9. "The streets were full of failure. Let them be . . . There was a *paragon*, a *paragon* loose . . . why had he come . . ." A ***paragon*** (356) is a

person who is (a) handicapped by his ambition (b) a model of excellence (c) a destroyer of confidence (d) a worthy opponent.

10. "Beneath me the *rapt* Slud sits on a bench and raises a weight." ***Rapt*** (360) means (a) totally engrossed (b) potential failure (c) bewildered (d) completely confident.

11. "This explains, incidentally, the *prevalence* of famine in western Europe, whereas famine is unrecorded in Asia . . . " ***Prevalence*** (361) means (a) appearance (b) horror (c) extensiveness (d) devastation.

12. "Only your knights *errant*—an *elite, crack corps*—ever had horses." ***Errant*** . . . ***elite, crack corps*** (361) mean (a) capable . . . wealthy, experienced fighters (b) in exile . . . wise well-trained leaders (c) wandering . . . highly select first-class group (d) in disguise . . . upper-class, capable engineers.

13. "*Appalled*, guessing what I miss, I rise alone." ***Appalled*** (362) means (a) excited (b) dismayed (c) embittered (d) triumphant.

14. "'You,' I shout, rubbing it in, '*Indulger, dispense* me no *dispensations*. Push the bully hates your heart!'" ***Indulger*** . . . ***dispense*** . . . ***dispensations*** (362) mean (a) coddler . . . allocate . . . exemptions (b) softy . . . issue . . . punishments (c) champion . . . deprive . . . benefits (d) hypocrite . . . bestow on . . . penalties.

15. "I am Push, Push the bully, God of the Neighborhood, its *incarnation* of envy and jealousy and need." ***Incarnation*** (363) means (a) defender (b) embodiment (c) victim (d) champion.

Thinking Critically About the Story

1. Why did the author choose to tell the story from the point of view of Push? Whom do we sympathize with? Is Push an antihero? Explain. What is the advantage of telling the story from the negative side? Can you cite other stories told from the same set of values?

2. Compare Push and the newcomer, John Williams. Both are leaders, but how do they differ? Which of the two is more effective? Which of the two do the leaders you know resemble? Which of the two will have the more lasting effect on the lives of others?

3. Would you choose John Williams as a friend? Which of his traits would bother you? How would you handle them?

4. Perseverance is one of Push's very few redeeming features. When is perseverance a positive quality? When does it become negative? Do

you have the right mixture? Explain. What is the formula for the right mixture?

5. How do you handle a Push in real life? How would you have handled Push? How is a Push treated on TV? Does he always receive his comeuppance? Who has the better chance of achieving success in this world, a Push or a John Williams?

6. Practically all of the characters in the story are either boys or men. Are there any female bullies? If there are, how do their tactics compare with Push's? Are all bullies, like Push, motivated by hatred? Do they ever reform? Relate your own experiences. Do bullies ever achieve happiness?

7. What motivates a John Williams to do good? To achieve at his level? Does he make a good parent? Does a bully make a good parent?

Stories in Words

Protean (351) is named for Proteus, classical sea god. Proteus was a popular one to get hold of because he had the gift of prophecy, but it was difficult to hold onto him because he could assume different shapes. If the questioner held on, however, Proteus eventually had to assume his own shape and answer the question. The word *protean* means "having the ability to assume *different* forms, *different* moods, *different* characteristics."

Mimic (355) comes from Greek through Latin. The *mim* root has the suggestion of *imitation.* A *mimic imitates* the speech and manner of others. By looking like the monarch butterfly, the viceroy uses *mimicry* to save itself. Birds avoid both the monarch and the viceroy, though the latter would be a tender morsel. A *mime* is *a mimic* who usually relies on body language, not words, to tell a story. Before the modern copier, the *mimeograph* machine was generally used to make duplicate copies.

Vandals (358) comes from the name of the tribe that overran Rome in 455 A.D. The Vandals were a savage Teutonic tribe that wantonly destroyed works of art as well as their owners. The word *vandalism* has come to mean "malicious, pointless destruction of property." Another tribe, the Goths, gave their name to the style of art and architecture called *Gothic*; yet the Goths had nothing to do with either the art or the architecture. Renaissance architects gave the name *Gothic* to all buildings characteristic of the Middle Ages. They considered such structures crude and barbaric, "suitable for the Goths."

Mixed Motivations

Getting Technical

Terms

conflict	positive values	understatement
point of view	symbol	

Definitions Match each of the above terms with the appropriate definition.

1. Presentation of something as less significant than it really is
2. The opposition of two characters, two forces in characters, or characters and society or environment
3. Something that stands for something else as a summary of ideas and attitudes
4. Indicators of what should be, not of what should not be
5. Frame of mind from which the story is told

Examples Write the term that is most appropriate to describe each of the following.

1. She was torn between wanting to help them and wanting to see them pay for their complete disregard of her feelings.
2. Tell me what I did right, not what I did wrong.
3. Our school song is so much more than just words and a melody.
4. The skilled journalist told the story through the eyes of the handicapped victim.
5. The crash victim, swaddled in bandages and confined to a hospital bed for weeks, summarized his experience with "I got a bang out of it."

6. Which will be his guide: his own need for political power or the needs of his desperately poor constituents?

7. Hitch your wagon to a star!

8. Stop thinking about how others will feel if you do it; think about how you will feel after doing it.

Application Choose the statement that best completes each of the following.

1. "A Poetics for Bullies" is told from the point of view of (a) Eugene who drools (b) Frank the fat boy (c) John Williams, the newcomer (d) Push the bully.

2. The title "Winterblossom Garden" (a) is an understatement (b) is symbolic (c) reveals positive values (d) exposes the point of view.

3. One of the conflicts revealed in "Wild Men of Borneo" is between (a) the father and the daughter-in-law (b) the son and the mother (c) the mother and the daughter-in-law (d) the ambitions of the father and son.

4. Introduced as a symbol in "Patterns of Love" is the (a) missing bantam (b) rat (c) wood thrush (d) ducklings.

5. In "Winterblossom Garden" the conflict is most intense between the (a) son and daughter (b) mother and daughter (c) mother and father (d) son and parents.

6. "Wild Men of Borneo" is told from the point of view of the (a) father (b) son (c) mother (d) daughter-in-law.

Thinking Critically About the Stories

1. What are some of the Do's and Don'ts in these stories? What are the chances for achieving happiness for

    The son in "Wild Men of Borneo"
    The son in "Winterblossom Garden"
    Kate Talbot, the mother in "Patterns of Love"

2. Compare Claire, the mother in "Wild Men of Borneo," with the mother in "Winterblossom Garden" in terms of

    Their self-images
    The goals they set for themselves
    The punishing blows life deals them
    Their acceptance of their lot in life

   How close do they come to your concept of an ideal parent?

3. Compare the young people in the four stories. Refer to instances in the stories to support your reactions. Which ones seemed to be caricatures, humorous exaggerations? Which had a mixture of traits that gave them the ring of truth? With which one do you empathize most?

4. Select the scene that you enjoyed most in these stories. Be prepared to read it to the class and explain why you chose it.

5. Prove the truth of the following quotation.
   "In 'A Poetic for Bullies' Elkin used satire and bitter humor to guide his readers. In 'Patterns of Love' Maxwell's joyful sentimentalism and positive models and values unveil the good life." Which method is more likely to capture the reader's interest? Which is more likely to convince the reader? Which method do you find is more effective with you? Which method is closer to the technique you use to convince others?

Writing and Other Activities

1. Take one of your grandparents' or parents' favorite tales of their youth and write the climax in dialog and action twice: once from your relative's point of view; once from the other person's point of view.

2. Write a scene in which a perennial practical joker does a monolog, using the opening of "A Poetic for Bullies" as your model.

3. Set up a class panel discussion on one of the following:
   a. When is it time for parents to give advice rather than telling a teenager what must be done?
   b. Mistakes in family living that I hope never to make when I have a family of my own
   c. How to handle the friend
      —who knows it all, especially what is best for you
      —who always finds fault with your contributions
      —who always goes you one better
      —who invariably turns the conversation to his (her) favorite topic: guess who!
      —who finds only good in everything
   d. How to influence siblings without being detected

4. Write a two-minute address to seniors on one of the following:
   a. How to Turn a New Leaf Week
   b. Love Yourself Week
   c. Look in the Mirror Week
   d. Reform Week

5. Write "A Poetic for ____________." (Select one of the following habitués of senior gathering places.)
   a. the gossip creators
   b. the influence peddlers
   c. the gloom spreaders
   d. the ego crushers

Stories in Words: A Review

A. April
B. calculate
C. camera
D. carnival
E. chaise longue
F. fondly
G. geranium
H. Greenwich Village
I. mimic
J. protean
K. resist
L. vandals

Answer the following questions by choosing a word from the list above. Use letters only.

Which of the words above . . .

1. ________ contains the root for *pebble?*
2. ________ literally means *farewell to meat?*
3. ________ contains the root for imitation?
4. ________ was named for a savage Teutonic tribe?
5. ________ is often confused for another quite similar word?
6. ________ is related to the word for *crane?*
7. ________ once meant *foolishly?*
8. ________ means *room* in Latin?
9. ________ contains the same root twice?
10. ________ is named for a slippery character in Greek mythology?

A good narrative depends upon plot. An important ingredient in plot is conflict. The classic plot line has been summarized: "Boy meets girl. Boy loses girl. Boy wins girl." How many plays, books, and movies have you seen with a variation of this basic plot? When boy loses girl, there is conflict: with other people, with nature, with fate, with society.

Conflict is at the heart of the stories in this unit, but they avoid the cliché-ridden "boy meets girl" device. The conflict in the first story is primitive, elemental, especially gripping because it is stated so matter-of-factly.

7

Conflict

No doubt there are other important things in life besides conflict, but there are not so many things so inevitably interesting. The very saints interest us most when we think of them as engaged in a conflict with the Devil.

Robert Lynd

The second story presents a sharp contrast. Here the conflict is subtle, not so obviously stated as in the Hemingway story, but the conflict is keen nevertheless. The conflict in the third story seems trite but it is deceptive. It is only at the end that we realize how different this story is. The conflict in the fourth story is the classic confrontation between the murderer and the amateur detective. The murderer is cleverer than most and almost certain to commit the perfect crime, but there is always chance.

All four stories engage the reader's attention, with contrasts aplenty.

The Killers

ERNEST HEMINGWAY

"I was up at Henry's," Nick said, "and two fellows came in and tied up me and the cook, and they said they were going to kill you."

It sounded silly when he said it. Ole Andreson said nothing.

Some stories handle conflict on an elemental level. There are no subtleties, no gradations of feeling, no insinuations or hidden suggestions. Everything is out in the open. The conflict may be someone against a beast, a person against nature, or the basic person *vs.* person struggle. "The Killers" is an elemental story, with no holds barred.

The setting is an ordinary lunchroom like hundreds of others scattered throughout the country. It's a quiet setting where nothing unusual ever happens. Then two strangers arrive, and the tension builds slowly until their horrible purpose is revealed.

Ernest Hemingway is outstanding as a literary stylist. His spare, direct style has many imitators, but few writers can capture the growing tensions in the conversations he reports. "The Killers" is almost a one-act play. It could be staged quite easily without any loss of impact. The second scene could be played at the side of the stage, suggesting the full implications of the impending tragedy.

This powerful story is one you won't soon forget.

The Killers

The door of Henry's lunchroom opened and two men came in. They sat down at the counter.

"What's yours?" George asked them.

"I don't know," one of the men said. "What do you want to eat, Al?"

"I don't know," said Al. "I don't know what I want to eat."

Outside it was getting dark. The streetlight came on outside the window. The two men at the counter read the menu. From the other end of the counter Nick Adams watched them. He had been talking to George when they came in.

"I'll have a roast pork tenderloin with apple sauce and mashed potatoes," the first man said.

"It isn't ready yet."

"What the hell do you put it on the card for?"

"That's the dinner," George explained. "You can get that at six o'clock."

George looked at the clock on the wall behind the counter.

"It's five o'clock."

"The clock says twenty minutes past five," the second man said.

"It's twenty minutes fast."

"Oh, to hell with the clock," the first man said. "What have you got to eat?"

"I can give you any kind of sandwiches," George said. "You can have ham and eggs, bacon and eggs, liver and bacon, or a steak."

"Give me chicken croquettes with green peas and cream sauce and mashed potatoes."

"That's the dinner."

"Everything we want's the dinner, eh? That's the way you work it."

"I can give you ham and eggs, bacon and eggs, liver——"

"I'll take ham and eggs," the man called Al said. He wore a derby hat and a black overcoat buttoned across the chest. His face was small and white and he had tight lips. He wore a silk muffler and gloves.

"Give me bacon and eggs," said the other man. He was about the same size as Al. Their faces were different, but they were dressed like twins.

Both wore overcoats too tight for them. They sat leaning forward, their elbows on the counter.

"Got anything to drink?" Al asked.

"Silver beer, bevo, ginger-ale," George said.

"I mean you got anything to *drink*?"

"Just those I said."

"This is a hot town," said the other. "What do they call it?"

"Summit."

"Ever hear of it?" Al asked his friend.

"No," said the friend.

"What do you do here nights?" Al asked.

"They eat the dinner," his friend said. "They all come here and eat the big dinner."

"That's right," George said.

"So you think that's right?" Al asked George.

"Sure."

"You're a pretty bright boy, aren't you?"

"Sure," said George.

"Well, you're not," said the other little man. "Is he, Al?"

"He's dumb," said Al. He turned to Nick. "What's your name?"

"Adams."

"Another bright boy," Al said. "Ain't he a bright boy, Max?"

"The town's full of bright boys," Max said.

George put the two platters, one of ham and eggs, the other of bacon and eggs, on the counter. He set down two side dishes of fried potatoes and closed the wicket into the kitchen.

"Which is yours?" he asked Al.

"Don't you remember?"

"Ham and eggs."

"Just a bright boy," Max said. He leaned forward and took the ham and eggs. Both men ate with their gloves on. George watched them eat.

"What are *you* looking at?" Max looked at George.

"Nothing."

"The hell you were. You were looking at me."

"Maybe the boy meant it for a joke, Max," Al said.

George laughed.

"*You* don't have to laugh," Max said to him. "*You* don't have to laugh at all, see?"

"All right," said George.

"So he thinks it's all right." Max turned to Al. "He thinks it's all right. That's a good one."

"Oh, he's a thinker," Al said. They went on eating.

"What's the bright boy's name down the counter?" Al asked Max.

"Hey, bright boy," Max said to Nick. "You go around on the other side of the counter with your boy friend."

"What's the idea?" Nick asked.

"There isn't any idea."

"You better go around, bright boy," Al said. Nick went around behind the counter.

"What's the idea?" George asked.

"None of your damn business," Al said. "Who's out in the kitchen?"

"The Black."

"What do you mean the Black?"

"The Black boy that cooks."

"Tell him to come in."

"What's the idea?"

"Tell him to come in."

"Where do you think you are?"

"We know damn well where we are," the man called Max said. "Do we look silly?"

"You talk silly," Al said to him. "What the hell do you argue with this kid for? Listen," he said to George, "tell the cook to come out here."

"What are you going to do to him?"

"Nothing. Use your head, bright boy. What would we do to a Black boy?"

George opened the slit that opened back into the kitchen. "Sam," he called. "Come in here a minute."

The door to the kitchen opened and Sam came in. "What was it?" he asked. The two men at the counter took a look at him.

"All right, Black boy. You stand right there," Al said.

Sam, standing in his apron, looked at the two men sitting at the counter. "Yes, sir," he said. Al got down from his stool.

"I'm going back to the kitchen with the cook and bright boy," he said. "Go on back to the kitchen, Black boy. You go with him, bright boy." The little man walked after Nick and Sam, the cook, back into the kitchen. The door shut after them. The man called Max sat at the counter opposite George. He didn't look at George but looked in the mirror that ran along back of the counter. Henry's had been made over from a saloon into a lunch counter.

"Well, bright boy," Max said, looking into the mirror, "why don't you say something?"

"What's it all about?"

"Hey, Al," Max called, "bright boy wants to know what it's all about."

"Why don't you tell him?" Al's voice came from the kitchen.

"What do you think it's all about?"

"I don't know."

"What do you think?"

Max looked into the mirror all the time he was talking.

"I wouldn't say."

"Hey, Al, bright boy says he wouldn't say what he thinks it's all about."

"I can hear you, all right," Al said from the kitchen. He had propped open the slit that dishes passed through into the kitchen with a catsup bottle. "Listen, bright boy," he said from the kitchen to George. "Stand a little further along the bar. You move a little to the left, Max." He was like a photographer arranging for a group picture.

"Talk to me, bright boy," Max said. "What do you think's going to happen?"

George did not say anything.

"I'll tell you," Max said. "We're going to kill a Swede. Do you know a big Swede named Ole Andreson?"

"Yes."

"He comes here to eat every night, don't he?"

"Sometimes he comes here."

"He comes here at six o'clock, don't he?"

"If he comes."

"We know all that, bright boy," Max said. "Talk about something else. Ever go to the movies?"

"Once in a while."

"You ought to go to the movies more. The movies are fine for a bright boy like you."

"What are you going to kill Ole Andreson for? What did he ever do to you?"

"He never had a chance to do anything to us. He never even seen us."

"And he's only going to see us once," Al said from the kitchen.

"What are you going to kill him for, then?" George asked.

"We're killing him for a friend. Just to oblige a friend, bright boy."

"Shut up," said Al from the kitchen. "You talk too much."

"Well, I got to keep bright boy amused. Don't I, bright boy?"

"You talk too damn much," Al said. "The cook and my bright boy are amused by themselves. I got them tied up like a couple of girl friends in the convent."

"I suppose you were in a convent?"

"You never know."

"You were in a kosher convent. That's where you were."

George looked up at the clock.

"If anybody comes in you tell them the cook is off, and if they keep after it, you tell them you'll go back and cook yourself. Do you get that, bright boy?"

"All right," George said. "What you going to do with us afterward?"

"That'll depend," Max said. "That's one of those things you never know at the time."

George looked up at the clock. It was a quarter past six. The door from the street opened. A streetcar motorman came in.

"Hello, George," he said. "Can I get supper?"

"Sam's gone out," George said. "He'll be back in about half an hour."

"I'd better go up the street," the motorman said. George looked at the clock. It was twenty minutes past six.

"That was nice, bright boy,"" Max said. "You're a regular little gentleman."

"He knew I'd blow his head off," Al said from the kitchen.

"No," said Max. "It ain't that. Bright boy is nice. He's a nice boy. I like him."

At six-fifty-five George said: "He's not coming."

Two other people had been in the lunchroom. Once George had gone out to the kitchen and made a ham-and-egg sandwich "to go" that a man wanted to take with him. Inside the kitchen he saw Al, his derby hat tipped back, sitting on a stool beside the wicket with the muzzle of a sawed-off shotgun resting on the ledge. Nick and the cook were back to back in the corner, a towel tied in each of their mouths. George had cooked the sandwich, wrapped it up in oiled paper, put it in a bag, brought it in, and the man had paid for it and gone out.

"Bright boy can do everything," Max said. "He can cook and everything. You'd make some girl a nice wife, bright boy."

"Yes?" George said. "Your friend, Ole Andreson, isn't going to come."

"We'll give him ten minutes," Max said.

Max watched the mirror and the clock. The hands of the clock marked seven o'clock, and then five minutes past seven.

"Come on, Al," said Max. "We better go. He's not coming."

"Better give him five minutes," Al said from the kitchen.

In the five minutes a man came in, and George explained that the cook was sick.

"Why the hell don't you get another cook?" the man asked. "Aren't you running a lunch counter?" He went out.

"Come on, Al," Max said.

"What about the two bright boys and the cook?"

"They're all right."

"You think so?"

"Sure. We're through with it."

"I don't like it," said Al. "It's sloppy. You talk too much."

"Oh, what the hell," said Max. "We got to keep amused, haven't we?"

"You talk too much, all the same," Al said. He came out from the kitchen. The cut-off barrels of the shotgun made a slight bulge under the waist of his too tight-fitting overcoat. He straightened his coat with his gloved hands.

"So long, bright boy," he said to George. "You got a lot of luck."

"That's the truth," Max said. "You ought to play the races, bright boy."

The two of them went out the door. George watched them, through the window, pass under the arc light and cross the street. In their tight overcoats and derby hats they looked like a vaudeville team. George went back through the swinging door into the kitchen and untied Nick and the cook.

"I don't want any more of that," said Sam, the cook. "I don't want any more of that."

Nick stood up. He had never had a towel in his mouth before.

"Say," he said. "What the hell?" He was trying to swagger it off.

"They were going to kill Ole Andreson," George said. "They were going to shoot him when he came in to eat."

"Ole Andreson?"

"Sure."

The cook felt the corners of his mouth with his thumbs.

"They all gone?" he asked.

"Yeah," said George. "They're gone now."

"I don't like it," said the cook. "I don't like any of it at all."

"Listen," George said to Nick. "You better go see Ole Andreson."

"All right."

"You better not have anything to do with it at all," Sam, the cook, said. "You better stay way out of it."

"Don't go if you don't want to," George said.

"Mixing up in this ain't going to get you anywhere," the cook said. "You stay out of it."

"I'll go see him," Nick said to George. "Where does he live?"

The cook turned away.

"Little boys always know what they want to do," he said.

"He lives up at Hirsch's rooming house," George said to Nick.

"I'll go up there."

Outside the arc light shone through the bare branches of a tree. Nick walked up the street beside the car tracks and turned at the next arc light down a side street. Three houses up the street was Hirsch's rooming house. Nick walked up the two steps and pushed the bell. A woman came to the door.

"Is Ole Andreson here?"

"Do you want to see him?"

"Yes, if he's in."

Nick followed the woman up a flight of stairs and back to the end of a corridor. She knocked on the door.

"Who is it?"

"It's somebody to see you, Mr. Andreson," the woman said.

"It's Nick Adams."

"Come in."

Nick opened the door and went into the room. Ole Andreson was lying on the bed with all his clothes on. He had been a heavyweight prizefighter and he was too long for the bed. He lay with his head on two pillows. He did not look at Nick.

"What was it?" he asked.

"I was up at Henry's," Nick said, "and two fellows came in and tied up me and the cook, and they said they were going to kill you."

It sounded silly when he said it. Ole Andreson said nothing.

"They put us out in the kitchen," Nick went on. "They were going to shoot you when you came in to supper."

Ole Andreson looked at the wall and did not say anything.

"George thought I better come and tell you about it."

"There isn't anything I can do about it," Ole Andreson said.

"I'll tell you what they were like."

"I don't want to know what they were like," Ole Andreson said. He looked at the wall. "Thanks for coming to tell me about it."

"That's all right."

Nick looked at the big man lying on the bed.

"Don't you want me to go and see the police?"

"No," Ole Andreson said. "That wouldn't do any good."

"Isn't there something I could do?"

"No. There ain't anything to do."

"Maybe it was just a bluff."

"No. It ain't just a bluff."

Ole Andreson rolled over toward the wall.

"The only thing is," he said, talking toward the wall, "I just can't make up my mind to go out. I been in here all day."

"Couldn't you get out of town?"

"No," Ole Andreson said. "I'm through with all that running around."

He looked at the wall.

"There ain't anything to do now."

"Couldn't you fix it up some way?"

"No. I got in wrong." He talked in the same flat voice. "There ain't anything to do. After a while I'll make up my mind to go out."

"I better go back and see George," Nick said.

"So long," said Ole Andreson. He did not look toward Nick. "Thanks for coming around."

Nick went out. As he shut the door he saw Ole Andreson with all his clothes on, lying on the bed looking at the wall.

"He's been in his room all day," the landlady said downstairs. "I guess he don't feel well. I said to him: 'Mr. Andreson, you ought to go out and take a walk on a nice fall day like this,' but he didn't feel like it."

"He doesn't want to go out."

"I'm sorry he don't feel well," the woman said. "He's an awfully nice man. He was in the ring, you know."

"I know it."

"You'd never know it except from the way his face is," the woman said. They stood talking just inside the street door. "He's just as gentle."

"Well, good night, Mrs. Hirsch," Nick said.

"I'm not Mrs. Hirsch," the woman said. "She owns the place. I just look after it for her. I'm Mrs. Bell."

"Well, good night, Mrs. Bell," Nick said.

"Good night," the woman said.

Nick walked up the dark street to the corner under the arc light, and then along the car tracks to Henry's eating house. George was inside, back of the counter.

"Did you see Ole?"

"Yes," said Nick. "He's in his room and he won't go out."

The cook opened the door from the kitchen when he heard Nick's voice.

"I don't even listen to it," he said and shut the door.

"Did you tell him about it?" George asked.

"Sure. I told him but he knows what it's all about."

"What's he going to do?"

"Nothing."

"They'll kill him."

"I guess they will."

"He must have got mixed up in something in Chicago."

"I guess so," said Nick.

"It's a hell of a thing."

"It's an awful thing," Nick said.

They did not say anything. George reached down for a towel and wiped the counter.

"I wonder what he did?" Nick said.

"Double-crossed somebody. That's what they kill them for."

"I'm going to get out of this town," Nick said.

"Yes," said George. "That's a good thing to do."

"I can't stand to think about him waiting in the room and knowing he's going to get it. It's too damned awful."

"Well," said George, "you better not think about it."

Reading for Understanding

☐ MAIN IDEA

1. The main point of the story is the (a) danger of running a restaurant (b) cold-blooded brutality of killers (c) heroism of a simple cook (d) thoughtfulness of strangers.

☐ DETAILS

2. The first person the killers verbally attacked was (a) Nick Adams (b) the cook (c) George (d) the motorman.

3. Al and Max couldn't get the meal they wanted because (a) the cook was ill (b) the restaurant had run out of chicken croquettes (c) George was afraid of the men (d) it wasn't time.

4. The victim was named (a) Max (b) Andreson (c) George (d) Nick Adams.

5. The caretaker of Andreson's rooming house was (a) Mrs. Bell (b) Al (c) Mrs. Hirsch (d) Andreson himself.

❑ INFERENCES

6. When Max said, "They all come here and eat the big dinner," he intended to be (a) funny (b) helpful (c) appreciative (d) deceptive.

7. The employees of the restaurant could be considered (a) foolish (b) vicious (c) lucky (d) disappointed.

8. The words *bright boy* were intended to be (a) appreciative (b) affectionate (c) appropriate (d) sarcastic.

9. Andreson's attitude could be considered (a) hostile (b) fatalistic (c) terrified (d) friendly.

❑ AUTHOR'S STYLE

10. The author's style can best be characterized as (a) simple and direct (b) wordy and inflated (c) light and humorous (d) roundabout and leisurely.

11. A major skill of the author's is (a) reporting conversation (b) writing a poetic prose (c) giving detailed descriptions (d) emphasizing the importance of kindness.

❑ ORDER OF EVENTS

12. Arrange the items in the order in which they occurred. Use letters only.
    A. Nick speaks to Andreson.
    B. The customers tie up Nick and the cook.
    C. Nick reports on his conversation with Ole.
    D. Max and Al ask for dinner.
    E. Max and Al leave the lunchroom.

❑ OUTCOMES

13. The probable outcome of the situation in the story would be (a) the reformation of Max (b) the departure of George from the restaurant job (c) the death of Andreson (d) a different procedure for serving dinner.

14. If George had chosen to defy the two customers, (a) Max and Al would have quarreled (b) Nick would have sacrificed himself for George (c) he'd have frightened the bullies (d) he could have been killed.

☐ FACT OR OPINION

Tell whether the following is a fact or an opinion.

15. George insisted that dinner would be served at 6:00, not before.

Words in Context

1. "They sat down at the *counter*." ***Counter*** (375) means (a) rear (b) booth (c) table for two (d) long serving table.
2. "Give me chicken *croquettes* with green peas . . ." ***Croquettes*** (375) means (a) white meat (b) roasted over charcoal (c) rounded, crumb-covered chopped meat or fish (d) fried in deep fat.
3. "He wore a *derby* hat and a black overcoat buttoned across the chest." Another name for ***derby*** (375) is (a) cap (b) beret (c) stetson (d) bowler.
4. "'*Silver beer, bevo, ginger-ale,*' George said." ***Silver beer, bevo,*** and ***ginger-ale*** (376) have in common the fact that (a) they contain artificial sweeteners (b) they are homemade (c) they contain no alcohol (d) they are natural drinks.
5. "He . . . closed the *wicket* into the kitchen." ***Wicket*** (376) means (a) arched opening (b) window (c) ramp (d) walkway.
6. "Henry's had been made over from a *saloon* into a lunch counter." The contemporary word for ***saloon*** (377) is (a) supermarket (b) boutique (c) bar (d) fast-food.
7. "He had *propped* open the slit that dishes passed through into the kitchen . . ." ***Propped*** (377) means (a) braced (b) cut (c) swung (d) jammed.
8. "Inside the kitchen he saw Al . . . with the *muzzle* of a sawed-off shotgun resting on the ledge." ***Muzzle*** (379) means (a) open end (b) trigger (c) safety catch (d) polished stock.
9. "George watched them . . . pass under the *arc light* and cross the street." ***Arc light*** (379) means (a) railroad overpass (b) street sign (c) traffic signal (d) street lamp.
10. "He was trying to *swagger it off*." The idiom ***swagger it off*** (380) means (a) forget all about it (b) disregard their fears (c) be helpful (d) put on a false front.

Thinking Critically About the Story

1. What devices does Hemingway use to make convincingly real the two men who seem to come right out of a movie script dealing with gangland characters?

2. What devices does Hemingway use to have tension and suspense begin at a high level—and then go higher?

3. At what point does Nick become aware of the dangerous position he is in? Why does he go to warn Ole Andreson? What would you have done? Why doesn't he go to the police? What have you learned about Nick as a person?

4. Why does Ole Andreson lie with his back to the door? Why is the door unlocked? What is the inevitable ending?

5. What answers can you guess at for some of the unanswered questions in the story?

    How were Al and Max able to learn about Ole Andreson's whereabouts?
    Why do they come to kill him?
    Why doesn't Andreson try to protect himself?
    Why don't they notify the police? Why do Al and Max allow George, Nick, and Sam to live to tell the tale?
    Why did Hemingway leave these questions unanswered?

6. Select committees of students to read aloud to the class the portions of dialog that are most tense. Have one of the students keep the continuity by reading the non-dialog sentences along with them. How effective is Hemingway at keeping the number of words down to a bare minimum?

Stories in Words

Sandwiches (375) forever recalls a famous gambler. At 5 A.M. on August 6, 1762, John Montagu, fourth earl of Sandwich, was hungry. He had been gambling all night, but he didn't want to get up from the gambling tables. To avoid the problem of having to eat a full meal, he ordered his servants to bring him some sliced meat between two pieces of bread. Thus the first *sandwich* was born. Though the Romans are said to have eaten a similar food, it was the earl of Sandwich who popularized it and gave it its name. It was the same earl who outfitted

Captain James Cook's ship, which explored the world. When Cook got to what is now the Hawaiian islands, he named them the *Sandwich Islands*.

Derby (375), like sandwich, is named for an English earl. The twelfth earl of Derby devoted most of his time to horse racing. In 1780 he started an annual contest for three-year-olds at Epsom Downs, near London. Derby day became an important social event at which men tended to wear bowler hats. The Americans admired the British and instituted their own races, calling one of them the Kentucky Derby. The Americans also admired those bowler hats, but they preferred to call them *derbies*.

Elbows (376) is one of those common words we use without thinking how appropriate is its origin. *Elbow* has two parts: *el* derives from an Old Norse word for "forearm"; *bow* derives from a word meaning "bend" or "curve." *Elbow* thus suggests "the place where the forearm bends." An ell was an old measure, presumably measuring the distance from elbow to wrist, though the actual distance was somewhat longer. The shape of the letter *L* suggests an arm bent at the elbow. An addition to a house at right angles is called an *ell*, as is an elbow in a pipe or conduit. The word *elbow* has several extended uses: *elbow room, to elbow one's way into a crowd, out at elbows*.

Graven Image

JOHN O'HARA

"Listen, Joe, are we talking like grown men? Are you sore at the Pork? Do you think you'd have enjoyed being a member of it? If being sore at it was even partly responsible for getting you where you are, then I think you ought to be a little grateful to it."

Confrontation and conflict take many forms. In an action movie, the conflict is physical: guns or fists. In some movies and stories, however, the conflict is civilized and subtle. You have to read between the lines to understand the nature of the conflict and the form it is taking.

"Graven Image" shows us a successful member of the government, a self-made man, a person who has had to rise in the ranks through hard work and honest merit. A much more self-assured friend from earlier times asks for a job that is in the power of the government member to grant. There are little digs and thrusts during the early part of the meeting, but all seems to be going well. The job is almost assured, but then . . . A single sentence sharpens our awareness of the basic conflict and completely changes the direction of the story. What is the "wrong thing" that the applicant says?

Graven Image

The car turned in at the brief, crescent-shaped drive and waited until the two cabs ahead had pulled away. The car pulled up, the doorman opened the rear door, a little man got out. The little man nodded pleasantly enough to the doorman and said "Wait" to the chauffeur. "Will the Under Secretary be here long?" asked the doorman.

"Why?" said the little man.

"Because if you were going to be here, sir, only a short while, I'd let your man leave the car here, at the head of the rank."

"Leave it there *anyway*," said the Under Secretary.

"Very good, sir," said the doorman. He saluted and frowned only a little as he watched the Under Secretary enter the hotel. "Well," the doorman said to himself, "it was a long time coming. It took him longer than most, but sooner or later all of them—" He opened the door of the next car, addressed a colonel and a major by their titles, and never did anything about the Under Secretary's car, which pulled ahead and parked in the drive.

The Under Secretary was spoken to many times in his progress to the main dining room. One man said, "What's your hurry, Joe?," to which the Under Secretary smiled and nodded. He was called Mr. Secretary most often, in some cases easily, by the old Washington hands, but more frequently with that embarrassment which Americans feel in using titles. As he passed through the lobby, the Under Secretary himself addressed by their White House nicknames two gentlemen whom he had to acknowledge to be closer to The Boss. And, bustling all the while, he made his way to the dining room, which was already packed. At the entrance he stopped short and frowned.

The man he was to meet, Charles Browning, was chatting, in French, very amiably with the maître d'hôtel. Browning and the Under Secretary had been at Harvard at the same time.

The Under Secretary went up to him. "Sorry if I'm a little late," he said, and held out his hand, at the same time looking at his pocket watch. "Not so very, though. How are you, Charles? Fred, you got my message?"

"Yes, sir," said the maître d'hôtel. "I put you at a nice table all the way back to the right." He meanwhile had wig-wagged a captain, who stood by to lead the Under Secretary and his guest to Table 12. "Nice to have seen you again, Mr. Browning. Hope you come see us again while you are in Washington. Always a pleasure, sir."

"Always a pleasure, Fred," said Browning. He turned to the Under Secretary. "Well, shall we?"

"Yeah, let's sit down," said the Under Secretary.

The captain led the way, followed by the Under Secretary, walking slightly sideways. Browning, making one step to two of the Under Secretary's, brought up the rear. When they were seated, the Under Secretary took the menu out of the captain's hands. "Let's order right away so I don't have to look up and talk to those two over there. I guess you know which two I mean." Browning looked from right to left, as anyone does on just sitting down in a restaurant. He nodded and said, "Yes, I think I know. You mean the senators."

"That's right," said the Under Secretary. "I'm not gonna have a cocktail, but you can. . . . I'll have the lobster. Peas. Shoestring potatoes. . . . You want a cocktail?"

"I don't think so. I'll take whatever you're having."

"O.K., waiter?" said the Under Secretary.

"Yes, sir," said the captain, and went away.

"Well, Charles, I was pretty surprised to hear from you."

"Yes," Browning said, "I should imagine so, and by the way, I want to thank you for answering my letter so promptly. I know how rushed you fellows must be, and I thought, as I said in my letter, at your convenience."

"Mm. Well, frankly, there wasn't any use in putting you off. I mean till next week or two weeks from now or anything like that. I could just as easily see you today as a month from now. Maybe easier. I don't know where I'll be likely to be a month from now. In more ways than one. I may be taking the Clipper to London, and then of course I may be out on my can! Coming to New York and asking *you* for a job. I take it that's what you wanted to see me about."

"Yes, and with hat in hand."

"Oh, no. I can't see you waiting with hat in hand, not for anybody. Not even for The Boss."

Browning laughed.

"What are you laughing at?" asked the Under Secretary.

"Well, you know how I feel about him, so I'd say least of all The Boss."

"Well, you've got plenty of company in this town. But why'd you come to me, then? Why didn't you go to one of your Union League or Junior League* or what-ever-the-hell-it-is pals? There, that big jerk over there with the blue suit and the striped tie, for instance?"

**Union League, Junior League* exclusive high-society organizations

Browning looked over at the big jerk with the blue suit and striped tie, and at that moment their eyes met and the two men nodded.

"You *know* him?" said the Under Secretary.

"Sure, I know him, but that doesn't say I *approve* of him."

"Well, at least that's something. And I notice he knows you."

"I've been to his house. I think he's been to our house when my father was alive, and naturally I've seen him around New York all my life."

"Naturally. Naturally. Then why didn't you go to *him?*"

"That's easy. I wouldn't like to ask him for anything. I don't approve of the man, at least as a politician, so I couldn't go to him and ask him a favor."

"But, on the other hand, you're not one of our team, but yet you'd ask me a favor. I don't get it."

"Oh, yes you do, Joe. You didn't get where you are by not being able to understand a simple thing like that."

Reluctantly—and quite obviously it was reluctantly—the Under Secretary grinned. "All right. I was baiting you."

"I know you were, but I expected it. I have it coming to me. I've always been against you fellows. I wasn't even for you in 1932, and that's a hell of an admission, but it's the truth. But that's water under the bridge—or isn't it?" The waiter interrupted with the food, and they did not speak until he had gone away.

"You were asking me if it isn't water under the bridge. Why should it be?"

"The obvious reason," said Browning.

"'My country, 'tis of thee'?"

"Exactly. Isn't that enough?"

"It isn't for your Racquet Club pal over there."

"You keep track of things like that?"

"Certainly," said the Under Secretary. "I know every club in this country, beginning back about twenty-three years ago. I had ample time to study them all then, you recall, objectively, from the outside. By the way, I notice you wear a wristwatch. What happens to the little animal?"

Browning put his hand in his pocket and brought out a small bunch of keys. He held the chain so that the Under Secretary could see, suspended from it, a small golden pig.* "I still carry it," he said.

"They tell me a lot of you fellows put them back in your pockets about five years ago, when one of the illustrious brethren closed his downtown office and moved up to Ossining."

"Oh, probably," Browning said, "but quite a few fellows, I believe, that hadn't been wearing them took to wearing them again out of simple loyalty. Listen, Joe, are we talking like grown men? Are you sore at the Pork? Do you think you'd have enjoyed being a member of it? If being sore at it was even partly responsible for getting you where you are, then I think

**small golden pig* charm worn by members of an exclusive, restricted college fraternity

you ought to be a little grateful to it. You'd show the bastards. O.K. You showed them. Us. If you hadn't been so sore at the Porcellian* so-and-so's, you might have turned into just another lawyer."

"My wife gives me that sometimes."

"There, do you see?" Browning said. "Now then, how about the job?"

The Under Secretary smiled. "There's no getting away from it, you guys have got something. O.K., what are you interested in? Of course, I make no promises, and I don't even know if what you're interested in is something I can help you with."

"That's a chance I'll take. That's why I came to Washington, on just that chance, but it's my guess you can help me." Browning went on to tell the Under Secretary about the job he wanted. He told him why he thought he was qualified for it, and the Under Secretary nodded. Browning told him everything he knew about the job, and the Under Secretary continued to nod silently. By the end of Browning's recital the Under Secretary had become thoughtful. He told Browning that he thought there might be some little trouble with a certain character but that that character could be handled, because the real say so, the green light, was controlled by a man who was a friend of the Under Secretary's, and the Under Secretary could almost say at this moment that the matter could be arranged.

At this, Browning grinned. "By God, Joe, we've got to have a drink on this. This is the best news since—" He summoned the waiter. The Under Secretary yielded and ordered a cordial. Browning ordered a Scotch. The drinks were brought. Browning said, "About the job. I'm not going to say another word but just keep my fingers crossed. But as to you, Joe, you're the best. I drink to you." The two men drank, the Under Secretary sipping at his, Browning taking half of his. Browning looked at the drink in his hand. "You know, I was a little afraid. That other stuff, the club stuff."

"Yes," said the Under Secretary.

"I don't know why fellows like you—you never would have made it in a thousand years, but"—then, without looking up, he knew everything had collapsed—"but I've said exactly the wrong thing, haven't I?"

"That's right, Browning," said the Under Secretary. "You've said exactly the wrong thing. I've got to be going." He stood up and turned and went out, all dignity.

Reading for Understanding

☐ MAIN IDEA

1. The main point of the story is (a) once a friend, always a friend (b) prejudice can wound deeply (c) the Washington scene is confusing (d) hunting for a job can be humiliating.

**Porcellian* member of the fraternity

DETAILS

2. The "little man" mentioned at the beginning of the story is (a) Browning (b) the doorman (c) the waiter (d) the Under Secretary.

3. The name of the Under Secretary is (a) Joe (b) Fred (c) Charles (d) not mentioned.

4. The purpose of the meeting was (a) preparing an interview (b) trying a new restaurant dish (c) seeking a job (d) preparing to meet the Secretary.

5. The small golden pig was (a) the symbol of an exclusive group (b) the Under Secretary's most prized possession (c) a precious antique (d) a detail on a necklace.

INFERENCES

6. When the doorman says to himself, "Well, it was a long time coming," he was referring to (a) Browning's limousine (b) the Under Secretary's display of self-importance (c) a sudden shower that had threatened all day (d) Browning's return to Washington.

7. A comparison of the Under Secretary and Browning suggests Browning was more (a) sensitive (b) intelligent (c) motivated (d) polished.

8. Browning suggests that his basic motive in approaching the Under Secretary was (a) need for money (b) friendship (c) patriotism (d) revenge.

9. The Under Secretary doesn't really approve of (a) the Secretary (b) the doorman (c) Browning's circle of associates (d) the way in which his own party has been acting.

10. On first consideration, the Under Secretary is (a) impressed with Browning's qualifications (b) unwilling even to listen to Browning (c) determined to join the Porcellians (d) certain that Browning is unqualified.

11. Which of the following comments might reasonably be made? (a) The relationship between Browning and the Under Secretary has always been cordial. (b) The Under Secretary is aware that rank has its privileges. (c) Grown men seldom remember the disappointing events of earlier days. (d) The fellow diners were all close friends of the Under Secretary.

12. *The Boss* probably refers to (a) the Secretary of State (b) one of the two senators in the dining room (c) a cabinet minister (d) the President.

❑ AUTHOR'S ATTITUDE

13. The author's attitude toward Browning is one of (a) ill-concealed admiration (b) subtle disapproval (c) amusement (d) indifference.

❑ OUTCOME

14. After the conclusion of the story, Browning (a) was made an aide to the Under Secretary (b) got into a violent disagreement with the Under Secretary (c) complained to the President (d) didn't get the job.

❑ CAUSE AND EFFECT

15. The Under Secretary carried a suppressed resentment for years because (a) of a carefully hidden disability (b) he had unsympathetic parents (c) Browning's party was in power (d) he had been the victim of prejudice.

Words in Context

1. "*Graven Image*" refers to the biblical commandment that one should not (a) steal (b) worship before other gods (c) bear false witness (d) be disrespectful of parents.
2. "The *little* man nodded *pleasantly enough* to the doorman." ***Little* . . . *pleasantly enough*** (388) mean (a) petty . . . warmly (b) short . . . barely politely (c) insignificant . . . courteously (d) undersized . . . coldly.
3. "'Will the *Under Secretary* be here long?' asked the doorman." ***Under Secretary*** (388) means (a) important elected official (b) well-known politician (c) chief assistant to Cabinet member (d) chief adviser to the President.
4. "The man he was to meet, Charles Browning, was chatting in French, very *amiably* with the *maître d'hôtel*." ***Amiably* . . . *maître d'hôtel*** (388) mean (a) quietly . . . waiter (b) loudly . . . attendant (c) officiously . . . manager (d) congenially . . . headwaiter.
5. "'Oh, no. I can't see you *waiting with hat in hand*, not for anybody. Not even for The Boss.'" ***Waiting with hat in hand*** (389) means in an attitude of (a) impatience (b) humility (c) extreme patience (d) condescension.
6. "'Why didn't you go to one of your *Union League or Junior League pals*?'" ***Union League or Junior League pals*** (389) would be peo-

ple who are (a) members of Congress (b) underprivileged (c) young (d) in high society.

7. "Reluctantly . . . the Under Secretary grinned. 'All right. I was *baiting* you.'" ***Baiting*** (390) means (a) complimenting (b) tempting (c) criticizing (d) needling.

8. "'I wasn't even for you in 1932 . . . it's the truth. But that's *water under the bridge*—or isn't it?'" ***Water under the bridge*** (390) means (a) past and forgotten (b) past but not forgotten (c) not significant (d) paid for.

9. "'I had ample time to study them all then, you recall, *objectively*, from the outside.'" ***Objectively*** (390) means (a) from personal experience (b) statistically (c) impartially (d) openly.

10. "'. . . when one of the illustrious *brethren* closed his downtown office and *moved up to Ossining*.'" ***Brethren . . . moved up to Ossining*** (390) mean (a) relatives . . . was fired (b) blood brothers . . . was expelled (c) well-known officials . . . was defeated (d) fraternity members . . . went to jail.

Thinking Critically About the Story

1. John O'Hara depicts his characters mainly by letting their actions speak for them. Be prepared to read aloud some of the lines that etch the Under Secretary in acid.

2. What is the purpose of the Under Secretary's meeting with Charles? How long have they known each other? What is the conflict between them? Why does Charles ask the favor of Joe? Why is Joe willing to grant it? If you were Charles would you put yourself in such a position? If you were Joe, would you agree to hire him?

3. Have the last two paragraphs read to the class. How does Charles fail? What do you learn about Washington politics from this excerpt? What are the advantages of a political appointment? The disadvantages? Why do people seek these jobs? Would you? Explain.

4. Was the confrontation inevitable? Who won? Who is the real loser? What has been done to lessen the effect of "to the victor belongs the spoils"? Should all political appointments be abolished? Explain.

5. To what extent are college clubs, fraternities, involved in the conflict? What criticism of such organizations is implicit in the story? Is it justified?

Stories in Words

Nickname (388) is an example of an interesting historical process in language. The word was originally *ekename. Eke* meant "also or added." It appears in the modern verb *eke,* as in *eke out a living.* An *ekename* was an added name. If you say *an ekename* in one breath, you almost transfer the *n* from *an* to *ekename: a nekename.* That roving *n* finally came to rest in front of *ekename,* and now we have *nickname.* Sometimes the process works in reverse. *An adder* was originally *a nadder,* and *an apron* was once *a napron.*

Wig-wagged (389) demonstrates the playfulness of many expressions in English. Speakers enjoy the kind of duplication evident in words like *hurry-scurry, hurly-burly, pell-mell, helter-skelter, nitty-gritty, willy-nilly, namby-pamby, teeter-totter, razzle-dazzle, pitter-patter,* and *hocus-pocus. Wigwag* actually says the same thing twice. *Wig* is an English dialectal word meaning "to move." *Wag* is a common word meaning "to move back and forth, with quick jerky motions." *Wig-wag* thus means "move-move back and forth." A similar sounding word, *zigzag,* is a series of short, sharp turns. Both *zig* and *zag* mean about the same: "short, sharp turn." The combined word is emphatic, though it doesn't add any information.

Menu (389) has an interesting history and strange cousins. It can be traced all the way back to the Latin *minutus,* "small." Apparently, menu was thought of as a small list of dishes available at a restaurant. The meaning has been extended to a list on the screen of a computer. The relatives of *menu* include *minute* and *minuet.* If we go back still further to the Latin root *min,* we find *minor, diminish, minus, minimum, minipark,* and *minuscule,* all of which have something to do with the idea *small.* Even the verb *mince* means to "chop into small pieces."

The Old Man

DAPHNE DU MAURIER

I could see it rattled the old man to have such an oaf of a son. Irritated him, too, because Boy was so big. It probably didn't make sense to his intolerant mind. Strength and stupidity didn't go together.

Of all conflicts, those within the family are most frequent. The closeness and intimacy of family life can generate difficulties, struggles, dangerous confrontations. Such a conflict is the subject of "The Old Man." Unit 1 is concerned with the relationship across the generations. This story is altogether different, as you will see when you have come to the end. The characters are unlike any of those in the earlier unit.

Daphne du Maurier is the author of several readable novels, notably *Rebecca,* famous both as a book and a classic motion picture. Even in her novels, though, she hasn't created a character more striking, more primitive, or more surprising than the Old Man.

The Old Man

Did I hear you asking about the Old Man? I thought so. You're a newcomer to the district, here on holiday. We get plenty these days, during the summer months. Somehow they always find their way eventually over the cliffs down to this beach, and then they pause and look from the sea back to the lake. Just as you did.

It's a lovely spot, isn't it? Quiet and remote. You can't wonder at the old man choosing to live here.

I don't remember when he first came. Nobody can. Many years ago, it must have been. He was here when I arrived, long before the war. Perhaps he came to escape from civilization, much as I did myself. Or maybe, where he lived before, the folks around made things too hot for him. It's hard to say. I had the feeling, from the very first, that he had done something, or something had been done to him, that gave him a grudge against the world. I remember the first time I set eyes on him I said to myself, "I bet that old fellow is one hell of a character."

Yes, he was living here beside the lake, along of his missus. Funny sort of lash-up they had, exposed to all the weather, but they didn't seem to mind.

I had been warned about him by one of the fellows from the farm, who advised me, with a grin, to give the old man who lived down by the lake a wide berth—he didn't care for strangers. So I went warily, and I didn't stay to pass the time of day. Nor would it have been any use if I had, not knowing a word of his lingo. The first time I saw him he was standing by the edge of the lake, looking out to sea, and from tact I avoided the piece of planking over the stream, which meant passing close to him, and crossed to the other side of the lake by the beach instead. Then, with an awkward feeling that I was trespassing and had no business to be there, I bobbed down behind a clump of gorse, took out my spyglass, and had a peep at him.

He was a big fellow, broad and strong—he's aged, of course, lately; I'm speaking of several years back—but even now you can see what he must have been once. Such power and drive behind him, and that fine head, which he carried like a king. There's an idea in that, too. No, I'm not joking. Who knows what royal blood he carries inside him, harking back to some remote ancestor? And now and again, surging in him—not through his own fault—it gets the better of him and drives him fighting mad. I didn't think about that at the time. I just looked at him, and ducked behind the gorse when I saw him turn, and I wondered to myself what went on in his mind, whether he knew I was there, watching him.

If he should decide to come up the lake after me I should look pretty foolish. He must have thought better of it, though, or perhaps he did not care. He went on staring out to sea, watching the gulls and the incoming tide, and presently he ambled off his side of the lake, heading for the missus and home and maybe supper.

I didn't catch a glimpse of her that first day. She just wasn't around. Living as they do, close in by the left bank of the lake, with no proper track to the place, I hardly had the nerve to venture close and come upon her face to face. When I did see her, though, I was disappointed. She wasn't much to look at after all. What I mean is, she hadn't got anything like his character. A placid, mild-tempered creature, I judged her.

They had both come back from fishing when I saw them, and were making their way up from the beach to the lake. He was in front, of course. She tagged along behind. Neither of them took the slightest notice of me, and I was glad, because the old man might have paused, and waited, and told her to get on back home, and then come down towards the rocks where I was sitting. You ask what I would have said, had he done so? I'm damned if I know. Maybe I would have got up, whistling and seeming unconcerned, and then, with a nod and a smile—useless, really, but instinctive, if you know what I mean—said good day and pottered off. I don't think he would have done anything. He'd just have stared after me, with those strange narrow eyes of his, and let me go.

After that, winter and summer, I was always down on the beach or the rocks, and they went on living their curious, remote existence, sometimes fishing in the lake, sometimes at sea. Occasionally I'd come across them in the harbor on the estuary, taking a look at the yachts anchored there, and the shipping. I used to wonder which of them made the suggestion. Perhaps suddenly he would be lured by the thought of the bustle and life of the harbor, and all the things he had either wantonly given up or never known, and he would say to her, "Today we are going into town." And she, happy to do whatever pleased him best, followed along.

You see, one thing that stood out —and you couldn't help noticing it— was that the pair of them were devoted to one another. I've seen her greet him when he came back from a day's fishing and had left her back home, and towards evening she'd come down the lake and on to the beach and down to the sea to wait for him. She'd see him coming from a long way off, and I would see him too, rounding the corner of the bay. He'd come straight in to the beach, and she would go to meet him, and they would embrace each other, not caring a damn who saw them. It was touching, if you know what I mean. You felt there was something lovable about the old man, if that's how things were between them. He might be a devil to outsiders, but he was all the world to her. It gave me a warm feeling for him, when I saw them together like that.

You asked if they had any family. I was coming to that. It's about the family I really wanted to tell you. Because there was a tragedy, you see. And nobody knows anything about it except me. I suppose I could have told someone, but if I had, I don't know . . . They might have taken the old man away, and she'd have broken her heart without him, and anyway, when all's said and done, it wasn't my business. I know the evidence against the old man was strong, but I hadn't positive proof, it might have been some sort of accident, and anyway, nobody made any inquiries at the time the boy disappeared, so who was I to turn busybody and informer?

I'll try and explain what happened. But you must understand that all this took place over quite a time, and sometimes I was away from home or busy, and didn't go near the lake. Nobody seemed to take any interest in the couple living there but myself, so that it was only what I observed with my own eyes that makes this story, nothing that I heard from anybody else, no scraps of gossip, or tales told about them behind their backs.

Yes, they weren't always alone, as they are now. They had four kids. Three girls and a boy. They brought up the four of them in that ramshackle old place by the lake, and it was always a wonder to me how they did it. God, I've known days when the rain lashed the lake into little waves that burst and broke on the muddy shore near by their place, and turned the marsh into a swamp, and the wind driving straight in. You'd have thought anyone with a grain of sense would have taken his missus and his kids out of it and gone off somewhere where they could get some creature comforts at least. Not the old man. If he could stick it, I guess he decided she could too, and the kids as well. Maybe he wanted to bring them up the hard way.

Mark you, they were attractive youngsters. Especially the youngest girl. I never knew her name, but I called her Tiny, she had so much go to her. Chip off the old block, in spite of her size. I can see her now, as a little thing, the first to venture paddling in the lake, on a fine morning, way ahead of her sisters and the brother.

The brother I nicknamed Boy. He was the eldest, and between you and me a bit of a fool. He hadn't the looks of his sisters and was a clumsy sort of fellow. The girls would play around on their own, and go fishing, and he'd hang about in the background, not knowing what to do with himself. If he possibly could he'd stay around home, near his mother. Proper mother's boy. That's why I gave him the name. Not that she seemed to fuss over him any more than she did the others. She treated the four alike, as far as I could tell. Her thoughts were always for the old man rather than for them. But Boy was just a great baby, and I have an idea he was simple.

Like their parents, the youngsters kept themselves to themselves. Been dinned into them, I dare say, by the old man. They never came down to the beach on their own and played; and it must have been a temptation, I thought, in full summer, when people came walking over the cliffs down to the beach to bathe and picnic. I suppose, for those strange reasons best known to himself, the old man had warned them to have no truck with strangers.

They were used to me pottering, day in, day out, fetching driftwood and that. And often I would pause and watch the kids playing by the lake. I didn't talk to them, though. They might have gone back and told the old man. They used to look up when I passed by, then glance away again, sort of shy. All but Tiny. Tiny would toss her head and do a somersault, just to show off.

I sometimes watched them go off, the six of them—the old man, the missus, Boy, and the three girls, for a day's fishing out to sea. The old man, of course, in charge; Tiny eager to help, close to her dad; the missus looking about her to see if the weather was going to keep fine; the two other girls alongside; and Boy, poor simple Boy, always the last to leave home. I never knew what sport they had. They used to stay out late, and I'd have left the beach by the time they came back again. But I guess they did well. They must have lived almost entirely on what they caught. Well, fish is said to be full of vitamins, isn't it? Perhaps the old man was a food faddist in his way.

Time passed, and the youngsters began to grow up. Tiny lost something of her individuality then, it seemed to me. She grew more like her sisters. They were a nice-looking trio, all the same. Quiet, you know, well-behaved.

As for Boy, he was enormous. Almost as big as the old man, but with what a difference! He had none of his father's looks, or strength, or personality; he was nothing but a great clumsy lout. And the trouble was, I believe the old man was ashamed of him. He didn't pull his weight in the home, I'm certain of that. And out fishing he was perfectly useless. The girls would work away like beetles, with Boy, always in the background, making a mess of things. If his mother was there he just stayed by her side.

I could see it rattled the old man to have such an oaf of a son. Irritated him, too, because Boy was so big. It probably didn't make sense to his intolerant mind. Strength and stupidity didn't go together. In any normal family, of course, Boy would have left home by now and gone out to work. I used to wonder if they argued about it back in the evenings, the missus and the old man, or if it was something never admitted between them but tacitly understood—Boy was no good.

Well, they did leave home at last. At least, the girls did.

I'll tell you how it happened.

It was a day in late autumn, and I happened to be over doing some shopping in the little town overlooking the harbor, three miles from this place, and suddenly I saw the old man, the missus, the three girls and Boy all making their way up to Pont—that's at the head of a creek going eastward from the harbor. There are a few cottages at Pont, and a farm and a church up behind. The family looked washed and spruced up, and so did the old man and the missus, and I wondered if they were going visiting. If they were, it was an unusual thing for them to do. But it's possible they had friends or acquaintances up there, of whom I knew nothing. Anyway, that was the last I saw of them, on the fine Saturday afternoon, making for Pont.

It blew hard over the weekend, a proper easterly gale. I kept indoors and didn't go out at all. I knew the seas would be breaking good and hard on the beach. I wondered if the old man and the family had been able to get back. They would have been wise to stay with their friends up Pont, if they had friends there.

It was Tuesday before the wind dropped and I went down to the beach again. Seaweed, driftwood, tar and oil all over the place. It's always the same after an easterly blow. I looked up the lake, towards the old man's shack, and I saw him there, with the missus, just by the edge of the lake. But there was no sign of the youngsters.

I thought it a bit funny, and waited around in case they should appear. They never did. I walked right round the lake, and from the opposite bank I had a good view of their place, and even took out my old spyglass to have a closer look. They just weren't there. The old man was pottering about as he often did when he wasn't fishing, and the missus had settled herself down to bask in the sun. There was only one explanation. They had left the family with friends in Pont. They had sent the family for a holiday.

I can't help admitting I was relieved, because for one frightful moment I thought maybe they had started off back home on the Saturday night and got struck by the gale; and, well—that the old man and his missus had got back safely, but not the kids. It couldn't be that, though. I should have heard. Someone would have said something. The old man wouldn't be pottering there in his usual unconcerned fashion and the missus basking in the sun. No, that must have been it. They had left the family with friends. Or maybe the girls and Boy had gone up country, gone to find themselves jobs at last.

Somehow it left a gap. I felt sad. So long now I had been used to seeing them all around, Tiny and the others. I had a strange sort of feeling that they had gone for good. Silly, wasn't it? To mind, I mean. There was the old man, and his missus, and the four youngsters, and I'd more or less watched them grow up, and now for no reason they had gone.

I wished then I knew even a word or two of his language, so that I could have called out to him, neighbor-like, and said, "I see you and the missus are on your own. Nothing wrong, I hope?"

But there, it wasn't any use. He'd have looked at me with his strange eyes and told me to go to hell.

I never saw the girls again. No, never. They just didn't come back. Once I thought I saw Tiny, somewhere up the estuary, with a group of friends, but I couldn't be sure. If it was, she'd grown, she looked different. I tell you what I think. I think the old man and the missus took them with a definite end in view, that last weekend, and either settled them with friends they knew or told them to shift for themselves.

I know it sounds hard, not what you'd do for your own son and daughters, but you have to remember the old man was a tough customer, a law unto himself. No doubt he thought it would be for the best, and so it probably was, and if only I could know for certain what happened to the girls, especially Tiny, I wouldn't worry.

But I do worry sometimes, because of what happened to Boy.

You see, Boy was fool enough to come back. He came back about three weeks after that final weekend. I had walked down through the woods—not my usual way, but down to the lake by the stream that feeds it from a higher level. I rounded the lake by the marshes to the north, some distance from the old man's place, and the first thing I saw was Boy.

He wasn't doing anything. He was just standing by the marsh. He looked dazed. He was too far off for me to hail him; besides, I didn't have the nerve. But I watched him, as he stood there in his clumsy, loutish way, and I saw him staring at the far end of the lake. He was staring in the direction of the old man.

The old man, and the missus with him, took not the slightest notice of Boy. They were close to the beach, by the plank bridge, and were either just going out to fish or coming back. And here was Boy, with his dazed stupid face, but not only stupid—frightened.

I wanted to say, "Is anything the matter?" but I didn't know how to say it. I stood there, like Boy, staring at the old man.

Then what we both must have feared would happen, happened.

The old man lifted his head, and saw Boy.

He must have said a word to his missus, because she didn't move, she stayed where she was, by the bridge, but the old man turned like a flash of lightning and came down the other side of the lake towards the marshes, towards Boy. He looked terrible. I shall never forget his appearance. That magnificent head I had always admired now angry, evil; and he was cursing Boy as he came. I tell you, I heard him.

Boy, bewildered, scared, looked hopelessly about him for cover. There was none. Only the thin reeds that grew beside the marsh. But the poor fellow was so dumb he went in there, and crouched, and believed himself safe—it was a horrible sight.

I was just getting my own courage up to interfere when the old man stopped suddenly in his tracks, pulled up short as it were, and then, still cursing, muttering, turned back again and returned to the bridge. Boy watched him, from his cover of reeds, then, poor clot* that he was, came out on to the marsh again, with some idea, I suppose, of striking for home.

I looked about me. There was no one to call. No one to give any help. And if I went and tried to get someone from the farm they would tell me

**poor clot* British: blockhead

not to interfere, that the old man was best left alone when he got in one of his rages, and anyway that Boy was old enough to take care of himself. He was as big as the old man: He could give as good as he got. I knew different. Boy was no fighter. He didn't know how.

I waited quite a time beside the lake but nothing happened. It began to grow dark. It was no use my waiting there. The old man and the missus left the bridge and went on home. Boy was still standing there on the marsh, by the lake's edge.

I called to him, softly. "It's no use. He won't let you in. Go back to Pont, or wherever it is you've been. Go to some place, anywhere, but get out of here."

He looked up, that same queer dazed expression on his face, and I could tell he hadn't understood a word I said.

I felt powerless to do any more. I went home myself. But I thought about Boy all evening, and in the morning I went down to the lake again, and I took a great stick with me to give me courage. Not that it would have been much good. Not against the old man.

Well. . . I suppose they had come to some sort of agreement, during the night. There was Boy, by his mother's side, and the old man was pottering on his own.

I must say, it was a great relief. Because, after all, what could I have said or done? If the old man didn't want Boy home, it was really his affair. And if Boy was too stupid to go, that was Boy's affair.

But I blamed the mother a good deal. After all, it was up to her to tell Boy he was in the way, and the old man was in one of his moods, and Boy had best get out while the going was good. But I never did think she had great intelligence. She did not seem to show much spirit at any time.

However, what arrangement they had come to worked for a time. Boy stuck close to his mother—I suppose he helped her at home, I don't know—and the old man left them alone and was more and more by himself.

He took to sitting down by the bridge, staring out to sea, with a queer brooding look on him. He seemed strange, and lonely. I didn't like it. I don't know what his thoughts were, but I'm sure they were evil. It suddenly seemed a very long time since he and the missus and the whole family had gone fishing, a happy, contented party. Now everything had changed for him. He was thrust out in the cold, and the missus and Boy stayed together.

I felt sorry for him, but I felt frightened too. Because I felt it could not go on like this indefinitely; something would happen.

One day I went down to the beach for driftwood—it had been blowing in the night—and when I glanced towards the lake I saw that Boy wasn't with his mother. He was back where I had seen him that first day, on the edge of the marsh. He was as big as his father. If he'd known how to use his strength he'd have been a match for him any day, but he hadn't the brains. There he was, back on the marsh, a great big frightened foolish fellow, and there was the old man, outside his home, staring down towards his son with murder in his eyes.

I said to myself, "He's going to kill him." But I didn't know how or when or where, whether by night, when they were sleeping, or by day, when they were fishing. The mother was useless, she would not prevent it. It was no use appealing to the mother. If only Boy would use one little grain of sense, and go . . .

I watched and waited until nightfall. Nothing happened.

It rained in the night. It was grey, and cold, and dim. December was everywhere, trees all bare and bleak. I couldn't get down to the lake until late afternoon, and then the skies had cleared and the sun was shining in that watery way it does in winter, a burst of it, just before setting below the sea.

I saw the old man, and the missus too. They were close together, by the old shack, and they saw me coming for they looked toward me. Boy wasn't there. He wasn't on the marsh, either. Nor by the side of the lake.

I crossed the bridge and went along the right bank of the lake, and I had my spyglass with me, but I couldn't see Boy. Yet all the time I was aware of the old man watching me.

Then I saw him. I scrambled down the bank, and crossed the marsh, and went to the thing I saw lying there, behind the reeds.

He was dead. There was a great gash on his body. Dried blood on his back. But he had lain there all night. His body was sodden with the rain.

Maybe you'll think I'm a fool, but I began to cry, like an idiot, and I shouted across to the old man, "You murderer, you bloody murderer." He did not answer. He did not move. He stood there, outside his shack with the missus, watching me.

You'll want to know what I did. I went back and got a spade, and I dug a grave for Boy, in the reeds behind the marsh, and I said one of my own prayers for him, being uncertain of his religion. When I had finished I looked across the lake to the old man.

And do you know what I saw?

I saw him lower his great head, and bend towards her and embrace her. And she lifted her head to him and embraced him too. It was both a requiem and a benediction. An atonement, and a giving of praise. In their strange way they knew they had done evil, but now it was over, because I had buried Boy and he was gone. They were free to be together again, and there was no longer a third to divide them.

They came out into the middle of the lake, and suddenly I saw the old man stretch his neck and beat his wings, and he took off from the water, full of power, and she followed him. I watched the two swans fly out to sea right into the face of the setting sun, and I tell you it was one of the most beautiful sights I ever saw in my life: the two swans flying there, alone, in winter.

Reading for Understanding

☐ MAIN IDEA

1. The main point of the story is (a) a picture of natural beauty by an English lake (b) the dominance of a powerful male swan and the tragic consequences (c) the character analysis of a young swan (d) the natural harmony in the wild when undisturbed by humans.

2. The old man's wife was (a) mean-spirited (b) as strong as he (c) a beauty (d) ordinary.

3. The number of children mentioned was (a) two (b) three (c) four (d) five.

4. The name of the male child was given by the (a) mother (b) father (c) sister (d) narrator.

5. The one who came back to the family was the (a) son (b) two daughters (c) mother (d) father.

☐ INFERENCES

6. The personality of the old man can best be described by the word (a) *hot-tempered* (b) *listless* (c) *cowardly* (d) *forgiving.*

7. The old man's behavior toward his wife was basically (a) cruel (b) loving (c) indifferent (d) difficult to describe.

8. The children (a) were almost carbon copies of the old man (b) were not all alike (c) all refused to leave the family home (d) all resembled the mother.

9. The tragedy would not have occurred if (a) Tiny had not rejoined the family (b) the weather had been different (c) Boy had not come back (d) fishing boats had not come near.

10. Apparently, the old man (a) was the victim of a strange fatal disease (b) really loved Boy more than he would admit (c) was disappointed when Tiny never came back (d) had become jealous of the closeness of his wife and Boy.

☐ AUTHOR'S TECHNIQUE

11. A clever device of the author is to (a) withhold the real identity of the family until the end (b) spend much time on speculating what makes a happy family (c) create an idyllic picture of life at an English resort (d) discuss regional accents in the British Isles.

12. Though the author doesn't give away the puzzle of the old man's identity, we must admit that she has been (a) verbose (b) dishonest (c) fair (d) indifferent.

❑ ORDER OF EVENTS

13. Arrange the items in the order in which they occurred. Use letters only.
    A. Boy is found dead.
    B. The author watches the swans fly into the sunset.
    C. The sisters leave home.
    D. Boy returns for good.
    E. The swans have four young.

❑ CAUSE AND EFFECT

14. Boy's death can reasonably be traced to (a) the old man's rage (b) the mother's indifference (c) a sister's jealousy (d) an accident of nature.

❑ FACT OR OPINION

Tell whether the following is a fact or an opinion.

15. On several occasions, the old man showed his dislike of Boy.

Words In Context

1. Prudent bird-watchers usually give "a wide berth" (397) to (a) heavyset passengers (b) friendly neighbors (c) suspicious-looking strangers (d) well-known celebrities.
2. "So I went *warily*, and I didn't stay to pass the time of day." ***Warily*** (397) means (a) quickly (b) guardedly (c) contentedly (d) angrily.
3. "I bobbed down behind a clump of *gorse*, took out my spyglass, and had a peep at him." ***Gorse*** (397) is a type of (a) large boulder (b) sheep (c) artificial hill (d) evergreen shrub.
4. "A *placid*, mild-tempered creature, I judged her." ***Placid*** (398) means (a) tranquil (b) slow-moving (c) heavyset (d) awesome.
5. "Occasionally I'd come across them in the harbor on the *estuary*, taking a look at the yachts anchored there . . ." ***Estuary*** (398) means (a) mainland peninsula (b) sea-drowned river mouth (c) leeside of the island (d) seaboard side.

6. "Perhaps suddenly he would be lured by the thought of . . . things he had either *wantonly* given up or never known . . ." ***Wantonly*** (398) means (a) irresponsibly (b) intentionally (c) generously (d) childishly.

7. ". . . anyone with a grain of sense would have . . . gone off somewhere where they could get some *creature comforts* . . ." Two examples of ***creature comforts*** (399) are (a) books and pamphlets (b) food and warmth (c) ideals and ambitions (d) facts and proofs.

8. "He had none of his father's looks, or strength, or personality; he was nothing but a great clumsy *lout*." ***Lout*** (400) means (a) noise-maker (b) youngster (c) self-seeker (d) clod.

9. ". . . it was something never admitted between them but *tacitly* understood—Boy was no good." ***Tacitly*** (400) means without (a) anger (b) rudeness (c) being expressed (d) fear of contradiction.

10. "The family looked washed and *spruced up*, and so did the old man and the missus . . ." ***Spruced up*** (401) means (a) enthusiastic (b) well-groomed (c) well-fed (d) well-prepared.

11. "The old man was *pottering about* as he often did when he wasn't fishing . . ." ***Pottering about*** (401) means (a) digging holes (b) repairing the nets (c) clearing the land (d) wasting time in idling.

12. ". . . the missus had settled herself down to *bask* in the sun." ***Bask*** (401) means (a) sleep (b) plan ahead (c) warm up (d) daydream.

13. "December was everywhere, trees all bare and *bleak*." ***Bleak*** (404) means (a) leafless (b) desolate (c) snow-covered (d) lifeless.

14. "His body was *sodden with the rain*." ***Sodden with*** (404) means (a) muddied over by the rain (b) washed clean by the rain (c) darkly outlined by the rain (d) soaked through by the rain.

15. "It was both a *requiem* and a *benediction*. An *atonement*, and a giving of praise." ***Requiem*** . . . ***benediction*** . . . ***atonement*** (404) mean (a) prayer . . . sermon . . . retribution (b) funeral service . . . finality . . . forgiveness (c) song for the dead . . . blessing . . . making amends (d) evening mass . . . praise . . . reparation.

Thinking Critically About the Story

1. What devices does du Maurier use to keep unrevealed the identity of the Old Man while at the same time developing our understanding of his inner nature?

2. What makes the Old Man so difficult to be with? Why is the missus able to get along with him? Is the Old Man typical of older men? Is the missus typical of older women? Cite examples to justify your statements.

3. What picture of family life does this story give us? How is the family run? Is it typical of life today? Of older times? How does the control of this family compare with that of your family? When you establish your own family, what interrelationships would you want to establish?

4. What role does the narrator play in the story? Does he give an objective, fair picture? What is his attitude toward the Old Man? What does he learn about nature from his observation of the Old Man's family? Can it be applied to human nature? Explain.

5. At what point should Boy have flown the coop? Why didn't he? At what point should children strike out on their own? What should be the relationship between parents and their grown children? What is the tragedy in this story? At what point did it become inevitable?

Stories in Words

Ambled (398) seems at first glance to be a simple Old English word, but it is not a Germanic word at all, rather a Romance word. It can be traced back to the Latin *ambulare*, "to walk." It refers to a specific kind of walking: easy, relaxed, unstressed. The dictionary suggests *saunter* as a synonym. The Latin root is found in *perambulator* and *ambulance*. *Perambulator*, another word for *baby carriage*, is used for taking the baby for a *walk*. The *walk* root in *ambulance* probably refers to the fact that an ambulance is a *moving* hospital. The pace of an ambulance does not, however, suggest idle walking.

Bewildered (402) is connected with wild beasts. The *wilder* root can be traced to the Old English *wild beasts*. The wilderness was the place where *wild beasts* dwelt. One of the scariest of all experiences is being lost in the wilderness. To be *bewildered* is to experience the confusion one might suffer in the deep woods.

Atonement (404) is the state of being *at one*. *Atonement* suggests *reconciliation*. The sinner or offender becomes *at one* with God. In the process, the word takes on a new pronunciation. The blending process is not unique with *atone*. Two words often merge to form one. *Don* was originally *do on*. *Doff* was originally *do off*.

The Avenging Chance

ANTHONY BERKELEY

"And the murderer, Mr. Sheringham?"

"The person whose photograph is in my pocket," Roger said unkindly. "By the way, do you remember what I was saying the other day about Chance the Avenger, my excellent film title? Well, it's worked again."

There have been great classic detective stories, but the highest rank must be reserved for a very few: flawlessly plotted, with all clues provided by the author. They have interesting characters, are well-written, and convey the spirit of a time. The reader watches the detective relentlessly tracking down every stray possibility until the revelation comes in a powerful conclusion.

The detective story authors and anthologists who took the name of *Ellery Queen* called "The Avenging Chance" "as nearly a perfectly plotted short story as had been written." It belongs in that select company of detective stories with the puzzle element so cleverly introduced that at the end, a reader can only say, "Yes, it had to be that way."

The earlier stories in this unit have dealt with conflict in a variety of contexts. In "The Avenging Chance," the conflict is more subtle. A brilliant murderer faces an unyielding amateur. There is no physical confrontation between murderer and sleuth, but there is an intellectual clash that results from the chance remark of a minor character.

The next time you are about to bite into a delicious chocolate-cream candy, you may hesitate just a moment. . . .

The Avenging Chance

Roger Sheringham was inclined to think afterwards that the Poisoned Chocolates Case, as the papers called it, was perhaps the most perfectly planned murder he had ever encountered. The motive was so obvious, when you knew where to look for it—but you didn't know; the method was so significant when you had grasped its real essentials—but you didn't grasp them; the traces were so thinly covered, when you had realized what was covering them—but you didn't realize. But for a piece of the merest bad luck, which the murderer could not possibly have foreseen, the crime must have been added to the classical list of great mysteries.

This is the gist of the case, as Chief Inspector Moresby told it one evening to Roger in the latter's rooms in the Albany a week or so after it happened:—

On the past Friday morning, the fifteenth of November, at half past ten o'clock, in accordance with his invariable custom, Sir William Anstruther walked into his club in Piccadilly, the very exclusive Rainbow Club, and asked for his letters. The porter handed him three and a small parcel. Sir William walked over to the fireplace in the big lounge hall to open them.

A few minutes later another member entered the club, a Mr. Graham Beresford. There were a letter and a couple of circulars for him, and he also strolled over to the fireplace, nodding to Sir William, but not speaking to him. The two men only knew each other very slightly, and had probably never exchanged more than a dozen words in all.

Having glanced through his letters, Sir William opened the parcel and, after a moment, snorted with disgust. Beresford looked at him, and with a grunt Sir William thrust out a letter which had been enclosed in the parcel. Concealing a smile (Sir William's ways were a matter of some amusement to his fellow members), Beresford read the letter. It was from a big firm of chocolate manufacturers, Mason & Sons, and set forth that they were putting on the market a new brand of liqueur chocolates designed especially to appeal to men; would Sir William do them the honor of accepting the enclosed two-pound box and letting the firm have his candid opinion of them?

"Do they think I'm a blank chorus girl?" fumed Sir William. "Write 'em testimonials about their blank chocolates, indeed! Blank 'em! I'll complain to the blank committee. That sort of blank thing can't blank well be allowed here."

"Well, it's an ill wind so far as I'm concerned," Beresford soothed him. "It's reminded me of something. My wife and I had a box at the Imperial last night. I bet her a box of chocolates to a hundred cigarettes that she wouldn't spot the villain by the end of the second act. She won. I must remember to get them. Have you seen it—*The Creaking Skull*? Not a bad show."

Sir William had not seen it, and said so with force.

"Want a box of chocolates, did you say?" he added, more mildly. "Well, take this blank one. I don't want it."

For a moment Beresford demurred politely and then, most unfortunately for himself, accepted. The money so saved meant nothing to him for he was a wealthy man; but trouble was always worth saving.

By an extraordinarily lucky chance neither the outer wrapper of the box nor its covering letter was thrown into the fire, and this was the more fortunate in that both men had tossed the envelopes of their letters into the flames. Sir William did, indeed, make a bundle of the wrapper, letter and string, but he handed it over to Beresford, and the latter simply dropped it inside the fender.* This bundle the porter subsequently extracted and, being a man of orderly habits, put it tidily away in the wastepaper basket, whence it was retrieved later by the police.

Of the three unconscious protagonists in the impending tragedy, Sir William was without doubt the most remarkable. Still a year or two under fifty, he looked, with his flaming red face and thickset figure, a typical country squire of the old school, and both his manners and his language were in accordance with tradition. His habits, especially as regards women, were also in accordance with tradition—the tradition of the bold, bad baronet which he undoubtedly was.

In comparison with him, Beresford was rather an ordinary man, a tall, dark, not handsome fellow of two-and-thirty, quiet and reserved. His father had left him a rich man, but idleness did not appeal to him, and he had a finger in a good many business pies.

Money attracts money. Graham Beresford had inherited it, he made it, and, inevitably, he had married it, too. The daughter of a late shipowner in Liverpool, with not far off half a million in her own right. But the money

**fender* low metal frame before the fireplace

was incidental, for he needed her and would have married her just as inevitably (said his friends) if she had not had a farthing. A tall, rather serious-minded, highly cultured girl, not so young that her character had not had time to form (she was twenty-five when Beresford married her, three years ago), she was the ideal wife for him. A bit of a Puritan perhaps in some ways, but Beresford, whose wild oats, though duly sown, had been a sparse crop, was ready enough to be a Puritan himself by that time if she was. To make no bones about it, the Beresfords succeeded in achieving that eighth wonder of the modern world, a happy marriage.

And into the middle of it there dropped with irretrievable tragedy, the box of chocolates.

Beresford gave them to her after lunch as they sat over their coffee, with some jesting remark about paying his honorable debts, and she opened the box at once. The top layer, she noticed, seemed to consist only of kirsch and maraschino.* Beresford, who did not believe in spoiling good coffee, refused when she offered him the box, and his wife ate the first one alone. As she did so she exclaimed in surprise that the filling seemed exceedingly strong and positively burnt her mouth.

Beresford explained that they were samples of a new brand and then, made curious by what his wife had said, took one too. A burning taste, not intolerable but much too strong to be pleasant, followed the release of the liquid, and the almond flavoring seemed quite excessive.

"By Jove," he said, "they are strong. They must be filled with neat alcohol."

"Oh, they wouldn't do that, surely," said his wife, taking another. "But they are very strong. I think I rather like them, though."

Beresford ate another, and disliked it still more. "I don't," he said with decision. "They make my tongue feel quite numb. I shouldn't eat any more of them if I were you. I think there's something wrong with them."

"Well, they're only an experiment, I suppose," she said. "But they do burn. I'm not sure whether I like them or not."

A few minutes later Beresford went out to keep a business appointment in the City. He left her still trying to make up her mind whether she liked them, and still eating them to decide. Beresford remembered that scrap of conversation afterwards very vividly, because it was the last time he saw his wife alive.

That was roughly half past two. At a quarter to four Beresford arrived at his club from the City in a taxi, in a state of collapse. He was helped into the building by the driver and the porter, and both described him subsequently as pale to the point of ghastliness, with staring eyes and livid lips, and his skin damp and clammy. His mind seemed unaffected, however, and when they had got him up the steps he was able to walk, with the porter's help, into the lounge.

**kirsch, maraschino* brandy, liqueur

The porter, thoroughly alarmed, wanted to send for a doctor at once, but Beresford, who was the last man in the world to make a fuss, refused to let him, saying that it must be indigestion and he would be all right in a few minutes. To Sir William Anstruther, however, who was in the lounge at the time, he added after the porter had gone:

"Yes, and I believe it was those infernal chocolates you gave me, now I come to think of it. I thought there was something funny about them at the time. I'd better go and find out if my wife—" He broke off abruptly. His body, which had been leaning back limply in his chair, suddenly heaved rigidly upright; his jaws locked together, the livid lips drawn back in a horrible grin, and his hands clenched on the arms of his chair. At the same time Sir William became aware of an unmistakable smell of bitter almonds.

Thoroughly alarmed, believing indeed that the man was dying under his eyes, Sir William raised a shout for the porter and a doctor. The other occupants of the lounge hurried up, and between them they got the convulsed body of the unconscious man into a more comfortable position. Before the doctor could arrive a telephone message was received at the club from an agitated butler asking if Mr. Beresford was there, and if so would he come home at once as Mrs. Beresford had been taken seriously ill. As a matter of fact she was already dead.

Beresford did not die. He had taken less of the poison than his wife, who after his departure must have eaten at least three more of the chocolates, so that its action was less rapid and the doctor had time to save him. As a matter of fact it turned out afterwards that he had not had a fatal dose. By about eight o'clock that night he was conscious; the next day he was practically convalescent.

As for the unfortunate Mrs. Beresford, the doctor had arrived too late to save her, and she passed away very rapidly in a deep coma.

The police had taken the matter in hand as soon as Mrs. Beresford's death was reported to them and the fact of poison established, and it was only a very short time before things had become narrowed down to the chocolates as the active agent.

Sir William was interrogated, the letter and wrapper were recovered from the wastepaper basket, and, even before the sick man was out of danger, a detective inspector was asking for an interview with the managing director of Mason & Sons. Scotland Yard moves quickly.

It was the police theory at this stage, based on what Sir William and the two doctors had been able to tell them, that by an act of criminal carelessness on the part of one of Mason's employees, an excessive amount of oil of bitter almonds had been included in the filling mixture of the chocolates, for that was what the doctor had decided must be the poisoning ingredient. However, the managing director quashed this idea at once: oil of bitter almonds, he asserted, was never used by Mason's.

He had more interesting news still. Having read with undisguised astonishment the covering letter, he at once declared that it was a forgery. No such letter, no such samples had been sent out by the firm at all; a new variety of liqueur chocolates had never even been mooted. The fatal chocolates were their ordinary brand.

Unwrapping and examining one more closely, he called the Inspector's attention to a mark on the underside, which he suggested was the remains of a small hole drilled in the case, through which the liquid could have been extracted and the fatal filling inserted, the hole afterwards being stopped up with softened chocolate, a perfectly simple operation.

He examined it under a magnifying glass and the Inspector agreed. It was now clear to him that somebody had been trying deliberately to murder Sir William Anstruther.

Scotland Yard doubled its activities. The chocolates were sent for analysis, Sir William was interviewed again, and so was the now conscious Beresford. From the latter the doctor insisted that the news of his wife's death must be kept till the next day, as in his weakened condition the shock might be fatal, so that nothing very helpful was obtained from him.

Nor could Sir William throw any light on the mystery or produce a single person who might have any grounds for trying to kill him. He was living apart from his wife, who was the principal beneficiary in his will, but she was in the South of France, as the French police subsequently confirmed. His estate in Worcestershire, heavily mortgaged, was entailed and went to a nephew; but as the rent he got for it barely covered the interest on the mortgage, and the nephew was considerably better off than Sir William himself, there was no motive there. The police were at a dead end.

The analysis brought one or two interesting facts to light. Not oil of bitter almonds but nitrobenzine, a kindred substance, chiefly used in the manufacture of aniline dyes, was the somewhat surprising poison employed. Each chocolate in the upper layer contained exactly six minims of it, in a mixture of kirsch and maraschino. The chocolates in the other layers were harmless.

As to the other clues, they seemed equally useless. The sheet of Mason's note paper was identified by Merton's, the printers, as of their work, but there was nothing to show how it had got into the murderer's possession. All that could be said was that, the edges being distinctly yellowed, it must be an old piece. The machine on which the letter had been typed, of course, could not be traced. From the wrapper, a piece of ordinary brown paper with Sir William's address hand-printed on it in large capitals, there was nothing to be learned at all beyond that the parcel had been posted at the office in Southampton Street between the hours of 8:30 and 9:30 on the previous evening.

Only one thing was quite clear. Whoever had coveted Sir William's life had no intention of paying for it with his or her own.

"And now you know as much as we do, Mr. Sheringham," concluded Chief Inspector Moresby; "and if you can say who sent those chocolates to Sir William, you'll know a good deal more."

Roger nodded thoughtfully.

"It's a brute of a case. I met a man only yesterday who was at school with Beresford. He didn't know him very well because Beresford was on the modern side and my friend was a classical bird, but they were in the same house. He says Beresford's absolutely knocked over by his wife's death. I wish you could find out who sent those chocolates, Moresby."

"So do I, Mr. Sheringham," said Moresby gloomily.

"It might have been anyone in the whole world," Roger mused. "What about feminine jealousy, for instance? Sir William's private life doesn't seem to be immaculate. I dare say there's a good deal of off with the old light-o'-love and on with the new."

"Why, that's just what I've been looking into, Mr. Sheringham, sir," retorted Chief Inspector Moresby reproachfully. "That was the first thing that came to me. Because if anything does stand out about this business it is that it's a woman's crime. Nobody but a woman would send poisoned chocolates to a man. Another man would send a poisoned sample of whiskey, or something like that."

"That's a very sound point, Moresby," Roger meditated. "Very sound indeed. And Sir William couldn't help you?"

"Couldn't," said Moresby, not without a trace of resentment, "or wouldn't. I was inclined to believe at first that he might have his suspicions and was shielding some woman. But I don't think so now."

"Humph!" Roger did not seem quite so sure. "It's reminiscent, this case, isn't it? Didn't some lunatic once send poisoned chocolates to the Commissioner of Police himself? A good crime always gets imitated, as you know."

Moresby brightened.

"It's funny you should say that, Mr. Sheringham, because that's the very conclusion I've come to. I've tested every other theory, and so far as I know there's not a soul with an interest in Sir William's death, whether from motives of gain, revenge, or what you like, whom I haven't had to rule quite out of it. In fact, I've pretty well made up my mind that the person who sent those chocolates was some irresponsible lunatic of a woman, a social or religious fanatic who's probably never even seen him. And if that's the case," Moresby sighed, "a fat chance I have of ever laying hands on her."

"Unless Chance steps in, as it so often does," said Roger brightly, "and helps you. A tremendous lot of cases get solved by a stroke of sheer luck, don't they? *Chance the Avenger*. It would make an excellent film title. But there's a lot of truth in it. If I were superstitious, which I'm not, I should say it wasn't chance at all, but Providence avenging the victim."

"Well, Mr. Sheringham," said Moresby, who was not superstitious either, "to tell the truth, I don't mind what it is, so long as it lets me get my hands on the right person."

If Moresby had paid his visit to Roger Sheringham with any hope of tapping that gentleman's brains, he went away disappointed.

To tell the truth, Roger was inclined to agree with the Chief Inspector's conclusion, that the attempt on the life of Sir William Anstruther and the actual murder of the unfortunate Mrs. Beresford must be the work of some unknown criminal lunatic. For this reason, although he thought about it a good deal during the next few days, he made no attempt to take the case in hand. It was the sort of affair, necessitating endless inquiries that a private person would have neither the time nor the authority to carry out, which can be handled only by the official police. Roger's interest in it was purely academic.

It was hazard, a chance encounter nearly a week later, which translated this interest from the academic into the personal.

Roger was in Bond Street, about to go through the distressing ordeal of buying a new hat. Along the pavement he suddenly saw bearing down on him Mrs. Verreker-le-Flemming. Mrs. Verreker-le-Flemming was small, exquisite, rich, and a widow, and she sat at Roger's feet whenever he gave her the opportunity. But she talked. She talked, in fact, and talked, and talked. And Roger, who rather liked talking himself, could not bear it. He tried to dart across the road, but there was no opening in the traffic stream. He was cornered.

Mrs. Verreker-le-Flemming fastened on him gladly.

"Oh, Mr. Sheringham! *Just* the person I wanted to see. Mr. Sheringham, *do* tell me. In confidence. *Are* you taking up this dreadful business of poor Joan Beresford's death?"

Roger, the frozen and imbecile grin of civilized chatter on his face, tried to get a word in; without result.

"I was horrified when I heard of it—simply horrified. You see, Joan and I were such *very* close friends. Quite intimate. And the awful thing, the truly *terrible* thing is that Joan brought the whole business on herself. Isn't that *appalling*?"

Roger no longer wanted to escape.

"What did you say?" he managed to insert incredulously.

"I suppose it's what they call tragic irony," Mrs. Verreker-le-Flemming chattered on. "Certainly it was tragic enough, and I've never heard anything so terribly ironical. You know about that bet she made with her husband, of course, so that he had to get her a box of chocolates, and if he hadn't Sir William would never have given him the poisoned ones and he'd have eaten them and died himself and good riddance? Well, Mr. Sheringham—" Mrs. Verreker-le-Flemming lowered her voice to a conspirator's whisper and glanced about her in the approved manner. "I've never told anybody else this, but I'm telling you because I know you'll appreciate it. *Joan wasn't playing fair!*"

"How do you mean?" Roger asked, bewildered.

Mrs. Verreker-le-Flemming was artlessly pleased with her sensation.

"Why, she'd seen the play before. We went together, the very first week it was on. She *knew* who the villain was all the time."

"By Jove!" Roger was as impressed as Mrs. Verreker-le-Flemming could have wished. "Chance the Avenger! We're none of us immune from it."

"Poetic justice, you mean?" twittered Mrs. Verreker-le-Flemming, to whom these remarks had been somewhat obscure. "Yes, but Joan Beresford of all people! That's the extraordinary thing. I should never have thought Joan *would* do a thing like that. She was such a *nice* girl. A little close with money, of course, considering how well-off they are, but that isn't anything. Of course it was only fun, and pulling her husband's leg, but I always used to think Joan was such a *serious girl,* Mr. Sheringham. I mean, ordinary people don't talk about honor, and truth, and playing the game, and all those things one takes for granted. But Joan did. She was always saying that this wasn't honorable, or that wouldn't be playing the game. Well, she paid herself for not playing the game, poor girl, didn't she? Still, it all goes to show the truth of the old saying, doesn't it?"

"What old saying?" said Roger, hypnotized by this flow.

"Why, that still waters run deep. Joan must have been deep, I'm afraid." Mrs. Verreker-le-Flemming sighed. It was evidently a social error to be deep. "I mean, she certainly took me in. She can't have been quite so honorable and truthful as she was always pretending, can she? And I can't help wondering whether a girl who'd deceive her husband in a little thing like that might not—oh, well, I don't want to say anything against poor Joan now she's dead, poor darling, but she can't have been *quite* such a plaster saint after all, can she? I mean," said Mrs. Verreker-le-Flemming, in hasty extenuation of these suggestions, "I do think psychology is so very interesting, don't you, Mr. Sheringham?"

"Sometimes, very," Roger agreed gravely. "But you mentioned Sir William Anstruther just now. Do you know him, too?"

"I used to," Mrs. Verreker-le-Flemming replied, without particular interest. "Horrible man! Always running after some woman or other. And when he's tired of her, just drops her—biff!—like that. At least," added Mrs. Verreker-le-Flemming somewhat hastily, "so I've heard."

"And what happens if she refuses to be dropped?"

"Oh dear, I'm sure I don't know. I suppose you've heard the latest."

Mrs. Verreker-le-Flemming hurried on, perhaps a trifle more pink than the delicate aids to nature on her cheeks would have warranted.

"He's taken up with that Bryce woman now. You know, the wife of the oil man, or petrol, or whatever he made his money in. It began about three weeks ago. You'd have thought that dreadful business of being responsible, in a way, for poor Joan Beresford's death would have sobered him up a little, wouldn't you? But not a bit of it; he—"

Roger was following another line of thought.

"What a pity you weren't at the Imperial with the Beresfords that evening. She'd never have made that bet if you had been." Roger looked extremely innocent. "You weren't, I suppose."

"I?" queried Mrs. Verreker-le-Flemming in surprise. "Good gracious, no. I was at the new revue at the Pavilion. Lady Gavelstoke had a box and asked me to join her party."

"Oh, yes. Good show, isn't it? I thought that sketch *The Sempiternal Triangle* very clever. Didn't you?"

"*The Sempiternal Triangle?*" wavered Mrs. Verreker-le-Flemming.

"Yes, in the first half."

"Oh! Then I didn't see it. I got there disgracefully late, I'm afraid. But then," said Mrs. Verreker-le-Flemming with pathos, "I always do seem to be late for simply everything."

Roger kept the rest of the conversation resolutely upon theaters. But before he left her he had ascertained that she had photographs of both Mrs. Beresford and Sir William Anstruther, and had obtained permission to borrow them some time. As soon as she was out of view he hailed a taxi and gave Mrs. Verreker-le-Flemming's address. He thought it better to take advantage of her permission at a time when he would not have to pay for it a second time over.

The parlormaid seemed to think there was nothing odd in his mission, and took him up to the drawing room at once. A corner of the room was devoted to the silver-framed photographs of Mrs. Verreker-le-Flemming's friends, and there were many of them. Roger examined them with interest, and finally took away with him not two photographs but six, those of Sir William, Mrs. Beresford, Beresford, two strange males who appeared to belong to the Sir William period, and, lastly, a likeness of Mrs. Verreker-le-Flemming herself. Roger liked confusing his trail.

For the rest of the day he was very busy.

His activities would have no doubt seemed to Mrs. Verreker-le-Flemming not merely baffling but pointless. He paid a visit to a public library, for instance, and consulted a work of reference, after which he took a taxi and drove to the offices of the Anglo-Eastern Perfumery Company, where he inquired for a certain Mr. Joseph Lea Hardwick and seemed much put out on hearing that no such gentleman was known to the firm and was certainly not employed in any of their branches. Many questions had to be put about the firm and its branches before he consented to abandon the quest.

After that he drove to Messrs. Weall and Wilson, the well-known institution which protects the trade interests of individuals and advises its subscribers regarding investments. Here he entered his name as a subscriber, and explaining that he had a large sum of money to invest, filled in one of the special inquiry forms which are headed Strictly Confidential.

Then he went to the Rainbow Club, in Piccadilly.

Introducing himself to the porter without a blush as connected with Scotland Yard, he asked the man a number of questions, more or less trivial, concerning the tragedy.

"Sir William, I understand," he said finally, as if by the way, "did not dine here the evening before."

There it appeared that Roger was wrong. Sir William had dined in the club, as he did about three times a week.

"But I quite understood he wasn't here that evening," Roger said plaintively.

The porter was emphatic. He remembered quite well. So did a waiter, whom the porter summoned to corroborate him. Sir William had dined, rather late, and had not left the dining room till about nine o'clock. He spent the evening there, too, the waiter knew, or at least some of it, for he himself had taken him a whiskey and soda in the lounge not less than half an hour later.

Roger retired.

He retired to Merton's, in a taxi.

It seemed that he wanted some new note paper printed, of a very special kind, and to the young woman behind the counter he specified at great length and in wearisome detail exactly what he did want. The young woman handed him the books of specimen pieces and asked him to see if there was any style there which would suit him. Roger glanced through them, remarking garrulously to the young woman that he had been recommended to Merton's by a very dear friend, whose photograph he happened to have on him at that moment. Wasn't that a curious coincidence? The young woman agreed that it was.

"About a fortnight ago, I think, my friend was in here last," said Roger, producing the photograph. "Recognize this?"

The young woman took the photograph, without apparent interest.

"Oh, yes, I remember. About some note paper, too, wasn't it? So that's your friend. Well, it's a small world. Now this is a line we're selling a good deal of just now."

Roger went back to his rooms to dine. Afterwards, feeling restless, he wandered out of the Albany and turned up Piccadilly. He wandered round the Circus, thinking hard, and paused for a moment out of habit to inspect the photographs of the new revue hung outside the Pavilion. The next thing he realized was that he had got as far as Jermyn Street and was standing outside the Imperial Theater. Glancing at the advertisements of *The Creaking Skull,* he saw that it began at half past eight. Glancing at his watch, he saw that the time was twenty-nine minutes past the hour. He had an evening to get through somehow. He went inside.

The next morning, very early for Roger, he called on Moresby at Scotland Yard.

"Moresby," he said without preamble, "I want you to do something for me. Can you find me a taximan who took a fare from Piccadilly Circus or its neighborhood at about ten past nine on the evening before the Beresford crime to the Strand somewhere near the bottom of Southampton Street, and another who took a fare back between those points? I'm not sure about the first. Or one taxi might have been used for the double journey, but I doubt that. Anyhow, try to find out for me, will you?"

"What are you up to now, Mr. Sheringham?" Moresby asked suspiciously.

"Breaking down an interesting alibi," replied Roger serenely. "By the way, I know who sent those chocolates to Sir William. I'm just building up a nice structure of evidence for you. Ring up my rooms when you've got those taximen."

He strolled out, leaving Moresby positively gaping after him.

The rest of the day he spent apparently trying to buy a second-hand typewriter. He was very particular that it should be a Hamilton No. 4. When the shop people tried to induce him to consider other makes he refused to look at them, saying that he had had the Hamilton No. 4 so strongly recommended to him by a friend who had bought one about three weeks ago. Perhaps it was at this very shop? No? They hadn't sold a Hamilton No. 4 for the last three months? How odd.

But at one shop they had sold a Hamilton No. 4 within the last month, and that was odder still.

At half past four Roger got back to his rooms to await the telephone message from Moresby. At half past five it came.

"There are fourteen taxidrivers here, littering up my office," said Moresby offensively. "What do you want me to do with 'em?"

"Keep them till I come, Chief Inspector," returned Roger with dignity.

The interview with the fourteen was brief enough, however. To each man in turn Roger showed a photograph, holding it so that Moresby could not see it, and asked if he could recognize his fare. The ninth man did so, without hesitation.

At a nod from Roger, Moresby dismissed them, then sat at his table and tried to look official. Roger seated himself on the table, looking most unofficial, and swung his legs. As he did so, a photograph fell unnoticed out of his pocket and fluttered, face downwards, under the table. Moresby eyed it but did not pick it up.

"And now, Mr. Sheringham, sir," he said, "perhaps you'll tell me what you've been doing?"

"Certainly, Moresby," said Roger blandly. "Your work for you. I really have solved the thing, you know. Here's your evidence." He took from his notecase an old letter and handed it to the Chief Inspector. "Was that typed on the same machine as the forged letter from Mason's, or was it not?"

Moresby studied it for a moment, then drew the forged letter from a drawer of his table and compared the two minutely.

"Mr. Sheringham," he said soberly, "where did you get hold of this?"

"In a secondhand typewriter shop in St. Martin's Lane. The machine was sold to an unknown customer about a month ago. They identified the customer from that same photograph. As it happened, this machine had been used for a time in the office after it was repaired, to see that it was O.K., and I easily got hold of that specimen of its work."

"And where is the machine now?"

"Oh, at the bottom of the Thames, I expect," Roger smiled. "I tell you, this criminal takes no unnecessary chances. But that doesn't matter. There's your evidence."

"Humph! It's all right so far as it goes," conceded Moresby. "But what about Mason's paper?"

"That," said Roger calmly, "was extracted from Merton's book of sample note papers, as I'd guessed from the very yellowed edges might be the case. I can prove contact of the criminal with the book, and there is a gap which will certainly turn out to have been filled by that piece of paper."

"That's fine," Moresby said more heartily.

"As for the taximan, the criminal had an alibi. You've heard it broken down. Between ten past nine and twenty-five past, in fact during the time when the parcel must have been posted, the murderer took a hurried journey to that neighborhood, going probably by bus or Underground, but returning, as I expected, by taxi, because time would be getting short."

"And the murderer, Mr. Sheringham?"

"The person whose photograph is in my pocket," Roger said unkindly. "By the way, do you remember what I was saying the other day about Chance the Avenger, my excellent film title? Well, it's worked again. By a chance meeting in Bond Street with a silly woman I was put, by the merest accident, in possession of a piece of information which showed me then and there who had sent those chocolates addressed to Sir William. There were other possibilities, of course, and I tested them, but then and there on the pavement I saw the whole thing, from first to last."

"Who was the murderer, then, Mr. Sheringham?" repeated Moresby.

"It was so beautifully planned," Roger went on dreamily. "We never grasped for one moment that we were making the fundamental mistake that the murderer all along intended us to make."

"And what was that?" asked Moresby.

"Why, that the plan had miscarried. That the wrong person had been killed. That was just the beauty of it. The plan had *not* miscarried. It had been brilliantly successful. The wrong person was *not* killed. Very much the right person was."

Moresby gasped.

"Why, how on earth do you make that out, sir?"

"Mrs. Beresford was the objective all the time. That's why the plot was so ingenious. Everything was anticipated. It was perfectly natural that Sir William should hand the chocolates over to Beresford. It was foreseen that we should look for the criminal among Sir William's associates and not the dead woman's. It was probably even foreseen that the crime would be considered the work of a woman!"

Moresby, unable to wait any longer, snatched up the photograph.

"Good heavens! But Mr. Sheringham, you don't mean to tell me that . . . Sir William himself!"

"He wanted to get rid of Mrs. Beresford," Roger continued. "He had liked her well enough at the beginning, no doubt, though it was her money he was after all the time.

"But the real trouble was that she was too close with her money. He wanted it, or some of it, pretty badly; and she wouldn't part. There's no doubt about the motive. I made a list of the firms he's interested in and got a report on them. They're all rocky, every one. He'd got through all his own money, and he had to get more.

"As for the nitrobenzine which puzzled us so much, that was simple enough. I looked it up and found that beside the uses you told me, it's used largely in perfumery. And he's got a perfumery business. The Anglo-Eastern Perfumery Company. That's how he'd know about its being poisonous, of course. But I shouldn't think he got his supply from there. He'd be cleverer than that. He probably made the stuff himself. Any schoolboy knows how to treat benzol with nitric acid to get nitrobenzine."

"But," stammered Moresby, "but Sir William . . . He was at Eton."

"Sir William?" said Roger sharply. "Who's talking about Sir William? I told you the photograph of the murderer was in my pocket." He whipped out the photograph in question and confronted the astounded Chief Inspector with it. "Beresford, man! Beresford's the murderer of his own wife.

"Beresford, who still had hankerings after a fast-pace life," he went on more mildly, "didn't want his wife but did want her money. He contrived this plot, providing as he thought against every contingency that could possibly arise. He established a mild alibi, if suspicion ever should arise, by taking his wife to the Imperial, and slipped out of the theater at the first intermission. (I sat through the first act of the dreadful thing myself last night to see when the intermission came.) Then he hurried down to the Strand, posted his parcel, and took a taxi back. He had ten minutes, but nobody would notice if he got back to the box a minute late.

"And the rest simply followed. He knew Sir William came to the club every morning at ten thirty, as regularly as clockwork; he knew that for a psychological certainty he could get the chocolates handed over to him if he hinted for them; he knew that the police would go chasing after all sorts of false trails starting from Sir William. And as for the wrapper and the forged letter, he carefully didn't destroy them because they were calculated not only to divert suspicion but actually to point away from him to some anonymous lunatic."

"Well, it's very smart of you, Mr. Sheringham," Moresby said, with a little sigh, but quite ungrudgingly. "Very smart indeed. What was it the lady told you that showed you the whole thing in a flash?"

"Why, it wasn't so much what she actually told me as what I heard between her words, so to speak. What she told me was that Mrs. Beresford knew the answer to that bet; what I deduced was that, being the sort of person she was, it was quite incredible that she should have made a bet to which she knew the answer. *Ergo*, she didn't. *Ergo*, there never was such a bet. *Ergo*, Beresford was lying. *Ergo*, Beresford wanted to get hold of those chocolates for some reason other than he stated. After all, we only had Beresford's word for the bet, hadn't we?

"Of course he wouldn't have left her that afternoon till he'd seen her take, or somehow made her take, at least six of the chocolates, more than a lethal dose. That's why the stuff was in those meticulous six-minim doses. And so that he could take a couple himself, of course. A clever stroke, that."

Moresby rose to his feet.

"Well, Mr. Sheringham, I'm much obliged to you, sir. And now I shall have to get busy myself." He scratched his head. "Chance the Avenger, eh? Well, I can tell you one pretty big thing Beresford left to Chance the Avenger, Mr. Sheringham. Suppose Sir William hadn't handed over the chocolates after all? Supposing he'd kept 'em, to give to one of his own ladies?"

Roger positively snorted. He felt a personal pride in Beresford by this time.

"Really, Moresby! It wouldn't have had any serious results if Sir William had. Do give my man credit for being what he is. You don't imagine he sent the poisoned ones to Sir William, do you? Of course not! He'd send harmless ones, and exchange them for the others on his way home. Dash it all, he wouldn't go right out of his way to present opportunities to Chance.

"If," added Roger, "Chance really is the right word."

Reading for Understanding

❑ MAIN IDEA

1. The main point of the story is that (a) chocolates are, at best, a possibly dangerous addiction (b) pure luck solves nearly every murder case (c) chance may play a crucial aid in the solution of a murder (d) Graham Beresford was more intelligent than Sir William Anstruther.

❑ DETAILS

2. The parcel was received by (a) Anstruther (b) Moresby (c) Sheringham (d) Mrs. Beresford.

3. When Anstruther received the chocolates, he was (a) delighted (b) appreciative (c) furious (d) made ill.

4. Mrs. Verreker-le-Flemming said that Joan Beresford was (a) frivolous (b) cruel and vindictive (c) unfaithful (d) fair and honest.

5. The name of the play was (a) *Chance the Avenger* (b) *The Creaking Skull* (c) *The Poisoned Chocolates Case* (d) *The Eternal Triangle.*

❑ INFERENCES

6. Sir William Anstruther may be called (a) a tool of the murderer (b) a jovial, good-humored baronet (c) an amateur detective of considerable talent (d) a connoisseur of fine candies.

7. Beresford's illness (a) was accidental (b) was a trick (c) never fooled anyone (d) could have killed him.
8. Sheringham solved the case because he believed that (a) Moresby was on the verge of solving it (b) Anstruther was really not a ladies' man (c) character traits tend to be consistent (d) Anstruther was too generous in giving away the chocolates.
9. Though Roger tried to avoid Mrs. Verreker-le-Flemming, she (a) proved to be less talkative than usual (b) gave Roger every opportunity to talk (c) indicated that she preferred Anstruther (d) provided the clue that broke the case.
10. Beresford can best be characterized by the adjective (a) *clever* (b) *compassionate* (c) *fearful* (d) *generous.*

☐ AUTHOR'S PURPOSE

11. A major purpose of the author was to (a) stress the character of Moresby (b) downplay the role of luck (c) concentrate on the foibles of Roger Sheringham (d) provide a challenging puzzle.

☐ ORDER OF EVENTS

12. Arrange the items in the order in which they occurred. Use letters only.
    A. Roger speaks to Mrs. Verreker-le-Flemming.
    B. Anstruther receives a box of chocolates.
    C. Beresford becomes ill.
    D. Roger reveals the name of the murderer.
    E. We learn of Beresford's marriage.

☐ OUTCOMES

13. At the close of the story, (a) Beresford was amazed that his plan miscarried (b) Sheringham sought out the company of Mrs. Verreker-le-Flemming (c) Moresby disagreed with Sheringham's solution (d) Beresford's greed was at last satisfied.

☐ CAUSE AND EFFECT

14. If Anstruther had not offered Beresford the chocolates, (a) Beresford would have tried another plan (b) Moresby would have suspected Anstruther (c) Sheringham himself might have been in danger (d) Anstruther would have been poisoned.

❑ FACT OR OPINION

Tell whether the following is a fact or an opinion.

15. Beresford never intended to kill Anstruther.

Words in Context

1. "This is the *gist* of the case, as Chief Inspector Moresby told it one evening to Roger. . ." ***Gist*** (410) means (a) substance (b) impact (c) origin (d) perplexing result.

2. ". . . would Sir William do them the honor of . . . letting the firm have his *candid* opinion of them?" ***Candid*** (411) means (a) professional (b) gustatory (c) sincere (d) biased.

3. "For a moment Beresford *demurred* politely and then, most unfortunately for himself, accepted." ***Demurred*** (411) means (a) smiled (b) refused firmly (c) hesitated (d) frowned.

4. "Of the three *unconscious protagonists* in the *impending* tragedy, Sir William was without doubt the most remarkable." ***Unconscious protagonists*** . . . ***impending*** (411) mean (a) injured victims . . . inevitable (b) unconscious participants . . . awesome (c) unsensing actors . . . coming (d) unsuspecting main characters . . . about to happen.

5. ". . . and both described him subsequently as pale to the point of *ghastliness*, with staring eyes and *livid* lips . . ." ***Ghastliness*** . . . ***livid*** (412) mean (a) sensationalism . . . discolored (b) infuriation . . . sensational (c) extreme fatigue . . . pallid (d) deathlike state . . . purplish.

6. "However, the managing director *quashed* this idea at once: oil of bitter almonds, he asserted, was never used . . ." ***Quashed*** (413) means (a) repudiated (b) accepted (c) modified (d) questioned.

7. "By about eight o'clock that night he was conscious; the next day he was practically *convalescent*." ***Convalescent*** (413) means (a) a new man (b) stronger than ever (c) out of danger (d) on the way to recovery.

8. "Roger's interest in it was purely *academic*." ***Academic*** (416) means (a) scholarly (b) professional (c) theoretical (d) practical.

9. "'. . . Chance the Avenger! We're none of us immune from it.' '*Poetic justice*, you mean?' twittered Mrs. Verreker-le-Flemming." ***Poetic***

justice (417) means an outcome with (a) equal justice to all (b) virtue rewarded and vice punished (c) rewards and punishments (d) trial by jury.

10. "Roger kept the rest of the conversation *resolutely* upon theaters." ***Resolutely*** (418) means (a) waveringly (b) considerately (c) undeviatingly (d) carefully.

11. "The porter was emphatic. He remembered quite well. So did a waiter, whom the porter summoned to *corroborate* him." ***Corroborate*** (419) means (a) rescue (b) confirm (c) assist (d) interrogate.

12. "'And now . . . perhaps you'll tell me what you've been doing?' 'Certainly, Moresby,' said Roger *blandly*. 'Your work for you.'" ***Blandly*** (420) means (a) boastfully (b) gleefully (c) quickly (d) smoothly.

13. "'He *contrived* this plot, providing as he thought against every *contingency* that could possibly arise.'" ***Contrived . . . contingency*** (422) mean (a) created . . . opposing force (b) devised . . . likelihood (c) foresaw . . . obstacle (d) constructed . . . advantage

14. "'. . . what I *deduced* was that, being the sort of person she was, it was quite incredible that she should have made a bet to which she knew the answer. *Ergo*, she didn't.'" ***Deduced . . . Ergo*** (422) mean (a) foresaw . . . Incidentally (b) discovered . . . But (c) anticipated . . . Since (d) concluded . . . Therefore.

15. "'Of course he wouldn't have left . . . till he'd seen her take . . . more than a *lethal* dose. That's why the stuff was in those *meticulous* six-minim doses.'" ***Lethal . . . meticulous*** (422) mean (a) killing . . . traceable (b) tragic . . . devilish (c) mortal . . . precise . . . (d) common . . . perfectionist . . .

Thinking Critically About the Story

1. The greatest satisfaction to most detective story aficionados comes from being able to follow the deductive reasoning that leads to the exposure of the perpetrator. Try the following checklist for this story. Did you get it?
   a. Why does each piece of chocolate contain precisely six-minim doses of nitrobenzine?
   b. How is Sheringham able to connect Beresford to the typed note without finding the typewriter?
   c. Why are the taxidrivers involved?
   d. Why does Sheringham shop for note paper?
   e. Why does Sheringham inquire about Joseph Lea Hardwick?

f. Why does Sheringham claim that he has a large sum of money to invest?

2. What is the pivotal point upon which the solution of the crime depends? What does the title mean? Do you believe that chance depends solely on probability, or is there a directing force? Cite examples to support your statement.

3. How does Roger Sheringham compare with the notable detectives of fiction? Holmes? Kojak? Hammer? Dupin? Your favorite TV sleuth? What are Sheringham's best assets? The best assets of the others? Whom would you consider best? Justify your response.

4. Be prepared to tell the class your favorite detective story from fiction or from real life. What makes it your favorite? How does "The Avenging Chance" compare to it?

5. Roger Sheringham is unique among great detectives. He alone lacks an identifying mannerism or idiosyncrasy. What are the identifying aspects of Holmes? Hammer? Kojak? The other detectives in current TV fare? Why are these peculiarities stressed? Do all adults have their quirks? Do all young adults? Do all people? How do we acquire them? Are they an advantage? A disadvantage? When do they become a handicap? Why must we beware of our own? What are yours?

Stories in Words

Mortgaged (414) is traceable to an old French expression that meant "dead pledge." A famous jurist, Sir Edward Coke, explained in the early 17th century that the word suggests the risk taken by the person who holds the mortgage. The borrower may not pay; then the land that supported the mortgage is forfeited to the lender. The pledge becomes dead to one or the other depending upon whether the money is paid or not. The root *mort* appears in *mortal, mortician,* and *mortify.* A person who is *mortified* might wish he or she were dead.

Lunatic (415) contains the root for the moon, *luna.* From ancient times it was believed that the mind is affected by the moon and that some people reach a peak of frenzy during the full moon. The slang word *looney* is derived from *lunatic. Lunatic* once had a medical association that is no longer valid. The root appears in *lunar, luna moth,* and *lunation.* The nearby word, *fanatic,* derives from the Latin *fanum,* or "temple." A fanatic was presumably "inspired by a deity, frenzied." The word *fan* for a "sports enthusiast" is probably a shortened form of *fanatic.*

Trivial (418) clearly comes from the Latin *tri* (three) and *via* (way). Most authorities think it comes from *crossroads,* where people meet to discuss unimportant things. Some think it comes from *trivium.* The quadrivium and the trivium made up the seven liberal arts. The quadrivium consisted of arithmetic, astronomy, geometry, and music. The trivium consisted of rhetoric, logic, and grammar. Do the latter pursuits encourage trivial conversation!

Conflict

Getting Technical

Terms

foreshadowing	inevitability	setting
genre	plausible	

Definitions Match each of the above terms with its definition.

1. The quality that makes a sequence of events inescapable, unavoidable
2. The where or when of a story; the time and place
3. Planting information in a narrative so that later events are prepared for
4. Label given to a story element—character, action, setting—that is credible or valid to the reader
5. Literary type or class to which a work belongs

Examples Match each of the following with the appropriate term.

1. It is the type of slushy soap opera that she always enjoys.
2. Early in the story the author casually tells us the date of a dime, and that date becomes the crucial key to the identity of the master criminal.
3. From the moment of weakness when she falls prey to her own greed, the tragic ending of the story had to result.
4. Once upon a time not so long ago in a small village near a large inland lake. . .
5. The characters seem to walk right out of my past.

6. It is one of those modern short stories that seems to begin nowhere, go nowhere, and end nowhere—a slice of life for the reader to puzzle over.

Application Choose the statement that best completes each of the following.

1. In "The Killers" the incident having the least inevitability in the following group is (a) the killers' finding Ole Andreson (b) the violent death of Ole Andreson (c) Nick's trying to warn Ole (d) the killers' sparing the three men in the diner.
2. An example of foreshadowing in "The Old Man" is in the (a) title (b) use of a first-person-singular narrator (c) death of Boy (d) girls' leaving home.
3. The murder in "The Avenging Chance" is made plausible by (a) Mrs. Verreker-le-Flemming's gossipy nature (b) Roger Sheringham's perseverance (c) Beresford's need for money (d) Mrs. Beresford's distaste for chocolate.
4. The only story in this group having a rural setting is (a) "The Graven Image" (b) "The Old Man" (c) "The Avenging Chance" (d) "The Killers."
5. The ending of "Graven Image" is made more plausible by (a) the short stature of the Under Secretary (b) the way the food is eaten (c) Browning's obvious wealth (d) the Under Secretary's idealism.
6. The setting of "The Avenging Chance" is (a) Washington many years ago (b) Winnipeg of today (c) winter in London (d) summer in Paris.
7. The only story in the group belonging to the genre of animal fable is (a) "The Graven Image" (b) "The Killers" (c) "The Old Man" (d) "The Avenging Chance."
8. Plausibility is achieved in "The Old Man" by (a) giving human motivations to birds (b) making Boy shy and strong (c) not revealing the mother's feelings (d) ending with a brutal killing.

Thinking Critically About the Stories

1. Poetic justice is two-edged: good is rewarded and evil is punished. Avenging chance, on the other hand, makes certain that the unjust pay the penalty. Avenging chance is at work in our detective story, but are either poetic justice or avenging chance at work in the other three

stories in this unit? Give specific references to substantiate your statement.

2. The stories in this unit have a wide appeal. Which one has most significance for you? Which one gave you most to think about? Which one will you remember longest? Justify your choices.

3. Compare Boy in "The Old Man" and Ole Andreson in "The Killers." Are they cowards? What made them quitters? (What's wrong with being a quitter?) Which one do you sympathize with more? Have you met people like them in real life? In other fictional stories?

4. Compare the following in their method of handling their problem.

the Old Man	the Under Secretary
Roger Sheringham	the missus

Which one is most effective? Least effective? Most mature? Least mature?

5. Which author do you consider the most skillful in creating plausible characters? In arousing and sustaining reader interest? Which is the best storyteller? Cite instances in the stories to support your point of view.

Writing and Other Activities

1. Write the dialog and action for one of the following:
   a. Several years later Mrs. Verreker-le-Flemming tells a friend about the tragic death of her dear friend, Joan Beresford.
   b. That night Sam tells his children about his encounter with big-time gangsters.
   c. Al and Max report back to Mr. Big on their temporary lack of success.
   d. Sir William tells a lady friend of how Graham Beresford did not fool him for a moment.

2. Be prepared to lead a class panel in a discussion on one of the following:
   a. It is isn't what you know but whom you know that counts when you want to get ahead.
   b. Mistakes teenagers make in handling parental anger.
   c. Mistakes parents should not make in handling the not-the-brightest of their children.
   d. The roles retaliation and sweet revenge should play in our public relations with friends and enemies.

3. From the daily newspaper clip a news item of interest to you. Take one of the events covered and convert it into a "Hemingway" dialog.

4. Write the inner dialog for one of the following moments:
   a. Nick Adams debates with himself whether he has done the right thing by not notifying the police.
   b. Graham Beresford probes his alter ego to find where he had erred.
   c. Charles Browning discusses the incident with himself and decides that he did the right thing.
   d. The narrator in "The Old Man" discusses with himself what he would have done if he had been in the Old Man's place.

5. Write the news article for the local paper on one of the following headlines:
   a. POISONED-CHOCOLATE KILLER CAPTURED
   b. MYSTERIOUS KILLING,
LOCAL MAN MURDERED
   c. BROWNING RETIRES
FROM PUBLIC OFFICE
   d. LOCAL WILDLIFE DIMINISHING.

Stories in Words: A Review

A. ambled	E. elbows	I. nickname
B. atonement	F. lunatic	J. sandwich
C. bewildered	G. menu	K. trivial
D. derby	H. mortgaged	L. wig-wagged

Answer the following questions by choosing a word from the list above. Use letters only.

Which of the words above. . .

1. _______ is a synonym of *sauntered*?
2. _______ is derived from an old superstition?
3. _______ contains a duplication common in English?
4. _______ once did not have its initial letter?
5. _______ is named for a hungry gambler?
6. _______ contains the suggestion of a *bend* or *curve*?
7. _______ is a word associated with words for *wild beasts*?
8. _______ contains within it a prepositional phrase?
9. _______ suggests a *dead pledge*?
10. _______ has roots suggesting *three ways*?

Though there are many different kinds of science fiction, stories tend to divide into two large categories. In the first, action is all. The famous Buck Rogers serials that occasionally surface on television are good examples. In this kind of story, the characters are almost comic-book creations, who have been created solely to further the rapid-action plot. The second kind of story goes deeper than the surface. Though action may be a part of the mixture, the emphasis tends to be upon character and theme. Many current social problems were foreseen in the science-fiction stories of yesterday. Many of tomorrow's problems and glories are foreshadowed in the stories of today.

Movies tend to prefer the first type, with a profusion of BEMs ("bug-eyed monsters"). Swamp things, creatures from mysterious lagoons, monsters created by radiation, giant reptilian forms from the sea bottoms, al-

8

Dateline—The Future

Science has not yet mastered prophecy. We predict too much for the next year and yet far too little for the next ten.

Neil A. Armstrong

iens from outer space—these are familiar to modern readers and moviegoers. Some stories of this type do try to introduce social commentary as well as action, but in most such stories the emphasis is upon what happens next. These satisfy the deep love we have for good stories.

The stories in this unit tend to fit into the second category. In these stories, action is subordinated to mood, character, and theme. Characters tend to be recognizable human beings under stress. You will be interested in them as people. Each story has a point to make, to leave you thinking about the story after it is over.

Both kinds of stories have a place, but the second category gives you more to wonder at. These stories encourage you to look deep inside yourself as a human being.

The Valley of Echoes

GÉRARD KLEIN
TRANSLATED BY FRANK ZERO

"This is the first time I've ever seen an acute angle on Mars," said Ferrier. "That's not erosion. Neither wind nor sand has managed to cut into this rock. Maybe it's just a giant crystal that has grown slowly, a gradual concentration of like atoms, or perhaps . . ."

Perhaps what? "We are not alone!" Such a statement would be the news event of the century. Is there somewhere in the vastness of space another race we might communicate with? On our planet, SETI, the Search for Extraterrestrial Intelligence, sends out signals and listens, waiting for some indication that there is other life "out there."

"The Valley of Echoes," by a French author, suggests the international appeal of science fiction. It transports us to Mars. Three space travelers cross the monotonous Martian landscape, looking for signs that at some time in the past, others have walked the now-barren hills of Mars. If only there were some substance that pointed to an ancient civilization, a fossil or artifact. Then they hear a persistent sound echoing through the valley, gradually becoming louder and louder. Is this the proof they are seeking? When you finish reading the story, decide for yourself.

The Valley of Echoes

This time we ventured a little beyond the pink mountains of Tula, the oasis of crystal, and for days on end we passed between innumerable dunes. The Martian sky was always like itself, very pure, a very dark blue with an occasional hint of gray, and with admirable pink efflorescences at sunrise and sunset.

Our tractors performed quite satisfactorily. We were venturing into regions that had hardly been explored thus far, at least by land, and we were reasonably sure of being the first to negotiate these desolate passes. The first men, at any rate; for what we were more or less vaguely searching for was some trace of an ancient civilization. It has never been admitted on Earth that Mars is not only a dead world, but a world eternally deserted. It has long been hoped that we would discover some remains of defunct empires, or perhaps the fallen descendants of the mythical masters of the red planet. Too many stories have been told about Mars for ten years of scientific and fruitless exploration on this point to undo all the legends.

But neither Ferrier nor La Salle nor I particularly believed in the possibility of so fantastic an encounter. We were mature and slightly disillusioned men, and we had left the Earth some years before to escape the wind of insanity which at that time was sweeping our native planet. This was something that we did not like to talk about, as it pained us. We sometimes thought it was due to the immense solitude of a species that had just achieved self-awareness, that confronted the universe, that hoped to receive a response, even a fatal one, to its challenge. But space remained silent and the planets deserted.

We were descending, then, toward the south, in the direction of the Martian equator. The maps were still imprecise at this time, and we had been assigned to make certain geological reports which could not be done from an airplane. As a psychologist, I was only moderately qualified for this task, but I also knew how to drive a tractor and how the instruments worked, and men were scarce on Mars.

The worst thing was the monotony that prevailed throughout these days. People on Earth, comfortably installed behind their desks, write things about us that bring tears of compassion to the eyes of thousands of readers; they speak of our heroism and the adventure that lies in wait for us at each step, of the eternally renewed splendors of unknown worlds. I have never encountered such things. We know danger, but it doesn't rise up from the dunes; it is insidious, a leak in our breathing apparatus or a corresponding defect in our tractors or in our radio antennas. It is, above all, the danger of boredom. Mars is a deserted world. Its horizons are short, curtailed. And there are more inspiring scenes than that of an immense plain of gray sand and scattered lichens. The landscape is not terrible in itself. But what one does feel, with poignant acuteness, is the awareness of these thousands of kilometers, all alike, stretching out in all directions as far as you can see and farther still, kilometers which slowly pass beneath your treads while you remain immobile. It's a little as if you were sure of finding in tomorrow the exact replica of yesterday.

And then you drive. For hours. Like a machine. And you are the machine, you are the tractor, you creep along between the dunes for hours on end, you avoid the heaps of stones, slowly modeled by the wind and themselves destined to become sand, and from time to time you lift your eyes to the sky and, through flinching lids, perceive the stars' sparkling in mid-day, which at first surprises and then bores you mortally, so that you would give anything for these eyes of the night to finally close.

Then you think of what you will do on Earth, when you return to it: you have heard the news; it is bad, always bad: no event occurs on Earth that is not aberrant: these are the "Insane Years," they say, and the desire to go back down there turns to a kind of loathing; nausea grips you.

Always, you drive. Without hoping for anything. At the end of a certain time, you see things rising up from among the dunes. You brake abruptly to avoid them, but there is never anything there. There are also those who fall asleep. The others notice it because the tractor suddenly loses its way; then they shake the driver or take the wheel themselves. This provides a little recreation.

As for me, it depends. Sometimes I make up stories. Stories that take place on Mars or in space or on another world, but never on Earth. I prefer not to think of Earth. La Salle is like myself. For Ferrier, it's worse, he can't stop thinking about it for a minute. I ask myself where this will lead him.

He's a geologist. I have watched him dig in the sand and hold up some tiny shell, the ancient abode of a creature long since withered, carried away by the soft winds of Mars. Never once has he discovered a more achieved fossil, the remains of a larger, more powerful (and more fragile) creature. I have seen him battling the evidence. I have seen him sweep his eyes over the hills of Mars, silently thinking that it will one day be necessary to turn over these millions of tons of sand in the hope of discovering, at the heart of the planet, the bleached fetus of a forgotten species. I don't think he talks enough. It is not good for a man to say nothing on Mars. Nor in space. He remains mute, as if the millions and millions of pounds of sand weighed down on him. Like La Salle and myself, he sought in space a way out, a means of escaping Earth, but he expected something else of it. He was hoping to encounter in it something other than himself; he thought to encounter the total stranger, he believed he would read on the cliffs of Mars the history of a world absolutely new for Earth. No doubt he had listened attentively, in his childhood, to the stories of the man in the moon.

Otherwise, he was just like La Salle and myself. There are things, you see, which we could not bear unless we were sure of discovering, one fine day, around the bend of space or between two hills, a glistening city and ideal beings. But La Salle and I, we know that this dream is not for today, or even for tomorrow, while Ferrier can no longer wait.

There are three of us, and that's an awkward number for playing cards. Sometimes we read. We also listen to the radio from time to time. But above all, we sleep. It is a way of economizing on oxygen. It is a way of projecting ourselves in time. We never dream.

When evening comes, we descend from the tractor, we unpack our apparatus. We proceed to take certain measurements. We forward the results. We start the catalytic stove; it functions tranquilly under its transparent bell glass, glowing red in the dusk like a hothouse flower. We eat. We unfurl the parasol-like thing that serves us as a tent, which prevents the mortal cold of Mars from freezing us to the bone, and we try once again to sleep. But it's no use—we've been sleeping nearly all day, you see, lulled by the jolting of the tractor, each taking his turn at the wheel; and when night comes, our respirator chafes us, we stifle, we're suddenly thirsty, and we lie there with our eyes open, staring at the milky dome of the tent, taking in the irritating faint gnashing of sandgrains blown against the plastic by the wind, the patter of insect feet.

Sometimes it happens, during these nights, that we ponder on what space might have been, on what these planets might have been. The thought comes to us that man, one day, will endow Mars with an atmosphere and with oceans and forests, that cities will rise here, fabulous, taller than all the cities of Earth, that spaceships will unite this planet and other worlds, and that the frontiers of the unknown will be situated elsewhere in space, always pushed back beyond the visible horizon. Our anguish is eased by the thought, and we know that man today is steering a false course in asking of this planet what it cannot give, in turning towards the past, in desperately sifting through the sieve of memory in hopes of finding once more the traces of an ancient downfall. We feel then, tremulously, that it is in the future that an answer lies, and that it is into the future that we must throw ourselves.

And we occasionally take stock of the paradoxical nature of our situation. We are at once the past and the future. We are included in the mad dreams of generations dead in the not distant past and we are going the way of infants yet to be born. Anonymous, we were myths; forgotten, we will be legends.

We do not go abroad at night because of the cold. The extreme tenuity of the atmosphere makes for great differences of temperature. But in the morning, around nine o'clock, we set out again.

Today we entered a zone of gray sand, then discovered a stretch littered with flat black stones, Aeolian* pebbles, strangely fashioned at times, and finally reached the extreme border of the reddish stretch that touches the Martian equator at certain points. Eroded mountains rise gently over the horizon. The dunes have thinned out and dispersed. The worn mesas that circumscribe the eye shelter this plain from the wind. Our tracks come to breach the hazardous irregularity of the desert. They will survive us.

The surface of the planet descended gently, as if we were plunging into the bosom of some dried-up sea, into the illusory depths of an imaginary littoral. And suddenly, we saw surge up and grow on the horizon translucent needles of rock, so thin and so high, with such sharp contours, that we did not believe our eyes. Ferrier, who was driving, gave a cry. He pressed the accelerator, and the sudden irresistible jolt of the tractor threw La Salle and myself from our seats.

"It's incredible."

"What a fantastic peak."

"No, it's a cliff."

But it was none of all this, as we saw later on in the day. It was a massif, probably crystalline, an accident that had spurted in ages past from the entrails of the planet, or perhaps even fallen from the sky, and some inconceivable tremor had cleaved it, so that it had the appearance, on this immutable plain, of a chipped yet tremendously sharp tooth.

"This is the first time I've ever seen an acute angle on Mars," said Ferrier. "That's not erosion. Neither wind nor sand has managed to cut into this rock. Maybe it's just a giant crystal that has grown slowly, a gradual concentration of like atoms, or perhaps . . ."

We looked at each other. There was one word on our lips. *Artifact.* Was this, at last, the evidence for which Earth had waited so long?

There is nothing worse, I think, than being deceived by an object. Because one cannot reproach it. We had suddenly put our trust in Mars. Like children.

And we were deceived. It was not an artifact.

But we did not want to accept what that meant. It had been crazy to hope. But we couldn't help it.

We spent the night at the foot of the crystalline mountains, and we experienced even more difficulty in getting to sleep than on previous days. We were both disappointed and satisfied. Our journey had not been in vain, and yet its secret goal was completely unfulfilled.

When morning came and the temperature became endurable, we ad-

**Aeolian* fashioned by the wind

justed our respirators and went out. We had decided to explore the rocky massif, to leave the tractor behind us and to carry only a light baggage of supplies and instruments.

The crystalline cliffs were not overly escarped. They contained faults and openings which permitted us to ascend. The rock was the color of ink, with here and there a murky transparency which reminded us of those blocks of ice that wander in space, the relics of incredibly ancient oceans, fragments of shattered ice packs, debris, finally, of pulverized planets.

We were trying to reach the largest fault, hoping to thus discover the very depths of the massif and to understand its structure. Perhaps a lake of mercury awaited us there, or engraved rocks, or even some creature, a door to another dimension, the traces of previous visitors, for this rock had survived for millions of years the slow burial by sand that lies in wait for all things on Mars. It had escaped the tide of dust that flows over the surface of the red planet, and the movement of the dunes that are incessantly shifted by the light winds, and in a way it was a witness to past ages, epochs in which men did not dare as yet to lift their faces to the sky; even less did they dream that one day they would voyage, weary, through these constellations.

But when it came, the thing took us unawares. La Salle, who was walking ahead, cried out. We heard him clearly and hurled ourselves headlong after him. Ferrier, who was following us, urged me ahead. Rounding a block, we saw La Salle, who seemed to be giving some object his utmost attention.

"Listen," he said to us.

We heard nothing at first; then, as we advanced another step, from those borderlines that separate silence from sound, we heard a gnashing noise arise.

We remained immobile. And this was neither the voice of the wind, nor its singing, nor even the light clatter of a stone or the cracking of rock split by the frost. It was a steady ssh-sshing, like the accumulated noise of millions of superimposed signals.

The air of Mars is too thin for our ears to perceive the sounds that it transmits. Moreover, our eardrums would not have withstood the difference of pressure which exists between the external milieu and our respiratory system. Our ears are entirely masked, and minuscule amplifiers allow us to hear the sound of our voices and to make out the noises of Mars. And this, I can vouch for it, was different from anything that I had heard up to that moment on the red planet. It was nothing human, and nothing mineral.

I moved my head slightly, and suddenly I perceived something else that dominated this ssh-sshing, reduced it to an insignificant and endless background noise. I perceived a voice, or rather the murmur of a million voices, the tumult of an entire race, uttering unbelievable, incomprehensible words, words I could never transcribe with any of the phonetic signs current on Earth.

"They're there," La Salle said to me, his eyes shining. He took a step or two forward, and I saw him hastily change the setting of his earphones. I followed him and did the same, for the murmur had become a tempest, the insect voices had been transformed into a strident and intolerable howling, a muffled and terrifying roar.

We were progressing along a narrow fault between two cliffs of rock. And the sound assailed us in successive, eddying waves. We were drunk on it. We sensed, we knew that at last we were about to find what we had come to see on Mars, what we had in vain implored space to give us.

Contact with another life.

For as the sound grew louder, we did not have the slightest doubt, not once. We were not easy men to deceive, nor were we liable to let our imagination run wild. This incredible richness in the modulation of the sound could only be the doing of live beings. It mattered little that we understood nothing; we had faith that Earth could solve problems of this sort, by its minds and its machines. We were merely the ambassadors of Earth.

At the last turn in the fault, the valley finally appeared. It resembled the basin of a dried-up lake, closed in by tall smooth cliffs which became more escarped the higher they rose. The opposite end of the valley narrowed and ended in a rocky bottleneck, finally coming up against a terminal wall.

There existed no other road that led to this valley except the one that we had taken, unless one were to let oneself drop from the sky. It was an arena rather than a valley, moreover: a vast oblong arena. And deserted.

And yet these incomprehensible voices assailed us.

It was a lake, you see, invisible, a lake of sounds and of dust, an impalpable dust that the years had laid down in this refuge, a dust fallen from the stars, borne by the wind, in which nothing had left its traces, a dust in which those who were calling to us had been swallowed up, perhaps, buried.

"Hello!" La Salle cried, his voice breaking.

He wanted to answer, he hoped for a silence of astonishment, but the arena was empty and the dense waves of sound came breaking in on us one after the other. Words whispered, words pronounced, phrases drawn out in a single breath, sprung from invisible lips.

"Where are you? Oh, where are you?" La Salle cried in a mournful voice. What he was hearing was not enough for him, he wished to see these unknown messengers, he hoped to see rise up from this lake of dust who knows what hideous or admirable forms. His hands were trembling and mine as well, and at my back I heard the short, hissing breath of Ferrier.

"Hello," cried an incredibly weak voice from the other end of the valley.

It was the voice of La Salle. It stood out, minutely, against the sonorous background of innumerable voices; it was a bit of wreckage carried to our shore.

"They are answering us," La Salle said to me, without believing it.

And his voice arose from a thousand places in the valley, an insect's voice, shrill, murmurous, shattered, diffracted. "Hello, hello, hello," it said. "Where are you, where are you-you-you-you-you . . ."

An echo, I thought. An echo. And La Salle turned again toward me, and I read in his eyes that he had understood, and I felt the hand of Ferrier weigh on my shoulder. Our voices, our mingled noises were grounded in the sound-matter that filled the valley, and created tricks of interference, returning to us as if reflected in strange mirrors of sound, transformed, but not at all weakened. Was it possible that such a valley existed on Mars, a valley of echoes, a valley where the transparent and thin air of Mars carried forever the sounds reflected by crystal walls?

Did there exist in the entire universe a place where the fossils were not at all mineral, but sounds? Were we, at last, hearing the voices of the ancient inhabitants of Mars, long after the sands had worn away and engulfed the last vestiges of their passing? Or was it, indeed, the evidence of other visitors come from worlds of which we were still ignorant? Had they passed by here yesterday, or a million years ago? Were we no longer alone?

Our instruments would tell us later and perhaps they would succeed in unraveling this skein of waves, undo these knots, and extract from this involuntary message some illuminating sense.

The valley was utterly deserted and dead. A receptacle. The whole of Mars was nothing but a receptacle that received our traces only to annihilate them. Except for this spot, except for this valley of echoes that would doubtless carry the sound of our voices through the ages to our distant successors, perhaps not human.

Ferrier took his hand from my shoulder, shoved me aside and pushed La Salle away, and began to run towards the center of the valley.

"Listen to them," he cried, "listen to them."

His boots sank into the impalpable dust, and it rose about him in an eddying. And we heard these voices breaking about our ears, in a tempest that he had raised. I saw him running and I understood what the sirens were, these voices that whispered in his ears, that called to him, that he had hoped for all these past years and vainly searched for, and he plunged into this sonorous sea and sank into the dust. I wished that I could be by his side, but I was incapable of making a move.

The voices hammered against my eardrums.

"The fool," said La Salle in a sad voice. "Oh, the poor fool."

Ferrier shouted. Ferrier called, and the immutable, the ancient voices answered him. He imbibed the voices. He drank them, devoured them, stirred them with his demented gestures.

And, slowly, they subsided. He had disturbed some instable equilibrium, destroyed a subtle mechanism. His body was a screen. He was too heavy, too material for these thin voices to endure his contact.

The voices grew weak. I felt them very slowly leave me, I felt them go away, in a last vibration I heard them shrivel up and die. And finally Ferrier fell silent. And in my earphones I made out a last whispering.

A kind of farewell.

The silence. The silence of Mars.

When Ferrier finally turned around, I saw, despite the distance, despite the cloud of dust that gradually settled, through his disordered respirator, tears that ran down his cheeks.

And he put his hands to his ears.

Reading for Understanding

☐ MAIN IDEA

1. The main point of the story is the explorers' (a) inability to function properly on the surface of Mars (b) hope of finding evidence of past intelligent life on Mars (c) homesickness for the green hills of Earth (d) constant communication with a base on Earth.

☐ DETAILS

2. The real danger to life on Mars arises from (a) the possibility of unknown monsters (b) overstimulation with the constant variety on the planet (c) too much activity and exertion (d) small problems like mechanical defects.

3. Night travel on Mars is avoided because of (a) poor visibility (b) rules set up by previous explorers (c) the cold (d) the Martian storms.

4. The person who first hears the eerie sound is (a) La Salle (b) Ferrier (c) the narrator (d) none of these.

5. The narrator suggests that Martian fossils might be (a) stones (b) sounds (c) bones (d) plants.

☐ INFERENCES

6. The personalities of the three explorers suggest (a) past disillusionments (b) naiveté (c) unchecked anger (d) buoyant optimism.

7. The narrator suggests that Earth (a) has sent out expeditions to the distant stars (b) has lost all touch with the Martian explorers (c) is having a period of great difficulty (d) is no longer in existence.

8. The geologist Ferrier (a) is satisfied with his discoveries on Mars (b) has found no example of any previous life on Mars (c) apparently dislikes La Salle (d) has had very limited success in finding fossils.

9. Most surface details on Mars (a) are buried by shifting sands (b) suggest a system of canals (c) can be seen from Earth with a

good pair of binoculars (d) are fixed and unchanging because of the slight atmosphere.

10. La Salle called Ferrier a "poor fool" because (a) he had fallen into a crevice and disappeared (b) there was no real basis for his hope (c) he had broken several rules the explorers always followed (d) he argued with his fellow explorers.

❑ TONE OF SELECTION

11. The tone of the story is one of (a) deep satisfaction (b) bitter antagonism (c) mournful resignation (d) heightened enthusiasm.

❑ ORDER OF EVENTS

12. Arrange the items in the order in which they occurred. Use letters only.
    A. The explorers reach the crystalline rock with the acute angles.
    B. The explorers set off toward the Martian equator.
    C. Ferrier weeps.
    D. The explorers begin to hear the gnashing noises.
    E. Ferrier runs off by himself toward the center of the valley.

❑ OUTCOMES

13. After the events described in the story, La Salle and the narrator probably (a) comfort Ferrier (b) split up (c) refuse to speak to Ferrier (d) return immediately to Earth.

❑ CAUSE AND EFFECT

14. The only place where traces of the explorers' visit might be retained is (a) the stone monument set up in honor of Ferrier (b) the tractor left behind (c) the valley of echoes (d) the crystalline peak.

❑ FACT OR OPINION

Tell whether the following is a fact or an opinion.

15. The Martian sky is dark blue.

Words in Context

1. "It has long been hoped that we would discover some remains of *defunct* empires." ***Defunct*** (437) means (a) powerful (b) ancient (c) recent (d) extinct.

2. "We were mature and slightly *disillusioned* men, and we had left Earth some years before to escape . . ." ***Disillusioned*** (437) means (a) free from false ideas (b) highly educated (c) romantic (d) adventurous.

3. "But what one does feel, with *poignant acuteness,* is the awareness of these thousands of miles, all alike . . ." ***Poignant acuteness*** (438) means (a) powerful distaste (b) sheer honesty (c) overwhelming awe (d) distressing intensity.

4. ". . . you avoid the heaps of stones, slowly modeled by the wind and themselves *destined* to become sand . . ." ***Destined*** (438) means (a) shaped (b) planned (c) fated (d) placed there.

5. ". . . no event occurs on Earth that is not *aberrant:* these are the 'Insane Years,' they say . . ." ***Aberrant*** (438) means (a) depressing (b) exhilarating (c) abnormal (d) violent.

6. "We feel then, *tremulously,* that it is in the future that the answer lies, and that it is into the future that we must throw ourselves." ***Tremulously*** (439) means (a) positively (b) with courage (c) truthfully (d) timidly.

7. "The extreme *tenuity* of the atmosphere makes for great differences in temperature." ***Tenuity*** (440) means (a) lack of density (b) volatility (c) variability (d) storminess.

8. "And suddenly, we saw surge up and grow on the horizon *translucent* needles of rock . . ." The needles of rock were ***translucent*** (440) because they were (a) so massive (b) semitransparent (c) clustered together (d) close to the horizon.

9. ". . . so that it had the appearance, on this *immutable* plain, of a chipped yet tremendously sharp tooth." ***Immutable*** (440) means (a) frightening (b) unusual (c) changeless (d) splendid.

10. "There was one word on our lips. *Artifact.* Was this, at last, the evidence for which Earth had waited so long?" ***Artifact*** (440) means a product of (a) human activity (b) volcanic action (c) erosion (d) meteors.

11. "There is nothing worse, I think, than being deceived by an object. Because one cannot *reproach* it." ***Reproach*** (440) means (a) reprimand (b) correct (c) argue with (d) control.

12. ". . . and the movement of the dunes that are *incessantly* shifted by the light winds . . ." ***Incessantly*** (441) means (a) rarely (b) occasionally (c) never (d) endlessly.

13. "I perceived . . . the murmur of a million voices . . . uttering . . . words I could never *transcribe* with any of the *phonetic* signs current on Earth." ***Transcribe . . . phonetic*** . . . (441) mean (a) forget . . . geo-

logical (b) write down . . . speech sound (c) recall . . . occult (d) describe . . . electronic.

14. "It was a lake, you see, invisible, a lake of sounds and of dust, an *impalpable* dust that the years had laid down . . ." ***Impalpable*** (442) means (a) incredible (b) imaginary (c) weightless (d) untouchable.

15. "It was the voice of La Salle. It stood out, *minutely*, against the *sonorous* background of innumerable voices." ***Minutely*** . . . ***sonorous*** . . . (442) mean (a) distinctly . . . unclear (b) vaguely . . . thunderous (c) scantly . . . resonant (d) startlingly . . . noisy.

Thinking Critically About the Story

1. How do the narrator, Ferrier, and La Salle compare with the explorers and early settlers who had flocked to the American continents? How does the trio compare with the astronauts of today? What motivates most of the people in each group? What qualities do they have in common? What drive that our early pioneers had is lacking in this Martian group? Would you be willing to be a pioneer? A Martian explorer? An astronaut? Explain.

2. What were the explorers on Mars searching for? Why? What would be the greatest achievement they could hope for? What is the danger to human beings on Earth if living beings are contacted anywhere else in the universe? Should such searches be encouraged? At what cost are such explorations made? Would that money be better spent fighting disease and hunger on Earth? Explain.

3. Recall other stories belonging to this genre. What gives these stories their enduring appeal? Why do some people find this genre unpalatable despite the charm? Why do other people develop a lasting satisfaction from them? How do you react? Explain.

4. How do the narrator, LaSalle, and Ferrier compare? How do their differences affect the story? Why did they join the expedition? Are there any such escape routes available to the earthbound people of today? Why is science fiction called escape literature?

5. What devices did Gérard Klein use to give verisimilitude to this story?

   In the setting?
   In the characters?
   In the action?
   In the conclusion?

   How would you rate this story? Explain.

Stories in Words

Planet (page 437) has a poetic origin. If you are a stargazer, you notice that the stars and constellations seem to move only because of the earth's rotation, but they do not move with respect to each other. Whatever real motion they have is on a vast time scale, undetectable by human eyes. Jupiter, Venus, Mars, and Saturn, on the other hand, move very noticeably against the background of the fixed stars. The ancient observers called them planets, or "wanderers," for that is what the word so appropriately means.

Murmur (page 441) is a member of a large class of words. It demonstrates in its own sound the sound it wishes to convey. Alfred Lord Tennyson talks about "the murmuring of innumerable bees" and thus suggests the insect noise. *Onomatopoeia* is the use of words whose sounds suggest their sense. Other examples include *buzz, hiss, clang, crash, mumble, clatter, swish, whoosh, bang, twitter, sizzle,* and *whiz.*

Atom (page 440) literally means "indivisible, undivided." A is a Greek prefix meaning *not,* as in *atypical, amoral,* and *achromatic.* The root *tom* meaning "cut" appears in *appendectomy, entomology,* and *diatom.* It was once thought that the atom was the smallest unit of matter, forever indivisible, but the atomic bomb proved that theory wrong. Scientists have divided the atom into neutrons, protons, and electrons. Modern physics divides the elements into ever smaller units like quarks, charms, hadrons, and gluons. The "unsplittable atom" is now seen to be an incredibly complicated collection of surprises.

Cephes 5

HOWARD FAST

"And remember, Third Officer, that we have no alternatives. This is a genetic factor in these poor souls, and had we not isolated them in this fashion, the whole galaxy would be infected."

Who is speaking? What is the context? What is the "genetic factor" that might threaten to infect the whole galaxy? You will find the answers to these questions in the following stimulating science-fiction story.

The setting is a time when space has been conquered. Scientists have solved the problem of moving faster than light, the major limiting factor in today's scientific thought. An interstellar ship is hurtling to a mysterious destination. A young ship's officer, new to the ship, is puzzled by certain feelings, strange disturbances that affect his moods. An unusual cargo is responsible for vibrations that permeate the ship.

Through the help of a Counselor, the young officer is permitted to see the cargo, contemplate the unusual danger the cargo represents, and wonder at a civilization that sometimes fosters the most irrational action of all. Cephes 5 is a most unusual planet.

Cephes 5

The Third Officer (in training, which meant that he was merely the aide to the regular third officer) walked through the corridor of the great interstellar ship toward the meditation room. Although he had spent four years studying the eleven classes of interstellar ships, the reality was new, awesome, and infinitely more complex—the more so since this was a Class Two ship, entirely self-sustaining and with an indefinite cruising range. Unlike other interstellar ships, it was named not for the planet of its origin but for the planet of its destination, Cephes 5, and like all medical ships, it carried clearance for any port in the galaxy.

He knew how fortunate he was to have been appointed to this ship to complete his training, and at the age of twenty-two he was young and romantic enough to doubt and bless his good fortune constantly.

The ship was only three days out of its last port of call—the port where he had come on board as an officer cadet—and since then he had been occupied constantly with medical examinations, inoculations, briefings, and orientation tours. This was his first free hour, and he very properly sought the meditation room.

It was a long, plain room with ivory-colored walls and ceiling, and lit by a pleasant golden light. Here and there were stacks of cushions, and perhaps a dozen of the ship's one hundred and twenty crew members were in the room, meditating. Each sat upon one of the thin cushions, legs crossed, body erect, hands folded, eyes cast down in a position that was more or less universal in every planet of the galaxy. The Third Officer selected a pillow and seated himself, crossing his bare legs. He was quite comfortable since he wore only a pair of cotton shorts.

He sought to lose himself in his awareness of himself, as he had learned a long time ago, to still his own wonders and doubts and fears and to immerse himself in the wholeness of the universe, his own self becoming part of an infinitely larger self; yet the process would not work. He was blocked, confused and troubled, his mind shaken and swept from thought to thought, while underneath these rushing thoughts, strange and unpleasant fantasies began to form.

He glanced at the other men and women in the meditation room, but they sat in silence, apparently untroubled by the strange and frightening thoughts that hammered at his mind.

For half an hour or so the Third Officer fought to control his own mind and kept it clear and quiet, then he gave up and left the meditation room; and he realized that he had been in this curious state of mental excitement ever since boarding *Cephes* 5, but had only become fully aware of it when he attempted to meditate.

Deciding that it was simply his own eagerness, his own excitement at being assigned to this great, mysterious interstellar cruiser, he went to one of the viewing rooms, sank into a chair, and pressed the button that raised the screen on outer space. The impression was of sitting in the midst of the galaxy, facing a blazing and uncountable array of stars. The Third Officer remembered that on his early training trips the viewing room had been a cure for almost any problem of fear or disquiet. Now it failed him, and his thoughts in the viewing room were as disquieting as they had been in the meditation room.

Puzzled and not untroubled, the Third Officer left the viewing room and sought out the ship's Counselor. He still had four hours of free time left to him before he began his tour of duty in the engine room, and while he had hoped to devote this time to making the acquaintance of other crew members in the off-duty lounge, he decided now that the first order of importance was to learn why the ship filled him with such a sense of chaos and foreboding.

He knocked at the door of the Counselor's office, and a voice asked him to enter, which he did gingerly, uncertainly, for he had never before gone to a Counselor on one of the great galactic ships. The Counselors were legendary throughout the galaxy, for in a manner of speaking they were the highest rank in all of humanity's table of organization—very old, very wise, and gifted in ways that could only fill a cadet of twenty-two years with awe and respect. On interstellar ships they ranked even above the captain, although it was rare indeed that one of them countermanded a captain's order or interfered in any manner with the operation of the ship. Legend had it that some of the Counselors were more than two hundred years old, and certainly an age of a century and a half was not uncommon.

Now, as the Third Officer entered the small, simply furnished office, an old man in a blue silk robe turned from the desk where he had been writing and nodded at the Third Officer. He was very old indeed, a black man whose skin was as wrinkled and dry as old brown leather and whose pale yellow eyes looked at the Third Officer with pleasant inquiry. Was it true that the Counselors were telepaths who could read minds as easily as ordinary men heard sound? the Third Officer wondered.

"Quite true," the old man said softly. "Be patient, Third Officer. There are more things for you to learn than you imagine." He pointed to a chair. "Sit down and be comfortable. There are a hundred and twelve years of difference in your age and mine, and while you may think that a matter of little account when you reach my age, it's very impressive at the moment, isn't it?"

The Third Officer nodded.

"And you were in the meditation room and you found that you could not meditate?"

"Yes, sir."

"Do you know why?"

"No, sir."

"And neither do you suspect why?"

"I have been on spaceships before," the Third Officer said.

"And you have been on this one for three days, and you have been examined, lectured to, shot full of a variety of serums and antibodies, and oriented—but never told what cargo this ship carries?"

"No, sir."

"Or its purpose?"

"No, sir."

"And quite properly, you did not ask."

"No, sir, I did not ask."

The Counselor regarded the Third Officer in silence for perhaps two or three minutes. The Third Officer by now found his own problems submerged in his excitement and curiosity at actually sitting face to face with one of the fabled Counselors, and finally he could contain himself no longer.

"Would you forgive me if I ask a personal question, sir?"

"I can't imagine any question that requires forgiveness," the Counselor replied, smiling.

"Are you reading my mind now, sir? That's the question."

"Reading your mind now? Oh, no—no indeed. Why should I? I know all about you. We need unusual young men in our crew, and you are quite an unusual young man. Reading your mind would take great concentration and effort; quite to the contrary, I was looking into my own mind and remembering when I was your age. But that's a problem of the aged. We tend to be too reflective and to wander a good deal. Now concerning the meditation—it will take a little time, but once you fully understand the purpose of *Cephes 5*, you will overcome these disturbances and indeed you will find that you meditate on a higher level than before—commensurate with a new effort of will. Let that be for a moment. Do you know what the word *murder* means?"

"No, sir."

"Have you ever heard it before?"

"No, sir. Not that I remember."

The old man appeared to be smiling inwardly, and again there was a minute or two of inner reflection. The Third Officer waited.

"There is a whole spectrum of being that we must examine," the Counselor said finally, "and thus we will introduce you to an area of being you have possibly never dreamed of. It won't damage you or even shake you overmuch, for it was taken into consideration when you were chosen to be a part of the crew of *Cephes* 5. We begin with murder as an idea and an act. Murder is the act of taking a human life, and as an idea it has its origin in abnormal feelings of hatred and aggression."

"Hatred and aggression," the Third Officer repeated slowly.

"Do you follow me? Do you understand?"

"I think so."

"The words are possibly unfamiliar. Allow me to go into your mind for just a moment—and you will feel this better than I could explain it."

The old man's face became blank, and suddenly the Third Officer winced and cried out in disgust. The old black man's face became alive again, and the Third Officer put his face in his hands and sat that way for a moment, shivering.

"I'm sorry, but it was necessary," the Counselor said. "Fear is very much a part of it, and that is why I had to touch the fear and horror centers of your mind. Otherwise, how do you explain color to a blind person?"

The Third Officer looked up and nodded.

"You will be all right in a moment. Murder is the act—the finality of what you just felt. There are other degrees, pain, torture, an incredible variety of hurts—tell me if any of these words elude you."

"Torture, I don't think I ever heard the word."

"It's a deliberate inflicting of pain, psychological pain, physical pain."

"For what reason?" the Third Officer asked.

"There you have the crux of it. For what reason? Reason implies health. This is sickness, the most dreadful sickness that humanity has ever experienced."

"And murder? Is it simply a syndrome? Is it something out of the past? Out of the childhood of the races of humanity? Or is it a postulate?"

"No indeed. It's a reality."

"You mean people kill other people?"

"Exactly."

"Without reason?"

"Without reason as you understand reason. But within the spectrum of this sickness, there is subjective reason and cause."

"Enough to take a human life?" the Third Officer whispered.

"Enough to take a human life."

The young man shook his head. "Incredible—just incredible. But consider, sir, with all due respect, I've had an education, a very good education. I read books. I watch television. I have kept myself informed. How can it be that I've never heard of this—indeed that I've never even heard the words?"

"How many inhabited planets are there in the galaxy?" the old man asked, smiling slightly.

"Thirty-three thousand, four hundred and sixty-nine."

"Seventy-two, since Philbus 7, 8 and 9 were settled last month. Thirty-three thousand, four hundred and seventy-two. Does that answer your question? There are thousands of planets where murder has never occurred, even as there are thousands of planets that have never known tuberculosis, or pneumonia or scarlet fever."

"But we heal these things—and almost every other disease known to humanity," the Third Officer protested.

"Yes, almost every other disease. Almost. We have no knowledge that is absolute. We learn a great deal, but the more we know, the wider the boundaries to the unknown become, and the one disease that defeats our wisest physicians and researchers is this thing we are discussing."

"Has it a name?"

"It has. It is called insanity."

"And you say it's a very old disease?"

"Very old."

It was the Third Officer's turn to be thoughtful, and the old man waited patiently for him to think it through. Finally the cadet asked, "If we have no cure, what happens to these people who murder?"

"We isolate them."

Realization came to the Third Officer like a cold chill. "On the planet Cephes 5?"

"Yes. We isolate them on the planet Cephes 5. We do it as mercifully, as kindly as we can. Long, long ago other alternatives were tried, but they all failed, and finally they came to the conclusion that only isolation would work."

"And this ship—" The Third Officer's voice trailed away.

"Yes—yes, indeed. This is the transport ship. We pick up these people in every part of the galaxy and we take them to Cephes 5. That is why we choose our crew with such care and concern, people of great inner strength. Do you understand now why your meditation went so poorly?"

"Yes, I think I do."

"No sensitive person can escape the vibrations that fill this ship, but you can learn to live with them and deal with them, and find new strength in the process. Of course, you always have the option of leaving the ship."

The old black man looked at the Third Officer thoughtfully, thinking rather wistfully of the precious, fleeting beauty of youth, the unfaded golden hair, the clear blue eyes, the earnest facing and assumption of the problem of life, and he remembered the time when he had been young and strong-limbed and beautiful, not with regret, but with the apparently eternal fascination in the life process that was a part of his being.

"I don't think I will leave the ship, sir," the Third Officer said after a moment.

"I didn't think you would." The Counselor rose then, standing tall and straight and lean, his blue robe hanging from his bony shoulders, his great height and wide shoulders a quality of the black people on the Rebus and Alma constellation of planets. "Come now," he said to the boy, "we will go into this somewhat more fully. And remember, Third Officer, that we have no alternatives. This is a genetic factor in these poor souls, and had we not isolated them in this fashion, the whole galaxy would be infected."

The Third Officer opened the door for him and then followed the Counselor down the corridor to one of the elevators. They passed other crew members on the way, men and women, black and white and yellow and brown people, and each of them made a gesture of respect to the Counselor. They paused at the elevators, and when a door opened, they stepped in. The Captain of the ship was just leaving the elevator, and she held the door for a moment to tell the Counselor that he looked well and rested.

"Thank you, Captain. This is Third Officer Cadet. He is with us only three days."

The Third Officer had not seen the Captain before, and he was struck by the grace and beauty of the woman. She appeared to be in her middle fifties, yellow-skinned with black slanting eyes and black hair hardly touched with gray. She wore a white silk robe of command, and she greeted the Third Officer graciously and warmly, giving him the feeling of being vitally needed and important.

"We were discussing Cephes 5," the Counselor explained. "I take him now to the sleep chamber."

"He is in good hands," the Captain said.

The elevator dropped into the bowels of the great spaceship, stopped, and the door opened. The Third Officer followed the Counselor out into a long, wide chamber that at first glance left him breathless and shaken—a place like a great morgue where on triple tiers of beds at least five hundred human beings lay asleep, men and women and children too, some as young as ten or twelve years, none much older than their twenties, people of every race in the galaxy. In their sleep, there was nothing to distinguish them from normal people.

The Third Officer found himself whispering. "That's not necessary," the Counselor said. "They cannot awake until we awaken them."

The old man led the young man down the long line of beds to the end of the chamber, where, behind a glass wall, men and women in white smocks were working around a table on which a man lay. A network of wires was attached to a band around his skull, and in the background there were banks of machines.

"We block their memories," the Counselor explained. "That we are able to do, and then we build up a new set of memories. It's a very complex procedure. They will have no recollection of any existence before Cephes 5, and they will be fully oriented toward Cephes 5 and the mores there."

"Do you just leave them there?"

"Oh, no—no indeed. We have our agencies on Cephes 5; we have maintained them there for many, many years. Feeding these people into the life of Cephes 5 is a most delicate and important process. If the inhabitants of Cephes 5 were to discover this, the consequences for them would be tragic indeed. But there is very small chance of that. Indeed, it is almost impossible."

"Why?"

"Because the entire pattern of life on Cephes 5 depends on ego structure. Every person on the planet spends his life creating an ego structure which subjectively places him at the center of the universe. This ego structure is central to the disease, for given the sickness that creates the ego, each individual goes on to form in his mind an anthropomorphic superman whom he calls God and who supports his right to kill."

"I am not sure I understand," the Third Officer said.

"In time you will. It is enough to accept the fact that the people on Cephes 5 place their planet and their own selves at the center of the universe, and then they structure their lives so that no uncertainty concerning this should ever arise. This is why we have been able to continue this process for so many years. You see, they refuse even to consider the fact that human beings might exist elsewhere in the universe."

"Then they don't know?"

"No, they don't know."

For a while they stood there, the Third Officer watching the work on the other side of the glass panel and growing more and more uneasy. Then the Counselor tapped his shoulder and said, "Enough. Even in their sleep, they think and dream, and you are still too new to this to suffer their vibrations for long. Come, we will go to one of the viewing rooms, sit and look at the universe, and talk a little more and compose ourselves."

In the viewing room, with the enormous, blazing glory of the stars in front of him and with the comforting presence of the Counselor beside him, the Third Officer was able to relax and begin to deal with the flood of ideas and impressions. He found that he was full of a great pity, an overwhelming sense of sadness, and he spoke of this to the old man.

"It's quite normal," the Counselor said.

"What do they do on Cephes 5?" he wondered.

"They kill."

"Then is the planet empty?"

"Hardly. You see, these poor demented creatures are aware of their function, which is to kill, and like all creatures with a sense of function, they place the function above all else. Thus they breed like no other people in the universe, increasing their population constantly, so that while their killing mounts, their breeding remains ahead of it."

"Are they normally intelligent?"

"Very intelligent—yet their intelligence is to no effect. Their egos prevent them from ever turning it inward."

"But how can they be intelligent and continue this thing you call murder?"

"Because the intelligence is directed toward only one end—the killing of their own kind. As I told you, they are insane."

"But if they are intelligent, won't they devise ways to move through space?"

"Oh, yes. They have done so, with very crude rockets. But we chose Cephes 5 originally because it is the farthest inhabitable planet from the center of the galaxy, almost forty light-years from another inhabitable planet. They will move through space, but the problem of warping space, of moving faster than light—this will always elude them, for this is a problem that we can solve only within ourselves.

For some time the Third Officer sat in silence, and then he asked softly, "Do they suffer a great deal?"

"I am afraid so."

"Is there any hope for them?"

"There is always hope," the old man replied.

"We call it Cephes 5 in our table of planets," the Third Officer said. "But every planet has a subjective name for itself. What do these people call their planet?"

"They call it the Earth," the old man said.

Reading for Understanding

❑ MAIN IDEA

1. The central point of the story is that (a) the people of Earth are immature, with many primitive traits (b) space travel will always be easier for Earth travelers than for others (c) Earth is probably the most advanced planet in the galaxy (d) hatred and aggression will always be found throughout the universe.

❑ DETAILS

2. The Class Two ship in the story is a (a) battle cruiser (b) surveying vessel (c) medical ship (d) fuel freighter.

3. The ship was named (a) after a Greek god (b) for its destination (c) after a scientist of the 21st century (d) for the captain.

4. The difference in ages between the Counselor and the Third Officer is (a) 20 years (b) 60 years (c) more than a hundred (d) never mentioned.

5. The sleep chamber contained (a) the major officers of the ship (b) the Third Officer's quarters (c) a place of relaxation (d) the ship's cargo.

☐ INFERENCES

6. The Third Officer had been chosen for his berth on the ship because of (a) his father's glorious record (b) the Captain's bias (c) his position on a list (d) his personal qualities.
7. The people being transported to Cephes 5 were (a) all from Earth (b) from our own solar system (c) from everywhere in the galaxy (d) from a science laboratory on an outer planet.
8. The major fault with the people on Cephes 5 is (a) complete self-centeredness (b) inability to make up their minds (c) vulnerability to physical ailments (d) lack of intelligence.
9. A major aspect of Cephes 5 is its (a) dense cloud cover (b) ever-growing population (c) reputation as the birthplace of many space heroes (d) closeness to the center of the galaxy.
10. The Third Officer, the Counselor, and the Captain are alike in their (a) smart appearance (b) knowledge of stellar navigation (c) life-enhancing qualities (d) understanding of the problems of Cephes 5.

☐ AUTHOR'S PURPOSE

11. A major purpose of the author in writing this story was to (a) praise the average human being (b) point out dismaying negative tendencies on the planet Earth (c) write a humorous tale of travel to the stars (d) continue the adventures of the *Star Trek Enterprise*.

☐ TONE OF SELECTION

12. The tone of the story is one of (a) quiet sadness (b) exuberant revelation (c) humorous gaiety (d) argumentative sarcasm.

☐ OUTCOMES

13. The spaceship will reach Cephes 5, disembark the cargo, (a) but the Third Officer will ask to remain on Cephes 5 (b) and the spaceship will take off to return to its home base (c) and the Counselor will accept a new role as ruler of Cephes 5 (d) and then have to wage war against the inhabitants.

☐ CAUSE AND EFFECT

14. The sleepers were being transported to Cephes 5 because (a) the spaceship commander was a dictator (b) they had asked to return home (c) they had demonstrated a genetic defect (d) Cephes 5 was underpopulated.

❑ FACT OR OPINION

Tell whether the following is a fact or an opinion.

15. Meditation was a regular therapeutic activity on board the spaceship.

Words in Context

1. "... and since then he had been occupied constantly with ... briefings, and *orientation tours.*" ***Orientation tours*** (450) have as their goal (a) promotion (b) familiarization (c) study (d) distinction.

2. "He sought to lose himself in his awareness of himself ... and to *immerse* himself in the wholeness of the universe." ***Immerse*** (450) means (a) engross (b) develop (c) find (d) analyze.

3. "Now it failed him, and his thoughts in the viewing room were as *disquieting* as they had been in the meditation room." ***Disquieting*** (451) means (a) disrespectful (b) relaxing (c) perturbing (d) exasperating.

4. "... the first order of importance was to learn why the ship filled him with such a sense of chaos and *foreboding.*" ***Foreboding*** (451) means (a) horror (b) panic (c) detestation (d) apprehension.

5. "He knocked at the door of the Counselor's office, and a voice asked him to enter, which he did *gingerly,* uncertainly, for he had never before gone to a Counselor ... " ***Gingerly*** (451) means (a) quietly (b) warily (c) hesitatingly (d) quickly.

6. "On interstellar ships they ranked even above the captain, although it was rare indeed that one of them *countermanded* a captain's order." ***Countermanded*** (451) means (a) reviewed (b) criticized (c) disobeyed (d) canceled.

7. "'... you will find that you meditate on a higher level than before—*commensurate with* a new effort of will.'" ***Commensurate with*** (452) means (a) lessened by (b) created by (c) consistent with (d) multiplied by.

8. "The old man's face became blank, and suddenly the Third Officer *winced* and cried out in disgust." ***Winced*** (453) means (a) clenched his fists (b) gritted his teeth (c) trembled (d) flinched.

9. "'There you have the *crux* of it. For what reason ... '" ***Crux*** (453) means (a) essence (b) cruelty (c) concept (d) reality.

10. "The old black man looked at the Third Officer thoughtfully, thinking rather *wistfully* about the precious, *fleeting* beauty of youth." ***Wistfully . . . fleeting*** . . . (454) means (a) contentedly . . . awesome (b) jealously . . . magnificent (c) sadly . . . short-lived (d) callously . . . fragile.

11. "'This is a *genetic factor* in these poor souls, and had we not isolated them in this fashion, the whole galaxy would be infected.'" ***Genetic factor*** (455) means (a) environmental element (b) inherited component (c) fatal defect (d) universal causation.

12. "'They will have no recollection of any existence before Cephes 5, and they will be fully *oriented toward* Cephes 5 and the *mores* there.'" ***Oriented toward . . . mores*** (455) mean (a) acquainted with . . . type of people (b) equipped for . . . regulations (c) defused for . . . climate (d) accustomed to . . . customs.

13. "'Every person on the planet spends his life creating an *ego structure* which *subjectively* places him at the center of the universe.'" ***Ego structure . . . subjectively*** . . . (456) mean (a) ambition . . . structurally (b) consciousness . . . in his thinking (c) world outlook . . . completely (d) self-acceptance . . . falsely.

14. "'Come, we will go to one of the viewing rooms, sit and look at the universe . . . and *compose* ourselves.'" ***Compose*** (456) means (a) analyze (b) placate (c) judge (d) calm.

15. "'You see, these poor *demented* creatures are aware of their function, which is to kill, . . . and they place the function above all else.'" ***Demented*** (456) means (a) deliberative (b) deranged (c) deferential (d) delineated.

Thinking Critically About the Story

1. Why does the Third Officer resort to meditation? Do you know real-life or other fictional people who have used it successfully? What is it supposed to accomplish? Have you ever tried it? Would doing so help you with some of your present problems? Explain.

2. Why does the Third Officer go to see the Counselor? What is the role of the Counselor? How does the Counselor compare with your school and vocational counselors? What tools beyond the control of his present-day counterparts are available to the Counselor? If you had a besetting problem, would you seek help from a guidance counselor? Why does the Third Officer go to him without hesitation? Explain.

3. At the beginning of the story, how did the Third Officer become aware of the unusual nature of the voyage? What communicated to him the sense of chaos and foreboding? How was it done? What are some other stories that deal with extrasensory perception (ESP) in action? Have you ever had an experience that seemed to involve ESP? Do you feel that there is ESP? Explain.

4. What does the Counselor do after he says,"Allow me to go into your mind for just a moment—and you will feel this better than I could explain it." What is a telepath supposedly capable of doing? Do you believe that people can implant feelings—and ideas from one mind to another—without using the usual means of communication? Have you ever seen a "mind reader" in action? Can people actually read your mind as though it were a computer screen? Cite your evidence.

5. According to the author, Howard Fast, what is the tragic flaw in human beings? Are human beings the only living creatures with a willingness to kill their kind? Explain. Do you agree that we have been irrevocably programmed to kill each other and that murder is inevitable? Justify your answer. Why did Fast develop these hypotheses?

Stories in Words

Inoculations (450) is ultimately derived from the Latin word *oculus,* or "eye." The Latin verb *inoculare* meant "to insert a bud in a plant, to graft." Besides meaning "eye," *oculus* meant "bud." The eye of the potato suggests this association with *eye* and agriculture. Now *inoculate* suggests implanting a microbe or vaccine rather than a *bud.* The *eye* root appears in *binoculars,* in which the prefix *bi* suggests *two.* An *oculist* is a doctor concerned with the *eye.*

Orientation (450) seems similar to *oriental*: indeed the two words are related by derivation. The basic root of both is the Latin *oriri,* "to rise." The Orient is the East, where the sun *rises.* One meaning of the verb *orient* is "to turn toward the east," or "cause to face toward the east." The verb now has a general meaning: "to adjust to one's surroundings, to get one's bearings." As used in the text, *orientation* refers to an adjustment period. In 1948 a new word came into existence: *orienteering.* This is a cross-country race involving the use of a map and compass and many checkpoints along the route.

Syndrome (453) contains two Greek elements: *syn,* "together, with"; "*dramein,* "to run." A *syndrome* is a *running together* of signs, symptoms, or characteristics. Though generally referring to disease, *syndrome* may also refer to other combinations of characteristics. *Syn* appears in words like *sympathy, syndicate, synthetic, synonym,* and *synopsis. Drom* appears in the word *hippodrome*—by derivation a "horse racecourse," and *dromedary*—a camel of unusual "running" ability.

Harrison Bergeron

KURT VONNEGUT, JR.

"Even as I stand here—" he bellowed, "crippled, hobbled, sickened—I am a greater ruler than any man who ever lived! Now watch me become what I *can* become!"

Extrapolation is a major tool of science-fiction writers. To extrapolate is to project, extend, or expand known facts into an area not yet experienced. Kurt Vonnegut, Jr., has taken certain trends he observes in today's society and extrapolated them into a future nearly a century from now.

In his opening paragraph, Vonnegut provides a clue to his disapproval of current trends. Equality before the law is a desirable goal, but *complete* equality is impossible. By the nature of things, some people are faster, brighter, taller, happier, livelier, more skilled than others. Mediocrity is scarcely admirable; yet, Vonnegut apparently feels, certain trends in society encourage mediocrity and deplore departure from the norm. Vonnegut then proceeds to extrapolate this trend to create a society that is nothing short of a nightmare.

"Harrison Bergeron" is outrageous and enthralling, stimulating and challenging. You will not soon forget Harrison Bergeron, who dared to challenge the supremacy of mediocrity, if only for a glorious moment. Vonnegut has dreamed up a society that even science-fiction writers haven't visualized.

Harrison Bergeron

The year was 2081, and everybody was finally equal. They weren't only equal before God and the law. They were equal every which way. Nobody was smarter than anybody else. Nobody was better looking than anybody else. Nobody was stronger or quicker than anybody else. All this equality was due to the 211th, 212th, and 213th Amendments to the Constitution, and to the unceasing vigilance of agents of the United States Handicapper General.

Some things about living still weren't quite right, though. April, for instance, still drove people crazy by not being springtime. And it was in that clammy month that the H-G men took George and Hazel Bergeron's fourteen-year-old son, Harrison, away.

It was tragic, all right, but George and Hazel couldn't think about it very hard. Hazel had a perfectly average intelligence, which meant she couldn't think about anything except in short bursts. And George, while his intelligence was way above normal, had a little mental handicap radio in his ear. He was required by law to wear it at all times. It was tuned to a government transmitter. Every twenty seconds or so, the transmitter would send out some sharp noise to keep people like George from taking unfair advantage of their brains.

George and Hazel were watching television. There were tears on Hazel's cheeks, but she'd forgotten for the moment what they were about.

On the television screen were ballerinas.

A buzzer sounded in George's head. His thoughts fled in panic, like bandits from a burglar alarm.

"That was a real pretty dance, that dance they just did," said Hazel.

"Huh?" said George.

"That dance—it was nice," said Hazel.

"Yup," said George. He tried to think a little about the ballerinas. They weren't really very good—no better than anybody else would have been, anyway. They were burdened with sash weights and bags of birdshot, and their faces were masked, so that no one, seeing a free and graceful gesture or a pretty face, would feel like something the cat drug in. George was toying with the vague notion that maybe dancers shouldn't be handicapped. But he didn't get very far with it before another noise in his ear radio scattered his thoughts.

George winced. So did two out of the eight ballerinas.

Hazel saw him wince. Having no mental handicap herself, she had to ask George what the latest sound had been.

"Sounded like somebody hitting a milk bottle with a ball peen hammer,"* said George.

"I'd think it would be real interesting, hearing all the different sounds," said Hazel, a little envious. "All the things they think up."

"Um," said George.

"Only, if I was Handicapper General, you know what I would do?" said Hazel. Hazel, as a matter of fact, bore a strong resemblance to the Handicapper General, a woman named Diana Moon Glampers. "If I was Diana Moon Glampers," said Hazel, "I'd have chimes on Sunday—just chimes. Kind of in honor of religion."

"I could think, if it was just chimes," said George.

"Well—maybe make'em real loud," said Hazel. "I think I'd make a good Handicapper General."

"Good as anybody else," said George.

"Who knows better'n I do what normal is?" said Hazel.

"Right," said George. He began to think glimmeringly about his abnormal son who was now in jail, about Harrison, but a twenty-one-gun salute in his head stopped that.

"Boy!" said Hazel, "that was a doozy, wasn't it?"

It was such a doozy that George was white and trembling, and tears stood on the rims of his red eyes. Two of the eight ballerinas had collapsed to the studio floor, were holding their temples.

"All of a sudden you look so tired," said Hazel. "Why don't you stretch out on the sofa, so's you can rest your handicap bag on the pillows, honeybunch." She was referring to the forty-seven pounds of birdshot in a canvas bag, which was padlocked around George's neck. "Go on and rest the bag for a little while," she said. "I don't care if you're not equal to me for a while."

George weighed the bag with his hands. "I don't mind it," he said. "I don't notice it any more. It's just a part of me."

"You been so tired lately—kind of wore out," said Hazel. "If there was just some way we could make a little hole in the bottom of the bag, and just take out a few of them lead balls. Just a few."

"Two years in prison and two thousand dollars fine for every ball I took out," said George. "I don't call that a bargain."

"If you could just take a few out when you came from work," said Hazel. "I mean—you don't compete with anybody around here. You just set around."

**ball peen hammer* having a spherical shape rather than a claw at the end of the hammerhead

"If I tried to get away with it," said George, "then other people'd get away with it—and pretty soon we'd be right back to the dark ages again, with everybody competing against everybody else. You wouldn't like that, would you?"

"I'd hate it," said Hazel.

"There you are," said George. "The minute people start cheating on laws, what do you think happens to society?"

If Hazel hadn't been able to come up with an answer to this question, George couldn't have supplied one. A siren was going off in his head.

"Reckon it'd fall all apart," said Hazel.

"What would?" said George blankly.

"Society," said Hazel uncertainly. "Wasn't that what you just said?"

"Who knows?" said George.

The television program was suddenly interrupted for a news bulletin. It wasn't clear at first as to what the bulletin was about, since the announcer, like all announcers, had a serious speech impediment. For about half a minute, and in a state of high excitement, the announcer tried to say, "Ladies and gentlemen—"

He finally gave up, handed the bulletin to a ballerina to read.

"That's all right—" Hazel said of the announcer, "he tried. That's the big thing. He tried to do the best he could with what God gave him. He should get a nice raise for trying so hard."

"Ladies and gentlemen—" said the ballerina, reading the bulletin. She must have been extraordinarily beautiful, because the mask she wore was hideous. And it was easy to see that she was the strongest and most graceful of all the dancers, for her handicap bags were as big as those worn by two-hundred-pound men.

And she had to apologize at once for her voice, which was a very unfair voice for a woman to use. Her voice was a warm, luminous, timeless melody. "Excuse me—" she said, and she began again, making her voice absolutely uncompetitive.

"Harrison Bergeron, age fourteen," she said in a grackle squawk, "has just escaped from jail, where he was held on suspicion of plotting to overthrow the government. He is a genius and an athlete, is under-handicapped, and should be regarded as extremely dangerous."

A police photograph of Harrison Bergeron was flashed on the screen—upside down, then sideways, upside down again, then right side up. The picture showed the full length of Harrison against a background calibrated in feet and inches. He was exactly seven feet tall.

The rest of Harrison's appearance was Halloween and hardware. Nobody had ever borne heavier handicaps. He had outgrown hindrances faster than the H-G men could think them up. Instead of a little ear radio for a mental handicap, he wore a tremendous pair of earphones, and spectacles with thick wavy lenses. The spectacles were intended to make him not only half blind, but to give him whanging headaches besides.

Scrap metal was hung all over him. Ordinarily, there was a certain symmetry, a military neatness to the handicaps issued to strong people, but Harrison looked like a walking junkyard. In the race of life, Harrison carried three hundred pounds.

And to offset his good looks, the H-G men required that he wear at all times a red rubber ball for a nose, keep his eyebrows shaved off, and cover his even white teeth with black caps at snaggle-tooth random.

"If you see this boy," said the ballerina, "do not—I repeat, do not—try to reason with him."

There was the shriek of a door being torn from its hinges.

Screams and barking cries of consternation came from the television set. The photograph of Harrison Bergeron on the screen jumped again and again, as though dancing to the tune of an earthquake.

George Bergeron correctly identified the earthquake, and well he might have—for many was the time his own home had danced to the same crashing tune. "My God—" said George, "that must be Harrison!"

The realization was blasted from his mind instantly by the sound of an automobile collision in his head.

When George could open his eyes again, the photograph of Harrison was gone. A living, breathing Harrison filled the screen.

Clanking, clownish, and huge, Harrison stood in the center of the studio. The knob of the uprooted studio door was still in his hand. Ballerinas, technicians, musicians, and announcers cowered on their knees before him, expecting to die.

"I am the Emperor!" cried Harrison. "Do you hear? I am the Emperor! Everybody must do what I say at once!" He stamped his foot and the studio shook.

"Even as I stand here—" he bellowed, "crippled, hobbled, sickened—I am a greater ruler than any man who ever lived! Now watch me become what I can become!"

Harrison tore the straps of his handicap harness like wet tissue paper, tore straps guaranteed to support five thousand pounds.

Harrison's scrap-iron handicaps crashed to the floor.

Harrison thrust his thumbs under the bar of the padlock that secured his head harness. The bar snapped like celery. Harrison smashed his headphones and spectacles against the wall.

He flung away his rubber-ball nose, revealed a man that would have awed Thor, the god of thunder.

"I shall now select my Empress!" he said, looking down on the cowering people. "Let the first woman who dares rise to her feet claim her mate and her throne!"

A moment passed, and then a ballerina arose, swaying like a willow. Harrison plucked the mental handicap from her ear, snapped off her physical handicaps with marvelous delicacy. Last of all, he removed her mask.

She was blindingly beautiful.

"Now—" said Harrison, taking her hand, "shall we show the people the meaning of the word dance? Music!" he commanded.

The musicians scrambled back into their chairs, and Harrison stripped them of their handicaps, too. "Play your best," he told them, "and I'll make you barons and dukes and earls."

The music began. It was normal at first—cheap, silly, false. But Harrison snatched two musicians from their chairs, waved them like batons as he sang the music as he wanted it played. He slammed them back into their chairs.

The music began again and was much improved.

Harrison and his Empress merely listened to the music for a while—listened gravely, as though synchronizing their heartbeats with it.

They shifted their weights to their toes.

Harrison placed his big hands on the girl's tiny waist, letting her sense the weightlessness that would soon be hers.

And then, in an explosion of joy and grace, into the air they sprang!

Not only were the laws of the land abandoned, but the law of gravity and the laws of motion as well.

They reeled, whirled, swiveled, flounced, capered, gamboled, and spun.

They leaped like deer on the moon.

The studio ceiling was thirty feet high, but each leap brought the dancers nearer to it.

It became their obvious intention to kiss the ceiling.

They kissed it.

And then, neutralizing gravity with love and pure will, they remained suspended in air inches below the ceiling, and they kissed each other for a long, long time.

It was then that Diana Moon Glampers, the Handicapper General, came into the studio with a double-barreled ten-gauge shotgun. She fired twice, and the Emperor and the Empress were dead before they hit the floor.

Diana Moon Glampers loaded the gun again. She aimed it at the musicians and told them they had ten seconds to get their handicaps back on.

It was then that the Bergerons' television tube burned out.

Hazel turned to comment about the blackout to George. But George had gone out into the kitchen for a can of beer.

George came back in with the beer, paused while a handicap signal shook him up. And then he sat down again. "You been crying?" he said to Hazel.

"Yup," she said.

"What about?" he said.

"I forget," she said. "Something real sad on television."

"What was it?" he said.

"It's all kind of mixed up in my mind," said Hazel.

"Forget sad things," said George.

"I always do," said Hazel.

"That's my girl," said George. He winced. There was the sound of a riveting gun in his head.

"Gee—I could tell that was a doozy," said Hazel.

"You can say that again," said George.
"Gee—" said Hazel, "I could tell that one was a doozy."

Reading for Understanding

❑ MAIN IDEA

1. The main point of the story is the (a) generally negative aspects of the typical television game show (b) disastrous results of trying to make everyone equal in every respect (c) ways in which future scientists will assure compatibility of spouses (d) ways in which true love rises above apparently insuperable obstacles.

❑ DETAILS

2. Harrison Bergeron was arrested in (a) February (b) March (c) April (d) none of these.

3. Unlike Hazel, George (a) is an underground spy for the Handicapper General (b) has less-than-average intelligence (c) is not related to Harrison Bergeron (d) carries a mental handicap radio.

4. The forty-seven pounds of birdshot (a) are around George's neck (b) act as ballast for their small boat (c) are reserved for an upcoming hunting party (d) have been left in the apartment by a previous tenant.

5. The person who answers Harrison Bergeron's call for an Empress is (a) Hazel (b) unintelligent (c) Diana Moon Glampers (d) a ballerina.

❑ INFERENCES

6. George is saddled with devastating handicaps because he is (a) bright (b) a traitor (c) Hazel's husband (d) talkative.

7. Surprisingly enough, when George and Hazel talk about the handicaps, George (a) agrees to take them off for a while (b) defends their use (c) telephones for permission to remove them (d) expresses his sense of being persecuted.

8. Of the use of handicaps in the story, it might be said that (a) the more trying the handicap, the more accomplished the person (b) there is nothing in modern society that relates in any way to the use of handicaps (c) the society of the future has found a sound, sensible way to eliminate inequalities (d) the parents of children carrying handicaps have petitioned the government to remove them.

9. Harrison Bergeron is apparently (a) an arm of the secret police (b) a weakling suffering many handicaps (c) superior in intelligence and physique (d) a brother of the new Emperor.

❑ AUTHOR'S METHOD

10. In "Harrison Bergeron," the author relies heavily upon (a) exaggeration and satire (b) realism and straightforward narration (c) subtle characterization of the Handicapper General (d) poetic narrative and gentle laughter.

❑ AUTHOR'S PURPOSE

11. The author's purpose in this story is to (a) show the best of all possible worlds (b) suggest the dangers of a mindless search for a fictitious "equality" (c) provide a practical blueprint for a brave new world without problems (d) prove that science fiction can equal ordinary fiction in the analysis of character.

❑ TONE OF SELECTION

12. The tone of the story may be characterized as (a) bitterly misanthropic (b) wickedly humorous (c) contagiously optimistic (d) conciliatory and apologetic.

❑ ORDER OF EVENTS

13. Arrange the items in the order in which they occurred. Use letters only.
    A. Diana Moon Glampers fires her double-barreled ten-gauge shotgun.
    B. George's son is taken away.
    C. The U.S. passes the 211th, 212th, and 213th Amendments.
    D. A news bulletin announces the escape of a prisoner.
    E. George sees Harrison on the tube.

❑ PREDICTING OUTCOMES

14. After the death of the Emperor and Empress, (a) Diana Moon Glampers will be court-martialed (b) Hazel and George will make a suicide pact in grief (c) nothing will change (d) the Amendments will be repealed.

❑ FACT OR OPINION

Tell whether the following is a fact or an opinion.

15. The society depicted by Vonnegut is generally sound and well-planned.

Words in Context

1. "All this equality was due . . . to the unceasing *vigilance* of agents of the United States *Handicapper* General." ***Vigilance* . . . *Handicapper*** (464) mean (a) intelligence . . . in charge of horse racing (b) expenditures . . . in charge of secret police (c) watchfulness . . . in charge of disadvantages (d) authority . . . in charge of drug control.

2. "They were burdened with *sash weights* and bags of birdshot, and their faces were masked . . ." ***Sash weights*** (464) today are used to (a) decorate dresses (b) balance windows (c) slow down cars (d) fasten belts.

3. "George *winced.* So did two out of the eight ballerinas." ***Winced*** (465) means (a) smiled (b) frowned (c) flinched (d) groaned.

4. "He began to think *glimmeringly* about his abnormal son . . . but a twenty-one gun salute in his head stopped that." ***Glimmeringly*** (465) means (a) sadly (b) angrily (c) hopefully (d) faintly.

5. "It wasn't clear at first as to what the bulletin was about, since the announcer . . . had a serious *speech impediment.*" An example of a ***speech impediment*** (466) would be (a) bass voice (b) stuttering (c) monotone (d) high volume.

6. "*Her voice was a warm, luminous, timeless melody.*" Her voice was like that of a (a) train announcer (b) cheerleader (c) singer of lullabies (d) newscaster.

7. "The picture showed the full length of Harrison against a background *calibrated* in feet and inches." ***Calibrated*** (466) means (a) marked off (b) confined (c) constricted (d) constructed.

8. "He had outgrown *hindrances* faster than the H-G men could think them up." ***Hindrances*** (466) means (a) weights (b) encumbrances (c) difficulties (d) devices.

9. "Ordinarily, there was a certain *symmetry,* a military neatness to the handicaps issued to strong people, but Harrison looked like a walking junkyard." ***Symmetry*** (467) means (a) balance (b) usefulness (c) ruthlessness (d) beauty.

10. "And to *offset* his good looks, the H-G men required that he wear at all times a red rubber ball for a nose . . . and cover his even white teeth with black caps *at snaggle-tooth random.*" ***Offset* . . . *snaggle-tooth random*** . . . (467) mean (a) emphasize . . . with the irregularity of baby teeth (b) control . . . with the regularity of capped teeth (c) contrast with . . . at regular intervals (d) counteract . . . with the irregularity of bad teeth.

11. "Screams and barking cries of *consternation* came from the television set." ***Consternation*** (467) means (a) panic (b) pain (c) surprise (d) danger.

12. "'Even as I stand here—' he bellowed, 'crippled, *hobbled*, sickened—I am a greater ruler than any man who ever lived!'" ***Hobbled*** (467) means (a) unloved (b) misunderstood (c) fettered (d) at bay.

13. "*He flung away his rubber-ball nose, revealed a man that would have awed Thor, the god of thunder.*" (467) He looked like (a) a desperate criminal (b) a mythical monster (c) a legendary champion (d) a badly injured man.

14. "Harrison and his Empress merely listened to the music for a while . . . as though *synchronizing* their heartbeats with it." ***Synchronizing*** (468) means (a) pulsating (b) contrasting (c) strengthening (d) timing together.

15. "They reeled, whirled, swiveled, *flounced, capered, gamboled,* and spun." ***Flounced, capered, gamboled*** (468) are (a) contrasting terms (b) synonymous terms (c) unrelated in meaning (d) abstract in meaning.

Thinking Critically About the Story

1. Separating the truth from the farcical, to what extent do Harrison Bergeron's parents, George and Hazel, resemble people you know? To what extent do they resemble people you meet in TV series?

2. Prove the truth of the following quotation: "Kurt Vonnegut, Jr., has taken certain trends he observes in today's society and extrapolated them into a future nearly a century from now." What is wrong with the society envisaged in this story? For what does it punish? What is rewarded? To what extent does it resemble the world we live in? Would you enjoy living in it? Cite examples from real life to prove your contentions.

3. To what extent are the characters of Harrison Bergeron, the ballet dancer, and Diana Moon Glampers based on reality? To what extent are they grossly exaggerated? What does the author expect to accomplish by juxtaposing such contrasts? Does he succeed? Explain.

4. Which of the gimmicks in the story did you find most ingenious? Which did you find cruelest? Would you use any of the training devices on your friends? On members of your family? Give the reasons.

5. How does the slapstick in this story compare with that found on TV? Think of animated cartoons and situation comedies. Cite specific examples to prove your contentions.

Stories in Words

Handicap (464) reveals its superficial origins quickly: *hand in cap*. What connection does a hand in cap have with the artificial advantage or disadvantage given to competitors in a sports contest? In the past, in various kinds of wagers, the two competing parties deposited their money in a cap or hat for the winner to take away. The word *handicap* has expanded its meaning beyond the sports scene. It can now apply to any disadvantage that makes achievement difficult.

Siren (466) is clearly and directly descended from the Greek temptresses who in the *Odyssey* tried to lure Odysseus onto the rocks by their singing. Odysseus was warned, "Whoever sails near and hears the song of the Sirens immediately forgets wife and children." Odysseus had the ears of his comrades stopped with wax so that they would not be tempted. He allowed himself to hear the Sirens' song, but, by prearrangement, his comrades did not untie him. Even today the word *siren* is sometimes used for an unusually alluring woman, a temptress. There is another meaning: a *penetrating warning sound*, as of an ambulance. Like the song of the Sirens, this sound is intended to get everyone's attention!

Calibrated (466) demonstrates that tracing a word's origins isn't always easy; often there are disagreements among the experts. Of *calibrate*, one thing seems certain: it is directly related to the word *caliber*. Caliber is the diameter of a circular section, especially of the inside of a gun's bore. Out of this come combinations like a *22-caliber gun*. Both *The Oxford Dictionary of English Etymology* and *The Random House Dictionary* trace *caliber* to the Arabic *calib*, or "mold." *Webster's New International Dictionary* takes it beyond the Arabic to the Greek *kalapous*, containing a root meaning "to burn." In addition, Ernest Weekley's *Etymological Dictionary*, suggests the Medieval Latin *aequilibrare*, with the suggestion of *measurement*, a link to the modern meaning of *calibrate*. Often the linkage to the past is easy. Sometimes, however, there are missing steps that make certainty impossible.

I Do Not Love Thee, Dr. Fell

ROBERT BLOCH

"I was sleeping," he told her. "There's nothing to worry about, my dear. From now on, we're going places. I've been in a pretty bad slump for the past month or so—someday I'll tell you all about it—but I'm all right now. Let's go out for dinner and we'll make plans."

There is an old rhyme written by Tom Brown, three centuries ago when Brown was a student at Oxford:

I do not love thee, Doctor Fell,
The reason why I cannot tell;
But this alone I know full well,
I do not love thee, Doctor Fell.

The rhyme has often been quoted to illustrate the perfectly irrational dislike one person may have for another. There is a Dr. Fell in our story, a person not easily pinned down. Who is he? Why has he been consulted by Mr. Bromely? What effect has he had upon the hapless Bromely?

Though classified as science fiction and a glance at a possible future, this is basically a story of irony. In the highly charged world of the present, with pressures and tensions on every side, how can people cope? In our story, by the author of *Psycho*, one person coped—perhaps not altogether successfully.

I Do Not Love Thee, Doctor Fell

Bromely couldn't remember who had recommended Doctor Fell. The name had popped into his mind (funny, something like that popping *into* his mind at a time when so many things seemed to be popping *out* of it!) and he must have made an appointment.

At any rate, the receptionist seemed to know him, and her "Good morning, Mr. Bromely" had a warm, pleasant sound. The door of the inner office, closing behind him, had a harsh, grating sound. Both seemed oddly familiar.

Bromely sensed the same misplaced familiarity as he gazed around the inner office. The bookshelves and filing cases to the left of the window, the desk to the right, the couch in the corner almost duplicated the arrangement in his own office. This was a good omen, he felt. He'd be at home here. At home. But, *you can't go home again. Home is where the heart is. You have stolen my heart, now don't go 'way. As we sang love's old sweet song on—*

It took a tremendous, conscious effort to pull out of that one, but Bromely did it. He wanted to make a good impression on the Doctor.

Doctor Fell rose to greet him from his chair behind the desk. He was a tall, thin man of about Bromely's age and build, and Bromely received a vague impression that his features were not dissimilar. The subdued lighting did not lend itself to a closer scrutiny of the psychiatrist's countenance, but Bromely was aware of a look of purpose and intensity quite foreign to his own face.

The same purpose and intensity drove Doctor Fell around the desk, communicated in his hearty handclasp.

"You're prompt, Mr. Bromely," said Doctor Fell. His voice was deep and low: *Deep and Low. Low and Behold. Behold, Bedad and Begob. Shadrach, Mesach and Abednego, Inc.*

How he got out of that one, Bromely never knew. He was somewhat surprised to find himself on the couch. Apparently he'd been talking to Doctor Fell for quite some time—and quite rationally, too. Yes, he remembered, now. He'd been answering all the routine questions.

Doctor Fell knew that he was Clyde Bromely, age 32, public relations counsel. Born in Erie, Pennsylvania. Parents dead. Business, lousy. No business. No *business like show business, there's no business I know—*

Had he said that? Apparently not, because Doctor Fell's rich, deep, comforting voice moved right along, asking the questions and extracting the answers. And it was quite all right to talk to Doctor Fell, tell him all he knew. Fell was a good psychiatrist.

Bromely knew a little something about psychiatry himself. Oh, not the technical terms of course, but more than a smattering of technique. This was a routine orientation, preliminary to probing. And Bromely cooperated.

When Doctor Fell began to ask questions about his health and his general background, Bromely took a sheaf of papers from his inside coat pocket and handed them over.

"Here it is, Doc," he said. "Complete report on the physical. Had it taken last week." He indicated a second folded sheaf. "And here's the autobiography. All the names you'll need—friends, relatives, teachers, employers, the works. Everything I could remember. Which isn't much, right now."

Doctor Fell smiled in the shadows. "Excellent," he said. "You seem to understand the necessity of cooperation." He put the papers on the desk. "I'll check over this later, " he told Bromely. "Although I imagine I'm already familiar with most of the contents."

Bromely got that panicky feeling again. Whoever had recommended Doctor Fell to him must also have talked to Doctor Fell about his case. Now who would that be? He hesitated to ask—not that he felt ashamed, but it would be an admission that he was pretty far gone if he couldn't even recall how he'd come here. Well, it didn't matter. He was grateful to be here, and that was the important thing. He needed Doctor Fell.

"You've got to help me, Doctor Fell," he was saying. "You're my last hope. That's why I've come to you. You must understand that, because it's the crux of the whole matter. I would never have come to you unless you were my last hope. I'm at the end of my rope. When you come to the end of your rope, you swing. I'm swinging, now. I'm swinging down the lane, Down Memory Lane. I wanted to be a songwriter, once. But my lyrics sounded as if they were stolen. That's my problem. Association. I've got too much association. Everything I do or say sounds like it's stolen from somebody else. Imitation. Mimicry. Until there's nothing original, nothing basic beneath to which I can cling. I'm losing myself. There's no real *me* left."

Bromely went on like this for about an hour. He said everything that came into his mind. The associative clichés poured out, and with them the desperate plea for help.

Doctor Fell scribbled in his notebook and said nothing. At the end of the session he tapped Bromely on the shoulder.

"That'll be enough for today," he said. "Tomorrow, same time? Let's plan on an hour a day, five days a week."

"Then you think you can help me?"

Doctor Fell nodded. "Let's say that I think you can help yourself. Five days a week, from now on."

Bromely rose from the couch. Doctor Fell's face wavered and blurred before him. He was very tired, very confused, but oddly relieved despite the physical strain that affected his vision. There was just one thing bothering him—and suddenly, he remembered it.

"But, Doc, I just happened to think. You know, I'm not doing too well with the business these days and five days a week—"

The hand gripped his shoulder. "I quite understand. But let's put it this way. Your case—your problem, that is—interests me, personally. And even a psychiatrist has been known to extend his services on occasion, without fee."

Bromely couldn't believe his ears at first. "You mean—it won't cost me anything?" His expression of gratitude was genuine. "Doc, you're a real friend. A friend in need. A friend in deed. Indeed."

Doctor Fell chuckled. "Believe me, Mr. Bromely, I am your friend. You'll find that out for yourself, in time, I trust."

As Clyde Bromely went out the door he felt the phrases flooding through his brain. *In God we trust, all others pay cash. My best and only friend. A man's best friend is his mother.*

The receptionist said something to him as he left, but Bromely was too preoccupied to catch her words. He was *engrossed in thought*, he was *deep in contemplation, Deep in the Heart of Texas. Death and Texas. Nothing's sure but.*

The rest of the day passed in a blur. Almost before he realized it, tomorrow had come and he had come and here he was back on the couch.

Doctor Fell listened as he told him about his father and mother, and about the peculiar feeling he now had—the feeling that Doctor Fell reminded him of his father and mother. Brother and sister I have none, but I am my father's only son. Who am I?

"Who are you?" Doctor Fell asked the question, softly. "That's really what's bothering you, isn't it? Who are you? You can answer that question if you want to, you know. So try. Try. Who are you?"

It was the *wrong* question. Bromely felt it, and he froze. Somewhere, deep inside, words formed an answer. But he couldn't find the words. He couldn't find that spot, inside him, where the words came from.

For the rest of the hour he just lay there on the couch.

Doctor Fell said nothing. When the time was up he tapped Bromely on the shoulder, muttered "Tomorrow, then," and turned away.

Bromely got out of the office. The receptionist stared at him oddly, half-opened her mouth to say something, and didn't. Bromely shrugged. Somehow he managed to find his way back to his own office.

He walked in and asked *his* girl for messages. Apparently whatever was wrong with him showed in his appearance, because she did that half-open-mouth trick too. Then she managed to control herself and tell him that CAA had called just a few minutes ago and wanted to see him. There was a chance to handle Torchy Harrigan.

That was the news he'd been waiting for. Bromely snapped out of it, fast. Torchy Harrigan—just signed for a new network video show—two pictures coming up with MGM—big deal with CAA, Consolidated Artists of America—personal representative—press releases to all dailies—

"Call them back and tell them I'm on my way over," he said. "Bromely rides again!"

Bromely was riding again. He was riding the couch in Doctor Fell's office. He was *riding for a fall, riding hell-for-leather—*

And all the while he was talking it out, gasping and sobbing and wheezing and choking it out.

"I can't explain it, Doc. I just can't figure it out! Here I had this deal sewed up with Harrigan, just the kind of setup I've been looking for. Two bills a week and all expenses, a chance to go out to the Coast with him, the works. Even turned out that his business manager is Hal Edwards—good friend of mine, known him for years. He gave Harrigan the pitch on me, built me up.

"So I walked in on Edwards and we talked it over, and then we went up to Harrigan's suite at the Plaza to talk it over. And Harrigan gave me the big hello, listened to Hal Edwards pitch for me—greatest flack in the business, all that kind of thing.

"You get the picture, Doc? The whole deal was in the bag. Harrigan was just waiting for me to give him the word on my plan for a publicity campaign. Edwards flashed me the cue and I opened my mouth.

"But nothing came out. You understand me? But *nothing*! I couldn't think of anything to say. Oh, there were words and phrases whirling around in my head, only they didn't add up. I couldn't think like a press agent anymore."

All the while he talked, Bromely had been watching Doctor Fell's face. At first it seemed far away, but now it was coming closer and closer, getting bigger and bigger until it blotted out everything.

And Doctor Fell's voice was like distant thunder, then thunder near at hand, thunder overhead.

Vision and hearing played their tricks, but Bromely clung to Doctor Fell, clung to *words that fell from Doctor Fell for he's a jolly good fellow which nobody can deny.*

Doctor Fell had been taking notes in shorthand. He glanced at them now as he spoke. In a moment, Bromely realized he was merely reading off a string of quotes from Bromely's previous conversation. The phrases droned on, louder and louder.

"Can't figure it out . . . sewed up . . . setup . . . two bills a week . . . the works . . . gave Harrigan the pitch on me, built me up . . . big hello . . .

greatest flack in the business . . . get the picture . . . in the bag . . . give him the word . . . flashed me the cue . . . but nothing . . . didn't add up."

Doctor Fell leaned forward. "What do those phrases mean to you, Bromely? What do they really *add up* to, in your mind?"

Bromely tried to think about it. He tried hard. But all he could come out with was, "I don't know. They're all slang expressions I used to use in public relations a few years ago. Come to think of it, they're a little dated now, aren't they?"

Doctor Fell smiled. "Exactly. And doesn't that tie in with your final statement, that you couldn't think like a press agent anymore? Isn't that part of your problem, Mr. Bromely—that you aren't a press agent anymore, really? That you're losing your identity, losing your orientation? Let me ask you once again, now: *who are you*?"

Bromely froze up. He couldn't answer because he couldn't think of the answer. He lay there on the couch, and Doctor Fell waited. Nothing happened.

Nothing seemed to happen for a long, long time. How Bromely got through the next two days he couldn't remember. All he recalled were the hours on the couch—and it seemed to him that he shuttled back and forth between his office and Doctor Fell's more than once a day.

It was hard to check, of course, because he didn't talk to anyone. He lived alone in a one-room walkup apartment and he ate at fast-food places. He wasn't talking to his office-girl, Thelma, anymore either. There was nothing to talk about—no calls since the unfortunate Harrigan affair—and he owed her for three weeks' back salary. Besides, she almost seemed afraid of him when he appeared in the office. Come to think of it (and it was so hard to come to think of it, or anything else, so very hard) even Doctor Fell's little receptionist looked frightened when he walked in, without a word.

Without a word. That was his problem. He had no words any longer. It was as though his final effort, talking to Harrigan and Hal Edwards, had drained him dry of the ability to communicate. All the clichés had flowed out of him, leaving . . . nothing.

He realized it now, lying on the couch in Doctor Fell's office. Once more Doctor Fell had asked the single question, the only question he ever asked. "Who are you?"

And he couldn't answer. There was nothing. He was nobody. For years, now, he'd been in the process of becoming nobody. It was the only explanation that fitted. But he couldn't seem to explain.

With a start, he realized that it wasn't necessary. Doctor Fell was sitting close to Bromely now, breaking the long silence, whispering confidentially in his ear.

"All right," he was murmuring. "Let's try a different approach. Maybe *I* can tell you who you are."

Bromely nodded gratefully, but somewhere deep within him, fear was rising.

"Your case is quite remarkable in a way," said Doctor Fell, "but only because it's one of the first. I don't believe it will be the last. Within several years, there'll be thousands of men like you. The schizoids and the paranoids will have to move over and make room for a new category."

Bromely nodded, waited.

"You know anything about disease germs, bacteria? These organisms undergo swift mutations. Men invent sulfa drugs and the germs develop tolerance to sulfa. Men use antibiotics—penicillin, streptomycin, a dozen others. And the bugs adapt. They breed new strains of bugs."

He thinks I'm bugs, Bromely told himself, but he listened. Fell went on, his voice rising slightly.

"Bugs change, but still they spawn on men. And aberration changes with the times, too—but still it spawns on men. Five hundred years ago the commonest form of insanity was belief in demoniac possession. Three hundred years ago men had delusions of witchcraft and sorcery. A man who couldn't integrate his personality created a new one—he became a wizard. Because the wizard was the symbol of power, who knew the secrets of Life and Death. The disintegrating personality seeks reaffirmation in Authority. Does that make sense to you?"

Bromely nodded, but actually nothing made sense to him anymore. The fear rose within him as Doctor Fell's voice rose without.

"Yes, three hundred years ago, thousands of men and women went to the stake firmly convinced that they were, actually, witches and wizards.

"Times change, Bromely. Look what happened to you. Your personality disintegrated, didn't it? You began to lose touch with reality.

"You lived alone, without personal ties to reaffirm identity. Your work was phony, too—the epitome of all phoniness—manufacturing lies to create artificial press-agent personalities for others. You lived in a phony world, used phony words and phrases, and before you knew it, nothing you did was quite real to you anymore. And you got panicked because you felt your sense of identity slipping away. True?"

Bromely felt the fear very close now, because Doctor Fell was closer. But he wanted Doctor Fell to stay, wanted him to solve this problem.

"You're not a fool, Clyde." Doctor Fell used his first name now and it underlined the intimacy of his words. "You sensed something was going wrong. And so you did what others are beginning to do today. You did that which will create, in years to come, a new kind of mania."

The fear was *here*, now. But Bromely listened.

"Some start by seeking the 'self-help' books, just as old-time sorcerers used to study grimoires. Some go further and experiment in all the odd bypaths of parapsychology—ESP, telepathy, occultism. And some go all the way. They cannot conjure up the Devil but they can commune with Freud, with Adler, with Jung and Moll and Stekel* and the other archfiends. They don't chant spells anymore, but they learn the new Cabala,

**Freud . . . Stekel* leaders of modern psychoanalytic practices

the new language of Mystery. *Schizophrenia, echolalia, involutional melancholia*—the words come trippingly from the tongue, do they not?

"You should know, Clyde. Didn't you visit the library on those long dull days when business was bad, and read endlessly in psychiatry? Didn't you bury yourself, these past several months, in a completely new world of delusion and hallucination and obsession, of neurosis and psychosis? In other words, when you felt you were going crazy—just as in the past, men felt they were becoming possessed of the Devil—didn't you seek to fight it by studying psychiatry as the ancients studied the black arts?"

Bromely tried to sit up. Doctor Fell's face loomed closer, swung away, loomed closer again.

"You know what happened to those men, Clyde. They became, in their own minds, wizards. And you know now—surely you must have guessed—what has happened to you. During the past week, you couldn't be a press agent anymore. You couldn't be a rational human being anymore. In an effort to project, to invest in a new identity, you became a psychiatrist. And *you invented me*!

"You've told yourself that this office is something like your own office, my receptionist resembles your girl, I resemble you. Don't you understand? This is your office. That is your girl. You've been coming in daily and lying down here on your own couch. No wonder she's frightened, hearing you talk to yourself. Now do you know who you are?"

Was it Doctor Fell or the fear screaming in his ears?

"This is your last chance, Clyde. You've got to decide once and for all. You can be yourself again, completely, if you have faith in your own identity. If not, you're the first of the new maniacs. Let me ask you once again, once and for all: *who are you?*"

Clyde Bromely lay there on the couch while the room whirled and swirled. He saw pictures, endless pictures: a faded snapshot of a little Clyde, clinging to Mamma's skirt—Bromely, Lt. j.g., U.S.N., in uniform—Speed Bromely, public relations, shaking hands with a top comic at a benefit show—Bromely sitting in the public library, seeking the answer in the ologies and the isms—Bromely lying on the couch, clawing at nothing.

Bromely saw the pictures, shuffled them, sorted them, and made his choice.

Then the fear fell away, and Bromely slept. He slept there on the couch for a long, long time. When he woke up it was dark and he was alone in the room. Somebody was rapping on the door.

It was his girl. He knew that now. He was in his own office, and his own girl came in, timidly and hesitantly, as he rose with a smile of renewed confidence.

"I was worried," she said. "You being in here so long, and—"

He laughed, and laughed again inside as he realized that the sound but dimly conveyed the new security he felt within himself.

"I was sleeping," he told her. "There's nothing to worry about, my dear. From now on, we're going places. I've been in a pretty bad slump for the past month or so—someday I'll tell you all about it—but I'm all right now. Let's go out for dinner and we'll make plans."

The girl smiled. She could sense the change, too. Dark as the room was, it seemed to fill with sudden sunlight.

"All right," she said. "All right, Mr. Bromely."

He stiffened. "Bromely? That patient? Don't you know me, my dear?"

Reading for Understanding

❑ MAIN IDEA

1. The main theme of the story is (a) the keen interest shown by many in psychiatry (b) a bitter denunciation of psychiatric methods in clinics (c) the gradual deterioration of a man's personality and sense of self (d) a clear explanation of how a psychiatrist gets at the root of difficulties.

❑ DETAILS

2. Clyde Bromely's business was (a) movie directing (b) public relations (c) legal counseling (d) politics.

3. Bromely considered his last hope to be (a) Dr. Fell (b) Mrs. Bromely (c) Hal Edwards (d) Torchy Harrigan.

4. When Bromely had an opportunity to speak to Torchy Harrigan, he (a) insulted Harrigan (b) succeeded brilliantly (c) criticized Hal Edwards (d) failed miserably.

5. *Speed* was (a) a nickname of Bromely's (b) Bromely's partner (c) Harrigan's chief counsel (d) another psychiatrist.

❑ INFERENCES

6. Bromely couldn't remember who had recommended Dr. Fell because (a) Dr. Fell was already famous around the country (b) Bromely usually avoided all doctors (c) nobody had recommended him (d) both Harrigan and Edwards had recommended the doctor.

7. The most important question asked by Dr. Fell was (a) "What do these phrases mean to you?" (b) "What do they really *add up* to, in your mind?" (c) "Doesn't that tie in with your final statement?" (d) "Who are you?"

8. When Bromely felt he was losing his mind, he (a) visited a wizard (b) studied psychiatry (c) tried an old herbal remedy (d) entered show business.

9. Dr. Fell was actually a (a) witch doctor (b) creation of Bromely's imagination (c) member of a dangerous cult (d) rejected former partner in Bromely's office.

❑ AUTHOR'S PURPOSE

10. Bromely has a habit of matching old song titles and phrases with a current experience. The author uses this device to show (a) Bromely's cleverness (b) the kind of times Bromely was living in (c) his own cleverness (d) Bromely's slow disintegration.

❑ AUTHOR'S ATTITUDE

11. The author's attitude toward the disintegration of Bromely's personality is one of (a) restrained enthusiasm (b) marked indifference (c) sad disapproval (d) healthy curiosity.

❑ ORDER OF EVENTS

12. Arrange the items in the order in which they occurred. Use letters only.
    - A. Bromely has a physical examination.
    - B. Bromely first goes to Dr. Fell.
    - C. Bromely first senses a deep dissatisfaction with his life.
    - D. Bromely gets a call about Torchy Harrigan.
    - E. Bromely awakens with a great feeling of relief.

❑ OUTCOMES

13. At the end of the story, Bromely (a) gets the job he lost previously (b) is completely cured (c) marries the receptionist (d) assumes the identity of Dr. Fell.

❑ CAUSE AND EFFECT

14. Bromely's difficulties were probably caused by (a) the pressures and tensions of life (b) a childhood disagreement with a boy who looked like Dr. Fell (c) a failure in college (d) an unhappy love affair.

❑ FACT OR OPINION

Tell whether the following is a fact or an opinion.

15. During the sessions with Dr. Fell, Bromely was actually talking to himself.

Words in Context

1. "The *subdued* lighting did not lend itself to a closer *scrutiny* of the psychiatrist's *countenance* . . ." ***Subdued* . . . *scrutiny* . . . *countenance*** . . . (475) mean (a) fluorescent . . . control . . . feelings (b) bright . . . realization . . . mien (c) flickering . . . examination . . . appearance (d) toned down . . . critical regard . . . face.

2. "Apparently he'd been talking to Doctor Fell for quite some time—and quite *rationally* too. Yes, he remembered now. He'd been answering all the *routine* questions." ***Rationally* . . . *routine*** . . . (476) mean (a) sensibly . . . written (b) understandably . . . subtle (c) sanely . . . customary (d) calmly . . . embarrassing.

3. "Bromely knew a little something about psychiatry himself. Oh, not the technical terms of course, but more than a *smattering* of technique." ***Smattering*** (476) means (a) mastery (b) little knowledge (c) theoretical survey (d) textbook summary.

4. "This was a routine *orientation*, preliminary to probing. And Bromely cooperated." ***Orientation*** (476) means (a) introduction (b) session (c) conference (d) consultation.

5. "'You're my last hope. That's why I've come to you. You must understand that, because it's the *crux* of the whole matter.'" ***Crux*** (476) means (a) cause (b) nub (c) consequence (d) defective aspect.

6. "He said everything that came into his mind. The *associative clichés* poured out, and with them the desperate plea for help." ***Associative clichés*** (476) means (a) wise sayings in a group (b) untruths accepted as truth (c) hysterical babblings (d) trite expressions randomly connected.

7. "The receptionist said something to him as he left, but Bromely was *too preoccupied* to catch her words. He was *engrossed in thought*, he was *deep in contemplation*." The three italicized expressions (477) all mean (a) he was meditating (b) he was filled with fears (c) he did not trust the receptionist (d) he was relieved when the doctor took his case.

8. "'The *schizoids* and the *paranoids* will have to move over and make room for a new category.'" ***Schizoids* . . . *paranoids*** . . . (480) mean (a) psychiatrists . . . psychologists (b) split personalities . . . people with abnormal fears (c) daydreamers . . . failures (d) self-deceptionists . . . habitual liars.

9. "'These organisms undergo swift *mutations*. Men invent sulfa drugs and the germs develop tolerance to sulfa.'" ***Mutations*** (480) means (a) biological changes (b) cures (c) severe treatments (d) emotional strain.

10. "'Five hundred years ago the commonest form of insanity was belief in *demoniac possession*.'" A person suffering from ***demoniac possession*** (480) was thought to be (a) a fiend from hell (b) controlled by a fiend from hell (c) completely harmless (d) an uncontrollable killer.

11. "'The *disintegrating personality* seeks *reaffirmation* in Authority.'" ***Disintegrating personality*** . . . ***reaffirmation*** . . . (480) mean (a) puzzled mind . . . facts (b) person who is physically ill . . . help (c) person becoming mentally ill . . . endorsement (d) growing mind . . . the truth.

12. "'Yes, three hundred years ago, thousands of men and women *went to the stake* firmly convinced that they were, actually, witches and wizards.'" ***Went to the stake*** (480) means (a) were sent to jail (b) confessed openly (c) were burned to death (d) lived.

13. "'Your work was phony, too—the *epitome* of all phoniness—manufacturing lies to create artificial press-agent personalities for others.'" ***Epitome*** (480) means (a) cause (b) essence (c) result (d) reward.

14. "'Some start by seeking the 'self-help' books, just as old-time *sorcerers* used to study *grimoires*.'" ***Sorcerers*** . . . ***grimoires*** (480) mean (a) scholars . . . commentaries (b) rulers . . . encyclopedias (c) knights . . . myths and legends (d) magicians . . . wizards' manuals.

15. "'They cannot *conjure up* the Devil but they can *commune* with Freud, with Adler, with Jung . . .'" ***Conjure up*** . . . ***commune with*** . . . (480) mean (a) gain control of . . . commute with (b) summon . . . communicate with (c) expose . . . denounce (d) confer with . . . renounce.

Thinking Critically About the Story

1. What are press agents? What are their functions in our society? Are they indispensable? Explain. According to the author, what is the occupational hazard for one who works in public relations? What are the symptoms? What evidence is offered to prove its virulence? Are there any other careers that could cause the same personality disintegration? How can we protect ourselves from this disease?
2. Do we choose careers because of our personality traits, or do our career choices develop our personalities along predictable lines? Cite examples from real life or fiction to support your answer.

3. To what extent do you agree or disagree with the following evaluation:

   "The unnamed secretary whom we meet several times, but very briefly, is the one who keeps the story from becoming a comedy. She is the base in reality, the Greek chorus-of-one who reveals to the reader the full horror of Bromely's fate."

4. Think about the significance of the last line in the story.

   He stiffened. "Bromely? That patient? Don't you know me, my dear?"

   What reaction does the author expect from the reader? How effective is this last line? Recall other stories that use this same last-line twist. What TV tales make use of this device? When could this device be unfair to the reader? Is it so in this story?

5. How does the author create a realistic sense of the immediate danger of an epidemic of personality disintegrations? Is there a crack in the logic offered to the reader? Explain. What was the author's purpose in writing the story?

Stories in Words

Psychiatrist (475) contains two important roots: *psyche*— "life, soul" and *iatr*—"healing." A psychiatrist is one who attempts to "heal the soul." *Psych* also appears in *parapsychology*, the search for psychology beyond the normal; for example, *telepathy* and *telekinesis*. The prefix *para* means "beside, alongside of." *Telepathy* and *telekinesis* both contain the *tel* root meaning "distant." *Telepathy* is communicating "at a distance" by thought alone. *Telekinesis* is moving objects "at a distance" by thought alone. These paranormal phenomena are not accepted by the majority of scientists.

Autobiography (476) is a treasure trove of Greek elements. *Auto*, meaning "self," appears in *automat*, *autograph*, *autonomy*, and *autistic*. *Automobile*, meaning "self-moving, " is a hybrid, with a Latin root *mob*, "move," as well as the Greek. *Bio*, meaning "life," appears in *biography*, *biology*, *biosphere*, *biodegradable*, *biophysics*, *bionic*, and *biofeedback* (another hybrid word). *Graph*, meaning "to write," appears in *graph*, *graphics*, *telegraph* (the *tel* root again), *photograph*, *phonograph*, *graphology*, and *holograph*. An *autobiography* is thus a "self-written life story."

Cliché (476) is borrowed from the French: "a stereotype plate." Such a plate prints the same thing over and over. A stereotype in English refers to something without individuality or originality. A cliché is something that has been used so often it has lost the power to arouse or please. Yet most clichés at one time were fresh and new. The first person who used "quiet as a mouse" created a vivid image, but overuse has dulled its effectiveness.

Dateline—The Future

Getting Technical

Terms

gimmick	retribution	tragic flaw
interior monolog	slapstick	

Definitions Match each of the above terms with its definition.

1. Comedy stressing satire, horseplay, and improbable plot
2. An ingenious or novel plot element
3. Stream of consciousness; flow of thoughts and feelings through the mind of a character
4. Defect in character that leads to the downfall of a protagonist
5. Dispensing or receiving rewards and punishments according to the deserts of an individual

Examples Match each of the following actions with the appropriate term.

1. While the runaway train races across the countryside, the engineer is polishing her nails, and the brakemen are throwing custard pies at each other.
2. Because of his overconfidence, the protagonist ignores the warnings and falls victim to the assassination plot.
3. I know that somehow, somewhere, he will have to pay for his cruel mistreatment of these innocent children.

4. Placing the suction cup against the wall enabled me to overhear the plotting in the adjacent room.
5. The entire story is just a transcript of the troubled youth talking silently to himself.
6. The driverless car with failed brakes raced down the winding mountain while on the rear seat the two hoodlums were playing cards and slapping each other for cheating.
7. "If I had not had such blind trust in them, I never would have lost my chance for success and happiness."

Application Choose the statement that best completes each of the following.

1. The interior monolog is in the form of a dialog when Bromely is with (a) his secretary (b) Dr. Fell (c) Hal Edwards (d) his mother. ("I Do Not Love Thee, Dr. Fell")
2. The cargo of beings are sent to Earth (a) to improve the quality of life there (b) to establish contact there (c) in retribution (d) as a gimmick. ("Cephes 5")
3. Slapstick is mixed with social significance in (a) the thinking of the third officer in "Cephes 5" (b) the revolt of Harrison Bergeron (c) the death of the echoes in "The Valley of Echoes" (d) Bromely's hiring of Dr. Fell.
4. The major gimmicks in "The Valley of Echoes" result in the (a) invasion of Mars (b) death of an explorer (c) destruction of sounds (d) proof of life having existed on Mars.
5. According to the Counselor in "Cephes 5," the tragic flaw in human beings is their (a) high intelligence (b) inability to follow orders (c) sense of self-importance (d) need to protect the Earth.
6. Retribution in "Harrison Bergeron" is brought about by the (a) parent (b) son (c) ballerina (d) handicapper.

Thinking Critically About the Stories

1. Compare the leadership qualities of the Counselor and the Handicapper General, Diana Moon Glampers. What are the major assets of each? How do they differ? Which one is the more effective? Which one would you prefer being led by? How do they compare with leaders in your school? With your coaches? With our national leaders? Give specific instances to justify your statements.

2. What flaws in our society are exposed in each of the four stories? Which story brings the problem into sharpest focus? What solutions are offered? How do the methods of the authors differ? Which is the best writer?

3. How do the stories in this unit differ from the other stories in this collection?
   (a) In appeal?
   (b) In contents?
   (c) In characterizations?
   (d) In specialized knowledge?

   What criteria do you use in judging the other stories? Upon what criteria do you judge science fiction? What makes one science-fiction story better than another?

4. Which is the best science-fiction story you ever read? You ever saw on TV? Cite instances in the story to support your statements. How do the stories in this unit compare to your favorite?

5. Compare the Third Officer and Harrison Bergeron in:
   (a) Their outlook on life.
   (b) Their attitude toward rebellion and obedience.
   (c) Their method of facing a problem.
   (d) Their attitude toward adults.

   Who has the better approach to life? Whom do you resemble more?

Writing and Other Activities

1. Write in a friendly, straight-from-the-shoulder style the two minutes of advice that you have been asked to give to one of the following:

George Bergeron	Dr. Fell
Hazel Bergeron	the Third Officer

2. Plan a class discussion on an idea that you would like to extrapolate to the year 2121. How would it affect the lives of adolescents and adults at that time? Will it increase or lessen their chances for happiness? Let the class decide.

3. Plan a panel discussion on the following statement: "The stories in this unit stress mood, character, and theme. The typical TV or movie science-fiction tale, on the other hand, is based on a rapid-action plot in an unfamiliar time or place."

   Be prepared to discuss:

   What do the readers expect to enjoy in reading the type of story found in this unit?

What do viewers look forward to in a TV or movie science-fiction tale?

Members of the panel should be prepared to cite recent plots to support or disprove the statement.

4. Write an evaluation of a science-fiction movie, a TV presentation that you saw, or a science-fiction novel that you read lately. Write it for a sitcom addict who has never read or watched science fiction.

5. The class is planning a printed list of leisure-time activities. The book and movie section will consist of five-line blurbs of recommendation. Write two five-liners for classics of science fiction, one for a book available in the library, and one for a videocassette that can be borrowed from the library or from the local rental center.

Stories in Words: A Review

A. atom	E. handicap	I. planet
B. autobiography	F. inoculation	J. psychiatrist
C. calibrated	G. murmur	K. siren
D. cliché	H. orientation	L. syndrome

Answer the following questions by choosing a word from the list above. Use letters only.

Which of the words above . . .

1. _______ contains the idea of *wandering*?
2. _______ suggests the idea of *indivisibility*?
3. _______ is derived from temptresses mentioned in the Greek epic, the *Odyssey*?
4. _______ is related to the name for the inside of a gun's bore?
5. _______ contains the root idea of *healing*?
6. _______ is related to the idea of *stereotype*?
7. _______ is a word whose sound suggests the sense?
8. _______ contains the root meaning *to rise*?
9. _______ suggests a *running together*?
10. _______ suggests competition and wagers?

Glossary

The best way to build a vocabulary is to meet new words in helpful contexts. A word's context is the setting it appears in, all the other words around it. The following list contains a great many new words that are worth adding to your word store.

All the words in the list appear in the stories you have read. Here you will find helpful definitions. In addition, you will meet the words in new contexts, sentences designed to suggest the meaning of the listed words. These sentences, together with the contexts in which the words originally appeared, will help you add the words to your use vocabulary.

A

abase to lower in rank, office, esteem, or prestige; humble
I would rather starve than *abase* myself by asking them to help me over this rough spot.

abashed embarrassed; humiliated; disconcerted
He was *abashed* by his own inability to recall the names of the visitors.

aberrant atypical; a person whose behavior departs substantially from the standard
The *aberrants* in the group were quickly weeded out.

aberration an irregularity; mental lapse; peculiarity; oddity
Her only *aberration* was an occasional lapse of memory.

abjectly hopelessly; inescapably; contemptibly; ignobly
The old couple lived *abjectly*, the victims of poverty, squalor, and neglect.

absorption entire occupation of the mind; act of taking in
His complete *absorption* in his work made him unaware of the sacrifices his family was making for him.

abstracted withdrew; summarized; absentminded
When she has that *abstracted* look, we know that her mind and attention are miles away from us.

abstraction a nonconcrete idea or term; a notional painting; absentmindedness
Don't give me *abstractions*; give me specific Do's and Don't's.

abstruse hard to understand; profound; obscure
Simple arithmetic can be an *abstruse* science for many.
abyss a bottomless pit; deep, empty space
One false step on this mountain pass, and you will fall into the *abyss*.
academic scholastic; scholarly; theoretical; not practical
How to talk to an extraterrestrial being is rather an *academic* question.
acquisitive selfish; grasping; greedy; covetous
She is so *acquisitive* that she is always thinking of what is in it for me, me, me, me, me.
adage saying; proverb; precept
"Don't give a child an adult's task" is an old *adage*.
administrative executive; managerial; supervisory
How best to expand the corporation is an *administrative* problem.
adroit skillful; clever
Only an *adroit* driver could weave his way through these crowded, narrow streets without an accident.
affably good-naturedly; amiably; graciously
She greeted us so *affably* that we never suspected that she was deeply annoyed by the turn of events.
affectation a false mannerism; artificiality; pretense
How was I to know that his British accent was just an *affectation* cultivated by a native of Chicago.
afflicted plagued; beset; distressed; oppressed
Humanity is still *afflicted* by famine and war.
affront to offend; insult; a slight; humiliation
Don't *affront* the speaker by interrupting her during her presentation.
agile quick; graceful
Though Owen seems half asleep part of the time, he is an *agile* champion on the tennis court when his opponent makes a good shot.
akimbo hands on hip with elbows turned outward
All he can do is stand there with his arms *akimbo* while shouting derisive remarks at us.
akin related; identical; resembling
The smirk on his face was *akin* to a challenge, and I rushed toward him with fists flying.
albeit conceding the fact; even though; although
She quickly conceded to our request *albeit* she knew that we had no right to ask it of her.
alchemy a medieval chemical science; unexplainable transforming of something common into something special
Alchemy never found the formula for converting iron into gold.
allay to calm; ease; lessen
This is the medicine the doctor ordered to *allay* the patient's pain.
alluded referred to; mentioned; intimated
She was annoyed when I *alluded* to the significant sum that she still owed me.
allure to tempt; lead on; an attraction; fascination
At every vacation time, the *allure* of foreign travel sends him to the far corners of the world.

allusion implied reference
The works of John Milton have many *allusions* to Greek and Roman mythology.
aloof cold; detached; indifferent; apart; unresponsive
Her *aloof* manner alienated many who could have been friendly and helpful.
alternative a choice; substitute; option
If you don't like his results, your only *alternative* is to do the work yourself.
ambience atmosphere; surroundings; milieu
We enjoy the quiet, pleasant *ambience* of this restaurant as much as we relish the delicious food.
amiable agreeable; sociable; genial
Helen's *amiable* demeanor masks an intensely competitive nature.
amphibious able to live on land and in water; relating to or adapted for both land and water
The *amphibious* plane took off on the lake and landed on the mountaintop airstrip.
amphitheater an auditorium; large room with a viewing gallery
The games are held in an *amphitheater* that can seat sixty thousand spectators.
analogy comparison; similarity; parallelism
The lecturer pointed out the *analogy* between a mechanical pump and the human heart.
anarchistic rebellious against any authority; lawless
He firmly believes in the *anarchistic* slogan: "No government is good government."
anguish suffering from grief, pain, or worry
When the coach saw the opponent's ball sail through the uprights for a field goal, he let out an involuntary cry of *anguish* .
aniline a poisonous derivative from nitrobenzene, used in dyes
Do workers handling *aniline* dyes have to avoid inhaling the fumes?
animated lively; spirited; vivacious
Clever observations and sharp questions kept the *animated* discussion at a high level of interest.
animation liveliness; high spirit; vivacity
His comments delivered without *animation* and in low tones soon lost him his audience.
anthropomorphic ascribing human characteristics to nonhuman things
Anthropomorphic deities dominated many ancient cultures.
apoplectic enraged; angry; infuriated
When Mr. Perkins saw the dent his daughter had put in the family car, he was *apoplectic.*
appalled filled with horror, shock, or dismay
The world was *appalled* by the great loss of life when Mt. Pelee on the island of Martinique erupted in 1902.
applejack an alcoholic beverage usually made by freezing hard cider
The homemade *applejack* was more potent than any of the store-bought liquors.
apprehension an uneasiness; anxiety; capture; understanding
The sheriff announced that his major task was the *apprehension* of the escaped convicts.

arbor a vine-covered bower; shaded walk; gazebo
We were all invited to walk through the *arbor* and taste the newly ripened grapes.

arcane mysterious; obscure; secret; known only to the one or few who have the key
Only the tribal chief was able to officiate over the *arcane* rites of initiation.

archfiend a chief devil; chief person of great wickedness
I cannot but loathe the *archfiends* who gain power and wealth from the sale of illegal drugs.

arc light streetlight; any electric bulb
Can you read the street signs at night even when they are not close to the *arc lights?*

ardent very eager; intense; impassioned; fervent
Nathan Hale has long been a national symbol of *ardent* patriotism.

argus hundred-eyed monster of Greek legend; watchful guardian
A pit bull is too vicious to be the *argus* guarding a property when neighbors have small children.

aright rightly; correctly
If I remember *aright*, they visited us last November 3 for about two hours.

artful cunning; crafty; skillful; shrewd
The *artful* defense lawyer played to the emotions of the jurors with every gesture and statement he made.

artifacts characteristic products of human activity
The archeologists sifted through the sand in the cave, looking for *artifacts* to prove that people had lived there at one time.

artlessly frankly; openly; straightforwardly; naturally
The child presented her requests so *artlessly* that we were charmed into instant agreement.

assail attack; assault; set upon
Members of the audience *assailed* the speaker for basing his arguments on disproved data.

assert to state strongly; maintain; insist
Helen was right when she *asserted* that the chair should have allowed her to read her report.

assertive positive; decisive; self-assured; forceful
An effective manager must be *assertive* in making routine decisions.

assiduous hardworking; diligent; industrious; persistent
It takes long hours of *assiduous* memorizing to master any foreign language.

associative of, resulting from, or causing linkage or connection; acquired by learning
Associative behavior results from imitation.

astrakhan cloth with a curled and looped pile
My bitter-winter hat is made of *astrakhan.*

atonement repentance; amends; penance
The reformed criminal promised *atonement* for his misdeeds.

au courant fully informed; up to date; conversant
To keep *au courant* in worldwide events, Alice reads the daily newspaper and two weekly news magazines.

auditor one who listens; one who checks accounts
I am not a student taking the course for credit; I have been given permission to attend as an *auditor.*

authoritative official; decisive; trustworthy; learned
Is there one *authoritative* book on English usage, one that is acceptable to most specialists?

autonomy self-government; independence; sovereignty
After World War II, most colonies were granted *autonomy* by their former ruling powers.

avail purpose; to take advantage of; profit from
All efforts of the emergency squad were to no *avail* in the attempt to revive the crash victim.

avant garde artistic innovators; pioneers; trailblazers
Her dream is to be the leader of the *avant garde* that sets the trends in fashion for the year.

avid eager; greedy; devoted; enthusiastic; ardent
During the season, this *avid* football fan views three games simultaneously on his giant TV screen.

awe respectful fear; astonishment; respect; to astonish
The sight of the Lincoln Memorial filled the visiting students with *awe*.

awed filled with wonder or reverence; dismayed; terrified
I refused to be *awed* by the prospect of being in the presence of someone who had shaken hands with Elvis.

B

badinage playful repartee; banter; wordplay; jesting
Her quick wit and nimble tongue made her a master of the *badinage* that enlivens social gatherings.

baize a coarse woolen or cotton fabric napped to imitate felt
Helen made a *baize* covering for the bulletin board.

balk to shirk; refuse; prevent; timber; a beam; pitcher's error
To be used as *balks*, the boards will have to be fifteen-footers.

basking sunbathing; warming oneself; reveling; delighting
Basking in the admiration of his loyal fans, the rock star felt fully confident of his future.

batten down to fasten secure with thin bars and strips
As the storm approaches, the crew will *batten down* the hatches that lead to the storage areas below deck.

benediction a blessing; prayer
At the end of the service, the visiting clergyman gave the *benediction* to the devoted congregation.

benevolence good will; kindliness; compassion; liberality
The American Cancer Society depends on the *benevolence* of the general public.

bibliopegy the art of binding books
Books resulting from advances in *bibliopegy* can be just as enduring as volumes produced in former years.

bijou a jewel; small, dainty, delicate ornament
She carefully selected from her collection, the one *bijou* that would best enhance her dress.

bizarre strange; fantastic; outlandish; unusual
A prize will be given to the designer of the most *bizarre* Halloween costume.

blandly smoothly; agreeably; mildly
With her sudden affluence, she was able to tell the supervisor *blandly* that he was intolerable—and quit!

bleakly desolately; depressingly; dismally; gloomily; icily
The manager announced *bleakly* that if business did not improve by the weekend, the store would be closed.

blight a plant disease; plague; to destroy
The *blight* destroyed all the stately elm trees that had lined our main street.

blubbering uttering while weeping
Stop your *blubbering* so that I can understand what had happened and how I can help you!

bluff outspoken; promontory; ridge; to deceive; pretense
The farm was perched on a *bluff* high above the river.

bohemian a person living an unconventional life in a colony
Soho has replaced Greenwich Village in New York City as the center for present-day *bohemians*.

boon benefit; favor; blessing; convivial
The heavy rains were a *boon* to the parched crops.

boorish crude; rude; coarse; unrefined; uncouth
She considers as *boorish* anyone whose manners are not highly polished.

botched spoiled; ruined; mismanaged; flubbed
The inexperienced typist *botched* the letter and had to redo it completely.

bottleneck a block; barrier; clog
The overturned truck caused a *bottleneck* at the exit from the bridge, and the traffic backed up for a mile.

box a type of evergreen; container
A shrub in the *box* family was used to form the hedge that separated the estate property from the highway.

brazen bold, impudent, saucy
In "The Taming of the Shrew" *brazen* Kate insults every suitor who comes to woo her.

bridle to curb; check; flinch; a head harness; harness
Anyone in his right mind would *bridle* at such insults.

brilliantine a light, lustrous fabric; a preparation for making the hair glossy
His smoking jacket was fashioned out of *brilliantine*.

brook stream; to allow; suffer; put up with
Enough! I will not *brook* any more of your insolence!

bubbleheaded foolish and stupid
How can you suffer that *bubbleheaded* assistant who seems incapable of doing anything right!

bullion uncoined gold or silver in bars or ingots
The gold *bullion* was placed in the vault for safekeeping.

C

cabala a traditional occult or secret matter; system of mysticism and magic
As a student of the *cabala*, Eric claimed that he could perform rare feats of magic.

callowness immaturity; lack of experience
The *callowness* of the youth was evident in his inability to handle the visitors with charm or politeness.

candid frank; open; direct; straightforward; informal
To be *candid,* I really don't think that you should have assumed that we were opposed to your suggestions.

canter a lope; type of gallop
The tough ponies were able to *canter* for hours as they crossed the plains.

canzonettas light and graceful songs; madrigals
The strolling singers delighted the street crowds with their rendition of familiar *canzonettas.*

capered pranced and leaped; skipped
The young goats *capered* among the rocks near the peak.

captivated fascinated; charmed; dazzled
The handsome speaker's ready wit and genial outlook *captivated* the audience.

carbolic soap a harsh soap for deep cleaning
Walls of the sick room were usually washed down carefully with *carbolic soap* used as the disinfectant.

cardigan a collarless sweater or jacket with a button-down front
Wear your *cardigan* when the evening chill settles in.

careening lurching from side to side; leaning sideways
Careening madly down the mountainside, the dislodged boulder thundered toward the hapless hikers.

casement a window frame that opens on hinges at the side
The thief must have entered through an unlocked *casement* since all the doors were bolted.

casual accidental; halfhearted; vague; informal
I am not a devoted fan; I have only a *casual* interest in TV football.

casualty an injured victim; a wounded or dead person
The train wreck and subsequent fires caused many *casualties.*

casuistical containing false reasoning; having a false look of truth
No *casuistical* argument can convince me that this serious loss is really a victory for our side.

catastrophic disastrous; calamitous; tragic; devastating
This flood is more menacing than the *catastrophic* flood of 1973 in which hundreds lost their lives.

censored edited; cleaned up; suppressed
The dictatorial leader has all news reports *censored* before they leave the country.

cerements burial garments for the dead; shrouds
The corpses of royalty were wrapped in gold *cerements.*

chafe to rub; scratch; irritate; exasperate
Chafed by the tight collar, his neck turned red.

chaffing ridiculing; kidding; joshing
Their good-natured *chaffing* him about his big ears never seems to bother him.

characterologies studies of character growth and differences
Her gossip contained lengthy *characterologies* of each of their many neighbors.

charger a horse for battle or parade; an appliance
In full uniform, the general mounted his *charger* and moved to the head of the parade.

chaussee a paved road; causeway; highway
When the traffic was light on the *chaussee*, Henry allowed the younger drivers to take over.

cheeky impudent; impertinent; bold; arrogant
The *cheeky* tourist decided to join the wedding party uninvited.

cheroot a cigar cut square at both ends
In Mark Twain's day, many celebrities were photographed with a lighted *cheroot* held chest high.

chiddened (chided) scolded; rebuked; reprimanded
Her father *chiddened* her for not offering to carry the heavy packages for her mother.

chiding scolding; rebuking; reprimanding
There is little gained by *chiding* him when he does not know what was wrong in what he had done.

chimerical illusionary; fantastic; improbably; imaginary
When will he ever learn to reject all get-rich-quick schemes as *chimerical* money consumers.

chinks loopholes; openings; small slits; a means of evasion
In vain did we stuff mud in the *chinks* between the logs to make the old cabin draft-resistant.

chit a child; pert young woman; short note; signed voucher
I read the *chit* several times to verify the time she had set for our appointment.

chow chow a relish; Chinese preserve; type of dog
Before taking his first bite, he ceremoniously put a layer of *chow chow* over the frankfurter in the roll.

civilities conventional patterns of social behavior
She was so angry that she called him a crude boor, unaware of the most common *civilities* of polite society.

clarion clear; shrill; sharp; blaring; a medieval trumpet
The *clarion* call of a bugle rent the morning air as it blasted over the loudspeakers to awaken us.

cleave to stick to; split
Sincere people always *cleave* to their principles.

cleft a split; crack; fissure; cloven; divided
A *cleft* in the ice offered the mountain climbers shelter from the sudden storm.

cliche trite phrase; overused saying; hackneyed expression
"As pretty as a picture" is a traditional *cliche*.

clientele a body of clients; those who use a service
Shops that cluster around Worth Avenue cater to an exclusive *clientele*.

cloven divided into two parts
Satan is traditionally represented as being *cloven-footed*.

colander a perforated utensil for washing or draining food.
We put the berries in the *colander* and ran cold water over them to clear out sand and loose stems.

colleague a fellow worker; associate
Ask every *colleague* in the office to sign the get-well card for Jan.

commensurate in accord; consistent; fitting; appropriate
We agreed on a salary that was *commensurate* with her ability and experience.

commune to share thought; communicate; a community
Her followers actually believe that she is able to *commune* with the spirits of the departed.

comparatively relatively; approximately; nearly
Since I was *comparatively* new to the group, they assumed that I was unaware of the blindspots of our neighbors.

compassion pity; sympathy; humanity
We chose her as our family physician because of the great *compassion* she has for her patients.

competent qualified; capable; fit
Competent judges are desperately needed to rate the diving form of Olympic contestants.

compiled collected; assembled; drew together
I *compiled* a list of the tenants' complaints and presented them to the management.

complimentary praising; congratulatory; free; without charge
How can you accept as *complimentary* a remark so tinged with sarcasm!

composed calm; quiet; coolheaded; controlled
The captain remained *composed* and fully in command of himself and his crew during the entire storm.

composure calmness of mind; poise; serenity
Even bitter disappointments cannot affect Betty's *composure*, for she always maintains a calm and pleasant manner.

confessor one who confesses; priest who receives confessions
To what extent is a *confessor* bound to keep secret what has been told to him in his official capacity?

congeal to harden; set; solidify
The custard *congealed* quickly in the refrigerator.

congenital innate; inherent; inborn; hereditary
Is eye-dominance a *congenital* trait?

conjecture to guess; suppose; infer; an inference; guesswork
How can you base so much of your future life on a mere *conjecture!*

conjure to practice magic; call forth; summon; bewitch
Wizards and witches are supposed to be able to *conjure* up spirits who will follow their commands.

conscientious high-principled; responsible; honest
A *conscientious* worker fulfills his obligations to the best of his ability with least fanfare.

consolidated combined; merged; strengthened
The two companies will soon be *consolidated* into one.

consternation a paralyzing fear; panic; terror
To our utter *consternation*, we saw a shark approaching the long-distance swimmer.

contender one who fights, combats, debates, quarrels, claims
It is difficult to be a *contender* against self-seeking leaders.

contiguous adjoining; adjacent; touching; abutting
New York and New Jersey are *contiguous* states.

contingency an emergency; urgency; likelihood; accident
During the height of the tourist season, the Rangers must be prepared for any *contingency*.

contrive to manage; plan; arrange
Though the McManuses live solely on his social security, they somehow *contrive* to be comfortable and happy.

conundrum a puzzle; riddle; enigma
I am convinced that some of the *conundrums* in life just do not have any solutions.

convalescent one who is recovering, recuperating
The one major task of a *convalescent* is to get well.

convulsed shaken violently
The children were so *convulsed* with laughter by the magician's tricks that he had to slow his delivery.

convulsively fitfully; violently; frantically; spasmodically
When she began to cry so *convulsively*, the mother silently embraced her.

cordial friendly; gracious; warm; affectionate; a liqueur
After being greeted so *cordially*, how can you say that you were an unwelcome guest!

corncrib storage place for corn
The *corncrib* is never far from the barn.

corps a military branch; combat unit; team; crew
A *corps* of doctors was sent to inoculate all of the children in the community.

corroborate to verify; confirm; affirm; authenticate
Investigators throughout the world are conducting experiments to *corroborate* these startling findings.

corrugated wrinkled; furrowed
The ridges in the *corrugated* roof ran at right angles to the slope.

countenance a face; look; feature; approval; to tolerate
I refuse to continue any longer to *countenance* such rude behavior!

countermand to revoke; rescind; cancel; set aside
We were thoroughly confused when the second set of instructions seemed to *countermand* the first.

coveter one who desires greedily, hankers after
The *coveter* rarely sees the disadvantages and the difficulties surrounding what he yearns for so strongly.

cracknel a hard, brittle biscuit
My hunger was so great that the stale *cracknel* tasted as delicious as the best pastry I have ever eaten.

creature comforts something (like food, warmth, shelter) that gives bodily comfort.
What I missed most on those cold mornings in the camp were the *creature comforts* we always take for granted.

credulity an undue readiness to believe; blind faith
Her unsupported assertions stretched even our *credulity* to the breaking point.

cretonne a strong, unglazed cotton or linen cloth
We made the window curtains of white *cretonne*.

crewel a slackly twisted, worsted yarn
She had variously colored skeins of *crewel* surrounding her embroidery frame.

crick a painful, sudden spasm of a muscle
I tried to move my head from side to side to get rid of the *crick* in my neck.

cringe to shrink in fear; cower; flinch; quail
The child *cringed* as the angry father looked in her direction and shouted a series of don't's.

croissant a flaky, rich crescent-shaped roll
What I wouldn't give for a fresh cheese *croissant* at this moment!

croquette small, rounded patty made of minced meat, fish, or vegetables, coated with eggs and bread crumbs and fried
The Monday night special in our home is mashed potatoes and chicken *croquettes*.

crotchet an eccentricity; peculiarity; idiosyncrasy
Fainting in the presence of company is only one of my aunt's *crotchets*.

crux the main point; essence; gist
The *crux* of the matter is that they will reject our offer regardless of how good it is.

crystalline made of quartz that is colorless and transparent; made of clear, colorless glass
The light of the sun reflected by the *crystalline* slab was so intense that no one could gaze at it for long.

cuffed slapped; hit with open hand
Any student whose ears were *cuffed* by this dreaded school guard never forgot the experience.

cult a sect; religious group; faction; zealots
The leader of the secret *cult* demanded unquestioning obedience from his followers.

curio something considered novel, rare, or bizarre
In the cabinet there were the many *curios* that we had gathered over the years of our extensive travels.

curriculum vitae a summary of one's career and qualifications
Before going for an interview, I sent a copy of my *curriculum vitae* to the employment officer.

curtail to cut short; abridge; abbreviate
Because of the bad weather, we had to *curtail* our trip.

custom the fashion; trade
When I realized how unreliable their service was, I curtailed my *custom* and opened an account elsewhere.

cynic a scoffer; faultfinder; pessimist; skeptic
She is a *cynic*, firmly believing that human conduct is motivated solely by self-interest.

cynically sneeringly; scoffingly; skeptically
He replied *cynically*, "When you reach my age, you too will learn to trust no one."

cynicism expression of disbelief in sincerity, benevolence, rectitude, or competence
Cynicism is sneering at everything that makes life worthwhile.

D

dapper stylish; smart; neat; trim; modish; sporty
The *dapper* young executive would rather disappear than be seen in an outfit of last year's styling.

daunted intimidated; discouraged; unnerved; frightened
The unforeseen dangers did not *daunt* the early pioneers crossing the country in wagons.

dearth a scarcity; lack; shortage; insufficient supply
When the business boom arrived, there was a *dearth* of skilled technicians in our area.

deduced concluded; reasoned; inferred; gathered
Given the basic facts, you too could have *deduced* that their hearts were not in this venture.

deficit a shortage in amount or quantity
Because of these unanticipated expenses, we ended the year with a *deficit*.

deft skillful; expert; handy
With a few *deft* motions of the needle, the tailor repaired the torn buttonhole.

defunct extinct; dead
That company has been *defunct* for more than ten years.

deign to consent to do something beneath one's dignity
Will Cynthia *deign* to answer those unfair criticisms of her term of office?

delete to remove; cut out; erase; cancel; omit
Your letter of request will be much more forceful if you *delete* the last two sentences.

deluge a flood; to inundate; submerge; swamp
The Red Cross was *deluged* with requests for help when the full force of the hurricane turned inland.

demeanor conduct; behavior; bearing; manner
His is not the *demeanor* of someone willing to submit to unfair pressure.

demented suffering from irreversible mental deterioration
A person who suddenly resorts to odd, irresponsible behavior is soon suspected of being *demented*.

demoniac fiendish; frenzied; one possessed by a demon
Present-day physicians, unlike their colleagues of old, are never called upon to treat a *demoniac*.

demonologist one who specializes in the branch of learning dealing with evil spirits
Demonologists are to be found much more in fiction than in real life.

demurred objected; hesitated; took exception
The veterans were in favor of the plan, but some of the new recruits *demurred*.

deplorable regrettable; shocking; unfortunate
Conditions in the slums of 18th-century London were more *deplorable* than conditions in the ghettos of today.

derby a stiff felt hat with dome-shaped crown and narrow brim; a race
Will the *derby* ever return to popularity as a head cover?

descant to discourse; discuss discerningly and at length
Who can resist the temptation to *descant* in detail on unusual tidbits of gossip?

desolation ruin; devastation; bleakness; loneliness; sadness
How can one book picture all the *desolation* resulting from a worldwide war?

despicable contemptible; detestable; disgraceful
Do not ask me to forgive such *despicable* behavior.

destined decreed beforehand; predetermined; set apart for a specific purpose or place
Her parents have always believed that Susanna is *destined* to be a notable physician.

detonation an explosion; a discharge; setting off
The *detonation* of the first atom bomb raised the real fear that humanity is now capable of destroying Earth.

devastate to destroy; wreck; demolish; lay waste
The heavy spring floods *devastated* the entire countryside.

diffracted deflected
When a ray of light is directed through a narrow slit, it is *diffracted* and some of its components can be seen.

diffuse to spread out; scatter; long-winded; wordy
Her calm response and logical reasoning quickly *diffused* his anger.

diligent industrious; hardworking; thorough
A *diligent* investigator, Alice leaves no clue unexplored or unresearched.

diplomatic ambassadorial; tactful; discreet
Edna is so *diplomatic* that she can get along with anyone.

disarrayed disorganized; disarranged; disordered; disheveled
The restless child had *disarrayed* the bed covers.

discernment quality of being able to grasp and comprehend what is obscure
His quick *discernment* of his opponent's weaknesses assured him of an easy victory.

disconsolately sadly; forlornly; despondently; dejectedly
The puppy wandered *disconsolately* from room to room, whining for the children who were in school.

discreetly tactfully; wisely and cautiously
The entourage *discreetly* followed several feet behind the royal couple.

disdain contempt; to scorn
The general treated the order to surrender with *disdain,* sending back a resounding NO.

disheveled unkempt; rumpled; mussed; untidy
With one gust, the strong wind *disheveled* the hairdo that she had struggled so long to achieve.

disillusioned undeceived; disenchanted; burst the bubble
Sarah was quickly *disillusioned* when their cruel actions belied their pious words of deep concern.

disinclined unwilling; indisposed; hesitant; reluctant
Because of the slight praise the critics had given the play, I am *disinclined* to see it.

disinterestedly without bias; impartially; indifferently
Adam was *disinterestedly* concerned in the proceedings that did not affect him in the least.

disjointed disconnected; detached; rambling; illogical
The sequences in the play were so *disjointed* that the plot just didn't make sense.

disorder a disease; disorganization; disturbance; riot
May was out of the office for two months last year when she was hospitalized with a kidney *disorder.*

disparagement a belittling; ridicule
I am convinced that Paula's *disparagement* of our efforts is the result of raw jealousy.

dispensed administered; prepared and distributed
For thirty years, he wisely *dispensed* justice and collected only praise and his monthly paycheck.

disposition temperament; tendency; placement; disposal; final settlement
His will clearly stated the *disposition* he had intended for his assets.

disquiet to disturb; upset; vex
His habit of staring at people would *disquiet* anyone.

dissipating destroying; scattering; squandering
The sun soon *dissipated* the heavy mists of the morning.

dissuading discouraging; advising against
His determination was so great that there was no *dissuading* him.

distracted having attention drawn away; preoccupied; puzzled; confused
Jeremy was so *distracted* by the television in the other room that he couldn't do his homework.

distraught upset; anxious; troubled; mentally confused
Clara was extremely *distraught* over the loss of her wedding ring.

dithered in a state of confusion or excitement; dazed
The sudden change in his fortunes left the old man too *dithered* and exhausted to be able to think clearly.

diversion an amusement; a pastime; turning aside
The only *diversion* available to him during the long winter months was supplied by an electronic chess game.

divert to entertain; deflect; turn aside from a path
During the height of the storm, our plane was *diverted* to an airport two hundred miles away.

divination a prophecy; prediction; premonition; an unusual insight
The high priest's power of *divination* enabled him to direct the political action in the country.

divine to foresee; figure out; heavenly; preacher; priest
People who have the gift of being able to *divine* the future are found mainly in storybooks.

docks weeds; piers; cuts short; links
The village medicine man sent the children into the field to gather *docks* to be used in his potions.

documentary contained or certified in writing; factual; objective
We saw a *documentary* film dealing with World War II.

dolefully sadly; mournfully; in a melancholic manner
After losing his no-hitter, the pitcher looked *dolefully* at the telltale scoreboard.

domestics servants; help
The owners of the estate employ twenty *domestics* during the height of the social season.

doozy an extraordinary one of a kind
In your entire lifetime, you won't see another *doozy* like that one.

dottier more mentally unbalanced; more amiably eccentric; amusingly absurder
The absentminded oldster became *dottier* and more lovable with the passing of the years.

dour gloomy; sullen; unfriendly
Phil has often been told that his *dour* expression is a strong discourager of would-be friends.

dowager a dignified elderly woman; a widow holding title or property from her deceased husband
The swindler preyed on lonely *dowagers* eager for human companionship.

dowry the money, goods, or estate that a woman brings to her husband at marriage; natural gift; talent
Her priceless *dowry* consisted of her native intelligence and her sensitive concern for the welfare of her family.

drop-leaf having an extension that is folded vertically when not used
The *drop-leaf* table can be extended to accommodate four additional guests.

E

eddying moving in circles; making small whirlpools
Because of the *eddying* pools, the bay in which the two rivers join is too dangerous for swimmers.

efflorescent flowering; culminating; eruptive
It was a period in which the *efflorescent* genius of the scientific mind burst forth and changed the human world.

elation a great joy; high spirits
The entire squad showed great *elation* when our captains won the gold medal for tennis doubles in the Olympics.

elite the best; choice; socially superior group
She is the leader of the power *elite* that, behind the scenes, runs the government.

emulate to copy; follow the example of; imitate
You must choose carefully traits and actions and not the totality of the person you try to *emulate.*

enamored infatuated; captivated; enthralled; charmed
He is so fickle that he has forgotten the name of the beautiful coed he was *enamored* of only two weeks ago!

engrossed fully attentive; absorbed; taken up
I was so engrossed in the TV drama that I was unaware that my parents had entered the room.

enigmatically mysteriously; unfathomably; inscrutably
He speaks so *enigmatically* that I need a seer and an interpreter to give me the gist.

entailed required; called for; inheritance-restricted
Since the property was *entailed,* it would be inherited by his cousin and not by his wife.

entrails the internal organs, especially the intestines
The prophet foretold the future by examining the *entrails* of sacrificial animals.

entrenchment the act of placing within a trench; act of establishing solidly
Their *entrenchment* in the business was based on many years of loyal and devoted service.

enumerate to specify; cite; count; add up; tabulate
Please *enumerate* the items again so that we can be certain that we have them all.

epitome essence; model; embodiment
The British monarchy itself is the *epitome* of tradition.

epoch a period; an era; age
This is the *epoch* of unparalleled scientific achievement.

ergo therefore; hence
We did not invite him to our party. *Ergo,* he will not invite us to his.

errant traveling; wandering; fallible; deviating from standard
They finally located the *errant* calf a mile from home.

erudite learned; well-informed; wise
To earn his reputation, the *erudite* professor has spent long years in the alcoves of the library.

escarped having a line of cliffs; having a low, steep slope along the beach
The valley was *escarped* close to the horizon.

espaliered trained to grow flat against a trellis or railing
Espaliered fruit trees decorated the long wall.

estuary an arm of the sea at the lower end of a river
New York harbor is the drowned *estuary* of the Hudson.

ethereal sublime; unearthly; celestial
The *ethereal* beauty of a Florida sunset cannot be captured on canvas.

eulogy an oration of praise; praise of the dead; encomium
The best known American *eulogy* is Lincoln's Gettysburg Address.

evince to show; reveal; demonstrate
We would have given her the painting if only she had *evinced* some desire to own it.

exalt to praise; extol; honor; celebrate; inspire; uplift
The quintet gave a performance that truly *exalted* the privileged audience.

exasperated irritated; annoyed; angered; infuriated
Exasperated by the hecklers, the speaker walked off the stage.

excrescences outgrowths or enlargements
Warts and pimples are *excrescences* that are most unwelcome to teenagers.

exemplary worthy of imitation; admirable; noteworthy; typical
His *exemplary* behavior had a good influence on the younger children.

exercised alarmed; drilled; practiced
Exercised by the increase in air pollution, the citizens demanded that the nearby mills be investigated.

exhilarate to fill with high spirits; excite; stimulate
As the skaters glided across the perfect ice, they were so *exhilarated* they shouted with glee.

expectancy an act or state of being awaited; awaited amount
The life *expectancy* of most butterflies ranges from a few days to weeks.

expertise a special skill, know-how
Assembling a bicycle requires a good deal of *expertise.*

expire to come to an end; terminate; conclude; perish
When does your subscription to the magazine *expire?*

extenuate to excuse; justify; lessen
The attorney hoped that his client's extreme youth would *extenuate* the act.

extrapolate to infer from values within an already observed interval; project from the known into the unknown
Knowing the intervals, we can easily *extrapolate* to find what may result in the future.

exult to be very joyful; rejoice
The students *exulted* when the home team won the unexpected victory.

F

facetious witty; joking (often inappropriately)
Winifred tried to cover her embarrassment with a *facetious* remark that no one else found funny.

factor a consideration; component; cause
Your welfare was the prime *factor* in their decision to delay their leaving until after your exams.

faculty a teaching staff; skill; talent; power
A copy of this notice must be given to every member of the *faculty* before meeting classes tomorrow.

falsetto an artificially high voice
He spoke into the tape recorder in a *falsetto*, hoping to mislead those who would try to identify the speaker.

fancy imagination; whimsy; illusion; dream; longing; to imagine
She had the weird *fancy* that somehow I would turn out to be her Prince Charming in disguise.

fastidious fussy; particular; overrefined; choosy
He is too *fastidious* to enjoy going on an overnight along the rough mountain trails.

fault a break in rock; error; defect; blame
The *fault* in the rock caused it to split under pressure.

feigning pretending; making believe
Feigning interest in our welfare, the visitor asked many polite questions about our progress in school.

feline of or relating to cats; catlike; sleek; graceful; sly; treacherous; stealthy
With *feline* grace, she slinked out of the room with all eyes riveted on her.

ferocity savagery; violence; fierceness
With all the *ferocity* of a bear defending her cubs, Rover barked, growled, and leaped toward the menacing stranger.

festoon a decorative chain hanging between two points; to decorate with such a chain
Festoons of welcome were stretched high across the street at right angles to the line of march.

feverish inflamed; fevered; fanatic; frenzied
With *feverish* haste, Edna rushed to have the house in order before the guests would begin to arrive.

figment something made up or invented; a product of the imagination
Is King Arthur just the *figment* of some writer's imagination or was he a real, live person?

figurative symbolic; not literal
"I am dead on my feet" can only be taken as a *figurative*, never as a literal, statement.

finality the condition of being irrevocable, settled, final; complete
The *finality* of our defeat and surrender shocked me into the depths of a depression.

fiscal financial; budgetary; monetary
The job of corporate treasurer involves many *fiscal* responsibilities.

fitful unsteady; changeable; uneven
I stayed by her bedside to be there whenever she awoke from her *fitful* sleep.

flaccid flabby; soft; limp
Exercise, exercise, and more exercise is the only cure for *flaccid* muscles.

flack a press agent; publicity agent; public relations representative
Many reporters look for an easier berth by taking on the job of being the *flack* for a rising singer.

florid rosy; ruddy
Geraldine had a *florid* complexion, completely unlike the tanned complexion of her sister.

flotsam floating wreckage; debris; floating goods
We searched among the *flotsam* where the canoe had sunk, hoping to find what had caused it to go down.

focus point of concentration; center; to center on
The giant telescope can be directed by the computer to *focus* on any of the stars.

foreboding a forewarning; premonition; ominous; threatening
Phyllis had a *foreboding* that something had gone wrong when Joel failed to return her urgent telephone call.

forestall to prevent; avoid; guard against
In order to *forestall* a strike, the government official called a conference of the parties involved.

forlorn lonely; unhappy; deserted; lone; forgotten
The stranger looked so *forlorn* sitting dejected on the park bench that we invited her to join our group.

formidable impressive size or excellence
Washington's *formidable* defensive line discouraged opposing runners from trying to find a hole off guard or tackle.

forthwith immediately; without delay; instantly
We said our goodnights and left *forthwith.*

fortissimo very loud
How in the world can I do my homework if Sylvi insists on turning the volume of the TV up to *fortissimo*!

fortitude endurance; courage; moral strength
Mr. Foster's faith in the future gave him the *fortitude* to face this most painful period of his life.

fortnight a two-week period
The magazine makes its regular appearance every *fortnight*, twenty-six times a year.

frangible breakable; brittle; fragile
So lovely a creation should not have been molded in *frangible* pottery.

frieze a sculptured or richly ornamented band around a building; a band or line suggesting a frieze
A constant *frieze* of visitors wound its way around the ruins of the amphitheater.

frigidly coldly; icily; distantly; stiffly
In a voice that was *frigidly* calm, she asked me to explain why I had not returned the car on time.

frustrate to hinder; defeat; thwart; baffle; dishearten
Giving children tasks beyond their comprehension or strength will only *frustrate* them.

G

galactic of or pertaining to a system of stars, the Milky Way galaxy; huge
It will take *galactic* sums of money to undo the damage our industrial waste has done to our earth.

galvanized aroused; charged; awakened
The sound of the alarm *galvanized* the fire fighters into action.

gamboled romped playfully; skipped about; frolicked
Freed from the confines of the pens, the young lambs *gamboled* in the open field.

gambrel a type of roof; a stick or iron to suspend slaughtered animals
To have a larger hayloft, we planned a *gambrel* roof for the new barn.

gamy brave; smelly; scandalous; corrupt; disreputable
Fearing that the *gamy* meat was not fit for human consumption, we buried it in a deep hole.

garbled confused; jumbled; mixed-up; unclear; distorted
Somehow the instructions were *garbled*, and the package ended up in the wrong city.

garrulous talkative; windy; wordy; gossipy
He is so *garrulous* that he can outtalk any tape recorder on the market.

gaunt very thin; scrawny; bleak; desolate
Her long illness had left her *gaunt* and pale.

gazelle a small graceful African or Asian antelope
With the grace of a *gazelle*, she raced ahead, outdistancing all of her pursuers.

gazetteer a geographical dictionary or index
The *gazetteer* section of current dictionaries is often labeled *Geographical Entries* or *Geographical Names*.

gentry the upper class; aristocracy; country society
The fox hunt, with all its fanfare, is traditionally associated with the British *gentry*.

gestapo a German secret police organization
The *gestapo* practiced ruthless brutality and terrorism against suspects.

gesticulate to gesture; signal; motion; make a sign
The troubled driver *gesticulated* for the police car to stop.

ghastly extremely unpleasant; dreadful; terrifying
The disaster at Chernobyl in Russia is a *ghastly* reminder that nuclear energy has not as yet been tamed.

gimps physically handicapped people; cripples; limps
Harsh sounding identifying terms like *gimps* are not usually employed today to identify the handicapped.

gingerly with great caution
She *gingerly* put down the cage containing the two rattlesnakes.

gist an essence; a main idea; theme; sum and substance
The *gist* of his long letter was that we should investigate carefully before accepting the offer.

glean to gather piecemeal; harvest
The investigator *gleaned* the data by talking separately to everyone associated with the events.

glimmeringly shimmeringly; flickeringly
The candle lighted, *glimmeringly*, only one small portion of the vast concert hall.

gnash to grind together; bite and grind; chomp; gnaw
You can *gnash* your teeth and scowl all you want; my answer is still a resounding, "Never!"

goaded prodded; urged; pressured; impelled; propelled
Goaded by her fear of failure, she became more and more frantic in her vain efforts to find a solution.

goetic of or relating to black magic; witchcraft; necromantic
Goetic is an adjective once used to describe magic in which witchcraft was used to evoke evil spirits.

gorse a European shrub
Spiny, yellow-flowered *gorse* filled the lower reaches of the mountain.

governess a woman entrusted with the care of children in a private home; dated title for woman governor
In the nineteenth century the job of *governess* was one of the very few positions available to educated women.

grackle a European starling; iridescent American blackbird
The boat-tailed *grackle* with its harsh calls is a welcome native of Southern Florida.

graphic vivid; realistic; visual
The reporter had to learn to write *graphic* descriptions with a minimum use of adjectives.

grapple a large hook; to hold tightly; struggle; fight; face
I need a clearer head than I have now if I am ever to *grapple* successfully with this problem.

grave (adjective) solemn; serious; thoughtful; critical
I think you made a *grave* mistake when you decided to challenge the truthfulness of her statement.

graven image an object of worship carved from wood or stone; idol
As an inveterate hero worshipper, Rose has stood reverently before many *graven images.*

gravity a mutual attraction of objects; seriousness; concern
The judge spoke of the *gravity* of the offense and its serious consequences before he pronounced sentence.

grimoire a magician's manual for invoking demons and the spirits of the dead
What would you try to do first if you ever got your hands on an authentic *grimoire?*

grisly gruesome; horrible; gory
It was the most *grisly* crime recorded by the police in recent years.

grizzled gray-haired
He tried in vain to retain a youthful appearance by dyeing his *grizzled* hair.

grossness the quality or state of being monstrously overweight, crude, obscene, massive
The *grossness* of the fat man in the sideshow made me feel repulsion rather than pity or awe.

grotesquely strangely; bizarrely; fantastically; distortedly
The *grotesquely* shaped trees on the wind-battered slopes reminded the climbers of witches and wizards in a child's cartoon.

guffaw a hearty laugh; burst of laughter; to laugh heartily
I was startled by the loudness of his *guffaw* when I finished telling him the mild joke I had just heard.

H

habitable reasonably fit to be dwelt in
How much longer will the world be *habitable* with so many pollutants being spewed out by our industrial plants?

haggard gaunt; having a wasted look; exhausted
When the trapped explorers were finally rescued, their *haggard* expressions revealed their fatigue and anxiety.

hagridden harassed; tormented; burdened unduly
Community colleges offer a key to escape for members of families *hagridden* by poverty.

handicapped disadvantaged; impeded; limited
I don't want him to be *handicapped* for the rest of his life by his lack of a formal education.

handmaiden female servant; attendant; something whose essential function is to serve and assist
Literature must never become the *handmaiden* of the state.

hankering a craving; desire; yearning; longing
How many of us have a *hankering* for the days before electrified air-conditioning, television, and computers?

heady intoxicating; strong; exhilarating; stirring
Being told that I was the one chosen to lead the expedition was *heady* news indeed.

hibiscus a shrub or small tree of the mallow family
The sudden appearance of the large *hibiscus* flowers was a pleasant reminder that spring had arrived.

hillock a small hill; mound
The multiple *hillocks* of sand on our lawn told us that the ants had come to stay.

hindrance an obstruction; blockage; limitation; snag
Sunken logs were the most serious *hindrances* that we encountered on our canoe trip through the lakes.

hitherto until now; thus far
Hitherto I had always found them most interesting.

hobbled fettered; shackled; limped; held back; hindered
Hobbled by superstitions and a closed mind, he lives unaware of the advantages of a modern way of life.

hokey sickly or affectedly sentimental; corny; mawkish; obviously contrived; phony
In the word store of youth, *hokey* and *corny* are present-day replacements for *oversentimental* and *mawkish*.

hovel a wretched dwelling; ramshackle building
The hermit lived for years in a *hovel* built of old sheet metal and cracked two-by-fours.

huffy haughty; easily offended; peevish; resentful; irritable
"Don't get *huffy* just because you didn't get your way!"

humbug a fraud; deception; sham; pretension; cheat; nonsense
That old *humbug* had the nerve to try to pass himself off as a knowledgeable lawyer.

hummocks slight rises of ground above a level surface; hammocks
In the Everglades, distant stands of tree visible above the marsh grass signal most welcome *hummocks*.

hurtle to speed; fly; race; go like a shot
With increasing destructive force, the boulders *hurtled* down the mountainside.

hypocritical insincere; false; deceitful; deceptive
She was so *hypocritical* when she complimented him on the excellence of his mediocre painting.

hypothesis theory; premise; assumption; supposition
The book is based on the *hypothesis* that life is possible on the satellites around some of the planets.

I

icon a conventional religious picture; emblem; symbol
The *icon*, surrounded by lace and lighted candles, was enshrined in a corner of the hut.

idyllic peaceful; pastoral; charmingly simple; romantic
How close to the drudgery in real life is this *idyllic* picture of the shepherd caring for his flocks?

illusory deceptive; false; erroneous; unreal
I don't want to be filled with *illusory* hopes that can be shattered at any moment.

imbibe to drink; consume; swallow
Will you charge more if I *imbibe* the soda pop rather than drink it?

immaculate spotless; clean and neat; faultless
The house was *immaculate* and peaceful until the children came in out of the rain.

immutable unchanging; unchangeable; enduring; stable
The scientist hoped to be able to catalog all the *immutable* laws of the universe.

impalpable intangible; incapable of being touched; unreal
At times she feels that life is as *impalpable* as a dream, always beyond her intellect's ability to grasp.

impediment a bar; block; hindrance; handicap
Her lack of confidence in her abilities was her major *impediment* to success.

impending menacing; threatening; about to occur
The *impending* takeover of the company by a corporate giant will throw many employees out of work.

imperceptible not noticeable
By *imperceptible* movements, the cat crawled ever slightly closer to the feeding birds.

imperious overbearing; dictatorial; domineering
His *imperious* manner made it impossible for others to confide in him.

impertinent rude; unmannerly; insolent; irrelevant
The judge quickly ruled that the manager's *impertinent* testimony be stricken from the record.

impetuous rash; impulsive; hasty; violent; relentless
Inviting the entire team to spend the weekend at our summer cabin was an *impetuous* move that I soon regretted.

implored begged; urged; pleaded with
I *implored* them not to take part in this rash effort that risks so much for so little.

impotent ineffective; powerless; unable to function
Impotent with rage, he stood before his tormenters with clenched fists and closed eyes.

impound to confine; to seize and hold in the custody of the law; to collect and confine
The judge ordered that the company's assets be *impounded* until the judgment was satisfied.

imprecision a vagueness; inexactness
Can you tell the difference between deliberate *imprecision* and an out-and-out lie?

inadvertent unintentional; accidental; heedless
He will receive an official letter from the chairman apologizing for the *inadvertent* omission of his name.

incantation a spell; charm; sorcery; witchcraft
I sought in vain for an *incantation* that would do away with all final examinations.

incantatory employing or dealing with or suitable for use in sorcery
The leader uttered the mystic words having supposed *incantatory* power and waited for the miracle to happen.

incarceration an imprisonment; a confinement
The *incarceration* of the Count of Monte Cristo made him bitter toward his enemies outside the prison.

incarnation a concrete or actual form of a quality or concept; actualization
She is the *incarnation* of goodness, sweetness and kindness, just too good to be true.

incessant constant; ceaseless; interminable
If only I had some relief from her *incessant* chatter!

inchoate beginning; shapeless; unorganized; disjointed
Because of the *inchoate* state of the planning, we are unable to refer to any specific features.

incidental secondary; minor; unexpected
Of course we shall gladly be responsible for the *incidental* expenses in hiring the car for the day.

incisive sharp; biting; precise; shrewd
She is fortunate to have the clear, *incisive* ability to state in a flash the exact point at issue.

inconclusive undetermined; unsettled; indefinite; doubtful
The committee's *inconclusive* findings left the final disposition of the case up in the air.

inconnue a stranger; a large food fish
Inconnue is a French term rarely used as an English synonym for an *unknown*, a *stranger.*

incredulous skeptical; unwilling to believe; doubtful
The jury was evidently *incredulous* when the defendant told his bizarre alibi.

indelicate coarse; crude; clumsy; vulgar

Because of his rough upbringing, his friends are ever ready to overlook his *indelicate* manners.

indifferently unconcernedly; with lack of feeling; uncaringly

I would have much preferred an outburst of anger from them rather than being treated so *indifferently*.

indignation anger; displeasure; resentment; dismay

He replied with *indignation*, "I never said that!"

induce to persuade; coax; influence; produce; bring on

His sincerity and willingness to listen soon *induced* me to reconsider our unfavorable judgment.

indulge to humor; yield to whims of oneself or another

Though Marcia is pretty strict in her dieting, she occasionally does *indulge* her craving for chocolates.

ineffectual useless; unsatisfactory

His unwillingness to make decisions made him an *ineffectual* manager.

inexorable relentless; immovable; merciless; inescapable

His *inexorable* logic and factual proofs convinced us to vote in the affirmative.

inexplicable unexplainable; not able to be accounted for

Though the appearance of some UFOs is still *inexplicable,* most reputable scientists disbelieve their existence.

infallible unable to do wrong; faultless; unerring

Our next-door neighbor has long been my *infallible* source of information about local happenings.

infatuated enchanted; captivated by; made foolish

She was so *infatuated* with the concept that there was nothing we could do to make her reconsider.

infer to conclude; deduce; conjecture

From her look of impatience as we spoke, we quickly *inferred* that ours was the lost cause.

infestation a plague; an annoyance; act of attacking in large numbers

The grain was sprayed to prevent further *infestation*.

ingenious clever; cunning; masterful; brilliant

None of the experts could figure out the magician's *ingenious* escape from the locked trunk under water.

inherent inborn; essential; inalienable

Freedom of religion is an *inherent* part of the Bill of Rights.

in memoriam in memory of

In memoriam is a Latin phrase often used on memorials and in funeral services.

innate inherent; inborn; inherited; intrinsic

An *innate* flaw doomed the program from the start.

inoculation an injection; a vaccination; immunization

The doctor gave us a series of *inoculations* before we left for our visit to China and Thailand.

insidious deceitful; treacherous; underhanded

The habit-forming side effect of this *insidious* drug does not become apparent for many months.

instinctive intuitive; inborn

The will to survive is *instinctive* in all living organisms.

inter to bury; entomb; lay to rest
Many of the men and women who died fighting for our country are *interred* in Arlington Cemetery.

interject to insert; throw in; inject; interpolate
To keep audience attention high, the skilled speaker *interjected* humorous anecdotes into his talk.

interminable endless; ceaseless; tediously long
Spoken in an unwavering monotone, the instructions seemed *interminable* to the impatient applicants.

interspersed spread; placed in or among; interjected
Many diagrams are *interspersed* throughout the text.

intimation a hint; suggestion; portent; innuendo
I regretted that I had not asked him frankly just what he meant by his *intimations* of dangers ahead.

intravenous situated, performed, or occurring within or entering by way of a vein
Because of the patient's weakening condition, the doctor ordered continuous *intravenous* feeding.

inure to accustom; habituate; harden; toughen; adapt
Growing up in the Minnesota lake country *inured* him to cold weather.

iridescence play of colors producing rainbow effects; glitter; sheen; opalescence
It has the *iridescence* and beauty of a peacock feather.

irony incongruity between the expected and the actual results
What *irony* to have the headquarters of the local police burglarized in broad daylight!

irreconcilable unadjustable; unappeasable; incompatible
The partnership broke up when the two owners reached *irreconcilable* differences on how to run the business.

irrelevant unconnected; unrelated; immaterial
What you have to say is most interesting, but it is completely *irrelevant* to the problem at hand.

J

jauntiness a lightheartedness; sprightliness; an unconcern
After so many somber happenings, the *jauntiness* and high spirits of the young people gave me a needed lift.

jittering making fast, continuous, repetitive motions; being nervous or acting in a nervous way
Under the spell of the chill wintry wind, the drying garments were *jittering*, white and stiff, on the line.

jocund cheerful; merry; elated
The merry group gathered for an evening of singing, dancing, and *jocund* feasting.

juncture an occasion; a moment; an intersection; a junction
At that *juncture*, we all agreed that the wisest thing to do was to do nothing but just wait.

jurisprudence a system or body of law; science or philosophy of law; the course of court decisions
When the judge retired, she devoted her time to the study of medical *jurisprudence*.

K

kaftan (caftan) a cotton or silk ankle-length outer garment with long sleeves, common in the Levant

As we walked through the narrow streets of Jerusalem, we passed many men wearing cotton *kaftans.*

keen to mourn, lament, or complain in a loud, wailing voice or sometimes in a wordless cry; lamentation for the dead

The sound of *keening* arising from the neighboring cottage told us that the ailing owner had died.

kindred like; similar; closely related; corresponding

We were fortunate to find *kindred* spirits among our fellow employees and spent our leisure time with them.

L

lacerate to wound; slash; cut; lance

The arms of the inexperienced berrypickers were *lacerated* by the sharp thorns of the blackberry bushes.

languishing becoming feeble; pining away; suffering neglect; hungering for

Guiltless political prisoners have been *languishing* in their jails for years.

lapse to cease; decline; vanish; an omission; mistake

If you let your driving license *lapse,* you'll be caught in the red tape of getting another.

lath a thin, narrow strip used as the basis of plaster or tile

Lath must be attached to the rafters or joists before the plaster can be applied for forming the walls of the room.

laurel a shrub or tree of southern European origin

In Ancient Greece, a wreath of *laurel* was traditionally given to the victor in athletic contests.

leeward situated away from the wind; opposed to windward

We sat huddled on the *leeward* side of the house, hoping to gain some warmth from the weak winter sunrays.

lethal fatal; deadly; toxic; virulent

An automobile too easily becomes a *lethal* weapon in the hands of inexperienced or careless people.

linguist a multilingual person; language scholar

The term *linguist* has replaced *grammarian* as the popular term for a language scholar.

literally actually; virtually; word-for-word

If this keeps up it will *literally* drive me insane!

littoral of, relating to, or situated or growing on or near a shore, especially of the sea

Littoral property is always more valuable than anything at a distance from the waterfront.

livid discolored; black and blue; bruised; enraged; provoked

Her sarcastic thrusts made me turn *livid,* but I avoided any confrontation by being absolutely silent.

loathing extreme dislike; disgust
After learning of his father's murder, Hamlet looked upon the villainous King with *loathing.*

lolling lounging; loafing; drooping; sagging
Find something to make you look busy; don't let the manager find you *lolling* around.

loom to tower; soar; emerge; come into view suddenly
As we turned the bend, we gazed at a magnificent chain of snow-covered mountains *looming* ahead.

lout stupid person; a term of contempt
I will teach that lazy *lout* not to interfere with me!

lull to quiet; soothe; calm; ease
The sounds of the waves breaking gently on the beach can quickly *lull* me to sleep.

luminous glowing; reflecting light; radiant; clear; enlightening
The report must be so *luminous* that even a nonscientist will have no difficulty in understanding it.

lupine wolfish; a type of herb
I shall never forget the villain's *lupine* grin.

lurch to lean to one side; tilt; stumble; stagger
I almost lost my balance every time the ship *lurched* in the rough seas.

M

machination a scheme; crafty maneuver; conspiracy; tricks
Week after week, the brave TV detective thwarts the *machinations* of baffling fiends throughout the world.

magenta a deep purplish red
As a color *magenta* is bluer and deeper than Harvard crimson.

maitre d'hotel a headwaiter; majordomo; type of sauce
For a considerable consideration, the *maitre d'hotel* seated us in a quiet corner near the windowed wall.

malice ill will; evil; spitefulness; resentment
Are there people who rejoice out of pure malice in seeing others suffer?

malignancy a cancer; virulence; evil nature or behavior
Fortunately, the *malignancy* was detected early, and the life expectancy of the patient was not affected.

mania a madness; insanity; rage; crazing; obsession
Jim has a *mania* for collecting old keys.

mansard a type of roof
The *mansard* roof has two slopes on all sides with the lower slope steeper than the other.

manse the residence of a clergyman
Often a large, imposing residence is called a *manse.*

marshal to put in order; usher; a high official; law officer
Before speaking extemporaneously to the group, the skilled leader carefully *marshalled* his facts.

masque a masquerade; type of play
The *masque* was a short allegorical play of the 16th and 17th centuries, performed by actors wearing masks.

massif a large mountain mass; group of connected mountains
A *massif* can be the principal mass of a mountain.

matronly of, like, or resembling a dignified, mature woman, married and of some social distinction
As she witnessed the chaos in the children's play, her *matronly* expression became more and more severe.

maunder to wander slowly and idly; speak indistinctly or disconnectedly; prattle on and on
I sat silent and impatient as she *maundered* on about the chances she had missed in her youth so many years ago.

mausoleum a stately tomb; family tomb
He has a morbid interest in comparing the *mausoleums* of the rich and famous of previous generations.

mea culpa a formal acknowledgment of personal fault or error
"All I can say is, '*Mea culpa!* I do not know why it happened, but it did happen, and I could have stopped it.' "

meager thin; lean; of poor quality or amount
The prisoners of war were given a *meager* amount of food each day, barely enough to keep them alive.

merganser any of a variety of fish-eating diving ducks
The *merganser* has a slender bill hooked at the end and usually a crested head.

mesa an isolated relatively flat-topped natural elevation; a broad terrace with an abrupt slope at one side.
The *mesa* is usually more extensive than a butte and less extensive than a plateau.

metaphysics a division of philosophy dealing with the nature of reality; abstract philosophical studies
Metaphysics deals with what is beyond the physical and the experiential.

methodical systematic; precise; orderly; exact
You could set the clock by his daily schedule—that's how *methodical* he has always been.

meticulous scrupulous; excessively careful; fussy; petty
Jeremy is *meticulous* about the order in which his suits are arranged in his closet, from light to dark.

mezzanine the lowest balcony of a theater; a low-ceilinged story between two main stories of a building
In recent years the first few rows of a theater balcony has been called a *mezzanine.*

mignonette a garden annual, an herb
The fragrant flowers of the *mignonette* are a yellowish green.

milieu environment; setting; background; surroundings
Opening night of the opera tends to be part of a snobbish *milieu.*

mimic to imitate; impersonate; a copyist; mime; copycat
During the lunch recess, Phil would regularly *mimic* the instructors of the day.

minim the smallest or least possible part
A *minim* is equal to 1/60 of a fluid dram.

minuscule very small in size or importance; diminutive; insignificant; petty
If only once in my lifetime I could say that I had a *minuscule* investment that paid colossal dividends!

mirthless sad; dejected; depressed; melancholy; morose
A *mirthless* laugh was her only comment.
misadventure a mishap; misfortune; disaster; bad break
The book is an uproarious tale of the *misadventures* that blighted his misspent youth.
misgivings anxiety; fear; doubt; apprehension
Such doubt and *misgivings* are the usual result of a lack of decision.
modulation moderation; adjustment to lower intensity
The children must be taught that *modulation* of the volume on the TV means keeping it at moderate levels.
mooted debated; questioned; disputed; unsettled
Whether life exists on other planets is often *mooted*; satellites and robots may someday settle the question.
morass marsh; wetlands; swamp; mire
One of us will have to wade through thc *morass* to reach the island.
mores customs; conventions; traditions; standards
The square-dance devotees have developed a whole set of costumes and *mores* of their own.
mortally in a deadly and fatal fashion; to the point of death
Both the messenger and the driver were *mortally* wounded when they tried to race past the machine-gun nest.
mortify to shame; embarrass; do penance; fester
I was *mortified* when I could not recall the name of the play we had seen last night.
moue a pout; a little grimace of distaste or playful insolence
His deliberate *moue* showed that he definitely did not expect to enjoy the occasion.
mulch a protective organic covering to protect plants and roots; to cover or dress with such a covering
We used grass clippings, leaves, and manure to *mulch* the orchard.
murky dim; gloomy; sunless; cheerless; obscure; foggy
The air was *murky* with the smoke of the brush fires.
muse to meditate; speculate; say or think reflectively
"I could run away," he *mused*, "but then what would become of my hopes and plans for the future?"
musicology the historical and scientific study of music
Musicology consists of investigations and analysis of specific types of music.
musty moldy; stale; damp; trite
The rack of harnesses in the hayloft is a *musty* relic of a time long since past.
muumuu a long, loose dress that hangs free from the shoulders
With its bright colors and patterns, the *muumuu* is the costume introduced to Hawaiians by the missionaries.
muzzle an animal's mouth; to bind; silence; suppress
The dictator *muzzled* the popular press, hoping to quell opposition and unrest.
muzzy muddled or confused in mind; dull; depressing; blurred
What future is available to the men and women with brains made *muzzy* by drug abuse?
mystical symbolic; obscure; occult; having a spiritual value
I frankly admit that I do not understand the symbolism in the *mystical* poems of Blake.

N

nettle a stinging plant; to annoy; irritate; provoke
The debater's clear thinking and direct attack *nettled* his weaker opponent.

noisome smelly; foul; injurious; harmful; poisonous
The *noisome* odors of the swamp seeped into the storage barn close to the water's edge.

nonplussed confused; baffled
We were completely *nonplussed* by his uncooperative attitude, especially after all we had done for him.

nostalgia a bittersweet memory; homesickness; regret
Janet suddenly felt a pang of *nostalgia* for the sights and sounds of her grandparents' home.

notable marked; conspicuous; outstanding; famous; eminent
The charity ball was attended by all of the *notable* persons in the community.

nuptial of or relating to marriage or the marriage ceremony
The *nuptial* day arrived with the same rising of the sun that usually announces another dawn.

O

objectively impartially; impersonally; fairly
The decision was reached so *objectively* that no one could claim that it was colored by bias.

obligatory compulsory; mandatory; required; unavoidable
When the financial crisis occurred, contributions of definite sums became *obligatory* rather than voluntary.

obliged required; demanded; coerced; favored; accommodated
Having been at his birthday party, Helena felt *obliged* to invite him to hers.

obsequies the rites or ceremonies relating to burial
The governor of the state officiated at the *obsequies* for the fire fighters who had died in the factory fire.

obsequious compliant to excess; fawning; servile
With *obsequious* bowing and scraping, the followers of the victorious duke led him into the throne room.

occidental Western as opposed to Oriental; one who is native of a Western country
Until recently, it was impossible to confuse *occidental* art with the artistic productions of the Orient.

occult supernatural; magical; mystical; esoteric
The magician claimed that he had *occult* powers and that he used no sleight of hand in his performance.

ominous threatening; foreboding; sinister
The children scuttled home when the *ominous* black clouds raced across the overhead sky.

ordained conferred holy orders on; appointed; decreed; ordered
Is my lot *ordained* by fate or do I have the ability to really choose and select?

orgy a wild revelry; wild party; drunken festivities; excessive indulgence in an activity
In an *orgy* of senseless destruction, the raiders set fire to the houses, and gunned down the villagers.

orient to accustom; familiarize; put into correct position

The entering first-year students attended a series of lectures planned to *orient* them to college life.

orientation sense of direction; familiarization; adjustment; general inclination; introductory instruction

Those with a Marxist *orientation* have had to reconsider many of their fundamental adjustments to government.

outright utter; complete; altogether; instantly; unreservedly

I shall prove to your satisfaction that what they told you was an *outright* lie.

overwrought overexcited; agitated; overdone

How can you tell *overwrought* parents to control their anxieties and handle the crisis calmly?

P

pagan one who has little or no religion; a heathen; follower of a religion with many gods; heathenish

The modern *pagan* in our midst is one who seeks only selfish pleasures and worldly possessions.

painstakingly carefully; meticulously; thoroughly

Her paintings look like beautiful photographs because of her scrupulous, *painstakingly* precise attention to detail.

palate roof of the mouth; an intellectual taste

It was a dish that could bring joy to the most sophisticated *palate.*

pander a go-between; intrigue; one who caters to and often exploits the weaknesses of others; to act as a pander

The theater owner expected to make huge sums of money by *pandering* to local seekers of sensationalism.

papaya an evergreen tropical tree; its fruit

The yellow fruit of ripe *papaya* is juicy and delicious.

paradox a seemingly contradictory statement; self-contradiction

He offered as an example of a modern *paradox*: The more terrible the prospect of nuclear war becomes, the less likely it is to happen.

paragon a model of excellence or perfection; example

Fortunate is the movie star who becomes the *paragon* of beauty for a generation.

paranoia a tendency to being oversuspicious, excessively distrustful, or having delusions of persecution

Paranoia is a technical term that has been moving from psychiatry into the general vocabulary.

pariah an outcast

Because he put up an ugly-looking fence, Mr. Murray became a *pariah* in his own neighborhood.

parody a ludicrous imitation; caricature; to satirize; lampoon

The college audience was delighted by the mimic's *parody* of a student preparing to cheat at test-taking time.

pasha a former title of honor placed after the name of Turkish military and civil officials

Today, the title of *pasha* is found mainly in fiction.

passel a large number; a group
A whole *passel* of notables floated across the TV screen as we watched the fanfare of a new play's opening night.
passivity submissiveness; apathy; unassertiveness; inertia
Her endless little setbacks in the struggle to achieve have left her with the deadly *passivity* of defeatism.
patchouli an East Indian shrubby mint
The perfume made from *patchouli* has a heavy scent.
pathos sadness; ability to arouse sympathy
The story of his downfall has so much *pathos* in it that I was weepy for hours after reading it.
patriarch a founding father; oldest member of a group; elder
The cypress is the *patriarch* of American trees, going back to the time of the dinosaurs.
patronize to do business with; shop at; act superior toward
After that incident, I vowed never to *patronize* that supermarket again.
peevishly crossly; grumpily; fretfully; crankily
"Everyone around here tries to order me around," the new clerk muttered *peevishly* to himself.
pensive thoughtful; sad; reflective; solemn
She struggled to break out of the *pensive* mood brought on by the dying beauty of a brilliant autumn day.
perceive to observe; become aware of
Through the mist, the hiker could dimly *perceive* the outline of the old barn.
perceptibly noticeably; obviously
We were *perceptibly* distressed by her behavior, and we made no attempt to hide our displeasure.
perception an awareness; recognition
He has no *perception* of how much he embarrassed us with his crude comments.
perpetually constantly; incessantly; endlessly
Mr. Eller's face *perpetually* wore a frozen frown which even laughter around him could not erase.
perplexed puzzled; confused; mystified
Only a Sherlock Holmes would not be *perplexed* by this most unusual problem.
persevere to persist; not give up; stick to it
We must learn to *persevere* in developing our inborn abilities if we are truly to succeed.
personage a person of rank, note or distinction; a notable
The hotel caters to the *personages* of the entertainment world.
perspective a sense of depth; panorama; overview
When you see the incident in its proper *perspective*, your anger will be replaced by compassion.
pertinent related; suitable
Unless your comments are *pertinent* to the matter under discussion, we ask you to hold them until later.
perturbed upset; worried; disturbed; disquieted
Since Mr. Ellson had not expected this turn of events, he was greatly *perturbed* by what he saw.

petite having a small, trim figure—usually used of a woman
Is it a bit incongruous that so *petite* a woman should write in such a large, bold hand?

petit point embroidery made with a special stitch
Petit point with its one-horizontal-and-one-vertical crosslines is found in almost every home.

petulant cross; cranky; irritable
When Jeb's wishes were not carried out, his reaction was always *petulant* and peevish.

philters potions, drugs, or charms credited with magical powers
Time alone supplies the *philters* that make tolerable our excruciatingly painful memories.

phobia an unreasonable fear; overwhelming anxiety; a dread
Catering to her *phobia*, Harriet trudges the ten flights rather than take the elevator up to the office.

piazza an open square; roofed gallery; veranda; porch
We sat on a bench in the main *piazza* of the small Italian town and watched humanity pass by.

picador the horseman in a bullfight
The *picador* jabs the bull with a lance to weaken its neck and shoulder muscles.

picturesque quaint; colorful; charming; striking
Pioneering conditions that are so *picturesque* to look back on today were trying and dangerous to live through.

placid peaceful; quiet; serene; undisturbed
The painting by John Constable showed a *placid* scene of Salisbury Cathedral, suggestive of a peaceful summer day.

plaintively sorrowfully; mournfully; pitifully
I can still hear the voice of the sick child asking *plaintively* for the missing doll.

platter a large plate; a record for a record player
The idiom "to get something on a *platter*" means *without effort, very easily*.

plumb a plumb line; to sound, measure; test; vertical; true
He stared at nothingness, *plumbing* the depths of his being, trying to find the source of his guilt feelings.

poignant heartrending; pathetic; penetrating; sharp
How can we ever forget that *poignant* look of regret on her face?

poltergeist a noisy, usually mischievous ghost said to be responsible for unexplained noises
The frantic children were convinced that the nightly creakings in the old house were caused by a *poltergeist*.

ponderous heavy; bulky; massive
The *ponderous* furniture of an earlier day has given way to lighter pieces in keeping with modern life-styles.

poring over studying carefully; examining; pondering
She was *poring over* the report, looking for any error that could delay its publication.

portly large; substantial; heavy; obese; stocky; rotund
His *portly* appearance attested to his enormous appetite.

postprandial referring to or occurring after a meal, especially dinner
She had reached that stage in life when a *postprandial* nap is not only essential but even enjoyable.

postulate to claim; presuppose; an axiom; assumption
He firmly believes in the *postulate* that the good we do lives after us.

pottering wasting time; puttering
While she was *pottering* over trifles, I had to make the important decisions.

pram a lightweight, flat-bottomed boat; baby carriage
The British prefer *pram* to *baby carriage.*

prattle the chatter of children; chitchat; to chatter; babble
The constant *prattle* of the children at play was a reassuring sound to the baby-sitter.

precaution safeguard; safety measure; caution
When you are in this weakened condition, you should take extra *precautions* to prevent your catching a cold.

precipitancy a headlong haste
Alice, in informal dress, ran from the room with startling *precipitancy* when the stranger appeared.

precluded prevented; stopped; forestalled; checked
The adoption of one choice often *precludes* the use of another.

premises bases for reasoning; assumptions; site; immediate area
He threatened to call the police if we did not vacate the *premises* and leave the vicinity immediately.

preoccupation engrossment; excessive concern with something
Mr. Finver's *preoccupation* with details of his business left little time for his family.

preoccupied lost in thought; engrossed; absorbed
From Lori's *preoccupied* expression, I could tell that she was miles away, reliving her recent vacation.

presentiment a premonition; foreboding; a sense of something about to occur
I have a strong *presentiment* that she will succeed.

prevail to succeed; to be widespread; in style; win out
Gloom *prevailed* when we realized how small our chances of succeeding really were.

prevalence frequent occurrence; general acceptance
We boiled all the water we used because of the *prevalence* of typhoid in the area.

prim overprecise; proper; prudish; smug; trim
The cliche, "a *prim,* old-fashioned schoolteacher," belongs to another era.

privation loss of some quality; lack of necessities
W. C. Fields, the great comedian, suffered *privation* as a child, but in later years, he became a financial success.

projectile a missile for a weapon; an object sent forward by external force
Any small object can become a fearsome *projectile* if it hits the unprotected surface of the eye.

prolix wordy; wordy and tedious; verbose; repetitious
Our *prolix* friend always makes twenty words do the work of five.

propped supported; braced; rested
They *propped* up the shaky platform with several braces.

propriety an appropriateness; suitability; due regard for the standards of social acceptance; decorum

They questioned the *propriety* of his coming in less than formal dress to this solemn gathering.

prosaic commonplace; ordinary
Even the most *prosaic* life has moments of high drama and excitement.

protagonist the central character; hero; principal lead
The *protagonist* of *Hamlet* is a Danish prince sorely beset by problems not of his making.

protean readily assuming different shapes and forms; variable
As an actor, he is as *protean* as an ameba.

protestations objections; emphatic expression of disagreement
With some proper *protestations* of modesty, she told us of her most remarkable qualities.

protrude to jut out; project; stick out
The nail head that *protruded* from the catch prevented the door from closing.

proverbial widely referred to, as of the subject of a proverb; famous; expressed in a proverb
He did not lack the *proverbial* wisdom of elder statesmen, only the self-assurance that leads to fame and power.

Providence divine assistance
I am certain that *Providence* played a major role when the speeding sports car just missed me.

prussic acid hydrocyanic acid; cyanide
The extremely poisonous *prussic acid* is a favorite quick dead end in mystery and detective tales.

psychic mental; psychological; spiritual; supernatural; occult; a clairvoyant; a medium
Has any medium ever agreed to have professed *psychic* powers tested in a scientific laboratory?

psychosis a mental disorder severe enough to make persons unfit to manage their own affairs
The diagnosis of *psychosis* usually has removal to institutional care as a concomitant.

pumice porous, light volcanic rock
As a stone *pumice* is used as an abrasive; in powder form it is both a polish and an abrasive.

pungent sharp and piercing; biting
Hal's *pungent* wit, though clever, made him no friends among those whose feelings he hurt.

punitive inflicting, awarding, or involving punishment; serving as a severe penalty
Punitive regulations were passed by the city council to discourage nighttime bicycling without lights.

pyrrhic victory a victory that is offset by staggering losses
Although he finally won his legal case, he was totally impoverished by the costs of this *pyrrhic victory*.

Q

qualms uneasiness; nausea; doubt; pang of conscience
I have no *qualms* when it comes to letting him know that he has not been playing fair with us.

quarry a mine; lode; to obtain stone from a quarry; an object of hunt or pursuit; prey
The posse cornered their *quarry* in a narrow canyon and waited patiently for him to surrender.
quashed suppressed; put down; set aside; nullified; voided
He boasts that his political connections *quashed* every indictment ever brought against him.
quavery shaky; wavering; wobbly; trembling
I believe that all of our voices suffer from *quavery* tones after a brisk run up five flights of stairs.
queried asked; made inquiries; investigated; questioned
The district attorney *queried* him on his whereabouts the night of the mass killings.
querulous habitually complaining; peevish; fault-finding
There is one sure way to handle the *querulous* boredom of a child with too many toys and no playmates.

R

rack one's brains to strain with great effort
I *racked my brains* to no avail, trying to recall the name of the street on which she lives.
rakish depraved; jaunty; dashing; debonair
Rakish is a dated term other than for its use in the phrase, "a hat tilted at a rakish angle."
rapt absorbed; spellbound
The children gave *rapt* attention to the snake-feeding exhibition.
rarebit see welsh rarebit
raspy grating; rough
The *raspy* quality of her voice was a first sign of a coming cold.
rationally reasonably; sensibly
The basic conditions for living *rationally* are lacking for many who live in poverty row.
raucous disagreeably harsh or strident; hoarse; boisterously disorderly
I had been away from the woods for so long that even the *raucous* calls of the crows were melodious to me.
ravaged ruined; badly damaged; wrecked; demolished; looted
After the air raid, the entire countryside looked as though it had been *ravaged* by an eternal fire.
rawboned having little flesh; gaunt
The starved horse looked so *rawboned* that its bones seemed to be pressing on its skin.
reaffirmation an act of strengthening or confirming again
The sacrifices made by the astronauts are a *reaffirmation* of our faith in progress.
recesses intermissions; slots; inmost parts
The drug reached deep into the *recesses* of his being to calm his fears and ease his agony.
recurrence a repetition; reappearance; a coming back to mind
With each *recurrence* of the disease, his body lost more of its magnificent ability to fight back.

reedy tenor having the tone quality of a reed instrument
The penetrating, poignant voice of the *reedy tenor* was admirably suited to his repertory of sad folk songs.

reflective thoughtful
Sam turned from his long *reflective* gaze down the Grand Canyon and said, "This is something!"

refute to disprove; contradict
The accused must be given an opportunity to *refute* these grave charges.

regale to amuse; entertain; delight; feast; ply
The TV comic *regaled* the guests with amusing anecdotes about some of the celebrities among them.

regally royally; nobly; stately; majestically
We were treated most *regally* by our grateful host who placed his vast resources at our disposal.

relegate to banish; assign; degrade; demote; commit
Much of the routine work of this national organization is *relegated* to special committees.

relentless persistent; never giving up
The *relentless* pursuit of the hunted in fox hunts has been strongly condemned by animal lovers everywhere.

renounce to relinquish; abandon; disclaim; repudiate
In order to prevent a bloody civil war, the princess *renounced* all rights to the throne and went into exile.

repose rest; peacefulness; calm; to lie at rest
I deserve an hour of *repose* in front of the TV before I begin my evening task of watching the ball game.

repressive in a restraining or an inhibiting fashion; curbing; controlling
The people vowed vengeance against the secret police who had been so cruelly *repressive* for years.

reprimand to scold severely; rebuke; a scolding
The teacher *reprimanded* the student for entering the room late and disrupting the class.

reproach to blame; criticize; condemn; shame; condemnation
His older brother *reproached* him for his rude behavior and compelled him to apologize.

reproof a rebuke; scolding; chiding; reprimand
She is so sensitive to criticism that even the gentlest *reproof* is most painful.

reprovingly in a scolding, reproachful, chiding manner
The child squirmed when her mother looked *reprovingly* at her.

reputed considered; supposed; deemed; believed
I have a tendency to steer clear of anyone who is *reputed* to associate with gangland figures.

requiem a mass or musical composition in honor of the dead
He composed a *requiem* for an orchestra and chorus of fifty voices as his memorial to those who died there.

resolutely with firmness of purpose; unwaveringly
Though all of his classmates gave up on the puzzle hours ago, Jim continues *resolutely* trying for a solution.

resourcefulness inventiveness; creativity; ingenuity
Anyone who is capable of devising so novel an approach has the *resourcefulness* we need in our chief executive.

retinue followers; courtiers; retainers; employees; entourage
The *retinue* of the candidate for the vice presidency consisted of two planeloads of aides and reporters.

rhetorical eloquent; grandiloquent; stylistic; verbal
The old-fashioned orator delivered long *rhetorical* speeches as though they were operatic solos.

ricocheted rebounded; skipped off surfaces
The golf ball *ricocheted* off a tree and fell within ten feet of the pin.

roan a horse whose base color is red
A *roan* usually has a chestnut, bay, or sorrel coat thickly sprinkled with white or gray.

rugged sturdy; rough; coarse; difficult
This *rugged* test will reveal the limits of your endurance.

S

sack to pillage; plunder; dismiss; a devastation; raid
The raiders *sack*ed the village, burned the houses, enslaved the natives, and moved on to more conquests.

sackcloth and ashes a garment of sackcloth worn as a sign of mourning and penitence
I am too proud to come to you in *sackcloth and ashes*, asking humbly for your support.

sagacity keen perception; sound judgment; wisdom; astuteness
She is a person of exceptional intelligence and unusual political *sagacity*—a born winner.

sallow yellowish; sickly; pallid; ashen
A *sallow* complexion usually suggests sickliness.

samaritan an inhabitant of Samaria; compassionate; kind
A good *samaritan* is one who is sympathetic, kind, and helpful.

samovar a Russian pot used for boiling water
The *samovar* is a tea urn, usually of copper, with a spigot at its base and some device to heat it.

sardonic bitter; scornful; disdainful
Perry's bitter sense of humor was revealed in his *sardonic* comments about the team's progress.

sash weight an iron bar or cylinder attached to a double-hung window as a counterweight
The *sash weight* hidden in the window frame allows the window to open and close more easily.

sassafras a tall, eastern North American tree
The dried root bark of the *sassafras* is often used as a source of an aromatic volatile oil used in perfumes.

savory tasty; aromatic; delicious; respectable; wholesome
This most unusual dressing made of exotic spices is what made the salad so *savory*.

scantling the dimensions of timber and stone used in building; a small piece of lumber
Scrap wood was gathered to form the *scantlings* used as upright pieces in framing the house.

scavenger a carrion eater; garbage or trash picker; salvager
The vulture is the *scavenger,* the sanitation department of the desert.

schizoid characterized by a split personality; disintegrating, mutually contradictory, or antagonistic parts; an individual with a split personality
Dr. Jekyll and Mr. Hyde were the two aspects of a *schizoid* personality.

screed a long, monotonous piece of writing; harangue; a friendly letter; informal essay or story
Screed as a term describing a piece of writing is dated and not often used today.

scrofulous having a diseased appearance; morally degenerate; corrupt
The old abandoned canvas canoe lay on the shore with its *scrofulous* sides peeling and chipping.

scruff the nape; back of the neck
The attendant grabbed the unruly customer by the *scruff* and escorted him to the street pavement.

scrutiny a close examination; inspection; study
Close *scrutiny* of the ancient map revealed a few lines showing the outline of the Cape of Good Hope.

scudding being driven forward swiftly; running before a gale
The *scudding* clouds racing across the wide expanse of sky warned us that a storm was building up.

scuttle to hurry; scamper; scurry; sink; wreck; destroy
We grew uneasy as we listened to the mice *scuttle* across the attic floor in the otherwise silent house.

sedated calmed; subdued; quieted; put under the influence of a calming drug
The *sedated* patients sat calmly staring into nothingness, silent, motionless, waiting, just waiting.

sedately in a calm, self-controlled manner
The elderly couples *sedately* proceeded to their designated seats at their designated tables.

sediment dregs; leavings; residue; grounds; debris
After the flood had subsided, the streets remained covered with a heavy *sediment.*

self-contained independent; self-controlled; composed; complete in itself; reserved
Each unit was *self-contained,* capable of operating independently of the others.

self-esteem pride; self-respect; confidence and satisfaction in oneself
Self-esteem is an admirable quality only in moderation.

semblance outward appearance; bearing; copy; duplicate
There was not even a *semblance* of truth in her version of what had happened.

seminar an advanced or graduate course; a meeting for giving and discussing information
I attended a three-session *seminar* on computerized learning.

sempiternal everlasting; eternal; of never-ending duration
The forces of good must never weaken in the *sempiternal* fight against ignorance and poverty.

sensual earthy; pleasure-seeking; licentious
She has the *sensual* contentment of a pampered cat!

serene calm; tranquil; quiet; cool
His *serene* smile made us realize how much in command he felt despite our objections.

shambled shuffled; walked awkwardly with dragging feet
The street beggar *shambled* up to me and asked for a handout.

shard a piece or fragment of a brittle thing; shell; scale
The archeologist collected varicolored *shard* from sites where pottery-making people had lived.

sheaf a quantity of stalks of plant material bound together; something resembling such a bundle
The wind quickly scattered the loose *sheaf* of notepaper into the four corners of the yard.

shorn cut off close; deprived
Shorn of all power, the exiled king lives simply and quietly on an isolated island far from cities.

sidle to move sideways, especially in a furtive advance
I was able to *sidle* edgewise through the narrow opening.

simultaneously occurring at the same time; coincidentally
The general planned to bomb the massive objective *simultaneously* by land, sea, and air.

singularity unusual or distinctive manner or behavior
Singularity of dress or speech often makes life a burden for their unfortunate possessors.

singularly unusually; in an odd or strange manner; uniquely
A person of a *singularly* frank temperament, Helen is most difficult to be with for any period of time.

sirens temptresses; enchantresses; charmers; signals
Have the *sirens* disappeared as characters in modern TV productions?

slug a snail-like creature; rounded metal piece
A close relative of the snail, the *slug* is long and wormlike, with a fairly thin shell.

smattering a slight amount; smidgen; superficial, piecemeal knowledge
My *smattering* of knowledge of Spanish was of no use when I had to describe the technical diagram to the class.

snaggletooth an irregular, broken, or projecting tooth
Only after the dentist had bonded a new facing on my *snaggletooth* was I willing to smile and laugh.

sodden soaked through; drenched; soggy; dull
The football field, made *sodden* by the storm, was a sea of mud.

soirees evening parties or receptions
I was invited to attend the *soirees* where the elite of the community displayed their formal splendor.

solace comfort; consolation; help in need; to console; calm
The parents of the victim drew *solace* from the many sympathy cards and notes they received.

sonorous resonant; full-toned; eloquent; flamboyant
The *sonorous* voice of the announcer quickly gained the undivided attention of the spectators.

soot carbon particles
The *soot* from the smoky fire smudged our faces.

sorcery witchcraft; wizardry; black magic; necromancy
The witch in the play used *sorcery* to gain control of the minds of the leading citizens.

sordid filthy; squalid; low; depraved; vile; corrupt
It is a *sordid* tale of graft and corruption, of people whose only interest was amassing ill-gotten wealth.

sparse thinly scattered; spotty; meager; scant
The *sparse* meal of the athletes on the day of the contest contrasted sharply with their daily fare.

spawn to deposit eggs; reproduce; engender; the offspring
Salmon return in great numbers from the ocean depths and swim upstream to *spawn* in their birthplaces.

species type; sort; category; kind; variety
The specimen he brought in was of a *species* that did not fit into any of the classifications I know.

spectrum a continuous sequence or range
The dean was pleased at the wide *spectrum* of academic interest exhibited by the student body.

speculatively theoretically; tentatively; in a risky fashion
She approaches problems *speculatively*, inclined to reach conclusions based on theory rather than proven facts.

spirituelle having or evidencing a refined mind and wit
She writes with a tenderness that is *spirituelle* rather than spiritual.

spruced trim; neat; well-groomed; chic; dapper
He bought a new car and came to town on Saturday night all *spruced* up in the latest fashion.

staccato made up of short, abrupt, distinct sounds
The woodpecker sent a burst of *staccato* sounds through the quiet forest.

stall a booth; shop; stand; to stop; delay
The shoe *stall* in the new arcade has just the running shoes I plan to buy.

stark utter; complete; bare
The room was as *stark* as an unfurnished, vacant apartment.

steadfastly in a steady manner; unwaveringly; inflexibly; unalterably; loyally
She may be narrow of vision, but she holds *steadfastly* to the principles she learned in her childhood.

stealthily slyly; secretly; cautiously
The cat *stealthily* approached the bird, but a sudden motion frightened away the intended prey.

steely resembling steel in hardness, firmness, color, keenness, or chilliness
It was a cloudless night with the *steely* stars out in full regalia.

stickler a purist; fanatic; martinet; enigma; tough problem
Only a perfectionist could satisfy the demands of this *stickler* for details.

stifled smothered; choked; suppressed; curbed; inhibited
Because I realized her sensitivity, I *stifled* my urge to smile when she made that verbal slip.

stipulated imposed a condition; specified; stated; provided
We *stipulated* in the contract that final payment would be made when the work was completed to our satisfaction.

stipulation an imposed condition; a specification; provision
This *stipulation* was included as a protection of the rights of the minors in the lawsuit.

stolid hard to excite; unemotional; sluggish
He is a *stolid* citizen, one who takes everything in stride and never loses his ever-present cool.

straggly arranged irregularly or without planned order
I had hoped that as I grew older my *straggly* beard would become full and luxuriant.

strains parentages; stocks; extractions; varieties; traits
She is so fortunate to have these tough, peasant *strains* as the basis of her heredity.

strident harsh; grating; shrill
The *strident* voice of the drill sergeant drowned out all other sounds.

subjective personal; individual; emotional; biased
I want to get your *subjective* reactions, not how you think others feel about this turn of events.

submissiveness obedience; meekness; passiveness
I just don't understand their utter *submissiveness*, their unwillingness to stand up and fight back.

subside to settle; to sink; diminish; lessen; ease
Only when the child's high fever had *subsided* did the weary mother take time out for a needed nap.

subtile subtle; elusive; cunning; sagacious; keenly felt
How can I explain the *subtile* joy of your knowing that your friend knows how you feel.

subversive treasonous; traitorous; a traitor; one who plans to overthrow a government by unlawful means
During wartime, the FBI had the responsibility of keeping *subversives* out of defense plants.

succinct brief; direct; compact; concise; terse
Instead of a *succinct* directive to get us started, she delivered a long speech that kept us immobilized.

suggestible easily influenced by opinions or suggestions
Because of her inner insecurity, she is so highly *suggestible* that others always make her mind up for her.

suggestive indicative; remindful; reminiscent; improper
Her choice of speakers for the ceremony is *suggestive* of her bias in favor of those who entertain, not teach.

superimpose to place over or above something
It is not easy to modify habits that have been *superimposed* over other habits of long standing.

suppress to hold back; subdue; crush; control; hide
The government tried in vain to *suppress* all news of the unrest among the workers.

surmise a guess; belief; opinion; to guess
We must have facts; *surmises* are not enough.

surreptitious done or acting in a secret way
The *surreptitious* message reached the authorities in time to prevent the act of terrorism.

swaggering walking boldly and arrogantly; strutting
In *Romeo and Juliet*, *swaggering* Capulet servants begin a brawl with the retainers of the Montagues.

symmetry correspondence of parts; balance; proportion
We take for granted the perfect *symmetry* of a wheel with its radiating spokes.

synchronize to make things occur at the same time or in order
His major responsibility was to *synchronize* artillery fire and troop movements during the attack on the enemy stronghold.

syndrome a characteristic pattern of symptoms or behavior
Is just letting go an effective antidote for the spring-fever *syndrome?*

T

tacitly silently without words or speech
The roommates agreed *tacitly* that anything borrowed from each other must be returned.

taint a stain; blemish; to spoil; damage; debase
The scandal has been a *taint* on the family's good name all these years.

talisman something supposed to bring good luck
Like many other ballplayers, Andy has his own *talisman*, a ring inherited from his grandfather.

tamp to pack down tightly by a succession of taps or blows
After he put the charge into the drill hole, he carefully *tamped* down a covering of sand.

tankard a tall one-handled drinking vessel
Give him a *tankard* of strong ale; he will entertain you with tales that amaze and astonish.

taper a small or slender candle; long, thin, waxed wick; to decrease gradually
At long last, the storm began to *taper* off.

tattoo a mark on the skin; steady beat
The rain beat a lively *tattoo* on the tin roof and kept us awake most of the night.

taut drawn tight; tense; tidy; rigid; unbending
The *taut* rope began to sing as the moored ship, tugged by the current, tried to move away from the dock.

tedious time-consuming; tiring; drawn-out; monotonous; boring
Cleaning out the attic is a *tedious* task that is best handled by postponement.

tedium monotony; dullness; sameness
Simple tasks with endless repetitions and no variety breed *tedium*.

telepath to communicate by or practice thought transference; one who uses thought transference
A *telepath* is one who communicates with others, not by words or actions but through thoughts.

tempered strengthened; hardened; moderated; temperate; having a specific temper
Temper the wind to the shorn lamb.

temporize to delay; hedge; stall; bow to practical necessities
He tried to *temporize* until we had worked out a more practical solution.

tender to present for acceptance or sale; offer freely
I shall expect you to *tender* your resignation in the morning.

tenderloin a strip of meat; district of a city
Tenderloin steaks come from a large internal muscle of the loin on either side of the spinal column.

tenor meaning; gist; intent; implication; trend
Were you able to grasp the *tenor* of her remarks?

tentative not final; under consideration
All of these plans are *tentative,* of course, dependent upon the director's final approval.

tenuity slenderness; thinness; rarity; feebleness; faintness
The *tenuity* of a thread separates life and death.

terrace a porch; open platform; level area adjoining a building; raised embankment; row of houses; street
We built a grassy *terrace* next to the house so that the children could play in a protected area.

terrapin turtle
A *terrapin* is a North American turtle living in fresh or brackish water.

testimonial a recommendation; reference; tribute
The entire faculty attended the *testimonial* for the retiring president.

thaumaturgist a performer of miracles (as a saint or magician)
The *thaumaturgist* held his young audience spellbound as he made flags disappear and bunnies hop out of the air.

timely well-timed; in time; opportune
Her *timely* warning saved me from racing into the speed trap and a citation.

toddle to walk with short, unsteady steps
Patience teaches that we must learn to *toddle* before we can walk or run.

tote to carry; cart; haul; a small handbag
I hope that you do not expect me to *tote* these heavy packages for the next two hours!

transcribe to make a written copy of; paraphrase; summarize; record; transliterate; translate
The library will *transcribe* the textbook into braille.

transient temporary; fleeting; passing through; homeless person; temporary state
I soon learned how *transient* are spring beauty and music once played.

translucent penetrating; semitransparent; clear; lucid
We were able to watch the divers at work in the *translucent* water beneath our canoe.

tread a tire surface; gait; stride; footfall; to walk along
When the *tread* is thin, tires are more likely to skid on wet or icy pavements.

treading walking; stepping
You are *treading* on dangerous ground when you accuse her of being concerned with only herself.

tremulously timidly; hesitatingly; fearfully; nervously; quiveringly; waveringly; affected with trembling
With *tremulous* hands, the enfeebled patient raised the spoon to her lips.

trivial commonplace; unimportant; slight
Sometimes a *trivial* event triggers a serious result.

triviality a trifle; something slight; commonplace
Time is too precious to be wasted on *trivialities.*

trough drinking box; depression; water course; ditch
You can lead the horses to the *trough,* but you cannot make them drink.

truculent hostile; savage and cruel; scathingly harsh
His *truculent* manner made the other students avoid him from fear or annoyance.

U

ultimatum a final proposition, condition or demand; final objective or end
A rejection of this *ultimatum* will end negotiations and cause a renewed resorting to force.

uncomplaisant uncooperative; unobliging; unfriendly; ungracious
The guide's *uncomplaisant* attitude made the visitors feel most unwelcome.

uncontainable not able to be held back or controlled
When the outburst revealed his *uncontainable* temper, he was immediately discharged.

undermine to weaken gradually; ruin; destroy
Your continual sarcasm has *undermined* the child's self-confidence and made her fearful and timid.

unfulfilled unsupplied; unsatisfied; not completely achieved; marked by failure to reach full potentialities
Political leadership must satisfy the vital *unfulfilled* needs of a nation.

ungrudgingly generously; wholeheartedly; without reluctance
When the emergency arises, Edna can be depended upon to give *ungrudgingly* of her time and energy.

unimpaired whole; not damaged or made less
His innocence having been proved, Henry emerged from the trial with his reputation and prestige *unimpaired.*

unindigenous foreign; alien
When *unindigenous* plants are introduced into an area, there is the danger that they may crowd out native ones.

unobtrusive shy; not conspicuous; not aggressive in action, manner, or appearance
These gentle people led a quiet *unobtrusive* life of self-denial.

unostentatious quiet; restrained; not showy or flamboyant
The mansion glowed with *unostentatious* elegance, the faultless furnishings filled with magnificent richness.

unprecedented unique; hitherto unknown; unparalleled
Admirers came in *unprecedented* numbers to pay tribute to the artist's genius.

unsavory ill-tasting; tasteless; disreputable; shady
The inn was quickly tainted as a place that offered a friendly haven for *unsavory* characters.

upbraid to scold; reprimand; find fault with
I am so tired of having him *upbraid* me for something that my older brother had done.

upwardly mobile moving easily to a richer, more cultured, or more respected class
Education is the most frequently employed key to becoming *upwardly mobile.*

urbane suave; polished; sophisticated; cosmopolitan
Urbane and witty, he was at his polished ease in the drawing rooms of the social elite.

V

vagaries whims; capricious, eccentric, or unpredictable actions
Farmers are almost completely at the mercy of the *vagaries* of the weather.

vantage something that provides superiority or advantage
From his *vantage* point as chairman, he was able to anticipate the strategic moves of his opponents.

veer to swerve; change direction
The car *veered* sharply to avoid hitting the dog.

vehement violent; impetuous
At the town meeting, several citizens raised *vehement* objections to the proposed plan to widen Main Street.

venal willing to be bribed; corrupt; dishonest
The *venal* police officer gleefully converted traffic violations into ready money in his own pockets.

vent an opening; outlet; expression; to let escape; express
She verbally *vented* all of her anger on the hapless children who had intruded into her garden.

verge to edge or border on; be near; approach
He'll never succeed; his present course of action *verges* on stupidity.

verisimilitude the quality of appearing to be true or real; probability; likelihood
Verisimilitude does not mean absolute truth.

vermillion a bright red pigment
Vermillion varies from vivid red to reddish orange.

vestiges traces; remains; remnants
The rubble and wreckage of machines of war were the only *vestiges* that marked where a proud city had been.

vie to compete; struggle; contend
Determined to *vie* for international trade, various nations fill the skies with fleets of cargo planes.

vigilante a member of a self-appointed policing force
Vigilante groups cropped up when the process of law seemed to be failing in the settling of our West.

vindictive wanting revenge; spiteful; unforgiving
After being fired for irresponsibility, the *vindictive* salesman spread vicious rumors about the company.

vintage date; period; era; prime; superior; antique
I bought my first antique, an old inkstand of 1915 *vintage* and in prime condition.

vista a view; scene; prospect; vision; mental picture
At the turn in the road was a memorable *vista* of distant snow-capped mountains.

vivacious lively; buoyant; bubbling; spirited
The experienced coach selected the most *vivacious* freshmen to join the squad of cheerleaders.

void empty; vacant; lacking; invalid; empty space; to eject; abolish; annul; invalidated
Their leaving left a *void* that no one else could fill.

vulnerable open to attack; defenseless; exposed
Every scientific statement is a *vulnerable* statement.

W

wainscot a lining of an inner wall; the lower three or four feet of a wall if lined with a different finish

The *wainscot* was made of oak stained to harmonize with the dominant color of the wallpaper.

wallow to luxuriate in; bask in; feast on

Ever since she won the lottery, she has learned to *wallow* in luxuries.

wanly in a pale, sickly, feeble, or spiritless manner

Mr. Walters smiled *wanly* to show that he understood the joke but felt that it may have been inappropriate.

wantonly maliciously; needlessly; senselessly

The gangleader was accused of *wantonly* destroying the heating system in the project building.

warily alertly; cautiously; guardedly

We listened more and more *warily* as the salesman lengthened his sales talk with vague promises.

warlock a sorcerer; person practicing the black arts

The *warlock* threatened to cast a spell over the cattle if the farmers persisted in crossing his fields.

wastrel a vagabond; one who wastes his resources foolishly and self-indulgently; spendthrift

Will this be labeled the *wastrel* era during which the world's stored energy was almost exhausted?

wavering trembling; hesitating; doubtful; faltering

The tired old man was *wavering* as he reached the last step and nearly fell.

waylay to attack from ambush; intercept; overwhelm; obstruct

In the 1930's economic deprivation once more *waylaid* a large segment of the world's working class.

wayward disobedient; unmanageable; changeable; erratic

Operating a sailboat in a *wayward* wind is not the task for a beginner.

wedge a V-shaped block; chock; to cram; stuff

Only a magician could *wedge* another item into her crammed suitcase.

welsh rarebit (rabbit) melted cheese sandwich

On a cool or cold afternoon, it is very easy to learn to enjoy a *welsh rarebit* accompanied by a hot drink.

whatnot a nondescript person or thing; a light open set of shelves for bric–a–brac

I placed the letter on the top shelf of the *whatnot* to make certain that she would see it there.

wicker a small, pliant twig or branch

Wicker furniture is usually made of entwined pliable osier or withe.

wicket a small gate or door; an opening like a window; an arch or hoop in croquet

One type of *wicket* is a grilled or grated window through which business is transacted.

wince to flinch; draw back; make a face; cringe

Doreen *winced* when the teacher held her paper up to show the class how not to head a theme.

windfall something (like a tree or fruit) thrown down by the wind; an unexpected, sudden gain or advantage

The detectives questioning the relatives soon found themselves with a *windfall* of leads.

wisp small amount; a small handful

Wisps of smoke rose from the embers of the dying fire.

wistfully yearningly; longingly

Cinderella, dressed in cast-offs, looked *wistfully* at the elegant gowns of her unsympathetic stepsisters.

withal together with this; besides; nevertheless; on the other hand

His voice was rough and hoarse but had an appealing warmth *withal.*

woolen-headed marked by vague or confused perception or thinking

That *woolen-headed* nitwit is the last person whose judgment I would trust.

wormwood a European plant; something bitter or grievous

The dark-green oil extracted from *wormwood* is used in absinthe.

wraith a ghost; spirit; phantom; apparition

According to legend, the *wraith* of the drowned sailor appears at midnight whenever danger threatens.

wrath anger; rage; fury; irritability; ire

You will feel the full force of her *wrath* when she learns that you were the one who hid her notebook.

wrought up excited over; upset by; concerned about

I still don't see why she let herself get all *wrought up* about an incident that did not concern her.

wry twisted; distorted; ironic; cynical; sarcastic

His *wry* remarks, intended to be funny, only irritate and hurt the feelings of his targeted victims.

Z

zenith the climax; summit; highest point; point in the sky directly overhead

At the *zenith* of her career, Marie Curie was the acknowledged leader in her field.